HUMAN
PHYSIOLOGY

HUMAN PHYSIOLOGY

BY

F. R. WINTON, M.D., D.Sc.

Professor of Pharmacology, University College, London

AND

L. E. BAYLISS, Ph.D.

Reader in Physiology, University College, London

THIRD EDITION

WITH 248 ILLUSTRATIONS

LONDON

J. & A. CHURCHILL LTD.

104 GLOUCESTER PLACE, W.1.

1948

First Edition   .   . 1930
  „   „   Reprinted 1932
Second Edition .   . 1935
  „.   „   Reprinted 1936
Third Edition   .   . 1948

Printed in Great Britain

In this edition, as in the second edition, certain sections, as indicated below, have been written by colleagues, who have special knowledge of the subjects they have presented. The authors of the new sections have allowed the original authors of the book considerable influence in the scope of the material included and in its presentation so as to secure as far as possible balanced exposition of the subject and continuity in style.

CIRCULATION . . .	By G. W. Pickering (London)
RESPIRATION . . .	By I. F. S. Mackay (Newcastle-on-Tyne)
DIGESTION . . .	By R. A. Gregory (Liverpool)
METABOLISM . . .	By D. H. Smyth (Sheffield)
CARBOHYDRATE METABOLISM	By F. G. Young (London)
REPRODUCTION . . .	By W. H. Newton (Liverpool)
MUSCLE CHEMISTRY . .	By P. Eggleton (Edinburgh)
NERVE	
THE SPINAL REFLEX SYSTEM	
LOCALISATION OF FUNCTION IN THE CENTRAL NERVOUS SYSTEM	By D. Whitteridge (Oxford)
THE AUTONOMIC SYSTEM AND CHEMICAL TRANSMISSION AT NERVE ENDINGS . .	By W. Feldberg (Cambridge)
THE EYE	By R. J. Lythgoe, revised by K. Tansley (Birmingham)
THE EAR	By A. F. Rawdon-Smith
THE DUCTLESS GLANDS .	By W. H. Newton (Liverpool) and F. G. Young (London)
INDEX	By M. G. Eggleton (London)

PREFACE TO THIRD EDITION

THE third edition of this book appears at the end of a turbulent decade, during which the applications of physiology to medicine and to other human activities have been intensely studied and more widely recognised than before. Less conspicuous but not less vital, fundamental research has proceeded, and much theoretical work has yet to be done on the empirical results hastily discovered and utilised under the pressure of war conditions. As leadership in the advance of more and more branches of the subject passes from the old to the new world, it is the privilege and good fortune of British physiologists to be able to appreciate easily and with relish the major contributions published by their American colleagues in their own tongue, while retaining the traditional intimate acquaintance with the many and active workers in European countries which were regarded as pre-eminent in these fields a generation ago.

In the preface to the first edition of this book the authors wrote that it was addressed primarily to the medical student, and aimed at encouraging " the intellectual attitude of an alert explorer " rather than allowing him to remain " the passive recipient of orthodox knowledge." These aims also pervade the present edition, and in the pursuit of them we have developed the policy begun in the second edition of inviting friends who had first-hand experience of exploring particular fields to present their branches of the subject with the shape and distribution of emphasis that seemed right, now rather than formerly, to one who was living and working with the material.

The student, however, needs not only guidance concerning methods of scientific enquiry in special fields ; he needs also a coherent picture of the whole subject. To this end the original authors have exerted considerable influence, whether by way of suggestion of topics to be included or modification of the way of treating them, on the sections written by their colleagues, and they would like to express their cordial appreciation of the comfortable collaboration and the sense of team-spirit which has added so much of interest and fun to a serious enterprise.

Many of the chapters have been written anew, and none have escaped radical revision. The authors believe, however, that medical students are expected to learn too much and think too little, and they have therefore prevented the book from growing out of its shape as one of the smaller textbooks of Human Physiology.

This edition contains many new illustrations : some of these have been specially prepared, while others have been taken unchanged from original publications. For all these, whether modified or unchanged, we would like to record our thanks to the authors concerned. Messrs. W. B. Saunders ; The Williams & Wilkins Co. ; The D. Appleton-Century Co. ; American Medical Association ; John Wiley & Sons

Inc.; Baillière, Tindall & Cox; Charles C. Thomas; Henry Kimpton; Macmillan & Co; Hinrichsen Editions; the Oxford University Press; and the Cambridge University Press have all been good enough to grant permission for the use of certain illustrations from the books and journals of which they are publishers. We are very grateful for their co-operation.

Finally, we must again express our appreciation of the courtesy and patience maintained by our publishers, and particularly of the skill and consideration shown by their artist, by Mr. J. Rivers and by Mr. A. S. Knightley.

F. R. WINTON

L. E. BAYLISS

LONDON

PREFACE TO THE FIRST EDITION

THE science of physiology has arisen as the confluence of a number of independent streams of inquiry. Chief among them, the problems of human disease called for a survey of the normal functions of the human body, and this inspired the development of experimental mammalian physiology and supplementary observations on the frog when the choice of a cold-blooded animal rendered the technique simpler. Hardly less in importance, the developments of chemistry in the direction of biochemistry, and of zoology in that of comparative physiology, have intermingled with the classical physiology, and the composite science of general physiology is now concerned more with the furtherance of natural knowledge than with applications to medicine. So it happens that the proper study of physiology demands an extensive knowledge of other sciences, and it is the more arduous since so young a science of necessity enjoys but few generalisations to co-ordinate the bewildering diversity of its biological material.

As the scope of physiology has expanded, the attempt to acquaint the medical student with the salient facts has trespassed overmuch on his opportunities for leisurely reflection ; any real assimilation of the matter presented to him has become increasingly difficult, and much of the subject is forgotten soon after the urgent need for its retention is passed. Hence the complaints of teachers of medicine that their students remember most of the relevant facts of human physiology so tenuously that they fail to apply them to clinical problems.

The medical student is expected to know too much and to think too little. He has two chief needs, a training in scientific methods and a knowledge of the properties of the human body. They can, it seems, best be satisfied, within the comparatively short period of his education available for physiology, by confining his attention to " Human Physiology," and eliminating from his curriculum those parts of physiology which have no immediate bearing on the happenings in the body of man.

If, then, it be convenient to distinguish Human Physiology as a separate subject for teaching purposes (and we are not here concerned with the organisation of research), it would clearly be desirable to base the subject on direct observations on man, and to proceed by way of analysis of these to experiments on animals directed to the solution of the problems raised by those initial observations. This arrangement often reverses the chronological sequence of discovery, and can only be adopted without loss of logical coherence in suitably developed parts of the subject. Muscular activity, for example, lends itself to such treatment, whereas the secretion of urine in man is still too little understood to make it a satisfactory approach to the systematic description of the functions of the kidney. Indeed, it is only the recent rapid progress in certain fields that has made it feasible now to attempt their presentation as an analysis of the properties of man instead of a synthesis of experiments on animals and isolated organs.

It would be interesting to conceive a book on Human Physiology entirely on these lines, but the following pages are intended to include the facts expected in medical examinations, and were it not so, the book would be of little practical value to a busy medical student. We have, therefore, hazarded only a step in the direction indicated, mainly by change of order and emphasis, and only occasionally by the omission of irrelevant or inclusion of unusual material.

The subjects in the medical curriculum may be divided into two groups, according as their matter is more or less stable. In the first group, the elementary aspects of chemistry, physics and anatomy, for example, have been known for so long and are generally accepted with such confidence that dogmatic presentation is a justifiable economy of effort. In the second group, physiology and medicine include many hypotheses, essential even to the beginner, which are provisional and often disputed ; even the classical distinction between fact and theory is apt to be obscured by the difficulty of isolating the essential from the incidental in an observation on the complex and variable material concerned. Training in these subjects should encourage the faculties of identifying the more significant of a group of observations, and of recognising the degree of likelihood attaching to any particular hypothesis. Unduly dogmatic teaching of physiology is therefore no part either of a university education or of the vocational training of a physician.

There is, of course, little doubt that the less intelligent student survives an examination more easily if he has been taught only the views fashionable at the moment, but later he will have good reason to discredit such teaching, and what purports to be the scientific outlook associated with it. In any case, the best medical practice depends on judgment rather than rule of thumb, and if a student has the wit to adopt the intellectual attitude of an alert explorer and to reject that of the passive recipient of orthodox knowledge, the sooner he starts the better. Too skilful piloting of the weakest students through their examinations may perhaps leave them improperly prepared for the just performance of their vocation towards an increasingly informed, but still trusting, public.

These are the principles which have guided us in the arrangement of this book. If it be argued that our insistence on the provisional nature of some of the most fascinating generalisations in physiology makes them more difficult to learn, we would urge the few who find them so to persevere if they seek admittance to a learned profession.

The book has been kept short by omissions rather than by compression. Much anatomy, histology and biochemistry that is commonly included in text-books of physiology is now so admirably treated in special books on these subjects that duplication here has been deemed unnecessary, and only an outline of the immediate facts needed to complete the description or argument under consideration has been included. The history of physiology has regrettably had to be omitted for lack of space, and when recently discovered evidence seemed more illuminating than classical experiments, they have received preference, for modern views are not necessarily advanced, nor are the older views always elementary.

Acknowledgment of the sources of those illustrations which were taken from other publications is made in each case below the figure. We would here express our appreciation to the authors concerned. Messrs. G. Bell & Son, Ltd., Messrs. Longmans, Green & Co., Ltd., and Messrs. Macmillan & Co., Ltd., have been good enough to supply blocks of illustrations from their various publications. Certain illustrations from Adrian's " Basis of Sensation " are included by permission of Messrs. Christophers. Unqualified thanks are due to our publishers, Messrs. J. & A. Churchill, and especially to their artist and to Mr. J. Rivers, for their unstinting trouble, skill and courtesy.

F. R. WINTON

L. E. BAYLISS

London

September, 1930.

CONTENTS

CHAPTER   PAGE

I. PHYSIOLOGICAL ACTIVITY 1
Muscular Exercise, 2 ; Physiological Equilibria, 14 ; Fatigue, 15.

II. THE CIRCULATION 18
THE HEART, 21 : The Origin and Conduction of the Heart-beat, 25 ; The Pressure Changes Accompanying the Cardiac Cycle, 29 ; The Output of the Heart, 31 ; The Output of the Heart in Man, 37 ; The Arterial Pulse, 43.

THE FLOW OF BLOOD THROUGH THE VESSELS, 44 : Methods of Determining the Blood-flow through an Organ, 46 ; The Blood Pressure, 48 ; Factors Determining the Arterial Blood Pressure, 55 ; The Control of the Peripheral Vessels, 61 ; The Vaso-motor Reflexes, 66 ; The Circulation to particular Organs, 71 ; The Regulation of the Blood Supply to the Tissues, 78 ; The Circulatory Changes during Exercise, 78.

III. THE BLOOD AND THE OTHER BODY FLUIDS. . 80
THE BLOOD, 80 : The Red Blood Corpuscles, 80 ; The White Blood Corpuscles, 81 ; The Reticulo-endothelial System, 83 ; The Platelets and the Coagulation of the Blood, 83 ; The Life History of the Red Blood Corpuscle, 86 ; Hæmolysis, 87 ; Immunity Reactions, 88 ; Rouleaux Formation and Sedimentation Velocity, 91 ; The Viscosity of Blood, 93 ; General Chemical Properties of the Blood, 95 ; Hæmoglobin, 98 ; The Regulation of the Hydrogen Ion Concentration, 107 ; The Carriage of Carbon Dioxide, 111 ; The Effect of Exercise, 118.

TISSUE FLUID, LYMPH 120

THE PERITONEAL, PLEURAL AND PERICARDIAL FLUIDS 124

THE INTRA-OCULAR FLUIDS 124

THE CEREBRO-SPINAL FLUID 124

IV. RESPIRATION 127
The Structure and Movements of the Respiratory Mechanism, 127 ; The Bronchial Muscles, 129 ; The Pleura and Pleural Cavities, 129 ; The Respiratory Movements, 130 ; Fœtal Respiration and Expansion of the Lungs at Birth, 131 ; Sounds Associated with the Movements of the Lungs, 131 ; The Volume of Air in the Lungs, 132 ; The Composition of the Gases in the Lungs, 133 ; The Nervous Control of Breathing, 138 ; Afferent Nervous Mechanisms Influencing the Activity of the Respiratory Centre, 139 ; The Mechanism of Gaseous Exchange between the Lungs and the Blood, 144 ; The Regulation of Breathing, 147 ; The Effects of Low Pressures of Oxygen, 154 ; The Effects of High Pressures of Oxygen, 159 ; Asphyxia, 161 ; Artificial Respiration, 161 ; The Respiration During and After Exercise, 162 ; The Action of Drugs on Respiration, 163.

CHAPTER   PAGE

V. DIGESTION 164

Swallowing, 168 ; Gastric Digestion, 169 ; Movements of the Stomach, 173 ; Intestinal Digestion, 177 ; The Bile, 178 ; The Movements of the Intestines, 181 ; Absorption of the Digestion Products, 184.

VI. METABOLISM AND NUTRITION 188

GENERAL METHODS OF METABOLIC STUDIES, 189 : The Respiratory Quotient, 189 ; Tissue Metabolism, 190 ; Metabolism of Isolated Organs, 191 ; The Metabolism of the Intact Animal, 192 ; Methods of Determining Metabolism in Man, 194 ; The Basal Metabolic Rate, 196 ; Specific Dynamic Action, 199 ; The Use of Isotopes in Metabolism, 200.

THE METABOLIC HISTORY OF THE FOOD SUBSTANCES, 201 : Protein Metabolism, 201 ; Lipoid Metabolism, 205 ; Carbohydrate Metabolism, 210.

NUTRITION, 217 : The Calorie Requirements, 218 ; Specific Requirements, 222 ; The Vitamins, 224 ; Alcohol, 227 ; Water, 228 ; Hunger and Appetite, 231.

TEMPERATURE REGULATION, 232 : Physiological Processes Involved in Production and Loss of Heat, 235 ; Climatic Conditions, 237.

VII. EXCRETION. 240

The Regulatory Function of the Kidney, 240 ; Normal Urine, 242 ; The Structure of the Kidney, 244 ; The Secretion of Urine, 247 ; Plasma Clearances, 259 ; The Renal Blood Flow, 263 ; The Control of Renal Secretion, 264 ; The Action of Diuretics, 267 ; Summary of Renal Factors Controlling the Urine Flow, 269.

MICTURITION 270

VIII. REPRODUCTION 275

Introduction, 275 ; Spermatogenesis and the Spermatozoon, 278 ; The Ovum and Ovulation, 280 ; Fertilisation, Sex Determination and the Differentiation of the Sexes, 285 ; The Endocrine Functions of the Testis and Ovary, 290 ; Pregnancy, 298.

IX. MUSCLE 308

The Classification of Motile Organs, 308.

SKELETAL MUSCLE, 309 : The Isometric Twitch, 311 ; Electrical Variations in Muscle, 312 ; The All-or-None Property of Muscle Fibres, 314 ; The Effects of Repeated Stimulation, 317 ; The Chemical Composition of Muscle, 320 ; The Chemical Basis of Contraction, 322 ; Heat Production of Isolated Muscles, 327 ; The Performance of External Work by Isolated Muscles, 329.

THE "OXYGEN DEBT" MECHANISM IN MAN, 331 : Intermediate Stages, 333 ; The Removal of Lactic Acid, 333.

HEART MUSCLE, 334 : Metabolism of the Heart Muscle, 339.

UNSTRIATED MUSCLE, 341 : The Speed of Muscular Movement, 345 ; Muscular Tone, 348 ; The Action of Electrolytes on Isolated Tissues, 351.

CONTENTS

XV

CHAPTER — PAGE

X. NERVE 354

The Structure of Nerve, 354; The Resting Potential of Nerve, 357; The Excitation of Nerve, 361; The Nerve Impulse, 368; The All-or-None Law, 372; The Changes in Excitability after a Nerve Impulse, 373; The Membrane Theory, 374; Energy Requirements, 376; The Excitation of Nerve Fibres in the Body, 377.

XI. THE SPINAL REFLEX SYSTEM 381

The Spinal Cord, 381; Conduction Across a Synapse, 381; Reflex Action, 387; Spinal Reflexes in Mammals, 390; The Theory of Reflex Mechanism, 398; The Reflex Response to Stretch, 403; Reflex Tonus, 404; Reciprocal Innervation, 408; Locomotion, 409; The Influence of Chemical and Physical Agents on Reflex Excitability, 410.

XII. LOCALISATION OF FUNCTION IN THE CENTRAL NERVOUS SYSTEM 412

Peripheral Nerves, 413; The Spinal Animal, 414; The Decerebrate Animal, 416; The Labyrinth, 420; The Mid-Brain Animal, 421; The Thalamus Animal, 422; The Cerebellum, 423; THE CEREBRAL CORTEX, 426: The Sensory Areas of the Cortex, 435; Speech, 436; The Frontal Lobes, 438; The Electrical Activity of the Cortex, 439; Conditioned Reflexes, 440.

XIII. THE AUTONOMIC NERVOUS SYSTEM AND CHEMICAL TRANSMISSION AT NERVE ENDINGS . . . 448

The Function of the Sympathetic System, 451; The Function of the Parasympathetic Nervous System, 454; Summary of the Effects of Stimulation on the Sympathetic and Parasympathetic Nerves, 455.

CHEMICAL TRANSMISSION AT NERVE ENDINGS, 456: Some Properties of Cholinergic and Adrenergic Nerves, 462; Pharmacology of Acetylcholine, 463; The Distribution of Adrenergic and Cholinergic Neurones, 464.

XIV. THE PHYSIOLOGY OF THE SENSE ORGANS . . 471

THE EYE, 476: The Formation of the Retinal Image, 481; The Duplicity Theory, 491; The Nerve Impulse and the Sensation, 498; The Functions of the Cones, 503; Vision with Two Eyes, 511.

THE EAR, 519: The Physical Properties of Sound, 524; The Physiology of Hearing, 529; Auditory Acuity, 533.

TASTE AND SMELL, 538: Taste, 538; Smell, 539.

XV. THE DUCTLESS GLANDS 541

THE SUPRARENAL GLANDS, 543: The Function of the Suprarenal Medulla, 543; The Functions of the Suprarenal Cortex, 547.

THE THYROID GLAND 550

THE PARATHYROID GLANDS 554

THE PITUITARY GLAND, 557; The Anterior Lobe, 558; The Posterior Lobe, 562.

HUMAN PHYSIOLOGY

CHAPTER I

PHYSIOLOGICAL ACTIVITY

THE problems of physiology are concerned with how the living organism works in its normal surroundings. We see a man raise his arm, and enquire what is happening inside him to lift the weight of his limb. We see him walk, and wonder how he manages to regulate the orderly movements without even thinking about it. To discover things of this sort, we have to take the machine to pieces, much as we should have to take a car to pieces if we wanted to know how it worked. We cannot, of course, take a man to pieces, so we have to content ourselves with investigating animals and the properties of their constituent parts, such as the muscles and the nervous system. If we find that a property of an organ is about the same in a variety of animals, such as frogs, rabbits, cats, and dogs, it is reasonable to suppose that the property will also be the same in man. When we have discovered some of the properties of the individual organs, the further question arises how they interact with each other, and how far the behaviour of the intact organism can be interpreted by reference to the known properties of its constituent parts. So it happens that although physiology is primarily concerned with the reactions of living organisms, the main body of knowledge which is ordinarily called " physiology " deals with the properties of the simpler parts of animals, including man.

The physician differs from the physiologist in various ways ; he is primarily concerned with diseased organisms, he cannot in practice simplify his problems by isolating special bits of his patients and studying their properties, and he has not the leisure under the urgent conditions presented by illness to investigate problems arising in particular cases except quite superficially. His skill in recognising a particular disease depends in great part on detecting such slight deviations from normality as can be seen from the outside, and on observing the reactions of his patient to a few simple tests which can be applied quickly and without undue distress. The success which attends the employment of such simple measures is due to the background of knowledge of the physiological processes in the body upon which the physician can draw to give meaning to the few observations he can make. To a motor mechanic, who is vividly enough aware of how an engine works, an engine knock has a precise meaning which points to the nature and position of the defect ; to an ordinary driver, the same knock only suggests that something is wrong, but does not indicate which of many possible mechanisms is to blame. In the same sort of way, a physician interprets symptoms by fitting them into the picture of the interactions of physiological mechanisms which he knows to be present. If he has at some time studied these mechanisms so thoroughly that his knowledge of how the body works has become almost intuitive, he will be quick and accurate in his interpretations.

Perhaps the most characteristic feature of health is that a man can move about as quickly and for as long as he likes. An active man moves freely, but his well-being is not measured directly by the extent or speed of his movements, but rather by the slightness of the changes produced in him by the severest exercise which he takes in the normal course of his life. Certainly, if an ordinary clerk and an athlete ran together for half a mile to catch a train, the former might arrive exhausted, panting and sweating, and remain in a relatively distressed condition for some time, whereas the latter might suffer little inconvenience, and that soon over. The clerk, however, is not necessarily less healthy than his fellow, and the difference between their physical resources is a problem of physiology which will be considered later. An invalid, on the other hand, might suffer as much distress after walking but a short distance, and such a further degree of reduction of his physical reserves would clearly be due to his illness.

Health and disease are primarily sociological concepts; they generally mean that a man can or cannot carry on his normal occupations. A particular disease may be alarming, though barely detectable, if experience indicates that it will progress rapidly. But, confining our consideration to the relatively permanent conditions of health and chronic disease, it is evident that the reserves with which a healthy organism meets a demand for exceptional exertion are likely to be of the same kind as those which enable a diseased organism to undergo moderate exertion. Consequently, whereas experience in the treatment of the sick enables rules to be laid down which roughly divide the degrees of disturbance in an organism into normal (physiological) and abnormal (pathological) ranges, the mechanisms which maintain an equilibrium in the body are equally concerned in health and in disease. Human physiology is therefore an essential part of medicine. General physiology as a science is, however, distinct from medicine in that it studies organisms without any special aim in elucidating the problems attaching to the activities of man.

Muscular Exercise

Any untrained observer is aware that strenuous exercise produces breathlessness, an increase in pulse frequency, a rise in temperature, and ultimately fatigue. A trained medical observer can judge, from the proportion between these effects and the severity of the exertion, just how fit a man may be, and if unfit, where the fault may be sought. The difference between the two observers depends not only on experience, but also on an understanding of all those happenings in the body which, as intermediate links, relate the various symptoms mentioned to the performance of muscular work. And indeed, the exploration of the consequences of exercise on various organs has been one of the most fertile fields of experimental inquiry. In order to arrive at an understanding of these factors, careful measurements are necessary ; and the knowledge resulting from these enables the clinician to employ the rough tests, which are all that opportunity allows him, and to infer valuable information from them about the condition of the functions which he is concerned to assess in his patients.

It is profitable in connection with the **source of energy** expended in muscular work to compare the performance of work in man and in machines, since the analogy with the simpler mechanisms has provided clues which have been followed up in the human body.

When a particular fuel is burnt in an engine, the total chemical energy used can be calculated from the weight of the fuel employed or from the volume of oxygen consumed. This chemical energy is usually expressed in terms of calories. Some of this energy is converted into heat, and wasted. The useful portion of the energy is converted into mechanical work, measured in foot-pounds, or an equivalent metric unit. If this mechanical work is then completely converted into heat, its equivalent can be measured, and when added to the wasted heat output it equals the input of chemical energy. This is an example of the Law of Conservation of Energy, and experiments on man and other animals will be described which show that it also applies accurately to them.

One calorie,[1] the energy required to warm 1 g. of water 1° C. (at 15° C.), is equivalent to 3·086 foot-pounds. The mechanical efficiency of a machine is measured by dividing the useful output of mechanical energy by the total energy used (both calculated as calories). Under favourable conditions its value may reach 20 per cent. for steam engines, over 30 per cent. for internal combustion engines, and 25 per cent. for the human body. The fraction of the total energy, which does not appear as external work, is wasted as heat.

There are several **ways of measuring the energy expenditure of man.** First, his chemical energy can be calculated from the weight and nature of his food, and in this way useful information can be obtained in a prolonged experiment. It is found, for example, that a diet corresponding to 1,200 to 1,800 kilocalories per day, depending on the size and probably on the previous history of the individual is sufficient to maintain the body weight constant during rest in bed ; whereas at least 2,000 kcals. and 4,000 kcals. are needed during sedentary and heavy manual work respectively.

Secondly, he may be placed in a calorimeter, and his output of heat and external work directly measured. Such experiments are, however, difficult to perform, take a long time and involve cumbersome and expensive apparatus ; for certain purposes they are essential, and will be described later (Chapter VI).

A third method depends on following the variations in the rate of oxygen consumed, and gives good indications of the changes of energy expenditure during even relatively short spells of exercise. This is considered below.

A fourth method, that of following the rate of carbon dioxide

---

[1] For most physiological purposes, it is convenient to use a unit one thousand times as great as the calorie, the kilocalorie, sometimes called " great calorie " or **Calorie** (with Capital C).

exhaled, is apt to give unreliable results owing to the presence of large stores of this substance in the body and the readiness with which some of them may be released by adventitious circumstances, as for example by deep breathing (see Chapter IV).

The calculation of energy derived from the oxidation of a given substance by 1 litre of oxygen depends on a knowledge of the chemical nature and heat of combustion of the substance. Fortunately the food-stuffs utilised in the body all yield approximately the same value, namely, 5 kilocalories per litre of oxygen. The quantity of oxygen stored in the body is relatively small and constant ; hence measurement of oxygen consumption is a relatively reliable index of the energy expenditure of the body.

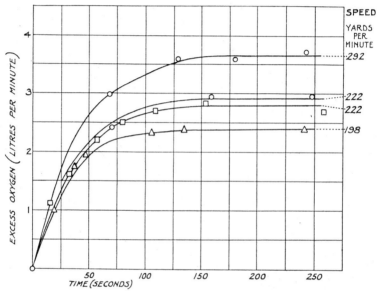

Fig. I. 1.   The **Oxygen Intake** corresponding with muscular exercise (running) of moderate severity, showing that (1) more oxygen is consumed when a man runs at higher speeds, and (2) the increased oxygen intake only rises gradually and reaches a steady value about two minutes after he begins to run. (A. V. Hill, " Muscular Move- ment.")

The problems which arise in connection with the expenditure of energy and the associated chemical changes in the body are considered in Chapter VI. Description of the technique of measurements of oxygen consumption will therefore be deferred. We will anticipate here only to give some figures which may be regarded as typical for a man of about 150 lb. weight.

If a man rests after a meal, his oxygen consumption gradually falls, till after about ten hours it reaches a steady value of some 200 c.c. per minute. This resting or " basal " value is increased by food or exercise, or by injection of glucose, extract of thyroid gland or other substances.   It corresponds, as we have seen, to about 1 kilocalorie per minute, which is about 1,500 kilocalories per day. This oxygen is absorbed in the lungs, about 6 litres of air being inhaled per minute. It is distributed throughout the body by all the available blood, which must circulate about once a minute ; the output of the heart being about 4 to 6 litres of blood per minute under resting conditions and the total volume of the blood in circulation about 4 litres.

If now this resting condition is interrupted by the performance of external work at a constant speed, the **oxygen consumption** generally rises, till in two minutes or more it reaches a new level, which in exercise of moderate severity may remain constant for a considerable period. This is illustrated in Fig. I. 1, which shows the relation between the excess of oxygen consumption over its resting value (vertical,) and the time measured from the beginning of exercise (horizontal) for the case of a particular man running at speeds of 198, 222, 222, and 292 yards per minute. It would seem, from the delay in the increase of oxygen consumption, that external work can be performed, at least for a few minutes, at the expense of energy stored in the body rather than of energy derived immediately from the extra oxygen taken in, and reasons will be given later for confirming this conclusion.

Under the influence of continued severe exercise, the oxygen consumption may rise from its resting value of 200 c.c. per minute to a maximum value of $2\frac{1}{2}$ to $4\frac{1}{2}$ litres per minute, depending on the individual. Later, the methods of calculation will be given, whereby it can be shown that in order to transfer 4 litres of oxygen from the lungs to the muscles, 34 litres of blood are required (100 c.c. of blood carries 18·5 c.c. oxygen, about 70 per cent. of which is removed by the muscles). Consequently, under conditions of extreme continued exercise, each side of the heart may have to pump 34 litres of blood per minute ; and since the total volume of blood in the body is about 4 to 5 litres, this implies a circulation of all the blood about seven times a minute. It is clear, therefore, that an enormous **output of the heart** is needed in continued exercise of considerable severity, and any impairment of its function

TABLE I. 1

The effect of Exercise on the Oxygen Consumption, Output of the Heart, and Pulse Frequency, in Man (Bainbridge after Lindhard)

	Oxygen Consumption c.c./min.	Output of Heart litres/min.	Pulse Frequency per min.
Rest	330	4·9	72
Work	606	6·3	86
,,	1,171	14·75	92
,,	1,759	16·65	128
,,	1,880	18·5	130
,,	2,407	22·6	148
,,	2,750	28·6	—

will be revealed by a reduction in the amount of exercise that can be tolerated. Probably 15 litres per minute would represent a nearly maximum output of the heart of a man with sedentary habits. The above table summarises an experiment which illustrates the close connection between the oxygen intake in the lungs, the heart output, and the pulse frequency, corresponding with the different amounts of work. It illustrates the way in which a simple observation, like the frequency of the pulse, may derive added significance from the results of physiological analysis which would be too elaborate to perform under ordinary hospital conditions.

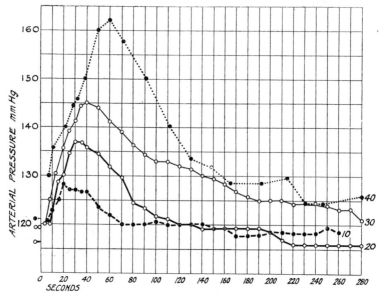

Fig. I. 2. The systolic **Arterial Pressure** changes following a period of exercise (lifting 20-lb. dumb-bells once in two seconds, a number of times given on the right of the chart). The vertical axis (0 sec.) represents the end of the period of exercise. (After Cotton, Rapport, and Lewis.)

Now if there should be any failure of the circulatory response to the demands of the muscles for oxygen during exercise, it is evident that the blood will become relatively de-oxygenated, and consequently blue in colour. This may be observed by the duskiness or blueness of the lips, nails, and other parts of the skin, and is termed *cyanosis*. If, however, the circulation responds adequately, by a considerable increase in its rate, an increased **arterial pressure** will be needed to drive the blood along the vessels. This has been observed, and is illustrated in Fig. I. 2 in connection with a form of exercise, the lifting of dumb-bells, which can conveniently be performed by patients who are not very ill. In more active exercise, the arterial pressure begins to rise at the beginning, or even just before the beginning, of the exercise; it rises further, and falls rather more slowly.

An oxygen intake of 4 litres a minute, which is a large value even for an athlete, corresponds with about 20 kilocalories per minute of energy liberated in the oxidative processes in the body, or with nearly two horse-power. Under certain conditions, as in rowing, a strong man may exert as much as ½ h.p. continuously for some time, and this represents a *mechanical efficiency* of 25 per cent., which is about the highest value attained by the human body.

Only a relatively small fraction of the chemical energy derived from oxidation is, therefore, transformed into external mechanical work ; the rest is converted to heat.

Most of the extra heat produced during exercise is lost from the

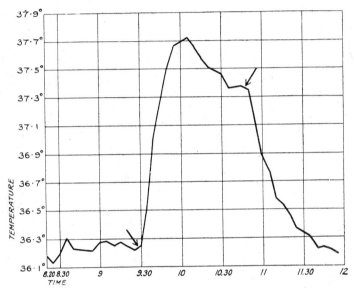

Fig. I. 3.   The **Body Temperature,** recorded by a thermocouple placed in the rectum, showing the changes due to severe exercise, the beginning and end of which are indicated by the arrows. (Benedict and Cathcart.)

skin and lungs, but some serves to raise the **body temperature,** which arrives at a balance between heat production and heat loss, at a rather higher level than normal. This rise sets in immediately at the beginning of exercise, and disappears soon after ; its magnitude depends on the severity of the activity, and on the conditions, such as clothes, subcutaneous fat and humidity, which delay heat loss from the body. Fig. I. 3 illustrates the course of the temperature changes. They may be much larger than this, and the temperature may rise from the normal value of about 37° C. as far as 40° C. The rise in temperature speeds up most of the processes in the body, and among them the frequency of the heart-beat, and so contributes to that augmentation of function with which the body responds to the urgent needs associated with considerable activity.

We have seen, therefore, that the rate of performance of *long-*

continued severe physical work is limited by factors such as the maximum rate of oxygen intake and the output of the heart. There are, however,

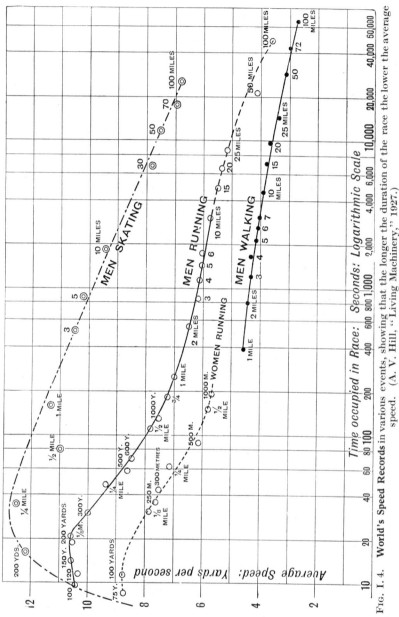

Fig. I. 4. World's Speed Records in various events, showing that the longer the duration of the race the lower the average speed. (A. V. Hill, "Living Machinery," 1927.)

further reserves in the body which enable *short* spurts of exercise greatly to exceed this rate ; under such conditions the oxygen intake, equivalent to the excess work, is postponed until the period of recovery,

and the man is said to incur an **" oxygen debt "** during his violent
exertion.   A. V. Hill's " ordinary middle-aged University Professor,"
for example, could incur an oxygen debt of 5·5 litres in 13 seconds by
running 100 yards at top speed ; that is, he consumed 5·5 litres of
oxygen over and above his resting oxygen consumption during the
period of recovery from the sprint.   His oxygen requirement during the
period of exercise was thus at the rate of 25 litres a minute, whereas
his maximum rate of oxygen intake was found to be only about 4 litres a
minute.   Consequently he exerted himself at least six times as strenu-
ously, for a short time, as he could have done if his supply of energy
had been limited to that obtained from current oxidation in the body.
Here again we are led to expect the existence of a mechanism whereby
the muscles can perform work for a short time without deriving energy
from simultaneous oxidation.

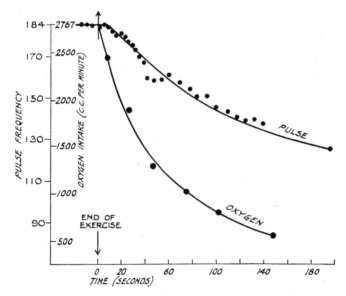

Fig. I. 5.   The changes in **Pulse Rate** and **Oxygen Intake** following severe
   muscular exercise (standing-running).   The horizontal axis represents
   the resting values.   (Lythgoe and Pereira.)

The greatest effort that can be maintained for more than a few
seconds is limited by the rate at which oxygen is utilised by the muscles
and at which it can be supplied to them.   This is made up of (1) the
current intake of oxygen, which depends on the circulation rate, and
(2) the oxygen debt.   The maximum oxygen debt which a man can
incur is approximately a fixed quantity, and does not increase with the
prolongation of his exertion ; consequently, the longer the duration of
exercise, the longer the period over which the oxygen debt must be
spread, and hence the lower the average speed.
   For long durations, the oxygen requirement of the muscles must

always be confined to the maximum rate of its absorption in the lungs. For very short durations, on the other hand, the oxygen required is almost entirely supplied by the oxygen debt mechanism, and the rate of working is limited by factors other than that of the rate of energy supply. This essential relation between duration and the maximum average speed of performance of exercise may be illustrated by Fig. I. 4, which shows the world's records, up to 1925, for various events.

The oxygen debt which is incurred to some extent even in moderate degrees of exercise, must be paid off subsequently by an excess oxygen intake. The duration of the recovery period depends on the duration and severity of the exertion, and on the " fitness " of the subject, and it may vary from a few minutes to an hour or more. The recovery process, therefore, is necessarily accompanied by a greater circulation rate, in

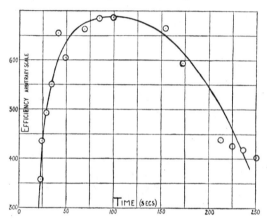

Fig. I. 6. Variation with the **Speed of Movement** of the efficiency (measured as the reciprocal of the excess oxygen consumption). Along the horizontal axis are the time taken in mounting seventy-eight steps (12.2 metres). The maximum efficiency, at 100 seconds, was 24.4 per cent. (Lupton.)

order that the oxygen may be transported from the lungs and distri-buted to the muscles ; and so the frequency of the heart-beat is usually considerably greater than its resting value. The duration of the per-sistence both of an increased **oxygen intake** and of an increased **pulse rate** during recovery from exercise is therefore a valuable rough indica-tion of the rate of a man's recovery, and consequently of his " fitness." The behaviour of the pulse provides one of the convenient clinical tests by which the reserves of a patient may be recognised as normal or pathological. An example of the variation of pulse frequency and oxygen intake after fairly severe exercise is given in Fig. I. 5.

The pulse quickens at the very outset of exercise, and accelerates till it approaches a steady rate in about two minutes. This increase of pulse frequency is due largely to a nervous mechanism originating in the brain. It usually begins before the actual start of the physical exercise, if the exertion is known to be immediately in prospect. At the end of a period of strenuous exercise the frequency falls rapidly, reaching a moderately increased value often in about fifteen minutes. This slight increase may persist for several hours, and is associated with a small increase in oxygen consumption above the " resting " value, though not necessarily accompanied by a raised temperature or an appreciably increased pulmonary ventilation. This close relation between changes of pulse rate and oxygen consumption is characteristic under many varying conditions of the body.

The recovery process would seem to indicate that some oxidative change occurs after muscular activity ; and since, after the recovery has occurred, the muscles are again able to perform work involving the liberation of energy without the consumption of an equivalent amount of oxygen, this oxidation is probably concerned with replacing the substance which is the source of " anaerobic energy " (*i.e.*, the energy which is expended without simultaneous use of oxygen).

Of the factors governing the mechnical efficiency of work performed by the human body, **speed** and skill are perhaps the most important. A man lifting a weight almost too heavy for him works hard but gains little. A fast bowler endows a ball with kinetic energy which represents only a small proportion of his total effort. That extreme slowness or quickness of movement is extravagant of energy is familiar in most human activities ; in going up stairs, for example, one of A. V. Hill's colleagues discovered that about one step per second was his most economical speed, and that a quicker or slower rate decreased the mechanical efficiency of the procedure (Fig. I. 6). In marching, again, a

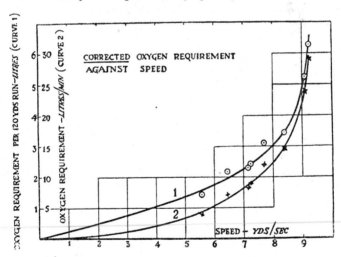

Fig. I. 7. The **Oxygen Requirement** when running 120 yards at various speeds (athlete, weight 139 lb.). Curve 1, oxygen requirement per 120 yards run. Curve 2, oxygen requirement per minute.

Note. The " oxygen requirement of the exercise " is equal to the total oxygen consumption during the exercise and recovery, minus the oxygen intake during a similar period of rest. (A. V. Hill, " Muscular Movement.")

given distance can be covered most economically at about 100 paces a
minute ; going faster or slower both involve greater intake of oxygen,
and combustion of food-stuffs. Running, on the other hand, is a form of
exercise in which there is no optimum speed, for the energy required
increases progressively with increased speed. In another example given
by A. V. Hill, an athlete weighing 139 lb. ran 120 yards at different
speeds on different occasions, and his oxygen requirements are shown in
Fig. I. 7 to increase enormously the more quickly he ran. The energy
required to run a given distance varied approximately as the cube of
the speed, and that required to run for a given time as nearly the fourth
power.

Unlike an elastic spring, a muscle performs less external work the
faster it contracts, and this property is referred to, for convenience, as

Fig. I. 8. **Inertia Flywheel** for measuring the external work done by human
arm muscles. The speed of bending the arm when a maximal pull is
exerted through a string on the flywheel depends on the diameter of
the pulley round which the string is wound. (A. V. Hill.)

the " **viscosity** " of muscle, although there is no reason to suppose that
there is any real flow of viscous fluids. In man, it may conveniently be
studied by opposing to the flexor muscles of the arm the inertia of a
flywheel, the effective mass of which can be varied (Fig. I. 8). One end
of the string is wound round the pulley on the wheel, and the other is
held in the hand, as in spinning a top. When the flywheel is made
" heavy," by winding the string round the smaller pulley, the arm
bends slowly from the extended to the flexed position ; and when the
wheel is made " light," by winding the string round the larger pulley, it
bends quickly. The more quickly it bends, the less external work it can
do, and when the movement takes only $\frac{1}{4}$ second, no external work
can be done at all ; it is, in fact, the shortest time in which an elbow can
be bent when the hand is empty. The external work performed in an
experiment of this kind can be found by calibrating the wheel and
measuring its speed of rotation at the completion of the movement.
The results shown in Fig. I. 9 are obtained from experiments in which the

same subject in each case exerted his maximum effort, and the speed of flexion of his arm was varied by varying the effective " weight " of the flywheel. The slower the movement, the greater the realised work, until, as the movement becomes very slow, the external work approaches a maximum value (some 10 or 11 kg.-metres).

Under ordinary conditions in the body, active muscles shorten, if only to a small extent, and the phenomenon which we have called the " viscosity " will evidently place a limit to the maximal effort a muscle can exert ; this restricts the force of its contraction and so prevents its rupturing a tendon, or straining a joint. If, however, the muscle be prevented from shortening, as may happen for example at the moment of

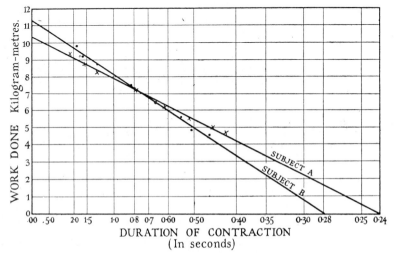

Fɪɢ. I. 9. Relation between **Maximum Realisable Work** and **Duration of Contraction** for human arm muscles, as observed on the Inertia Flywheel.

The duration of the contraction is plotted on a reciprocal scale, *i.e.*, as average speed of contraction. The straight lines show that the amount of external work done is inversely proportional to the speed of movement. Extrapolation of these lines to zero speed shows that the maximum work which might conceivably be obtained if the contractions could be made infinitely slow, would be 10·3 kg. m. for Subject A and 11·2 kg. m. for Subject B. Extrapolation to zero work shows that the minimum durations of the contraction would be 0·24 secs. and 0·28 secs. for the two subjects, respectively.

(From data by Lupton.)

kicking a ball, the muscle (extensors of the knee joint) is not restrained by this factor, and may develop an enormous tension, sufficient, on occasion, to tear apart the upper and lower portions of the knee-cap.

The individual movements in the foregoing experiment are assumed to be short and infrequent enough to be unaffected by fatigue or oxygen demand. It is of such short, quick movements that an activity like running essentially consists. Hence an enormous increase of energy is needed in proportion to increased speed of running, as was shown above in Fig. I. 7.

In slower forms of exercise, such as walking up stairs or up a hill, a too rapid performance of work is equally extravagant of energy ; but here we do not become more economical the more slowly we proceed, beyond a certain point, for energy must be expended in maintaining sustained tension of the muscles which control the posture of the body, and the intermediate position of the limbs. Consequently, though going more slowly involves less expenditure of energy in unit time, the time taken to perform a given piece of external work becomes so great that the total energy required to complete a particular task, such as mounting a certain number of steps, becomes larger. In such kinds of exercise, therefore, there is a speed at which it is performed with a maximum efficiency (*cf.* Fig. I. 6).

The problems concerned with muscular exercise will be discussed in greater detail in connection with its effects on the various systems in the body, which are considered in the chapters that follow.

Physiological Equilibria

The higher animals, including man, possess what Claude Bernard has termed an " internal environment." The individual cells are protected from the fluctuations of the external world by being enclosed in a system whose physical and chemical properties are regulated by sensitive and often elaborate, mechanisms. The preservation of these properties at steady values is one of the most remarkable feats which physiological processes have to perform, and it is undoubtedly of supreme importance in the maintenance of health. The temperature of the body, for example, is substantially constant, at a value at which the many chemical processes proceeding are in step ; if the temperature rises slightly, some of these processes are quickened more than others, and profound derangements ensue ; a rise of temperature of only $5°$ C. may be fatal. Owing to the poor conductivity of the tissues, the circulation of the blood is necessary to convey heat from the places, such as muscles, where it is mainly produced, to other places, such as the skin, where it is mainly dissipated. Elaborate arrangements exist in the nervous system which regulate the production and loss of heat so that the body temperature is steady in spite of large fluctuation of temperature in the outer world. Heat is produced by various chemical reactions and is lost from the body by a number of different routes. It is clear, therefore, that the control of even a simple property like body temperature depends on the integrity of many contributing mechanisms ; a partial failure of any one of them is compensated by an appropriate rearrangement of others, but an extensive failure results in dislocation.

The composition of the blood may be cited as another example of physiological equilibrium, for although the chemical constituents of the blood are so numerous, the variation of the concentration of any one of them, compatible with health, is quite small. Keeping these concentrations at a steady value involves again a large number of different mechanisms, failure of any one of which may have deleterious consequences throughout the body.

The constant conditions, *e.g.*, temperature and the composition of the blood, which animals maintain in their bodies are referred to as " steady states " or " physiological equilibria " ; it is one of the most fortunate characteristics of such equilibria that any change which tends to disturb the equilibrium induces a response in the organism tending to neutralise the effect of the change. To this extent, physiological equilibria resemble the true equilibria of thermodynamics. In the animal, the response is usually the resultant of a considerable number of contributing mechanisms, as in the two examples given above. W. B. Cannon has, therefore, introduced the special term **physiological homeostasis,** to describe the property of maintaining the constancy in all respects, of the " internal environment."

We must include, also, as a process of physiological equilibrium, the co-ordination brought about by the action of the central nervous system. The perfection of this co-ordination determines, to a large extent, the skill with which we can perform the various actions necessary in our daily life. Co-ordination by the central nervous system consists essentially in the receipt of information from the sense organs, in the integration of this information, and in the adjustment of the activity of all the organs and tissues in such a way that the body works as a whole in the most efficient way possible. Consider an athlete running a race. The leg muscles must first be activated in such a way that they produce the movement of running ; in this process there must be a continuous nice adjustment of the activities of opposing muscles. Then the activities of the greater part of the musculature of the body must be regulated so as to maintain balance ; in this, information is derived from the eyes, the semicircular canals and the receptors in the muscles themselves. The supply of blood to the active muscles must be regulated, and the supply of oxygen to the blood in the lungs, as we have already discussed. Finally, the extra heat generated must be dissipated by a further regulation of the distribution of the blood, and possibly by sweating. All these activities must be varied continuously, as conditions change slightly, throughout the period of exercise and recovery ; and on the efficiency with which the co-ordination is performed, depends largely the skill and efficiency with which the race is run.

Fatigue

Few problems in physiology demand so intimate an understanding of the whole subject as the nature of fatigue ; in an introductory chapter we can only indicate the kind of problems involved, so that they can be borne in mind when the more detailed descriptions of the diverse mechanisms concerned are considered in the later chapters. In ill-health, a man tires more rapidly than in good health ; fatigue, therefore, is one of the most disabling features of many maladies, and merits the closest attention of a physician.

By fatigue, we mean a condition of an organism due to sustained activity which reduces the activity, in spite of undiminished inducement to continue it ; a further essential feature of the condition is that the organism recovers completely during a sufficient period of rest. It was at one time supposed that a special physiological mechanism was at the root of the state of fatigue, which was attributed to the action of products of activity, " fatigue products," circulating in the blood. No one would now attempt to give so simple an explanation of the various sorts of fatigue. It is becoming recognised that fatigue involves the failure of one or more of a very large number of processes which normally interact so as to preserve the condition of homeostasis. If a disturbance is too large, or too long continued, or some of the compensating mechanisms are impaired, a shift in the equilibrium will take place, with consequences which incapacitate the organism. Such shifts of equilibria are of several kinds ; one kind involves fatigue, and is characterised by the facts that the disturbing agent may be attributed to continued activity of the organism, and that the shift in equilibrium disappears during rest. Even this one kind of disturbance of equilibrium may, however, involve almost any physiological system in the body ; it follows that no single cause for the sorts of fatigue which ensue after different sorts of activity, can reasonably be sought.

We may illustrate these general principles by considering a few special kinds of fatigue. We have already discussed the way in which a short spell of severe exercise is limited by the fact that its continuance would depend on incurring an oxygen debt greater than the fixed amount, which is the maximum for the particular man at the time. In long-continued exercise of less severity, fatigue may be due to shortage of fuel ; if, for example, a dog is trained to run on a treadmill, it will continue to do so for several hours before stopping from exhaustion ; if, however, glucose be administered periodically, and other conditions are favourable, the dog will continue to run for a period many times as long as that which would otherwise have led to exhaustion. Again, if a man be covered with a rubber coat or oilskin which prevents loss of heat and moisture, or if a dog is kept in a warm, moist atmosphere, the period during which he can keep up exercise of even moderate severity is quite short, and is not increased by administering glucose. Another familiar condition which closely resembles fatigue may be attributed to a reduction in blood volume to such an extent that the blood supply to the brain is inadequate and proper co-ordination fails ; few men can stand strictly at attention for more than about thirty minutes without fainting ; as far as we know, this is due to the loss of fluid from the blood resulting from the high pressure which develops in the veins of the legs when the legs are not moved, the pressure being transmitted back into the capillaries and driving some of the blood plasma across their walls into the tissue spaces.

In these examples, then, we have found fatigue to be due to disturbances of mechanisms concerned with things as widely different as oxygen debt, blood sugar, body temperature, blood volume, and the functioning of the central nervous system ; the kinds of fatigue due to mental work, and of that due to continued activity of a small group of muscles, as in lifting a weight up repeatedly with a single finger, are attributed to yet other sorts of disturbances. Of the many physiological processes described in the chapters which follow, relatively few can be exonerated from being concerned in bringing about fatigue or distress under suitable provocation, such as excessive activity or disease. It will add not a little to the value of the study of physiology if the reader will consider these processes from the point of view of what reserves they can provide to meet the demands of enhanced activity of the whole organism, and how they can interact so as to compensate for partial failures in other processes.

CHAPTER II

THE CIRCULATION

THE activity of each cell of the body consists in a variety of delicate chemical and physico-chemical reactions which can only take place under well-defined chemical and physico-chemical conditions ; if the reagents are lacking, or if the end products of chemical change accumulate, activity ceases and the cell ultimately dies. The chief function of the circulation is to maintain around the cells conditions that are optimum for their activity ; the blood brings the raw materials, it takes the waste products away. The life history of the organism is one of alternating periods of rest and of industry ; thus the blood needs of the organs are not constant and fixed but widely varying, and, as we shall see, the circulation responds to the calls that are made upon it. The blood flow to the tissues is varied by alterations in the total output of the heart per minute and by the proportion of this output which is distributed to individual organs. The regulation of the cardiac output and of the eventual distribution of the blood are thus the central problems of the physiology of the circulation.

It is common knowledge that the blood circulates, that it passes through the arteries to minute vessels in the tissues and returns thence through the veins to the heart. It was believed at one time that the vascular system connected with the right side of the heart was separate and distinct from that connected with the left, and it was supposed that in each system blood ebbed and flowed with the heart beat. This belief was supported by the fact that the system connected with the right heart, the venous system, consists of thin-walled vessels containing a dark purple fluid at low pressure, whereas the system connected with the left heart, the arterial system, consists of thick-walled vessels containing a bright scarlet fluid at high pressure. We owe to Harvey the conception and proof of the idea that the blood circulates, and as this step marks the beginning of modern physiology, it is of more than usual interest to note his argument.

Harvey was able to show that the valves in the heart are so arranged as to allow the passage of blood in only one direction. Further, by watching the motion of the heart in the living animal he concluded that blood is expelled from the ventricles into the pulmonary artery and aorta during systole, and enters the heart from the venæ cavæ and pulmonary veins during diastole. He calculated that if only a drachm of blood were expelled at each beat, the heart would in half an hour use up all the blood in the body, and so empty the veins completely and distend the arteries ; from this he concluded that the blood must move in a circle, entering the veins from the arteries. Proof that the blood flows continuously in one direction he found in the cutaneous veins of the human arm (Fig. II. 1). It had been shown previously by Fabricius that if a ligature is tied around the arm the veins swell up distally, and present along their course little swellings which mark the position of valves allowing the passage of blood in only one direction, towards the heart. The significance of this discovery was lost to Fabricius, but

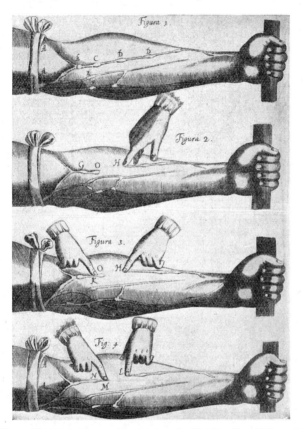

FIG. II. 1. Harvey's Figures illustrating the **Unidirectional Flow of Blood** in the Veins.

(1) The bandage A A is tied round the arm above the elbow, constricting the veins which become distended. The position of each valve is indicated by a swelling or knot, B, C, D, E, F. (2) The blood is pressed out of a vein from H to O with one finger, while another keeps the vein closed at H. No blood runs back past the valve at O. (3) If the vein is pressed by another finger at K, no blood can be forced backwards past the valve at O. (4) The vein is closed with one finger at L, as before, and emptied by stroking with another finger, M, towards the valve at N ; the vein continues empty until the finger at L is removed, when it rapidly fills up from the periphery.

was appreciated by Harvey, who made a further observation, which anyone may repeat on his own arm. The middle finger of the left hand is pressed firmly on a prominent cutaneous vein of the right forearm, and blood is massaged out of the vein proximally by rubbing the forefinger firmly up the vein past the next valve. If the forefinger is lifted, the vein fills from above only as far as the valve, but when the middle finger is lifted the whole stretch of collapsed vein rapidly fills from below. This process may be repeated indefinitely, blood always entering from the periphery; we must conclude with Harvey that blood is always entering the veins from the distal side, and the only source of this blood is the arterial system.

The missing link in Harvey's argument, namely, the connection

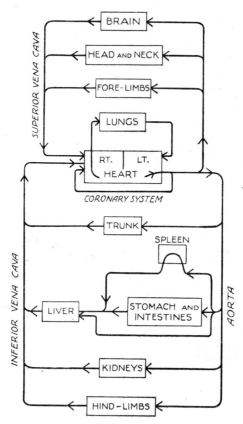

Fig. II. 2. Scheme of the **Human Circulation.**

between the arteries and veins, was supplied forty years later by Malpighi, when he discovered the capillaries.

The general arrangement of the circulation is shown in Fig. II. 2. In man, as in all mammals, the circulation consists of two circuits connected in series, the greater or systemic, and the lesser or pulmonary circuit; accordingly the heart consists of two pumps, one for the lungs and the other for the rest of the body. Blood is pumped by the right heart into the pulmonary artery and on through the pulmonary capillaries to the pulmonary veins, whence it enters the left heart. The left heart ejects the blood into the aorta, whence it is distributed to the other organs of the body, returning *via* the inferior and superior venæ cavæ to the right heart. During its passage through the pulmonary capillaries oxygen diffuses into, and carbon dioxide diffuses out of, the blood ; the blood distributed to the organs by the left side of the heart parts with oxygen to, and absorbs carbon dioxide from, the active tissues.

THE HEART

The heart is divided longitudinally into the right and left hearts, each consisting of two communicating chambers, auricle and ventricle. The capacity of each ventricle when fully relaxed is about 140 to 200 c.c. in man. The heart wall consists essentially of muscle (the myocardium), which has an inner covering (the endocardium), lined by

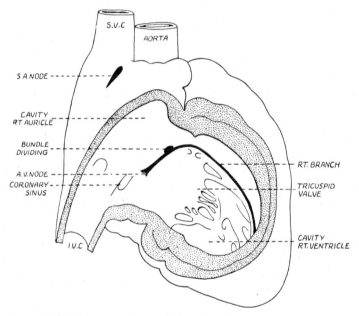

Fig. II. 3. A diagram of the human heart to show the **Sino-auricular Node** (S.A. node), the **Auriculo-ventricular Node** (A.V. node) and **Bundle of His.** The walls of the inferior vena cava, right auricle and right ventricle have been partially removed to expose the septa. The cut surfaces are stippled.

endothelium, and an outer covering (the epicardium). Covering the heart is a fibrous sac, the pericardium, which at its attachment to the great vessels is reflected over the outer surface of the heart, thus leaving between its outer or parietal layer and its inner or visceral layer a potential space, the pericardial cavity. The pericardium is attached to the surrounding structures, and thus partially fixes the heart while it allows it such freedom of movement as is essential for its contraction.

The heart muscle consists of quadrilateral cells, which are joined longitudinally to form fibres and anastomose with neighbouring cells by short bridges. It is an arrangement in which the cells communicate with one another and is termed a syncytium. The properties which these muscle cells possess in common with other contractile tissues will be dealt with in the chapter on Muscle (Chap. IX). Over the auricles the muscular wall is relatively thin, over the ventricles relatively thick; the wall of the left ventricle is four times as thick as that of the right. The thickness of the muscular wall of each chamber thus corresponds to the tension developed during its contraction. The muscle fibres of the right auricle are continuous with those of the left, those of the right ventricle are continuous with those of the left ventricle. The muscle fibres of the auricles, however, are separated from those of the ventricles by a fibro-tendinous ring, the auriculo-ventricular ring. The heart muscle is modified to form two important structures (Fig. II. 3). The first or **sino-auricular node** lies close to the junction of the superior vena cava with the right auricle and is about 2 cm. long and 2 mm. wide in man. It consists of a plexus of fine muscle fibres embedded in fibrous tissue. The second is the **auriculo-ventricular connection,** which forms the only functional junction between the muscular tissues of the auricles and the ventricles. This begins at the base of the inter-auricular septum close to the mouth of the coronary sinus as the auriculo-ventricular node, composed of slender interlacing muscle fibres. Continuous with the auriculo-ventricular node is the auriculo-ventricular bundle (of His), which runs across the fibrous ring between auricles and ventricles and enters the inter-ventricular septum, where it divides into right and left branches distri-buted to the appropriate ventricles. Each branch is continuous with a network of large, poorly striated, glycogen rich cells, the Purkinje tissue, which forms a plexus under the endocardium of each ventricle.

The cavity of each auricle is separated from that of the corresponding ventricle by an auriculo-ventricular valve, a fibrous membrane covered with endocardium and arising from the auriculo-ventricular ring. On the right side the valve is divided into three flaps (tricuspid), on the left into two (mitral). To the ventricular aspects of the margins of these valves are attached tendinous chords (chordæ tendineæ), which ter-minate in nipple-like projections of the ventricular muscle (papillary muscles). These valves are so arranged that when blood flows from auricle to ventricle the valves lie flat against the ventricular wall. When the ventricular pressure rises above the auricular pressure the valves are floated out by eddies and seal the auriculo-ventricular openings; the chordæ tendineæ, aided by the contraction of the papillary muscles, prevent the valves from being thrust out into the auricular cavity. The openings of the right ventricle into the pulmonary artery and of the left ventricle into the aorta are each guarded by semilunar valves, consisting of three semi-circular pockets whose cavities face away from the ventricles. The openings of the caval veins into the right, and of the pulmonary veins into the left auricle are unguarded; they are, however, sealed at the beginning of auricular systole by the contraction of the auricular muscle fibres surrounding them.

The Cardiac Cycle. The contraction of the heart can be seen in man by means of X-rays, and in experimental animals directly by opening the chest (Fig. II. 4). The cardiac cycle begins with a simultaneous contraction of both auricles (auricular systole), which are seen to become paler and smaller in size. After a short pause both ventricles contract (ventricular systole), at first becoming paler and more rounded, then smaller in size. As the ventricles empty, the aorta and pulmonary artery fill. After contraction, each chamber relaxes (diastole) and then gradually fills, to empty again at its next beat. The hardening and change in shape which constitute the first phase of ventricular contraction are accompanied by a thrusting of the apical region of the ventricles against the chest wall. This thrust commonly moves the overlying

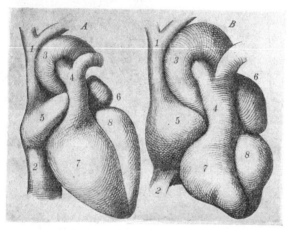

Fig. II. 4. The General Aspect of the **Mammalian Heart** in Auricular Systole (A) and at the end of Ventricular Systole (B).

1, superior vena cava ; 2, inferior vena cava ; 3, aorta ; 4, pulmonary artery ; 5, right auricle ; 6, left auricle ; 7, right ventricle ; 8, left ventricle. (Modified from Rollett.)

intercostal space, and the movement, known as the cardiac impulse (" apex beat "), indicates the point at which the region of the apex of the heart lies. The position of the impulse has great importance clinically in indicating the size and position of the heart.

In physiological terminology the terms " systole " and " diastole " are applied to each chamber of the heart. Clinically it is customary to refer to systole and diastole, meaning the activity of the ventricle alone ; the auricular contraction thus comes to be at the end of diastole, or in presystole.

In man the sequence of contraction of auricles and ventricles is recorded by the following graphic methods.

(1) **Mechanical Records—The Polygraph** (Fig. II. 5). The ink polygraph

records simultaneously on a strip of moving paper pulsations of the jugular vein and of the radial artery or heart's impulse. The pulsations of the jugular vein or heart's impulse are received by shallow metal cups pressed lightly on to the overlying skin so as to make an airtight junction. The receiver must

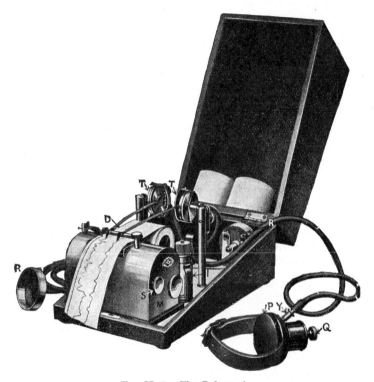

Fig. II. 5. **The Polygraph.**

R, R are cups for recording the apex beat and the venous pulse. T, T are the recording tambours, furnished with ink writing points, D. P is the glycerin pelotte for recording the arterial pulse ; it is strapped to the wrist over the radial artery, and consists of two rubber membranes tied, one over the other, on the end of a metal tube, the space between them being filled with glycerin ; the tube communicating with the tambour is attached behind the inner membrane, and contains air. If the outer membrane is indented, as by the pulse in the artery, the inner one bulges and so displaces air into the tambour. Y is a valve for opening the tambour to the air while strapping the pelotte to the wrist. Q is a screw for pressing the pelotte into good contact with the artery. M is the clockwork motor for driving the paper, started and stopped by the thumb-nut S. (Cambridge Instrument Co. Ltd.)

be placed over the jugular vein at a point where the veins are seen to be pulsating freely ; in normal subjects this is at about the level of the manubrium sterni, when the subject is lying down with the head a little raised (see p. 53). Chief interest in the records so obtained (Fig. II. 6) attaches to those of the venous pulse. In normal subjects this consists of three waves in each cycle, *a*, *c*, and *v*. The *a* wave is due to auricular contraction and is caused by the arrest of venous inflow to the heart by constriction of the mouths of the great veins. The *c* wave corresponds to ventricular systole and is largely transmitted from the carotid artery. The *v* wave is of less importance and is largely due to slowing of the venous flow consequent on the filling of the heart in diastole. The object of the radial pulse tracing is to time ventricular systole and thus to identify the *c* wave of the jugular pulse ; the *c* wave of the jugular pulse occurs about 1/10th second before the radial pulse, the difference in time corresponding to the difference in their distances from the heart (see p. 43). The most important feature of the jugular pulse is the *a* wave. In the early stages of heart block where conduction through the bundle of His is impaired, the interval between auricular and ventricular contractions and that between the *a* and *c* waves is prolonged. In the later stages, the ventricle ceases to respond to each auricular systole, and the *a* waves are not always followed by *c* waves. Lastly, in auricular fibrillation, where co-ordinate contraction of the auricles has ceased, the *a* wave is absent.

(2) **Electrical Changes—the String Galvanometer.** The contractions of the heart, like those of other muscular organs, are associated with changes in electrical potential, and if the subject is at rest the quick changes of potential

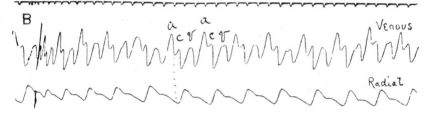

Fig. II. 6.   A simultaneous **record of the jugular and radial pulses** obtained by the polygraph ; the time marker records ⅕ second. In the radial pulse curve the main upstroke is the primary wave ; the small hump following it is the dicrotic wave. The *form* of the radial pulse is better shown by the sphygmograph. (From Lewis' " Mechanism and Graphic Registration of the Heart-beat.")

which may be led off from a pair of limbs are almost entirely cardiac in origin. The corresponding currents may be recorded by the string galvanometer, an instrument in which the current led off from the limbs is carried through a fine quartz or glass thread filmed with silver or gold and stretched between the poles of a strong electromagnet. Any current passing through the string sets up a surrounding magnetic field and the string is thus deflected. The shadow of the string is projected by a strong beam of light on a moving photographic plate, and records of its movements are obtained. In normal subjects the record (electrocardiogram) has the form shown in Fig. II. 7. The three leads commonly taken form the three sides of a triangle. As Einthoven first showed, no matter what the direction of the electrical axis in the plane of the triangle, the sum of the potential differences recorded in Leads I and III will equal that recorded in Lead II. This is the basis for the interpretation of electrocardiograms. Observation and experiment has shown that the P wave is due to the auricular contraction. the QRST complex to ventricular systole. Such records give us accurate information as to the spread of the cardiac excitation wave and have helped greatly to elucidate the nature of many irregularities of the heart's action.

The Origin and Conduction of the Heart-beat

If a mammalian heart is excised, it will continue to beat for hours, provided that an adequate supply of warm oxygenated fluid is supplied to the muscle through the coronary vessels (the fluid is passed under pressure into the aorta). It is clear, then, that the origin of the heart-beat is independent of any connection with the rest of the body. Now the heart contains nerve ganglia, chiefly derived from the vagus, but even if these are dissected out in the cold-blooded heart, the beat continues ; strips of auricular and ventricular mammalian muscle devoid of ganglia may contract rhythmically if placed in warm oxygenated Ringer-Locke solution. Further, in the chick embryo the heart

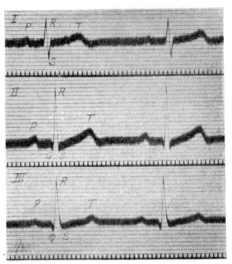

Fig. II. 7.   Typical **Electrocardiograms.**
I. Lead *I*, right arm to left arm.   II. Lead *II*, right arm to left leg.
III. Lead *III*, left arm to left leg.   (From Lewis' " Mechanism and Graphic Registration of the Heart-beat.")

begins to beat before it has received any nerves. Thus we may conclude that the beat originates in the heart muscle itself.

Although heart muscle is thus endowed with the property of contracting rhythmically, different parts of the heart behave differently in this respect. This is most easily shown in the classical experiments of Stannius on the heart of the frog (Fig. II. 8). If a ligature is tied tightly around the junction of the sinus venosus with the auricles, the auricles and ventricle stop beating while the sinus continues at the same rate as before. After five to thirty minutes the detached part of the heart begins to beat, but at a slower rate than that of the sinus ; the auricle contracts before the ventricle. If now a ligature is tied tightly between auricles and ventricle (second Stannius ligature), the auricles continue to beat as before, while the ventricle stops, after making a few rapid beats due to the stimulus of the ligature ; the ventricle begins to beat again after about an hour at a very slow rate. Thus, although each chamber of the heart is able of itself to contract rhythmically, the frequency of contraction varies from the sinus venosus at one end to the ventricle at the other ; in the intact heart the rate of beating is that of the fastest chamber—the sinus venosus. This experiment thus suggests that in the frog the heart-beat begins in the sinus region and spreads over the chambers successively ; that the same is true of the mammalian heart will now be shown.

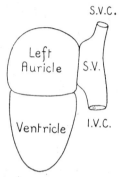

Fig. II. 8.   **Diagram of the frog's heart** from the side to show the position of the Stannius ligatures. The first ligature is tied tightly round the junction of the sinus venosus and right auricle (lying behind the left in the figure), the second between auricles and ventricle.   S.V. = sinus venosus ;   S.V.C. = superior vena cava and I.V.C. = inferior vena cava.

Nature sometimes performs in man an experiment analogous to the second ligature just described, when the auriculo-ventricular bundle is interrupted by some pathological process. On such occasions the ventricle, which may before have been contracting at a normal rate, suddenly stops for several seconds, after which it begins again at a new and unvarying rate of 30 to 40 beats per minute. The new rate is due to the onset of independent contractions of the ventricles after their only connection with the auricles, the bundle of His, has been severed. During the period in which the ventricles are quiet, consciousness is lost and an epileptiform seizure may occur, due to the cessation of the circulation to the brain.   (Adams-Stokes attacks.)

The Origin and Spread of the Electrical Changes in the Mammalian Heart. By placing electrodes, connected to a string galvanometer, on various parts of the heart's surface, the electrical changes there taking place can be accurately timed. In this way it has been shown by Lewis that the electrical change associated with the contraction of the mammalian heart begins in the sino-auricular node which lies in that part of the heart corresponding with the sinus venosus of the frog. From here the wave of electrical disturbance radiates in all directions over the auricular muscle, for the heart muscle cells are joined together as a syncytium, and for a short distance up the great veins. When the wave arrives at the auriculo-ventricular node it passes thence along the auriculo-ventricular bundle through the Purkinje tissue and into the ventricular muscle. The rate of conduction through the Purkinje tissue is very rapid (500 cm. per second) as compared with its rate through the ventricular muscle (50 cm. per second). Thus in spite of their size all parts of the ventricles contract almost simultaneously. That the normal heart-beat actually originates in the sino-auricular node (the pace-maker) is confirmed by the fact that when this structure alone is warmed or cooled, the heart-beat quickens or slows respectively ; when other parts of the heart are similarly warmed or cooled the frequency of the heart-beat is unaltered.

Auricular Flutter and Fibrillation. These two forms of disordered heart action in man are characterised by extremely rapid auricular beats as judged by the waves of electrocardiogram. In auricular fibrillation the auricular waves occur irregularly at the rate of about 400 to 500 per minute ; in flutter the waves are regular at 250 to 300 per minute. The bundle of His is incapable of conducting impulses at such rates and a variable degree of heart block is always present, the ventricle usually beating at about 100 to 150, perhaps regularly in flutter, always irregularly in fibrillation.

A condition analogous to flutter can be produced as a sequel to stimulating the dog's auricle with rapid rhythmic break shocks. If in such animals the excitation wave is followed, it is found to circulate continuously along a patch around the mouths of the caval veins.

In human flutter the course of the wave cannot be followed by leads placed directly on the heart, but the direction taken by the wave, as judged from records taken from leads placed on the chest, suggests that it follows a

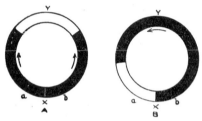

Fig. II. 9.   Genesis of Flutter and Fibrillation.   For explanation, see text.

course similar to that of experimental flutter. In fibrillation the circular path followed by the wave is shorter and more irregular.

These two forms of disordered heart action thus seem to be examples of what is known as circus movement, a condition first observed in a ring excised from the umbrella of the jelly fish. The genesis of circus movement depends on a simple property of all excitable tissue, namely the refractory period. If the heart is stimulated electrically it contracts, but will fail to respond to a second stimulus unless this follows the first after an adequate interval, the so-called refractory period. Now if we consider a ring of resting muscle as in Fig. II. 9 and stimulate this at X, then the wave of muscular contraction will spread in each direction a and b and join at the point Y, leaving the tissues behind refractory ; such is the normal spread and automatic extinction of the excitation wave over the auricle, each wave spreading out from the pace-maker, the sino-auricular node. Now if when X is stimulated the muscle at b is quiescent and that at a is refractory, the wave will spread in only one direction, anti-clockwise, and will pass Y and approach a. If the dimensions of the ring are such that by the time the wave reaches a and returns to X the muscle at these points has recovered from its refractory state, then the wave will always approach muscle that is capable of responding and so will continue to circulate indefinitely. It is clear that the existence of circus movement depends on the dimensions of the muscular ring, the rate of conduction of the wave, and the length of the refractory period. Now if the refractory period is prolonged, for example by quinidine, then it is evident that when the wave, originally starting from X, returns there, it may find the muscle still refractory and the wave will be extinguished. This is probably what happens in certain cases of auricular fibrillation ; the administration of quinidine stops the circus movement, and the rhythm of the heart becomes once more controlled by the pace-maker.

The Pressure Changes accompanying the Cardiac Cycle

Although the heart consists of two pumps, the right and left hearts, these work simultaneously and in the same way, and it will be convenient to describe the pressure changes only of the left auricle and ventricle ; those of the right auricle and ventricle are similar and simultaneous though of less magnitude. Of the various events of the cardiac cycle whose time relations are shown in Fig. II. 10 the jugular pulse and electrocardiogram have been considered already ; the pressure changes in heart and aorta and the change in ventricular volume will now be described. The pressure changes have been recorded by optical manometers (Fig. II. 17) connected by means of rigid tubes filled with fluid to cannulæ thrust into chambers of the heart. The volume changes were recorded by means of the cardiometer to be described on p. 40.

The **intra-auricular pressure curve** shows waves of rise of pressure (positive waves) corresponding to auricular systole (first positive wave) and the sudden closure of the auriculo-ventricular valves (second positive wave). The pressure then abruptly falls as the relatively emptied auricle relaxes. Blood flows into the auricles from the great veins, producing a gradual rise of pressure (third positive wave), which is interrupted when the auriculo-ventricular valves open and put the relaxed and relatively emptied ventricle into connection with the auricle. It will be noted that during diastole both intra-auricular and intra-ventricular pressures are below atmospheric pressure, which is represented as O mm. in Fig. II. 10. This is not due to any sucking action of the heart, but to the transmission of the negative pressure in the thorax through the slack heart wall.

Ventricular and Aortic Pressure. While the ventricles are quiescent, blood is flowing into them from the auricles, and the intra-ventricular pressure is slightly lower than, and closely follows, the intra-auricular pressure. With the onset of ventricular contraction the intra-ventricular pressure rises abruptly until it exceeds the aortic pressure, the aortic valves now open, blood is forced into the aorta, and the two pressures mount together. As ventricular ejection begins to decline the ventricular and the aortic pressures begin to fall, at first slowly, then rapidly, as the ventricle passes into diastole. The aortic valves now close ; the aortic pressure falls slowly as blood flows out at the periphery, ventricular pressure falls abruptly. The ventricular pressure now falls below auricular pressure, which has been rising owing to the venous inflow, the auriculo-ventricular valves open and blood flows into the ventricle, gradually raising its pressure until the next cardiac cycle begins.

Ventricular Volume. The volume of the ventricles is slightly increased during auricular systole. The onset of ventricular contraction is associated with no diminution of volume, for the ventricle is now a closed cavity separated from the auricle by the auriculo-ventricular valves and from the aorta by the aortic valves. The first period of ventricular systole is thus a period in which the muscular contraction is isometric (associated with no change in length). With the opening of the aortic valves the ejection phase begins and the ventricular volume

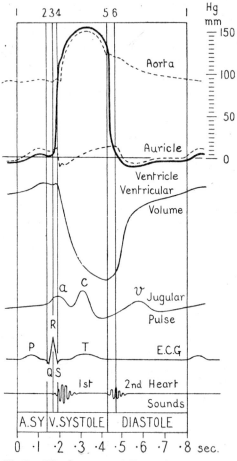

FIG. II. 10. **The Sequence of Events in the Cardiac Cycle.**

The upper four curves have been taken from actual records obtained from the dog's heart (Wiggers); they represent the pressure changes in aorta (broken line), left ventricle (continuous line), and left auricle (broken line), and the curve of ventricular volume. The lower three curves, representing the jugular pulse, the electrocardiogram, and the heart sounds, have been reconstructed from data obtained on human subjects (Lewis). The vertical lines represent the following events: 1 = auricular excitation (P wave of electrocardiogram), 2 = ventricular excitation (Q wave of electrocardiogram), 3 = auriculo-ventricular valves close, 4 = aortic valve opens, 5 = aortic valve closes, 6 = auriculo-ventricular valves open. A.SY represents the duration of auricular systole (more usual times for the duration of auricular systole would be 0·10 second, of ventricular systole 0·24 second, and of diastole 0·46 second).

rapidly diminishes. The rate of ejection gradually lessens as the ventricle empties and ceases as the aortic valves close, and the ventricle passes into diastole. With the opening of the auriculo-ventricular valves blood enters the ventricles, whose volume increases rapidly.

The Heart Sounds. The sounds associated with cardiac contraction may be heard by placing the ear on the chest wall over the heart ; they are usually detected by placing over the heart a hollow metal or vulcanite cone connected through rubber tubing to ear-pieces (the stethoscope). Each contraction of the normal heart is associated with two sounds, the first prolonged and of low pitch, the second abrupt and of higher pitch. They are usually somewhat crudely imitated by the sounds " lubb," " dup." The first sound is produced in part by muscular contraction and in part by eddies set up by closure of the auriculo-ventricular valves, the second is produced by closure of the aortic valves. Occasionally a third heart sound is heard, and is said to be due to the floating up of the auriculo-ventricular valves as the ventricle fills with blood in the early part of a long diastole.

Murmurs. When the valves of the heart are diseased, the heart sounds are usually accompanied or followed by abnormal sounds termed murmurs. Murmurs occurring with the first sound or between it and the second are associated with ventricular systole and are termed systolic. Systolic murmurs are not infrequent in normal subjects when the action of the heart is augmented, as after exercise. Murmurs occurring after the second sound and between it and the next first sound are associated with ventricular diastole and are termed diastolic ; they are purely pathological and are of first importance in detecting valvular disease of the heart. These murmurs are probably produced by the vibrations set up in the neighbourhood of diseased valves by the rapid stream of blood passing over them. When a particular valve is diseased it is thus to be expected that the murmur will be the loudest when the flow of blood is greatest, and this accords with practical experience. When the aortic valve fails to close properly (aortic regurgitation), a soft blowing murmur is heard over the second costal cartilages and left edge of the sternum ; this murmur is loudest when the difference between aortic and ventricular pressures is greatest, that is just after the second sound. In mitral stenosis the valve margins become fused and puckered and fail to open properly ; a murmur is heard at the heart's impulse when auricular pressure is most in excess of ventricular pressure and the flow into the ventricle is greatest. From Fig. II. 10 this point may be expected to be the early part of diastole just after the opening of the mitral valve and a little after the second sound, and this is in fact one of the most common periods at which the murmur is heard. But in mitral stenosis the auricular muscle hypertrophies, and it is probable that auricular systole produces a bigger ventricular inflow than in the normal heart shown in Fig. II. 10. At all events the other common period of the cardiac cycle at which the murmur is heard is during auricular systole, thus constituting a late diastolic or presystolic murmur. In advanced mitral stenosis a murmur is heard throughout diastole.

The Output of the Heart

The supply of blood to the tissues depends in the first place on the circulation rate or output of the heart per minute, and in the second place on the proportion of the output that is tapped off to each organ. By far the most important aspect of the physiology of the heart is thus

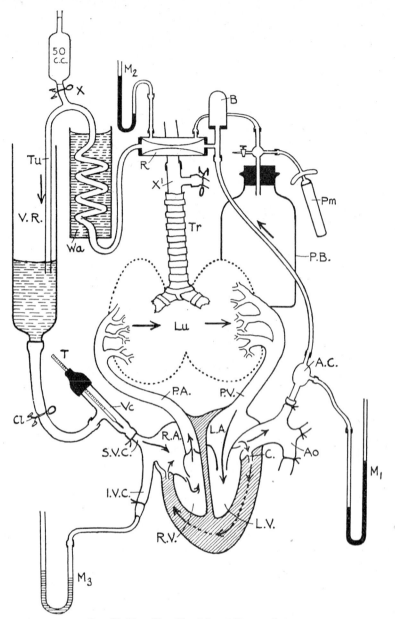

FIG. II. 11. The **Heart-Lung Preparation.**

The direction of the flow of blood is shown by arrows. V.R., venous reservoir ; Cl, clamp for adjusting the rate of inflow to the heart ; Vc, venous cannula, with thermometer, T ; S.V.C., superior vena cava ; I.V.C., inferior vena cava, connected to the manometer M_3 for measuring the venous pressure ; R.A., right auricle ; R.V., right ventricle ; P.A., pulmonary artery ; Lu, lungs ; Tr, trachea, with cannula X^1 ; P.V., pulmonary vein ; L.A., left auricle ; L.V., left ventricle ; C, coronary artery ; Ao, aorta, ligatured ; A.C., arterial cannula in brachiocephalic artery, connected to the manometer M_1 for measuring the arterial pressure ; B, elastic cushion ; R, arterial resistance ; pressure is applied to the outside of the sleeve by the pump Pm, is stabilised by the pressure bottle P.B., and measured by the manometer M_2 ; Wa, warming coil in hot water ; X, clamp for admitting blood to the graduated vessel when it is desired to measure the output of the heart ; Tu is then temporarily clamped. (From Starling's " Principles of Human Physiology.")

the regulation of its output. The output of the heart may be studied under two conditions, first when the heart is isolated, and secondly, when the heart is undisturbed in the body. Most of the observations on the output of the isolated mammalian heart have been made with Starling's heart-lung preparation.

The Heart-Lung Preparation. In studying the behaviour of the isolated heart it is of great advantage to leave the lungs in full functional connection with the heart, because the blood can be aerated and the necessary oxygen

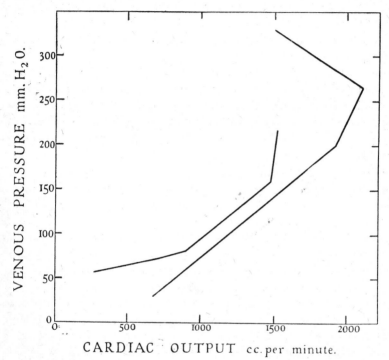

Fig. II. 12.   Relationship between **Venous Pressure and Cardiac Output.**
Two curves obtained in experiments with the heart-lung preparation.
It will be seen that equal increments in venous pressure are accompanied
by progressively smaller increments in cardiac output, until finally cardiac
output no longer rises ; subsequently, cardiac output may fall if the venous
pressure is pushed still higher.   (After Patterson and Starling.)

supplied to the heart by ventilating the lungs, and because the lungs remove vasoconstrictor substances which develop in shed blood and make perfusion of isolated mammalian preparations difficult.

The preparation is shown diagrammatically in Fig. II, 11, and is made briefly as follows. The venous reservoir, having been filled with warm defibrinated dog's blood, a dog's chest is opened under artificial respiration ; cannulæ are tied into the brachiocephalic artery and superior vena cava and all the other systemic vessels (inferior vena cava, azygos vein, subclavian artery and aorta) are tied. The blood entering the heart from the venous reservoir must now pass from the aorta through the arterial cannula and artificial circulation. In the artificial circulation the two important features are (a) the air cushion (B, Fig. II. 11) consisting of an inverted bottle containing suitably compressed air which simulates the elastic reservoir provided by the aorta and larger arteries, and (*b*) the resistance R consisting of a thin rubber sleeve inside a glass tube containing air under the known pressure of a large reservoir with which it is connected ; blood will only flow through the sleeve at a pressure higher than that of the air outside it, and thus the arterial pressure may be kept constant and independent of output. By these two devices the blood pressure in the aorta is prevented from falling too far during diastole and so the coronary circulation to the heart is well maintained.

In this preparation the nerves to the heart are severed and the heart beats at a constant rate, which may, however, be varied by altering the temperature of the blood (action on the sino-auricular node).

Using the heart-lung preparation it is found that the following factors determine the output of the heart :—

(1) **Venous Inflow and Venous Pressure.** A dog's heart of 60 g. will, if in good condition, expel just what it receives from the venous reservoir when the venous inflow is varied from a few cubic centimetres up to 3 litres a minute. With increasing rates of inflow the venous pressure, which distends the heart in diastole, rises slowly at first, but more rapidly with larger inflows (Fig. II. 12).

(2) **The Arterial Pressure.** With a moderate inflow the arterial pressure may be varied from, say, 60 to 160 mm. Hg without affecting the output ; a rise of arterial pressure is accompanied by a corresponding but smaller rise in the pressure of the venous blood entering the heart (see Fig. II. 14). With very high pressures the heart dilates and fails ; with very low pressures the heart is inadequately nourished through the coronary circulation and so fails.

(3) **The Frequency of the Heart.** With a moderate inflow (say 1 litre per minute for a heart of 60 g.) the heart rate may be varied from 70 to 150 beats per minute (by rhythmic electrical stimulation) without affecting the output per minute ; the venous pressure is, however, raised when the rate is reduced. Very slow or very fast rates reduce the output.

The Mechanism by which the Output of the Heart is varied. It is clear from what has been said that the isolated heart is an extremely efficient self-regulating pump. Within wide variations of venous and arterial pressure and of heart rate the heart puts out into the arteries just what it receives from the veins. The manner in which this adjustment is effected is shown by recording the volume changes of the ventricles.

Their volume changes are recorded by slipping over the ventricles a glass cup the shape of a wine glass (cardiometer), the stem of which is hollowed and connected to a volume recorder ; the open end of the cup is fitted with a rubber membrane in which a suitably sized hole has been burned. The ventricles are slipped through this hole, the edge of which grips lightly but securely the auriculo-ventricular groove.

Fig. II. 13 shows the results of an experiment in which the volume changes of the ventricles are recorded (upper tracing), while the arterial pressure is maintained constant and the inflow varied. A movement downward in the tracing indicates an increase in size of the heart; the volume at the end of diastole is thus given by the lower limit of each movement, and the volume at the end of systole by the upper limit;

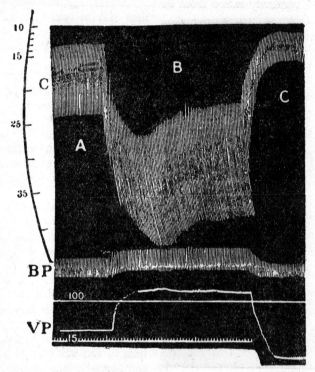

Fig. II. 13. Effect of Alterations in the **Venous Supply on the Volume of the Heart.** Heart, 67 g.

			Arterial pressure mm. Hg.	Venous pressure mm. H₂O.	Output of heart c.c. per min.
A	.	.	124	95	516
B	.	.	130	145	840
C	.	.	124	55	198

C = cardiometer curve; the curved line at the side indicates the value of the cardiometer excursions, *i.e.*, of alterations of ventricular volume in cubic centimetres. B.P. = arterial blood pressure. V.P. = pressure in the inferior vena cava. (Patterson, Piper and Starling.)

the total excursion gives the output of the heart per beat (stroke volume). When the inflow is increased from 516 c.c. per minute at A to 840 c.c. per minute at B, the venous pressure rises and the ventricles distend, at first putting out less at each beat than they receive. The diastolic volume of the ventricles thus gradually increases, and this is associated with a gradual rise in the output per beat, until finally the output equals the inflow and the heart ceases to dilate. The heart remains at this new size until at C the inflow is suddenly reduced to 198 c.c. per minute, when the heart puts out more per beat than it receives and the diastolic volume gradually falls. Finally, at a new and smaller diastolic volume the heart again puts out precisely what it receives.

In Fig. II. 14 the inflow remains constant, and when at C the arterial pressure is suddenly raised from 98 to 128 mm. Hg, the ventricles at

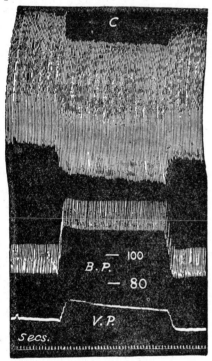

first fail to put out as much blood as they receive and so increase in size. The increase in diastolic volume is associated with a progressive recovery in the output per beat until the heart, at an increased diastolic size, is again ejecting all that it receives. When the arterial pressure is again reduced the ventricles at first expel more than they receive and so decrease in size.

The Work Done by the Heart. The external work done by each ventricle during a single contraction is the sum of the potential and kinetic energy imparted to the expelled blood. In symbols, work done per minute $= (\text{P.V} + \frac{1}{2}\rho\,\text{V}v^2)\,\text{N}$, where P represents the mean aortic pressure, V the stroke volume or output per beat, v the velocity of blood in the aorta,[1] ρ the density of the blood and N the number of beats per minute.

Assuming that the pressure developed in the right ventricle is one-sixth that of the left, the external work done by the whole heart per minute becomes:
$$\text{V} \left(\tfrac{7}{6}\,\text{P} + \rho v^2\right)\text{N}.$$

Fig. II. 14. Effect of **Increased Arterial Pressure on the Volume Changes of the Heart,** with a steady inflow of 924 c.c. Blood per minute.

C. = cardiometer curve. B.P. = arterial blood pressure. V.P. = pressure in the inferior vena cava. The lines 100 and 80 show the height of the blood pressure in mm. Hg. (Patterson, Piper and Starling.)

Now we have seen that when the work done by the heart is increased, either by an increase of output or by an increase of the pressure to which the blood is raised in systole, the diastolic volume increases. Experimentally it is found that similar increases in the rate of work, whether produced by augmented output or by raised aortic pressure, are accompanied in a given heart by similar expansions of diastolic volume. It

---

[1] This is derived by simple calculation from the stroke volume, the area of the opening through the aortic valves, and the ejection time (usually about three-eighths of the duration of a complete cardiac cycle).

will be shown elsewhere (Chaper IX) that the energy set free by skeletal muscle during contraction varies with the initial length of its fibres, and so it seems to be with the heart. When the diastolic volume of the heart is increased, the muscle fibres are stretched, the energy set free in systole is increased and the heart is able to perform more work. This relationship between the energy of contraction of the heart and its diastolic volume was formulated by Starling as " The Law of the Heart."

The oxygen consumption of the heart beating at constant rate is found to be proportional to the external work done and thus to the diastolic volume of the heart. If the heart rate is varied, then it is found that the oxygen consumed per unit of work done is greater at fast than at slow rates. Since the oxygen consumption is a measure of the total energy liberated, we may say that the efficiency of the heart, $\dfrac{\text{external work done}}{\text{energy set free}}$, is greater at slow than at fast rates. The efficiency of the isolated heart is usually about 0·2 (20 per cent.).

The Output of the Heart in Man

In determining the circulation rate in man, indirect methods alone are available, and unless these methods are to defeat their end it is essential that they should not of themselves alter the cardiac output. The methods now used all depend on measurement of the amount of gases absorbed or liberated by the blood as it passes through the pulmonary capillaries.

The Fick principle states that the total amount of any gas lost from the lungs in a given time must be equal to the difference between the amount taken away in the arterial blood and the amount brought back in the venous blood. Thus if c_a is the volume of oxygen contained in each c.c. of arterial blood, and c_v the volume in each c.c .of venous blood, and Q is the volume of oxygen absorbed by the lungs per minute, then the volume of blood flowing through the lungs per minute $= \dfrac{Q}{c_a - c_v}$. The same equation may be used for the corresponding values for carbon dioxide.

For example, in a normal subject engaged in sedentary occupation such as reading, the ventilation rate of the lungs is about 8 litres per minute ; since inspired air contains 21 per cent. oxygen and practically no carbon dioxide, while expired air contains 16 per cent. oxygen and 4 per cent. carbon dioxide, the amount of oxygen absorbed $= \dfrac{8{,}000 \times (21 - 16)}{100} = 400$ c.c., and the amount of carbon dioxide liberated $= \dfrac{8{,}000 \times (4 - 0)}{100} = 320$ c.c. Now in such a subject normal values for the oxygen and carbon dioxide content of the arterial blood may be taken as 18·5 c.c. per 100 c.c. and 50 c.c. per 100 c.c. respectively, while for the venous blood the corresponding values are 11 c.c. per 100 c.c. and 56 c.c. per 100 c.c. respectively.

The circulation rate may now be calculated from the Fick equation.

(1) From the oxygen figures the circulation rate $= \dfrac{400}{0 \cdot 185 - 0 \cdot 11} =$ 5,300 c.c. (5·3 litres) per minute. (2) From the carbon dioxide figures the circulation rate $= \dfrac{320}{0 \cdot 56 - 0 \cdot 50} = 5{,}300$ c.c. per minute.

In practice this method is used as follows. Since the composition of the inspired air is known, the volume of oxygen absorbed and of carbon dioxide liberated may be obtained by collecting the expired air over a known period, measuring it and estimating its oxygen and carbon dioxide content. Arterial blood may be obtained from puncture of an artery and analysed for its oxygen and carbon dioxide content.

If the oxygen or carbon dioxide pressure in a specimen of alveolar air is determined, the oxygen or carbon dioxide content of the arterial blood may be calculated from the dissociation curve of blood, after the total oxygen capacity has been determined on a specimen of venous blood (see Chapter III). This method is not valid in diseased subjects, since in certain conditions it is untrue that the arterial blood is in gaseous equilibrium with the mixed alveolar air.

The real difficulty of this method lies in determining the gaseous content of the venous blood, for the composition of venous blood from different parts of the body is variable, and the venous blood here in question is the mixed venous blood entering the lungs. In animals the right ventricle may be punctured and venous blood withdrawn for analysis, but to do this in man is unjustifiable. Recently it has been found possible to obtain blood from the right auricle and ventricle by means of an ureteric catheter introduced through the median basilic vein, and maintained in situ for an hour or more. The method of cardiac catheterisation has been used over 400 times on human subjects without accident, and therefore seems to be the method of choice for determining cardiac output in man. A No. 12 radio-opaque unwettable ureteric catheter is introduced through a wide bore needle into the median anti-cubital vein of the left arm and passed up through the innominate and superior caval veins into the right auricle where its position is verified by X-ray. A slow drip of 3·8 per cent. sodium citrate solution through the catheter prevents clotting round the hole at its tip. A citrate manometer connected to the catheter records right auricular pressure. Samples of right auricular blood are withdrawn into a syringe under oil, and their oxygen content estimated. The oxygen consumed by the subject per minute is also estimated.

An older and indirect method of estimating the oxygen and carbon dioxide contents of the mixed venous blood depended on the following reasoning. It is clear that if we stop breathing, the gas in the lungs will gradually tend to come into equilibrium with the venous blood, the oxygen content falling and the carbon dioxide content rising. Unfortunately we cannot measure the composition of the venous blood as simply as this would suggest, because equilibrium takes too long to be established. It is clear that if this method is to be used at all, the whole operation must be completed in a time less than that taken for any part of the blood to circulate once (about 23 seconds at rest) ; if a longer time is taken, then the composition of the venous blood will be altered, because such blood before traversing the tissues and returning to the lungs will already have been equilibrated with an abnormal gas mixture in the lungs. We can, however, determine the rate of change of composition of the air in the lungs, and the line expressing this rate of change must, if prolonged, pass through the equilibrium value. A deep breath is taken from a bag filled with a gas containing oxygen and carbon dioxide at about the same partial pressures as they are thought to have in the venous blood ; 5 seconds later half of it expelled and the last portion expired is taken for analysis ; 10 seconds later the remainder is expelled and similarly analysed. This experiment is repeated twice more, starting each time with a gas of slightly different composition in the bag. In each experiment the carbon dioxide content of each sample is plotted against the oxygen content, and the three lines so obtained are prolonged until they intersect. If these three lines intersect in a single point, then this point gives the oxygen and carbon dioxide content of the mixed venous blood. This procedure is known as the **Method of Triple Extrapolation.**

The Foreign Gas Principle. A foreign gas which is soluble in blood is breathed for a given time, and the amount removed from the lungs, and the amount taken up by each c.c. of arterial blood are measured. The circulation rate (in litres per min.) is then given by the amount of gas absorbed per minute divided by the amount dissolved per litre of blood ; this last is calculated from the concentration of gas in the alveolar air and its known solubility in blood.

It is clear that if an appreciable quantity of foreign gas is returned to the lungs by the pulmonary artery during the experimental period, the net loss of gas from the lungs will be less than that actually carried away by the arterial blood, and the calculated circulation rate will be too low. The whole observation must therefore be completed in less than the time taken by any significant amount of blood to flow once round the body, *i.e.*, in about twenty-three seconds in man at rest.

Although nitrous oxide and ethylene have also been used, acetylene appears to be the most suitable gas for this method, for it is harmless and easily estimated, diffuses readily through the lungs, and has a convenient and constant solubility in the blood. The results obtained appear to be accurate so long as the circulation rate is not too great, and they have been found to agree well with results obtained by a method involving the Fick principle, in which the composition of the mixed venous blood has been determined on samples withdrawn from the right ventricle.

After emptying the lungs the subject breathes quickly and deeply six times in and out of a rubber bag containing about 2 litres of air and 500 c.c. pure acetylene, and a sample is then taken at the end of expiration ; after a further 5 to 8 seconds of rebreathing a second sample is taken. From the composition of these two samples, and from the total quantity of gases in the lungs and bag, the amount of acetylene absorbed and its partial pressure in the alveolar air are determined.

The output of the heart is remarkably constant for each individual under conditions of complete physical and mental rest, that is after the subject has been lying down and fasting for ten or more hours (basal condition). In different individuals the output varies from 3 to $4\frac{1}{2}$

litres per minute, being closely related to the surface area of the body (2·2 litres per sq. metre), as estimated by the acetylene method, though rather higher values have been obtained by the method of cardiac catheterisation.

The cardiac output is reduced by a change from the recumbent to the standing position, which produces a fall in right auricular pressure. It is unaltered during sleep. Small increases are produced by excitement (about 1 litre per minute), and by the ingestion of food and drink (up to 2 litres per minute); but it is in muscular exercise that the greatest increases are found. Even such slight exercise as flexing the thigh once every second doubles the cardiac output. With more severe exercise, such as cycling, running, or swimming, the cardiac output increases proportionately to the rate of work, commonly reaching 20 litres per minute, and in trained individuals values of over 30 litres per minute have been attained. As Table I shows, the increase in cardiac output is due partly to an increased output per beat and partly to an increased frequency of the heart. The accuracy of the figures in this Table for cardiac output at the higher rates of work is questionable.

TABLE II. 1 (*after Christiansen*)

Subject.	Work performed. Kg-metres per min.	Oxygen consumption. Litres per min.	Pulse rate per min.	Cardiac output. Litres per min.	Output per beat. c.c.
Untrained female	0	0·24	·77	4·6	60
	600	1·57	131	14·5	111
	720	1·79	145	17·4	120
	840	2·05	159	19·0	120
	960	2·45	168	23·8	142
Trained male . . .	0	0·25	70	4·2	60
	720	1·93	118	16·5	140
	960	2·22	140	20·6	147
	1,200	2·83	174	23·0	132
	1,440	3·26	180	26·9	149
	1,680	3·94	179	37·3	208

Recent experiments have shown that in the human subject at rest, the output of the heart is largely determined by the pressure at which blood enters the right auricle from the great veins, and there seems little reason to doubt that changes in output are achieved by a mechanism very similar to that which operates in the heart-lung preparation. It is probable that the rise in cardiac output during exercise in man is also occasioned by a rise in right auricular pressure, but technical difficulties do not permit a definite answer to the questions whether the rise in venous pressure and increase in diastolic size in severe exercise are alone adequate to account for the very large increase in cardiac output that occurs. So far as our knowledge goes, however, the increase in size of the heart during exercise in man seems less than would be expected if the rise in stroke volume were due entirely to increase in diastolic size ; and it is therefore probably due in part to a more efficient emptying of the heart. The behaviour of the intact human heart during exercise also differs from that of the heart-lung preparation in that the increased cardiac output is due not only to an increased stroke volume (in Table I from 60 c.c. at rest to 208 c.c. during exercise), but also to an increased frequency of the heart beat. These differences in behaviour of intact and isolated hearts may be attributed mainly to the action of the cardiac nerves ; the increased frequency and the increased force of contraction of the intact heart are probably due to an inhibition of vagal and to an augmentation of sympathetic nerve impulses to the heart, and also perhaps to the action of adrenaline. Such changes in the nerve impulses playing on the heart occur in two ways. First they arise from impulses transmitted from the cerebral hemispheres to the nuclei of the medulla, and secondly, they arise reflexly from distension of the great veins and right auricle produced by the increased venous return to the heart. It has been shown experimentally that a rise of pressure in the great veins and right auricle causes impulses to pass up the vagus to the medulla, where they decrease the number of vagal and increase the number of sympathetic impulses sent to the heart, whose rate is thus increased (**Bainbridge reflex**).

The Innervation of the Heart. The heart receives two sets of nerve fibres from the autonomic system, parasympathetic fibres from the vagus, and sympathetic fibres (see Fig. XIII. 1). The vagal fibres terminate in ganglion cells in the heart, from which fibres pass to the sino-auricular and auriculo-ventricular nodes and the auricular muscle. Stimulation of the vagus slows the heart by action on the pace-maker, and also depresses the conduction from auricle to ventricle by action on the auriculo-ventricular node ; it may also reduce the force of the auricular contractions, but in the mammal has little action on the ventricles themselves. The sympathetic fibres arise from cell stations in the middle and inferior cervical ganglia and terminate around the sino-auricular and auriculo-ventricular nodes and in the heart muscle. Stimulation of the sympathetic fibres quickens the heart by action on the pace-maker, facilitates conduction from auricle to ventricle, and augments the force of the auricular and ventricular contractions. It may thus be seen that the action of the vagus on the heart is almost the converse of that of the sympathetic (*cf.* reciprocal innervation p. 408). Normally impulses are passing to the heart along each set of nerves, for section of the vagus quickens the heart and section of the sympathetic slows it.

The Control of the Frequency of the Heart. The number of impulses passing along the vagus and sympathetic nerves to the heart, and thus the heart rate, are chiefly determined reflexly through the Bainbridge, depressor, and carotid sinus reflexes (see pp. 66–71). By means of the Bainbridge reflex a rise of pressure in the great veins and right auricle quickens the heart, and a fall of pressure slows it ; by means of the depressor and carotid sinus reflexes a rise of pressure in the aorta and carotid arteries slows the heart, and a fall of pressure quickens it. The heart rate is also altered through the cardiac nerves by the activity of the cerebral hemispheres, becoming quickened in emotion, fright and exercise ; it is greatly slowed in a fainting attack. The heart is quickened when the body temperature rises (action on the sino-auricular node), when the rate of secretion of the thyroid gland is abnormally high, and in asphyxia.

Heart Failure. The function of the heart is to propel blood through the vessels at a rate fast enough to meet the metabolic requirements of the tissues ; failure to do so may result either from a lesion of the heart itself or because the supply of blood to the heart from the great veins is inadequate (peripheral circulatory failure). Heart failure in man is frequently accompanied by a condition of stenosis (narrowing) or incompetence (leakiness) of one or more valves, the heart then working at a mechanical disadvantage ; yet it will readily be appreciated that the origin of heart failure is usually to be sought in disease of the heart muscle itself. The earliest symptom of heart failure is undue breathlessness on exertion. In advanced heart failure the patient is breathless at rest and more so in the recumbent than the sitting posture ; venous pressure in the cervical veins is increased, the liver is enlarged and extensive accumulations of fluid occur, in the tissues (œdema) of the legs and in the peritoneal (ascites) and pleural cavities. In such an advanced case the cardiac output may be reduced to half the normal. It is now known that this reduction is not the chief cause of the symptoms since a similar or greater reduction of cardiac output in peripheral circulatory failure is associated with an entirely different clinical picture. The chief factor in producing the symptoms in cardiac failure is the rise in venous pressure which, on the left side of the heart, produces engorgement of pulmonary veins and capillaries, and by thus increasing the rigidity of the lungs leads to breathlessness and may lead to œdema of the lungs ; on the right side of the heart the raised venous pressure distends the hepatic veins and thus enlarges the liver, and by raising capillary pressure favours the passage of fluid out of the capillaries into the tissues.

An understanding of the mechanism of heart failure is of the first importance in clinical medicine and it is provided by the experiments on the heart lung preparation already described and particularly by the relationship of venous pressure to cardiac output shown in Fig. II. 12. The normal human heart works at a low venous pressure ; it thus has a large reserve, for relatively small rises in venous pressure produce considerable increases in cardiac output. In advanced heart failure, however, the heart is working at a high venous pressure, probably in the region where the curves of Fig. II. 12 become vertical, for a small increase of venous pressure now no longer produces a rise in cardiac output ; and even at these high venous pressures, the cardiac output is much less than it is in a healthy heart at a much lower pressure. The heart really consists of two pumps, the right and the left, and it is theoretically possible for one of these to show a greater degree of failure than the other. This is most conspicuous in diseases which cause a great rise in systemic arterial pressure and thus increase the load thrown on the left ventricle ; in such conditions attacks of breathlessness (cardiac asthma) which may progress to acute pulmonary œdema may be the chief manifestation of heart failure ; the essential factor in the production of such attacks is believed to be a rise in left auricular and thus in pulmonary venous pressure.

The most instructive example of cardiac failure in man is that seen in paroxysmal tachycardia in which the heart suddenly begins to beat at a rate of 180 to 200 beats per minute ; at such rates even previously healthy hearts may after some hours display the phenomena of cardiac failure. With the onset of the paroxysm the patient gradually becomes breathless, the neck veins swell, the liver enlarges, and the cardiac impulse moves outwards for perhaps 2 inches. This movement of the impulse is due to the enlargement of the diastolic size (cardiac dilatation) consequent on the increased venous pressure. Even with such a cardiac dilatation the output of the heart is found to be reduced. With the end of the paroxysm, the neck veins collapse, the liver decreases in size and the heart's impulse returns to its normal position ; the relationship between cardiac output, diastolic size and venous pressure once more becomes normal.

The Arterial Pulse

The sudden ejection of blood into the aorta that occurs with ea beat of the ventricles produces a wave of increased pressure that i propagated along the arteries towards the periphery ; this is known as the pulse wave, and it may be felt and recorded in any of the superficial arteries of the body as the pulse beat. The velocity at which this pressure wave is propagated may be determined by recording the times of its arrival at two different points such as the subclavian and radial arteries, and dividing the time differences by the difference in the distance from the heart of the two points at which measurements are taken. The pulse wave velocity varies in different subjects chiefly with the thickness and elasticity of the arterial wall, and since the arteries tend to become more rigid with advancing years (arteriosclerosis), the velocity increases from an average rate of 5·2 m. per second at the age of five to an average of 8·6 m. per second at the age of eighty-four. It is important not to confuse the pulse wave, which is simply a wave of increased pressure, with the movement of the blood itself ; the velocity of blood-flow is nowhere greater then 0·5 m. per second at rest and is considerably less in the smaller vessels.

The Form of the Pulse. The changes in pressure and their spacing in time that occur in a superficial artery such as the radial may be recorded by the *sphygmograph,* an instrument in which the pulsations of the artery are transmitted to a lever writing on a piece of smoked paper moving at a suitable speed. With practice the main features exhibited by such a record can usually be ascertained with the finger. The main deflection in the pulse record, the primary wave (Fig. II. 6), is the result of the sudden distension of the aorta during ventricular systole. Following the primary wave are a number of secondary waves, which arise in several ways. The most constant and conspicuous secondary wave results from closure of the aortic (semi-lunar) valves. At the end of ventricular systole the pressure in the ventricle falls rapidly, and blood begins to flow back from the aorta, but is suddenly checked by closure of the aortic valves. This sudden check causes a rise of pressure in the aorta, and this wave travels down the arterial tree with the same velocity as the primary wave which it follows. This secondary wave is known as the dicrotic wave and is preceded by a notch, the dicrotic notch. From what has been said it will be realised that the upstrokes of the primary and of the dicrotic waves are separated by the same interval of time as the opening and closure of the aortic valves. In addition to those two waves there are a number of inconstant and small waves arising from the reflection of the primary wave by obstacles such as the bifurcations of the arteries.

The form of the pulse wave is modified by such conditions as affect the discharge of blood from the heart and its escape through the arteries. Thus, when the aortic valves are narrowed by disease (aortic stenosis) the distension of the aorta during systole is very slow and the pressure in the peripheral arteries rises slowly to a maximum; this slow-rising pulse is termed anacrotic. When, on the other hand, the aortic valves do not close properly (aortic regurgitation), the pressure in the aorta falls very quickly during diastole and is suddenly and greatly raised during systole; in this condition the upstroke of the primary wave is unusually sudden and its downstroke rapid; from the sudden thrust on the finger feeling the artery this pulse is described as " water-hammer." In conditions of low pressure and rapid blood-flow, as may occur in children and in fevers, the dicrotic wave may be so pronounced as to be easily felt at the wrist; the frequency of the heart may thus be mistaken for twice its true value.

THE FLOW OF BLOOD THROUGH THE VESSELS

The blood is expelled from the ventricles in jets at high pressure into the aorta and pulmonary artery. The **aorta** is a wide tube, the thick walls of which are largely composed of elastic tissue; like any other elastic structure, its capacity is determined largely by the pressure of the blood it contains. When blood is expelled during ventricular systole, the aortic pressure rises, the aorta is distended and so accommodates a large part of the blood expelled, the remainder escaping through the arteries. During ventricular diastole, the tension in the aortic walls maintains the flow of blood onwards through the arteries, and the aorta diminishes in size until it is again distended at the next heart beat. In this purely passive way the aorta (and to a less extent its larger branches, which are similar in structure) converts the intermittent flow from the heart into a continuous though pulsating flow in the arteries. The blood passes from the aorta into its branches, **arteries,** which divide repeatedly until they become capillaries. With each subdivision, the arterial lumen becomes smaller and the arterial wall becomes more predominantly muscular. By the contraction or relaxation of their muscular walls the arteries (particularly the smaller branches or arterioles) are capable of great variation in calibre, and it is this calibre which largely determines the proportion of the total cardiac output distributed to the individual organs.

The finest branches of the arterioles lose their muscular coat and are termed **capillaries.** The capillaries are about 10μ in diameter and the blood they contain is separated from the tissues by a single layer of flat endothelial cells which forms the capillary wall; it is accordingly here that the interchange of substances between the blood and the tissues takes place. In spite of their thin walls, the capillaries are capable of active contraction, and of exerting pressure of 60 mm. Hg or more when contracted. In some resting tissues the majority of the capillaries are closed ; during activity they open, and thus they also play a part in regulating the distribution of the blood to the organs. Although the capillaries are under nervous control, they are pre-eminently the vessels which react to chemical substances released during the activity of tissues which they supply.

The blood from the capillaries is collected into venules and thence in the **veins** returns to the heart. The veins are wide and relatively thin-walled, and offer little resistance to the flow of blood. They are capable of active variation of calibre and are under nervous control. All but the smallest and largest veins contain valves, consisting of a number of semi-circular folds of the intima projecting into the lumen. As a rule two such folds are placed opposite one another, and are so formed that when the blood is forced in a direction away from the heart, the folds float out into the blood-stream and block the vein. When the muscles contract the thin-walled veins are squeezed and blood is forced in the only direction it is free to travel, namely towards the heart. When the muscles relax the tension on the veins is relaxed and blood is free to enter, but only from the arterial side. The " muscular pump " is thus an important mechanism for facilitating the venous return to the heart and for increasing the output of the heart during exercise.

TABLE II. 2

Blood vessels.	Number.	Radius cms.	Total cross-section sq. cms.	Velocity of blood cms./sec.	Length cms.	Fall in pressure mm.Hg.	Fall in pressure per cm. length.
Mesenteric artery . .	1	0·15	0·07	16·8	6·0	0·8	0·15
Main branches of mesenteric artery . .	15	0·05	0·12	10·1	4·5	3·3	0·73
Final branches of mesenteric artery . .	45	0·03	0·13	9·3	3·9	7·7	1·98
Intestinal arteries . .	1900	0·0068	0·20	5·8	1·42	24·5	17·2
Final branches of intestinal arteries . .	26,600	0·0025	0·57	2·1	0·11	6·3	57
Branches to the villi .	328,000	0·00155	2·48	0·48	0·15	4·0	26·5
Arteries of the villi .	1,050,000	0·00112	4·18	0·28	0·20	5·2	26·0
Capillaries of the villi .	47,300,000	0·00040	23·78	0·04	0·04	1·2	30
					Total	53·0	
Veins of the villi .	2,102,400	0·00132	11·59	0·1	0·10	0·7	7·0
Veins between the villi and the submucosa	131,400	0·00375	5·80	0·2	0·10	0·3	3·0
Submucosal veins .	18,000	0·0064	2·32	0·5	0·15	0·4	2·7
Final branches of intestinal veins . .	28,800	0·0032	0·93	1·3	0·11	2·3	21·0
Intestinal veins . .	1,899	0·0138	0·84	1·4	1·42	1·5	1·0
Final branches of mesenteric vein . . .	45	0·075	0·79	1·51	3·91	0·2	0·05
Main branches of mesenteric vein . .	15	0·12	0·67	1·7	4·5	0·1	0·02
Mesenteric vein . .	1	0·3	0·28	4·2	6·0	0·05	0·01
					Total	5·55	

The figures for the velocity of the blood and the fall in pressure along the various vessels have been calculated on the assumption that the rate of blood flow in the mesenteric artery is 70 c.c. per minute, and that this is evenly divided amongst the subsequent branches. It has been assumed also that the apparent viscosity of the blood in all the vessels whose radius is greater than 0·007 cm. is 4·5 times that of water (*i.e.*, 3·1 centipoises at 37·5° C.) and that it falls as the blood vessel becomes smaller according to the relation described on p. 93, Fig. III. 2. The total fall in pressure adds up to only 59 mm. Hg, a figure considerably smaller than the normal blood pressure of a dog. This is probably due to the fact that under normal conditions, a considerable proportion of the capillaries, and small arteries supplying them, are closed, so that the total effective cross-section is reduced and the fall in pressure increased.

At rest the **velocity** of the blood entering the aorta during ventricular systole is about 50 cm. per second. As the vascular tree branches the total area of cross-section increases, and the velocity of blood-flow correspondingly lessens, becoming minimal in the capillaries, where it is important that enough time be given for interchange to take place. At rest, the average particle of blood takes about one second to traverse the average capillary; during exercise the time is much shorter. The table on the preceding page gives some idea of the dimensions of the circulation; it shows the relationship between the total areas of cross-section and the velocity of blood-flow in the branches of the mesenteric artery of a dog weighing 5·7 kg.

Methods of Determining the Blood-flow through an Organ

The blood-flow through an organ may be measured in one of the following ways :—

(1) A cannula is tied into the vein draining that organ and the blood is collected and measured over a given time.

(2) If the main artery or vein is heated at a constant rate, then the rise in temperature of the blood in this vessel will vary inversely as the rate of flow. In Rein's " thermostromuhr." the artery is heated by a pair of plates connected to a steady source of alternating current of such high frequency that it fails to stimulate nerves and muscles. Two thermocouples placed on the artery above and below the point of heating are connected to a sensitive galvanometer whose deflection measures the temperature difference. The instrument is calibrated on a vessel through which the flow is known. Several of these devices may be placed on different vessels with very little operative interference and left there for a considerable time. In this way very complete records of the changes of blood-flow in response to various stimuli have been obtained.

(3) The human forearm is placed in a plethysmograph (Fig. II. 15), which is a rigid case closed with rubber diaphragms perforated to fit the arm snugly; a side tube leads from the plethysmograph to a volume recorder. Any change in the volume of blood in the arm is transmitted through the fluid in the plethysmograph to the volume recorder. The blood-flow may now be measured by observing the rate of increase of

volume when the venous drainage is temporarily obstructed by throwing a pressure of 60 mm. Hg into a cuff wrapped on the upper arm (see Fig. II. 18). This method is also applicable to other organs.

The following methods, while they do not actually measure the blood-flow, are used to detect changes in blood-flow or in vascular calibre :—

(1) If the organ is exposed to the air, its surface temperature is determined by the rate of blood-flow through it. This method is particularly useful for the human skin.

(2) The hand or foot may be placed in stirred water in a calorimeter ; the rate of heat elimination is proportional to the blood-flow.

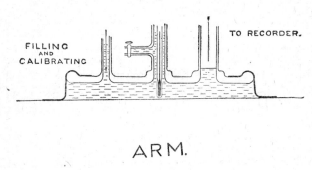

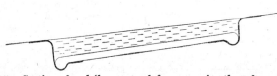

ARM.

FIG. II. 15. Section of a **plethysmograph** for measuring the volume changes of the human forearm. It consists of a truncated metal cone, fitted at each end with perforated diaphragms of strong rubber (black line) through which the forearm is inserted. The arm and plethysmograph are placed in a bath of water at suitable temperature (*e.g.*, 32° C.), the elbow and wrist are supported and wedged by sandbags and the plethysmograph is filled with water. All outlets from the plethysmograph are closed except that connected with a volume recorder, which thus records the volume changes of the forearm enclosed in the apparatus. (Lewis.)

(3) In a transparent tissue lying superficially, like the frog's web or the conjunctiva, or in an organ that can be exposed, the vessels may be observed microscopically and measured.

(4) The organ may be placed in a plethysmograph (Fig. II. 15) and its changes in volume recorded. These changes represent changes in the volume of blood in the organ, and may be ascribed to active changes in calibre of its vessels if unaccompanied by changes in general arterial and venous pressures.

(5) Colour Changes. The depth of colour of a tissue is determined by the diameter of the capillaries and venules (minute vessels) ; it tint by the rate of blood-flow.

Since the colour of the skin is determined by the calibre of its minute vessels, and its temperature by the rate of blood-flow through it, simple observation shows that different orders of vessels may change in size independently. Thus the hot pale hand, common in summer, is one in which the arteries and arterioles are wide, the capillaries narrow. Most of the blood is, in fact, by-passing the capillaries through short wide arteriolo-venous communications, which are found in the nail-bed, the volar surface of the fingers and the palm of the hand, and in similar parts of the foot. These vessels have thick muscular walls, are supplied by sympathetic nerves and are important in regulating the blood flow to, and thus the heat loss from, the extremities. They are thus important in the control of body temperature (see page 235). The cold red hand often seen in winter is one in which the arteries are narrow and the capillaries dilated ; the redness is due to the slow rate of removal of oxygen from the blood, occasioned by cold. The cold blue hand is one in which the arteries and arterioles are still further narrowed.

The Blood Pressure

If the effects of respiration and of muscular movement on the veins are excluded, the flow of blood through the vessels is produced

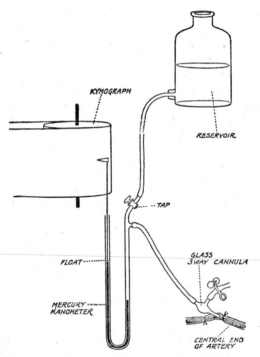

Fig. II. 16. **Apparatus for taking Blood Pressure in Animals.**

entirely by the pressure differences established by the heart. Although the blood pressure thus falls continuously from its highest value in the aorta to its lowest in the great veins entering the heart, it is most conveniently measured in three situations, the larger arteries, the capillaries and the great veins.

The Arterial Blood Pressure. The pressure in the arteries varies with each heart beat, and thus has a **maximum or systolic** value and a **minimum or diastolic** value ; the difference between the two is termed the **pulse pressure.** In the experimental animal the arterial pressure is commonly measured by inserting into the carotid or femoral artery a glass cannula filled with an anti-coagulant solution (half saturated Na_2SO_4), and connected through pressure tubing filled with the same liquid to a mercury manometer (Fig. II. 16). When, in determining the pressure in a vessel, the flow is obstructed, as in the case under consideration, the recorded value gives the pressure at the point of junction of that vessel with the larger vessel that supplies it ; for since there

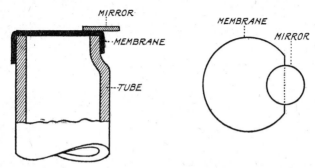

FIG. II. 17. A Membrane Manometer (Wigger's pattern.)

The tube on the end of which the membrane is tied is rigidly connected to a cannula in the ventricle, aorta, etc., and the whole is filled with saline solution. Movements of the membrane are recorded photographically by means of a beam of light reflected from the mirror attached to it. This manometer accurately records rapid changes in pressure, as its moving parts have a high natural frequency and are very light.

is no flow along the obstructed vessel there is also no fall of pressure. The levels to which the mercury rises in systole and diastole do not accurately represent systolic and diastolic pressures, since they are largely determined by the momentum of the heavy column of mercury. When true systolic and diastolic pressures are required the arterial cannula must be connected through a fluid system to a manometer that will respond quickly enough to record the pressure changes without lag, such as the membrane manometer shown in Fig. II. 17. When the arterial cannula is connected to a mercury manometer of very wide bore and hence of very low frequency, the mercury column does not oscillate and records the **mean pressure** of the blood ; more usually this value is recorded by using a mercury manometer of narrow bore with very high damping. The mean arterial pressure can be calculated from the systolic and diastolic values if the form of the pulse wave is also known ; it approximates more closely to the diastolic than to the systolic pressure, since the pressure falls more rapidly at the beginning than at the end of diastole.

The arterial pressure may be measured in man by a similar method. A needle filled with sodium citrate solution may be thrust into a large artery such as the brachial or femoral and connected through thick rubber and lead tubing filled with the same solution to a membrane manometer. For routine work an indirect method based on the following principle is used. If an artery is compressed, then the minimum pressure serving completely to stop the flow must be at

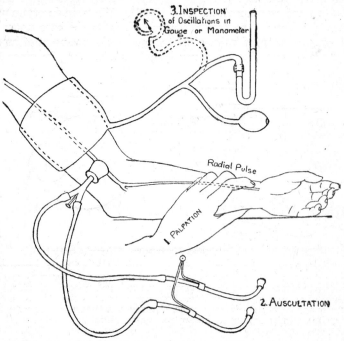

FIG. II. 18.   The Measurement of the Arterial Blood Pressure in Man.
(From Harris' " Experimental Physiology.")

least as great as the highest pressure (systolic) attained inside the vessel. As the pressure outside the artery is reduced, so blood will flow through the artery for longer and longer periods of the cardiac cycle, until finally when the compressing force is just less than diastolic pressure, blood-flow will be unimpeded, and the artery will cease to be deformed at any point of the cardiac cycle. A flat rubber bag contained in a loose but inextensible silk case is wrapped snugly around the upper arm. The interior of the bag is connected to a small hand pump through which air can be introduced or removed, and to a mercury manometer which measures the pressure of the air in the cuff. The cuff must be sufficiently wide to transmit the pressure of air it contains to the centre of the limb (12 cm. for the upper arm) and sufficiently long to encircle the limb completely. The systolic and diastolic pressures are deter-mined with this **sphygmomanometer** (Fig. II. 18) as follows.

(1) **By Palpation.** The cuff is inflated until the pulse can no longer be felt at the wrist. Air is allowed to leak out until the pulse returns. The pressure at which the pulse beat can first be felt is taken as systolic pressure.

(2) **By Auscultation.** The bell of the stethoscope is placed over the brachial artery at the bend of the elbow, and the cuff on the upper arm inflated until all sounds disappear. Air is allowed to leak out until pulse sounds just reappear; this is the systolic pressure. As the pressure is lowered the sounds become louder and louder and then abruptly die away. The point at which the loud sounds begin abruptly to die away is taken as diastolic pressure, for below this point the pressure of the cuff has failed to deform the artery. It is to be noted that while this index is probably a reliable measure of diastolic pressure in most subjects, patients are occasionally encountered in whom the sounds continue to be well heard when the pressure in the cuff is reduced to zero; in these cases this index of the diastolic pressure is clearly unreliable.

(3) **By the Oscillometer.** In some forms of the instrument the bag is connected to a high-frequency diaphragm type of pressure gauge. The oscillations of the diaphragm record the volume changes of the main artery of the limb transmitted to the air in the cuff. When the pressure in the cuff is slowly reduced, the point at which the oscillations of the manometer first increase is taken as systolic, the point of maximum oscillation as diastolic pressure.

The auscultatory method is that most commonly used in England and is probably the most reliable. The oscillatory method gives values for the systolic and diastolic pressures that are usually 5 to 10 mm. Hg higher than those obtained by the auscultatory method. Systolic pressures obtained by palpation are in experienced hands in fairly close agreement with those obtained by auscultation; owing, however, to the difficulty of feeling the first weak pulse beat, the values particularly in inexperienced hands are frequently some 5 to 10 mm. lower. It seems unimportant which method is actually used, since the possible errors are too small to be of much significance; it is more important for the student to learn to use one method accurately and to know its limitations.

The Capillary Pressure. Accurate estimation of the capillary pressure in man is extremely difficult. Until recently the best available method was to seal a small glass chamber on to the skin. The chamber is open on the side next the skin, and its interior is connected to a manometer and source of air pressure. The pressure of air necessary to cause the capillary loop (observed microscopically) to disappear is taken as the capillary pressure. This method gives variable results and is less reliable than the following direct method. A finger is immobilised in a bed of plasticine and the cuticle is shaved off from the base of the nail. If a drop of glycerine is placed on the skin, the capillary loops can easily be seen with a binocular microscope and surface illumination. By means of a micro-manipulator a fine glass micro-pipette containing physiological saline and sodium citrate solution is introduced into one of the capillaries, and blood allowed to enter its orifice. The pressure at which the blood neither enters nor leaves the pipette but oscillates with each heart beat is the mean capillary pressure. Owing to difficulties of fixation and of observing sufficiently large capillaries, the base of the nail is as yet the only place where the method is practicable in man.

The Venous Pressure. The veins offer little frictional resistance, and the blood flows through them with only a small fall of pressure. The venous pressure at some distance from the heart is thus very close to that in the superior vena cava. The most accurate and direct method of determining the venous pressure in man is to introduce into the median basilic vein at the elbow a wide needle connected with a manometer containing a solution of sodium citrate. The solution is allowed to flow into the vein until the meniscus shows small respiratory oscillations about a fairly constant mean value. The height of this meniscus gives the venous pressure in the vein at the point of measurement. To obtain a gauge of general venous pressure such values must be corrected for the difference in level between the vein punctured and the heart, since the pressure in the veins, as in all the vessels, is affected by gravitational forces. It is not easy to say precisely at what level the heart is in man, and so the pressures are usually referred to an easily accessible structure bearing a fairly constant relation to the heart, the junction of the manubrium with the body of the sternum (angle of Louis).

In recumbent healthy subjects when the arm lies at or below the level of the heart, the meniscus in the venous manometer comes to rest at the same level as the angle of Louis, or a centimetre or two below it. Relative to the angle of Louis the venous pressure in health is thus 0 to — 2 cm. H_2O.

Now the veins, being wide lax vessels, are distended when the pressure of their contained blood is greater than that of the atmosphere. When the venous pressure is a little below that of the atmosphere the veins collapse. If therefore in the recumbent subject we trace a superficial vein, such as the external jugular, from a point well below the level of the manubrium sterni to a point above it, we see that for the lower part of its course the vein is distended, and then at some higher point it collapses and ceases to be visible (Fig. II. 19). At the junction of distended and collapsed vein, pulsations synchronous with the heart beat and respiration will be observed. From what has been said it is clear that the junction of distended and collapsed vein should give the level at which the venous pressure is equal to that of the atmosphere, and in fact it is found that when the venous pressure is measured manometrically, the meniscus lies at the same level as that to which the jugular veins are distended. The point of collapse of the jugular veins is therefore used clinically to measure the venous pressure in man. In so doing it is essential to ensure that the point at which the vein ceases to be visible is not simply the point at which it plunges deeply into the neck ; this may be ascertained by noting that the vein fills to a higher level when it is obstructed below by a finger. In some subjects the external jugular vein is too small to use, and in these the venous pressure is most easily determined by noting the level reached by the slow wide pulsations of the neck produced by the blood in the internal jugular veins.

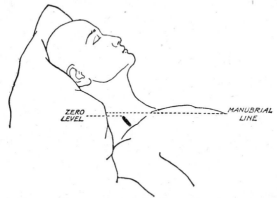

.Fig. II. 19.   Measurement of the Venous Pressure in Man.

The subject lies down with his head supported by pillows ; the jugular vein is seen distended with blood up to a point which usually lies just below the level of the notch of the *manubrium sterni*.   (Lewis.)

It has been pointed out that within certain limits the output of the heart is determined by the venous inflow. With moderate inflows, the venous pressure, distending the healthy heart in diastole, rises but little when the inflow increases ; when, however, the heart is nearing the limit of its capacity to perform work, the venous pressure rises rapidly (Fig. II. 12). In resting man the venous inflow is small ; the healthy heart requires but a small distending pressure to expel this inflow and maintains the venous pressure low. The failing heart, which is working at the limit of its capacity, requires a venous pressure that is several centimetres (2 to 10 cm. H_2O) higher to accomplish its task ; and under such circumstances the venous pressure is raised. It may be readily understood, therefore, that in the resting subject a rise of venous pressure above its normal value is the most usual and most important sign of failure of the heart. For this reason measurement of the venous pressure is of unusual importance clinically.

Normal values for the blood pressure in resting man at various parts of the vascular circuit are as follows :—

Axillary artery {	systolic . . 115 mm. Hg	
	diastolic . . 70 ,,	
	(pulse pressure . 45 ,,)	
Capillary of nail fold {	arterial limb . 32 ,,	
	summit of loop . 20 ,,	
Superior vena cava . . . 0 to — 2 ,,		

Of these values the venous pressure is the most constant, rarely varying by more than 2 mm. Hg (3 cm. H_2O) from the mean ; the capillary pressure shows slightly greater variations (5 mm. Hg) and the arterial pressure considerably greater fluctuations. Thus in an individual examined at rest on several occasions, the systolic pressure may vary from 110 to 130 mm. Hg and the diastolic pressure from 60 to 80 mm. Hg ; psychical factors are amongst the more important causes of these variations. Average values for the systolic blood pressure rise from 80 to 100 mm. at the age of five, to 115 mm. at the age of puberty and to 140 mm. Hg at the age of sixty.

Fig. II. 20 shows the blood pressure determined directly in various parts of the vascular circuit of the guinea pig by the introduction of a micropipette into the appropriate vessel. It will be seen that there is no appreciable fall of pressure until the smaller arteries are approached, then the pressure falls rapidly until the capillaries are reached, when the

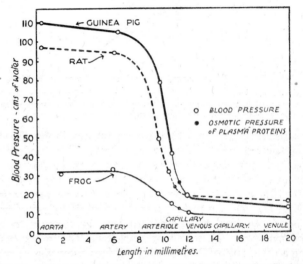

Fig. II. 20. Shows the **mean blood pressure** (circles) determined by inserting a micropipette into different parts of the mesenteric circulation of the guinea-pig, rat and frog. In each curve the thin line represents the fall of pressure along the capillaries. The dots indicate determinations of the osmotic pressure of the plasma proteins in each species. (After Landis.)

fall becomes more gradual. The fall of pressure as the blood traverses the veins is very small. The figure also shows that the pressure in the arterial limb of the capillary is higher, and in the venous limb lower, than the colloid osmotic pressure of the blood ; fluid thus tends to pass out of the blood at one end of the capillary and to be absorbed at the other. In an active organ, as we shall see, there is both arterial and capillary dilatation ; the resistance offered by these vessels falls and their intra-vascular pressure rises. As a result of the raised capillary pressure (and of increased capillary permeability) the lymph flow is increased, as will be considered in the next chapter. Owing to the large and variable resistance offered by the arterioles, the capillary pressure is largely independent of the general arterial pressure. The capillary pressure is more greatly influenced by alterations in venous pressure since there is little resistance to the flow from capillaries to veins.

The Effect of Gravity. The above values of the blood pressure are all given for vessels lying at the same level as the heart. When the vessels lie below this level, then to the pressure which is imparted to the blood by the heart must be added the pressure due to gravity, that is the pressure exerted by a column of blood equal in height to the vertical distance of the vessels examined from the heart. This relationship holds good for all the vessels of the perfectly flaccid limb; but in dependent limbs the venous pressure is reduced by the repeated movements which are usual during active life. Even the smallest movements empty the veins which, owing to the action of the valves, can only fill up from below. Thus in health the venous pressure in dependent limbs rarely rises very much above that of the atmosphere. This is important because if the venous pressure becomes greatly raised, then the capillary pressure is correspondingly raised and fluid tends to pass out of the capillaries and waterlog the tissue spaces. If the leg of a normal person is allowed to hang down for several hours without movement, it thus becomes œdematous. When the veins of the leg are distended by disease (varicose veins), the valves become incompetent, and after a day's work the feet become swollen because of the raised capillary pressure.

Factors Determining the Arterial Blood Pressure

As we shall see later, the maintenance of an adequate supply blood to the brain and to the heart is intimately dependent on the level of the arterial pressure, and it is convenient at this point to review the factors which determine this. The general arterial pressure depends on the cardiac output and on the peripheral resistance; the resistance offered by the vessel being determined by the diameter of the vessels and the viscosity of the blood. In health the cardiac output is mainly determined by the venous return to the heart, and this again largely depends on the relationship of the total blood volume to the capacity of the circulation.

The Peripheral Resistance. From the data already given for the blood pressure in different parts of the vascular circuit (p. 45 and Fig. II. 20), it will be seen that the main fall of pressure occurs in the smaller arteries and arterioles and to a less extent in the capillaries. The peripheral resistance is thus chiefly constituted by these vessels. The magnitude of the peripheral resistance depends on the diameter of these vessels, which is controlled by the central nervous system and by certain chemical substances. The effect of an alteration of peripheral resistance due to nervous action may be seen after stimulation of the splanchnic (sympathetic) nerve to the abdominal viscera (Fig. II. 21). The initial rise of blood pressure is due to constriction of the vessels of the gut as direct response to nerve stimulation; the secondary rise is due to the liberation of adrenaline from the suprarenal glands, and is absent if these glands are removed or their nerves cut. Of the chemical substances affecting the peripheral resistance, five are important as they are normal constituents of the body. Adrenaline (see p. 544) produces a constriction of the arterioles and to a less extent of the capillaries and veins, the arterial pressure rises while the capillary pressure is relatively unaffected. Pituitary extract constricts chiefly the capillaries and to a less extent

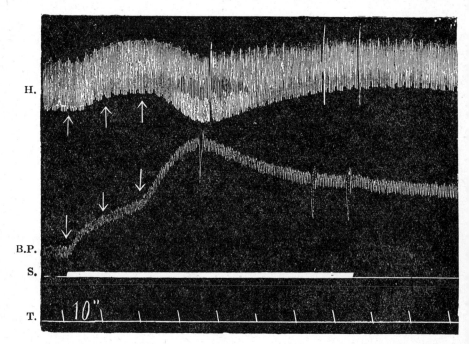

Fig. II. 21. The Effect of **Stimulating the Splanchnic Nerve** on the Arterial Blood Pressure, and on the Output and Volume of the Ventricles.

H., heart volume (a rise in the curve indicates an increase in volume). B.P., arterial blood pressure. S, signal showing duration of stimulation of the splanchnic nerve. T., time marker, showing 10 sec. intervals. Note that the first rise in arterial pressure is associated with an increase in the volume of the heart, owing to the greater power needed in order to expel the blood against the raised pressure, but that the secondary rise, due to the **secretion of adrenaline,** is associated with a decrease in the volume, showing that the tone of the heart is improved. Note also that the output is increased by the presence of adrenaline, as shown by the increased excursion of the cardiometer record (stroke volume). (From Starling's " Principles of Human Physiology.")

the arterioles, and in man produces a slight rise of arterial blood pressure and intense pallor of the skin. Renin, from the cortex of the kidney, has its chief action on the small arteries and arterioles, and produces a rise of arterial pressure without change in the colour of the skin. Acetyl-choline and histamine can be extracted from a number of organs, and both cause a fall of blood pressure by dilating the peripheral vessels. The action of acetyl-choline is chiefly on the arterioles, and the capillary pressure is but little altered ; the chief action of histamine is on the capillaries and so the fall of pressure along these vessels almost disappears (Fig. II. 22.)

Hypertension. Raised arterial pressure is not uncommon in man and may arise in several diseases. In most, both systolic and diastolic values are high, the cardiac output and blood viscosity are normal, and vasoconstriction is clearly the cause of hypertension. The vasoconstriction affects small arteries and arterioles chiefly and affects the organs of the greater or systemic circulation more or less equally so that the distribution of blood to the tissues is little affected. In the hand and in the efferent glomerular arterioles of the kidney, vasoconstriction has been shown to persist when vasomotor nervous tone is abolished. It is presumed, therefore, that hypertension is due to a pressor substance, but this has not yet been identified.

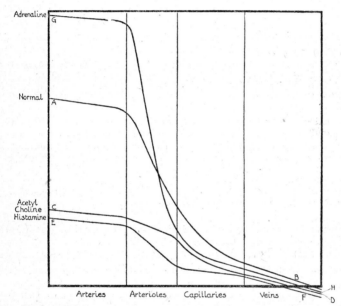

Fig. II. 22, Diagram showing the Rate of Fall of Blood Pressure in the Arteries, Capillaries and Veins in different conditions.

Note that adrenaline constricts, and acetyl-choline dilates, the arterioles, and that histamine dilates the capillaries. (From Lovatt Evans' " Recent Advances in Physiology.")

Of known pressor substances renin and hypertensin (see p. 65) stand alone in that they raise arterial pressure without diverting blood from the skin. The renin-hypertensin system is therefore thought to be concerned in human hypertension, but of this there is as yet no direct proof.

Factors Determining the Venous Return to the Heart. As we have seen the cardiac output is largely regulated by the pressure in the caval veins entering the right auricle and thus by the venous return to the heart. The venous return to the heart is determined in large part by the relationship between the total amount of blood in the circulation and the state of expansion or constriction of the vessels as a whole (the capacity of the circulation).

The volume of the blood in the body was first measured by bleeding the animal as far as possible, washing out the vessels with salt solution and determining the amount of hæmoglobin in the washings. It can be measured on the intact animal in one of two ways. (*a*) If the animal be made to breathe a given volume of a gas mixture containing a known small amount of carbon monoxide, and to continue until all the carbon monoxide has been absorbed, a certain fraction of the hæmoglobin will combine with it. This fraction, as we shall see in the next chapter, is very easily estimated by matching the colour of the diluted blood, or by examining its absorption spectrum. Suppose 50 c.c. of carbon monoxide were taken originally, and the blood were found to be 25 per cent. saturated. A separate experiment is now performed *in vitro*, in order to find out how much carbon monoxide is required to saturate a given volume of the animal's blood completely. Suppose this turns out to be 20 c.c. per 100 c.c. of blood; 50 c.c., therefore, will saturate $100 \times \dfrac{50}{20} = 250$ c.c.; the whole of the blood in the animal, however, was only 25 per cent. saturated, so that its volume must have been $250 \times \dfrac{100}{25} = 1,000$ c.c.

(*b*) Alternatively, we can inject into the blood-stream a known quantity of a dye, take a sample of blood after time has been given for it to become uniformly distributed, and determine its concentration by comparison with a solution of the dye of known concentration in a colorimeter. The total volume of the blood can thus be calculated from the ratio of the absolute quantity of the dye administered to its concentration in the sample of blood examined. It is necessary, of course, that the dye have the following qualifications : It must not be toxic, it must not leave the blood vessels easily and be distributed throughout the tissues, it must not be excreted rapidly, and it must have a strong colour in dilute solution. Evans Blue (T1824) appears to approximate most closely to the ideal dye for this purpose.

(*c*) A method of considerable value in man is to inject human erythrocytes. Anæmic subjects may be transfused with a known volume (V) of a concentrated suspension in plasma of red cells from a compatible donor. If the hæmoglobin contents of the recipient's blood be Hb_1 before and Hb_2 after transfusion, and if the suspension of red cells transfused be Hb_v, then the blood volume of the recipient before transfusion is $V\left(\dfrac{Hb_v - Hb_2}{Hb_2 - Hb_1}\right)$. This equation assumes that there is no loss of plasma from the circulation after transfusion, an assumption which usually holds in anæmic subjects. Finally, recipients of Groups A, B or AB may be transfused with a known volume of Group O blood, and the dilution of the transfused cells be determined in a sample of the recipient's blood by agglutinating out the recipient's cells with a suitable serum, and counting the unagglutinated donor cells. In this method the blood volume at the end of transfusion is given by the formula :

Final blood volume (c.c.) =

$$\frac{[\text{Vol. of blood transfused (c.c.)}] \times [\text{Red cell count of transfused blood}]}{[\text{Count of donor cells in recipient's blood}]}$$

It should be noted that the first method measures the total quantity of hæmoglobin in the body, and hence the blood volume only if we know its concentration accurately, while the second method measures the total volume of the plasma, and to some extent that of the tissue fluids, since the dye is not completely indiffusible. The two methods, therefore, do not always give the same answer. All these methods used in the intact animal make the assumption, which is only approximately true, that the composition of the blood with respect to cells and plasma is everywhere the same as that of the sample used.

In most animals the blood makes up from 5 to 8 per cent. of the body weight, there being about 3 to 5 litres in an average man, and 500 to 1,500 c.c. in an average dog of 6 to 20 kg.

At the pressures normally ruling in the vascular system, the veins are the most distensible vessels, and it is to be anticipated that when blood is added to the circulation most of it will be accommodated in the veins and thus increase the venous return to the heart. The same result should occur if the vessels in a given territory constrict so that blood drains out of them into the great veins. The venous return to the heart should be increased, therefore, either if the total blood volume increases, or if the capacity of the circulation is decreased. This can be shown very simply in a preparation in which the heart propels blood through a closed system analogous to that formed by the intact vessels ; injection of blood into this system greatly increases the output of the heart ; withdrawal of blood diminishes the output. The capacity of the circulation is determined by the general tonus (state of contraction) of the arterioles, capillaries and veins, but there are a number of situations in which blood is particularly liable to accumulate and which merit the term **blood reservoirs.** Of these the spleen is peculiar in that the blood is accommodated, and concentrated by loss of plasma, in the spleen pulp, a bypass of the circulation ; in the dog the spleen can accommodate one-fifth of the total blood volume. The other reservoirs, the liver and portal system, the sub-papillary venous plexus of the skin, and the great veins are, unlike the spleen, part of the general circulation, but are, like the spleen, capable of considerable variations in capacity ; the liver and portal system (including the spleen) at rest contain about one-quarter to one-third of the total blood volume in the cat and dog, the skin very much less. The capacities of these structures in man are not accurately known, but it is probable that the skin is relatively more and the spleen relatively less capacious than in the cat and dog.

The effect on the circulation of an alteration of the blood volume is seen after hæmorrhage. In the anæsthetised dog removal of about 10 per cent. of the blood volume leaves the arterial pressure unaltered, and it is clear that a reduction of blood volume of this order is compensated by other changes in the vascular system. This compensation is absent after section of the spinal cord in the neck and is thus effected through the central nervous system. If the blood flow through the liver, the gut, the splenic artery and vein, are simultaneously measured, it is found that when blood is removed, the outflows from spleen and liver immediately and temporarily exceed the inflows ; thus the blood content of these organs is largely expelled into the great veins and partly compensates for that removed. The cardiac output is reduced but with successive bleedings the arterial pressure does not fall until the cardiac output is 30 to 50 per cent. below normal. The blood flow through the gut and through the limbs is reduced showing that in these areas the vessels constrict. The reduced cardiac output is thus balanced by an increase in the peripheral resistance. It is probable that the preservation of the level of arterial pressure here is due to the activity of the carotid sinus and depressor reflexes, and that this serves to maintain the blood flow through heart and brain. In the rabbit and cat another compensatory mechanism quickly comes into action to restore the blood volume, namely dilution of blood by absorption into it of tissue fluid through the capillary wall. In the dog and man dilution of the blood is much slower, and in man is not complete until 24 to 72 hours after removing 1 litre of blood. With a profuse hæmorrhage the fall of arterial pressure may be profound enough to produce loss of consciousness through anæmia of the brain but even from this state the mechanism of the body may suffice for complete recovery. When the circulation in the anæsthetised dog is so disturbed by bleeding that the mean arterial pressure has fallen to 30 or 40 mm. Hg and remained so for six hours, a return of all the blood removed does not lead to a lasting recovery of the circulation (irreversible shock). If, after severe hæmorrhage, the irreversible state is to be prevented, prompt measures must be taken to restore the depleted blood volume. This can be most effectively done by transfusing fresh or stored blood from a healthy donor of the same or a compatible blood group (see next chapter). In an emergency, stored plasma or serum may also be used, but in any case the amount transfused must be adequate to restore arterial pressure to normal. Saline is useless for the purpose for, having no colloid osmotic pressure, it quickly passes out into the tissue spaces.

Peripheral Circulatory Failure and Shock. A condition resembling that seen after frank hæmorrhage in which the blood pressure falls, and in which the reduction in cardiac output is to be ascribed not to cardiac weakness but to changes in the vessels or circulating blood volume, is described as peripheral circulatory failure or, more loosely, shock. The following are some of the more important examples.

(1) The vaso-vagal or fainting attack is characterised by low blood pressure, slow pulse, pale cold sweating skin, loss of consciousness and sometimes nausea or vomiting. The slowing of the heart is effected through the cholinergic vagal fibres and is abolished by atropine. The fall of blood pressure is due to vasodilatation in voluntary muscle effected through the nerves ; the skin vessels are actually constricted ; the cardiac output may fall during the attack.

(2) **Burns.** In severe burns there is a rapid and profuse loss of plasma into the burned and adjacent tissues. The blood volume falls and the hæmoglobin content of the blood rises, and in severe cases the circulation may fail. Failure is prevented by transfusion of adequate amounts of plasma or serum.

(3) **Wound Shock.** Circulatory failure frequently occurs after extensive wounds, and sometimes without clear evidence of severe blood loss, in which case it has been attributed to vasodilatation from release of a histamine-like substance. Experience in the war of 1939–45 has confirmed that in the war of 1914–18, in showing conclusively that wound shock is not a single entity ; but the most important cause of peripheral circulatory failure after wounds is undoubtedly loss of blood, either externally, or into the tissues of the body. In fact the enormous saving of life after wounding in the recent war has been due to the provision of proper supplies of blood for early and adequate transfusion (amounts up to 7 litres have been given before and during operation) and to the use of antibacterial agents.

(4) **Infection.** Circulatory failure in the terminal stages of infection is not due to depleted blood volume but presumably to vascular paralysis and

it does not respond to transfusion. As yet comparatively little is known of this condition.

Severe Anæmia. A very interesting problem is presented by the circulation in severe anæmia. A patient with a hæmoglobin of 20 per cent., and a blood volume of 2·3 litres yet may have a cardiac output of 8 litres a minute. The considerable rise in cardiac output despite the much reduced blood volume indicates the importance of the mechanism regulating the capacity of the circulation ; exactly how the regulation is effected is not yet known.

It will now be evident that the state of the blood vessels exerts a very profound influence on the characteristics of the circulation. Thus, within limits, the output of the heart is determined by the venous pressure and thus by the relationship between circulating blood volume and the capacity of the circulation. Most of the blood in the circulation is accommodated in veins and capillaries, and it is the state of these two orders of vessels that most profoundly affects cardiac output. Arterial pressure is determined by cardiac output and by the peripheral resistance. The chief peripheral resistance is in the small arteries and arterioles, and thus the state of these vessels chiefly influences arterial pressure. The function of the circulation is to supply blood to the individual tissues of the body according to their needs ; not only must the total cardiac output be sufficient and the head of arterial pressure adequate but the blood must be distributed in such a way that active tissues receive a relatively large, and inactive tissues a relatively small, proportion of the total. The adjustment of the distribution is again determined by the state of the vessels in the various tissues. The regulation of the circulation is thus effected largely through control of the blood vessels and this will now be considered.

The Control of the Peripheral Vessels

The state of contraction or " tone " of the peripheral vessels is controlled by the vaso-motor nerves and by the action of certain chemical substances, which are either released generally into the blood stream or locally in the active tissues. In general it seems that the co-ordinated vascular responses of the organism, that is the restriction of blood-flow to some organs and its augmentation to others, are achieved mainly through the vaso-motor nerves, and through the action of certain chemical substances released into the circulating blood, of which the best known are adrenaline and renin. Local vascular changes consequent on injury or activity are produced chiefly by the release of vasodilator chemical substances from the tissues concerned.

The Vaso-motor Nerves. The nervous control of the blood vessels is chiefly effected through the autonomic system, which, as will be considered in Chapter XIII, consists essentially of two sets of nerve fibres, sympathetic and para-sympathetic, having different origins from the central nervous system. Most of the sympathetic fibres are adrenergic, i.e., act by releasing an adrenaline-like substance at their nerve endings, while most of the para-sympathetic fibres are cholinergic, i.e., act by releasing an acetyl-choline-like substance. Adrenergic and cholinergic fibres have inverse actions on the vessels. In the regulation of vascular tone the sympathetic fibres are considerably more important than the para-sympathetic. The action of the vaso-motor nerves was discovered by Claude Bernard, who found in the rabbit that when the cervical sympathetic chain was divided on one side, the ear on that side became flushed and warm, remaining so for a considerable time. Conversely, stimulation of the cervical sympathetic produces pallor and coldness of the corresponding ear. We now know that if the appropriate branches of the sympathetic nerves are stimulated under suitable conditions, then the blood vessels in all parts of the body (except perhaps the heart) constrict. The degree of constriction, however, varies in different organs. Thus stimulation of the appropriate sympathetic fibres produces intense narrowing of the vessels (vaso-constriction) of the skin and alimentary canal, but only slight narrowing in those of the brain and lungs (Fig. II. 23). The vessels constricted by stimulation of the sympathetic are particularly the arteries and arterioles, to a less extent the capillaries and the veins. Section of the sympathetic nerves supplying an organ leads to an increase in the blood-flow through it, and it thus appears that normally there is a steady stream of constrictor impulses passing along these nerves to the blood vessels. Further, since in the majority of organs the vessels cease to participate in the vaso-motor reflexes, shortly to be

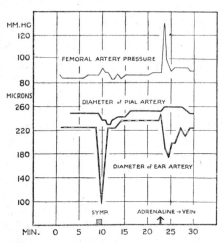

Fig. II. 23. The lower two curves record in microns the diameters of an artery of the pia mater of the brain, and of an ear artery, observed microscopically in a cat. The pial artery was seen through a glass window screwed into the skull. At the signal "symp." the cervical sympathetic trunk was stimulated and produced a pronounced constriction of the ear artery but only a slight narrowing of the pial artery. At the next signal 0·01 mg. adrenaline injected into a vein produced a marked constriction of the ear artery and a small dilatation of the pial artery which is to be attributed to a passive effect of the coincident rise of blood pressure. (Forbes, Firnley and Mason.)

described, after their sympathetic fibres have been cut, it seems that changes in vascular calibre of vaso-motor origin are chiefly determined by an increase or decrease (inhibition) of sympathetic vaso-constrictor impulses. Though of secondary importance there are also a number of vaso-dilator (cholinergic) nerves belonging to the sympathetic and para-sympathetic systems. Thus raising body temperature to beyond the point of sweating, produces a greater vaso-dilatation in the skin than can be produced by paralysing the vaso-motor (sympathetic) nerves ; again stimulation of the chorda tympani to the submaxillary gland, the lingual nerve to the tongue muscles and the nervi erigentes to the penis leads to vaso-dilatation in these parts. In addition to the autonomic nerves just considered, stimulation of the posterior spinal (sensory) roots as they leave the spinal cord produces vaso-dilatation in the area of skin to which the fibres eventually run ; since the impulses set up by this stimulation pass in the reverse direction to the impulses normally travelling along these nerves and entering the spinal cord, these impulses have been termed antidromic. The function of the antidromic fibres is in producing changes of vascular calibre by means of the cutaneous axon reflex (see p. 76).

The maintenance of vaso-motor tone is intimately dependent on the integrity of a group of nerve cells known as the " vaso-motor centre " lying in the floor of the fourth ventricle close to the vagus nucleus ; electric stimulation of these cells leads to generalised vaso-constriction and a rise of blood pressure. Section of the hind-brain below the level of these cells leads to generalised vaso-dilatation, and the blood pressure falls from, say, 120 to 80 mm. Hg. After several days, if the animal survives, the blood pressure may rise again almost to its previous level ; destruction of the spinal cord reduces the blood pressure almost to zero. It thus appears that there are also vaso-motor centres in the spinal cord, but in ordinary circumstances these are mainly controlled by that of the hind-brain (medulla) ; when this is destroyed, then the spinal centres gradually take over control. The activity of the vaso-motor centre in maintaining general vaso-motor tone is, as we shall see, profoundly modified by the influence of the cerebral hemispheres and by afferent impulses arising from certain receptors in the vascular system itself. The vaso-motor centre is also sensitive to chemical stimuli, being stimulated by CO_2 and by oxygen lack.

The *rôle* of carbon dioxide in determining the activity of the cells of the vasomotor centres is well shown when the gas is excessively removed from the blood by over-ventilating the lungs. If the lungs of an anæsthetised cat are artificially ventilated with air, by a pump working very rapidly at 180 strokes per minute, the blood pressure may fall in 2 minutes from 140 to 40 mm. Hg. If air containing 5 per cent. carbon dioxide is substituted for the ordinary air previously used, the rate of ventilation remaining the same, the blood pressure returns to its original level.

After a cerebral hæmorrhage the blood pressure may rise to 150 mm. Hg and the pulse is slowed. The rise of blood pressure is usually attributed to anæmia of the vaso-motor centre, arising from compression of the brain by the hæmorrhage ; in this way the cells of the centre would be stimulated by oxygen lack and the accumulation of metabolites.

Mode of Action of the Vaso-motor Nerves. It has been known for many years that the injection of acetyl-choline into an animal produces slowing of the heart, vaso-dilatation, and other effects resembling those produced by stimulation of the para-sympathetic nerves. Similarly, the injection of adrenaline produces acceleration of the heart, a rise of blood pressure and other effects also obtained by stimulation of the sympathetic nerves. Evidence is now accumulating that the nerves of the autonomic system produce their peripheral effects by releasing at their terminations substances closely resembling, if not identical with, acetyl-choline and adrenaline (see Chapter XIII). The antidromic fibres also seem to produce vaso-dilatation by releasing at their terminations a chemical substance, probably allied to histamine, which remains *in situ* when the circulation is stopped.

For if, while the antidromic fibres are stimulated the circulation to the cat's leg is stopped by a ligature and maintained so for a time equal to that normally taken by the vaso-dilatation to subside (about 6 minutes), then on releasing the circulation the antidromic flush still appears in undiminished vigour.

Sympathectomy. Division of the sympathetic fibres supplying a limb, either by removal of the appropriate sympathetic ganglia or section of the preganglionic sympathetic fibres is followed by vasodilatation, by loss of vascular responses to change of body temperature, and loss of reflex sweating and pilomotor response. The vasodilatation chiefly affects the skin, muscle blood flow being little altered. With the progress of time, the vasodilatation subsides a little and the vessels are found to be abnormally sensitive to adrenaline, histamine and other vaso-active substances. Complete sympathectomy, by removal in separate stages of the chain of sympathetic ganglia on both sides, has been performed in the cat and dog. The completely sympathectomised cat is sluggish, and very susceptible to exposure to cold, to oxygen lack, and to hæmorrhage. The sympathectomised dog is normally active and its arterial pressure at rest is little below normal. It is evident that while in the normal animal the vasomotor nerves are extremely important in regulating the circulation, yet other and probably chemical mechanisms can in the dog take over much of this function.

Chemical Regulation of the Circulation. We have seen that when the splanchnic sympathetic nerves are stimulated there is liberated from the suprarenal glands a substance termed *adrenaline*, which has a powerful effect on the circulation resembling that of a generalised stimulation of the sympathetic nerves. Adrenaline applied directly to the vessels constricts them, except those of the heart and skeletal muscle which it dilates. Injected into the general circulation, adrenaline seems to act mainly by increasing the rate and force of contraction of the heart beat (Fig. II. 21) and as a redistributor of blood. Thus in the dog it causes emptying of the spleen and liver; its constrictor action is greatest on the vessels of the skin and alimentary canal, in the brain such constrictor action as it has is more than outweighed by the rise in arterial pressure (Fig. II. 23); it dilates the vessels of the heart and active muscles. In man adrenaline in *small* doses increases cardiac output, produces intense constriction of arterioles, capillaries and veins of the skin, and increases the rate of blood flow through voluntary muscle; the blood flow through the kidney is reduced by constriction of the efferent glomerular arterioles; the systolic arterial pressure is increased while the diastolic remains stationary or may fall. In larger doses both systolic and diastolic pressures are increased. The effect of adrenaline is thus to divert blood from quiescent organs to active organs and to the brain and heart. Adrenaline is probably released into the human circulation during fright, asphyxia and muscular exercise; probably it is also liberated through the agency of the carotid sinus and depressor reflexes when the blood pressure falls.

The action of *post-pituitary* extract in constricting the capillaries has also been described. In the frog, pituitary extract seems to be normally concerned in maintaining the state of contraction of the melanophores (pigment cells of the skin), and perhaps the tone of the capillaries, for after removal of the pituitary the melanophores constrict and the capillaries are said to dilate, and both are said to be restored to their normal state by injection of the extract. In man, there is no evidence that the pituitary normally takes part in maintaining capillary tone.

The cortex of the kidney, but not the medulla, contains a substance *renin* which produces a prolonged rise of arterial pressure on intravenous injection. Renin is a protein, salts out with the globulins, and is destroyed by temperatures above 60° C. It is now known that it is not itself vaso-active, but that it is an enzyme which splits a constituent of the plasma globulins (hypertensinogen) into a simple substance

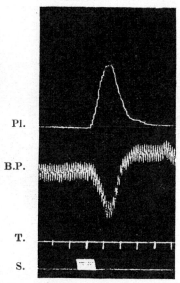

Fig. II. 24. **The Depressor Reflex,** producing Vaso-dilatation and a Fall in Arterial Pressure.

From above downwards : Volume (plethysmograph) of a loop of intestine, arterial blood pressure, time in 10 sec. intervals, signal showing period of stimulation of the central end of the vagus (containing the depressor fibres). (W. M. Bayliss.)

(hypertensin) which is thermo-stable, dialysable and soluble in alcohol. Hypertensin has a direct vaso-constrictor action, and when injected intravenously produces a rise of systolic and diastolic arterial pressure without a rise in cardiac output ; the renal blood flow is reduced through constriction of the efferent glomerular arterioles. Unlike other known pressor substances, the renin-hypertensin system does not divert blood from the skin. In the experimental animal renin is released into the renal vein blood when the renal artery is constricted and when the general arterial pressure is reduced by bleeding or by intravenous injection of vaso-dilator substances such as histamine. Just as the carotid sinus and depressor reflexes presently to be described may be regarded as safeguarding the blood supply to the brain and heart, so the renin-hypertensin system may be regarded as a mechanism for maintaining the intra-glomerular arterial pressure on which the function of the kidney as an excretory organ depends.

The Vaso-motor Reflexes

We have seen that the tone of the peripheral vessels and the frequency of the heart are controlled by the central nervous system through the autonomic nerves. This control depends on the activity of the vaso-motor centres in the hind-brain and spinal cord, and is adjusted to the varying needs of the organism by vaso-motor reflexes.

A simple vaso-dilatation in any organ will exert a two-fold effect on the general circulation. It will in the first place lower the peripheral

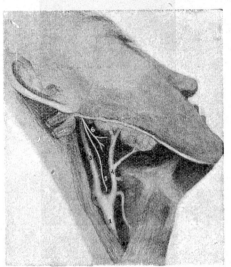

FIG. II. 25.   Showing carotid sinus in man : (1) common carotid ; (2) carotid sinus ; (3) internal carotid ; (4) external carotid ; (5) nerve to carotid sinus ; (6) glosso-pharyngeal nerve. (C. Heymans, " Le sinus carotidien.")

resistance and hence the arterial pressure, and it will increase the capacity of the circulation and thus reduce the venous return and output of the heart. Uncompensated and extensive vaso-dilatation would not only embarrass the blood supply to other organs, but would finally defeat its end by bringing the circulation to a standstill. It is not surprising, therefore, that mechanisms exist which ensure that when vaso-dilatation occurs in one part of the body, this is compensated by vaso-constriction elsewhere ; the arterial pressure and cardiac output are thus maintained. Our knowledge of such mechanisms is still rather imperfect, but four examples are well recognised and will now be described. Of these the depressor and carotid sinus reflexes are of fundamental importance and are constantly in play ; they ensure that the arterial pressure is maintained at a suitable level. The Lovèn reflex and the reflex responses to temperature are significant only in special circumstances.

(1) **The Depressor Reflex.** Nerve fibres arising from endings in the arch of the aorta ascend to the hind-brain in the trunk of the vagus (as in man) or as a separate " depressor " nerve (rabbit). Stimulation of these fibres produces a slowing of the heart and fall of blood pressure. The slowing of the heart is largely but not entirely abolished by previous section of the vagi ; it is thus due mainly to a reflex augmentation of vagal

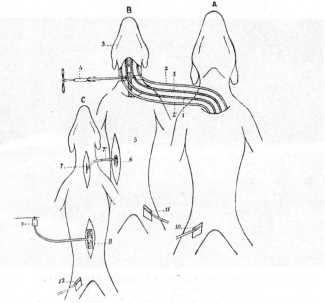

FIG. II. 26.   Arrangement of Animals in a **Cross-Circulation Experiment.**
  The head of dog B (3) is perfused from dog A by anastomosis of the carotid arteries and also of the jugular veins (1, 1′, 2, 2′), the vertebral arteries and veins being tied, the muscles of the neck divided between ligatures, and the rest of the tissues compressed round the vertebral column by the *écraseur* of Chassaignac (4).   Blood from the suprarenal of B (6) is led into one of the jugular veins (7) of C, which has been adrenalectomised ; the spleen of C (8) is enclosed in a plethysmograph, and contracts whenever adrenaline is secreted by the suprarenals of B.   The arterial blood pressures of the three dogs are recorded from the femoral arteries 10, 11, 12.   (From C. Heymans.)

tone, and partly to a reflex inhibition of sympathetic tone (an example of reciprocal innervation, see Chapter XI). The fall of blood pressure is independent of slowing of the heart and is due to a vaso-dilatation that effects all the organs of the body except perhaps the brain (Fig. II. 23). Thus stimulation of the depressor nerve produces an increase in the volume of a limb or of a loop of intestine, and an increase in blood-flow from the submaxillary gland. It can be shown that the physiological stimulus exciting the depressor reflex is a rise of pressure in the arch of the aorta.

(2) **The Carotid Sinus Reflex.** It has long been known that in man
pressure over the bifurcation of the common carotid artery
produces a sensation of faintness accompanied by slowing of
the pulse and fall of blood pressure. This effect has lately been
shown to be due to stimulation of nerve endings lying under
the adventitia of the carotid sinus, the name given to the
expansion at the origin of the internal carotid artery (Fig. II. 25).
If the sinus is compressed, or if the pressure of the blood inside

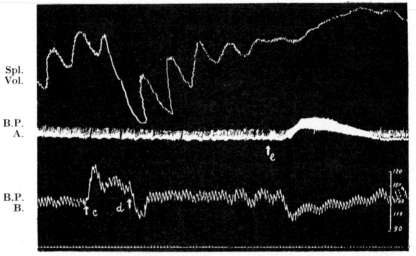

Spl.
Vol.

B.P.
A.

B.P.
B.

FIG. II. 27.   **The Regulation of the Arterial Blood Pressure.**   (Cross-circulation experiment, see Fig. II. 26.)

From above downwards : Volume of the spleen of dog C ; arterial pressure of dog A (perfusing the isolated carotid sinus of dog B), arterial
pressure of dog B.

At *c* the pressure in the carotid sinus of dog B was reduced by partially
clamping the inter-connecting artery, and at *d* the pressure was returned
to the initial value.   A **fall in pressure in the carotid sinus** leads to a reflex
rise in pressure in the rest of the body, and a reflex secretion of adrenaline, .
as shown by the contraction of the spleen of dog C ; a rise in pressure in
the carotid sinus has the reverse effect.   At *e* 0·1 mg. of adrenaline was
injected into the circulation of the perfusing dog, A, **raising** its arterial
pressure, and hence, also, **the pressure in the carotid sinus** of dog B.   This
resulted in a reflex fall in the arterial pressure of B, and an inhibition of the
secretion of adrenaline, as shown by the dilatation of the spleen of dog C.
(From C. Heymans.)

is raised, or if the sensory nerve to it (a branch of the glosso-
pharyngeal) is stimulated, the blood pressure falls and the
heart slows, changes produced reflexly in a manner similar to
those of the depressor reflex.   Conversely, if the common
carotid artery is compressed so as to produce a fall of pressure
within the sinus, the heart accelerates and the blood pressure
rises.   The paths followed by both this and the depressor reflex
are very similar.   The afferent impulses entering the hind-
brain through the glosso-pharyngeal and vagus nerves reach

the cardio-inhibitory and vaso-motor centres lying close by in the medulla. The impulses sent out by these centres through the vagus and sympathetic nerves are thus modified in the way described.

The methods used by Heymans and his co-workers in investigating the functions of the carotid sinus are interesting as an example of physiological technique (Fig. II. 26). One or both carotid

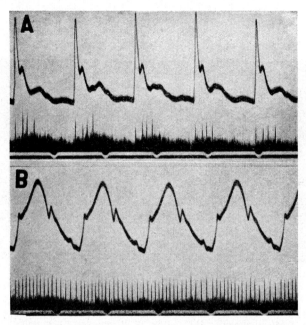

FIG. II. 28. In each record the upper curve represents the arterial blood pressure registered by a membrane manometer (Fig. II. 17), and the lower, the electrical discharge from the carotid sinus nerve of the rabbit severed so that it transmits the response of a single end organ in the sinus. In the upper record (A) the mean arterial pressure was 55 mm. Hg. and even at this low level a discharge of 4 impulses accompanied each ventricular systole. In the lower record B the mean arterial pressure was 135 mm. Hg., and here there was a larger and more continuous discharge from the end organ. (Bronk and Stella.)

arteries of one dog B are perfused with blood from a second dog A (cross-circulation). The head of dog B is completely severed from its trunk, except for the spinal cord and vagus nerves. On raising the arterial pressure in dog A and thus in the carotid sinuses of dog B, the blood pressure in the trunk of dog B falls and the heart rate diminishes ; the opposite changes occur when the blood pressure of dog A is lowered (Fig. 36). If now the suprarenal vein of dog B is anastomosed with the internal jugular vein of a third dog C (Fig. II. 26), then a fall of blood pressure in dog A produces, in addition to the effects mentioned, a contraction of the spleen of dog C (Fig. II. 27). Thus a fall of pressure in the carotid sinus of dog B leads in this dog to an increased secretion of adrenaline, as shown by the effect of blood from its suprarenal vein on the spleen of C.   The effects are abolished by denervating the carotid sinuses of dog B.

If electrodes connected to a sensitive recording device are placed on the depressor or carotid sinus nerves during life, a volley of impulses is found to accompany each heart-beat (Fig. 37).   If the carotid sinus and depressor nerves are cut, the blood pressure and pulse rate rise permanently.   In normal life, therefore, the constancy of blood pressure and pulse rate is due largely to impulses ascending these nerves ; any variation in blood pressure produces an inhibition or augmentation

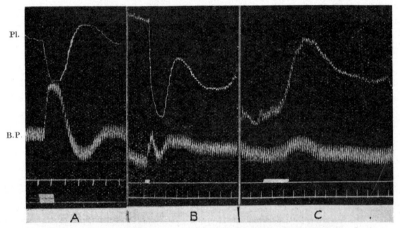

Fig. II. 29.   Lovèn Reflex in the Dog, producing **Vaso-dilatation in the Active Organ, and Vaso-constriction in Inactive Organs.**

A. From above downwards : Volume of intestine (plethysmograph), arterial blood pressure (B.P.), time in 10 sec. intervals, signal showing time of stimulation of the median nerve.   In general, stimulation of any sensory nerve leads to a rise in arterial pressure and vaso-constriction.

B. and C. From above downwards : Volume of the hind leg, arterial blood pressure, signal showing time of stimulation, time in 10 sec. intervals. In B, the median nerve was again stimulated, with the result that the blood pressure rose and the vessels of the leg constricted.   In C, the central end of a sensory nerve to the hind leg, *i.e.*, the sixth lumbar dorsal root, was stimulated ; again the blood pressure rose, but there was a considerable *vaso-dilatation* in the leg itself.   (W. M. Bayliss.)

of these impulses (see Fig. II. 28) and so reflexly initiates changes which restore the blood pressure to its normal level.

When the arterial blood pressure falls, these reflexes produce a general increase in vaso-motor tone, and this effect is sustained by the simultaneous release of adrenaline (Fig. II. 27). The vessels that actually constrict to this two-fold stimulus vary according to circumstances and appear to be those in which it is unimportant to maintain a large flow.   Thus the vessels of the brain are little constricted and those of the heart are dilated by sympathetic stimulation or by adrenaline and do not appear to participate in the general vaso-constriction evoked through

the carotid sinus and depressor reflexes ; in the warm animal
the vessels of the skin are dilated and constrict little in the
reflex ; in the cool animal the narrow skin vessels constrict
very markedly. These two reflexes are thus of extreme
importance in maintaining the distribution of blood to the
tissues according to their needs ; at the same time they prevent
undue strain on the heart by keeping the blood pressure within
convenient limits.

(3) **The Lovèn Reflex.** Stimulation of the sensory nerve fibres
supplying the limb of a dog produces vaso-dilatation in that
limb and vaso-constriction elsewhere, the constriction usually
being sufficient to cause a general rise of blood pressure, so that
the blood-flow to the stimulated limb is greatly increased
(Fig. II. 29). This reflex has not, as yet, been demonstrated in
man, and its precise position in the economy of the circulation
remains doubtful.

(4) **Reflex Changes to Temperature.** In temperate climates heat is
lost from the body chiefly by conduction and radiation from
the skin, and this is controlled by the sympathetic nerves
regulating the rate of blood-flow through the skin. The chief
factor in this control is a central mechanism which responds to a
rise in blood temperature by cutaneous vaso-dilatation and to a
fall by cutaneous vaso-constriction. The central receptor in
man responds to changes in blood temperature of the order of
0·1° C. or less. A subsidiary factor is reflex cutaneous vaso-
constriction from stimulation of cold receptors in the skin. In
man muscle blood flow is not altered by usual changes in
environmental temperature unless shivering occurs.

The Circulation to Particular Organs

It is important for the student to grasp at once that a given agent
may affect differently the blood vessels to different tissues. The organs
of the body have quite different *rôles* in the concerted actions of the
organism and the behaviour of the vessels supplying these organs is
adjusted to these different rôles.

The Brain. While the cerebral vessels are probably influenced by
vaso-dilator metabolites released during cerebral activity, they are
little affected by vaso-motor impulses ; persistent inquiry failed to
reveal any vaso-motor supply, until recently it was shown that stimulation of the cervical sympathetic produced a slight narrowing of the
pial arteries observed through a glass window screwed into the skull
(Fig. 32). The cerebral blood-flow is thus determined in the main by the
height of the arterial blood pressure, and it is rather surprising that this
should be regulated exclusively by receptors (see Chapter XI) lying
outside the brain, in the carotid sinus and arch of the aorta. For if
these receptors are excluded, then alterations in blood-flow to the
brain lead to no reflex changes altering the height of the arterial pressure,

unless the cerebral blood-flow is so reduced that it produces asphyxia of the vaso-motor centre.

The importance and significance of the reflexes controlling blood pressure is now evident, for the brain is the master organ of the body and is extremely sensitive to alterations in its blood supply ; if the blood-flow to the brain ceases for five seconds consciousness is lost and after twenty seconds epileptic twitching begins. By means of the carotid sinus and depressor reflexes the arterial blood pressure, and thus the cerebral blood-flow, are maintained by appropriate regulation of the rate and force of the heart-beat and of the blood-flow through organs other than the brain.

The Coronary Circulation. The heart muscle in mammals is supplied with blood from two coronary arteries arising from the aorta just beyond the semilunar (aortic) valves. The blood is returned to the right auricle by a number of openings of which by far the largest is the coronary sinus. The rate of the coronary blood-flow may be measured by inserting a cannula into the coronary sinus ; the blood issuing represents three-fifths of the total flow through the whole coronary system. Like that of the brain, the coronary blood-flow is determined in the main by the mean aortic pressure, as the following table shows (after Starling).

TABLE II. 3

Dog. Heart Weight 107 *g. Total Systemic Output* 1,400 *c.c. per minute.*

Arterial pressure. mm. Hg.	Coronary circulation. c.c. per minute
60	50
100	90
128	124
166	208
190	500

Like the brain the heart is peculiarly sensitive to its blood supply, and the importance to the animal of maintaining an adequate arterial pressure is again evident ; if the aortic pressure falls too low the heart fails through inadequate nutrition.

The coronary flow is also greatly increased by lowering the oxygen content of the blood. Stimulation of the sympathetic accelerator nerves, or the administration of adrenaline, increases the coronary blood-flow, in part by a direct effect on the vessels, in part by chemical substances produced as a consequence of the increased work of the heart muscle. The vagus seems to constrict the coronary vessels. The coronary circulation is thus so regulated that the nutrition of the heart muscle is varied according to the work done by the organ—a fact which is but an illustration of what might be stated of organs generally.

Coronary Occlusion and Angina Pectoris. The function of the heart, like that of every organ, is intimately dependent on its blood supply and the arrangements that we have discussed are such that in health, increased work of the heart is accompanied by increased blood-flow. If a coronary artery is suddenly blocked by a clot, then the patient may die at once from ventricullar fibrillation or after some hours from congestive cardiac failure ; in a large number of cases, particularly if the area deprived of its blood supply is small, the remaining healthy heart muscle is adequate to maintain the circulation at rest, the bloodless area is slowly converted into fibrous tissue and the patient recovers. Such small coronary occlusions are accompanied by intense substernal pain, probably due to the stimulation of sensory nerves in the heart itself by chemical substances released locally from the ischæmic muscle. If the coronary arteries are thickened and narrowed by disease, they are incapable of dilatation, and the circulation becomes inadequate to the demands of muscular work. In this condition substernal pain (angina pectoris) is produced on exercise, probably again by the release of metabolites from the inadequately oxygenated heart muscle. A somewhat similar pain known as intermittent claudication is experienced in the muscles of the legs on walking, when the arteries are narrowed or blocked by disease. The student may reproduce this pain by working the muscles of his forearm, after the circulation has been arrested by inflating a cuff on the upper arm to above systolic pressure. He may ascertain that the rate at which pain develops depends on the frequency and the force of the muscular contractions. On stopping work the pain remains present until the circulation is restored, when it quickly disappears. The pain thus seems to be due to stimulation of the nerve endings in the muscles by a substance released during muscular contraction, and normally removed by the circulating blood.

The Pulmonary Circulation. The whole output of the right ventricle is delivered into the pulmonary artery at a pressure of 15 to 20 mm. Hg. The blood-flow through the lungs is the same as the outflow through the aorta, *i.e.*, at rest about 4 litres per minute ; in exercise it may rise to 30 litres per minute or more. The resistance offered by the pulmonary vessels appears to be low. Since there is no alternative route for the blood between the right and left sides of the heart, it is not surprising that the vaso-motor supply is unimportant, though it appears that the vagus can dilate and the sympathetic constrict the vessels of the lungs.

The chief factor modifying the pulmonary circulation is the pressure change accompanying respiration. The lungs are elastic structures which are kept open by the chest wall ; if the chest is opened the lungs collapse. In consequence of this pull of the lungs, if a needle is thrust into the pleural cavity of man and connected to a manometer, this will normally register a pressure about 4 cm. H_2O below that of the atmosphere. During inspiration the lungs are further stretched and the intrapleural pressure falls by as much as 20 cm. water. These negative pressures affect all intra-thoracic structures but particularly the pulmonary capillaries, the great veins and the chambers of the heart in diastole, whose walls are yielding ; the effect on the thick-walled arteries is of less consequence. The effects of respiration on the systemic arterial blood pressure are complex and variable. In man during quiet respiration of the thoracic type (*i.e.*, mainly by the intercostal muscles) the blood pressure falls during inspiration and rises during expiration. This effect which is usual in man is probably due to mechanical changes in the pulmonary vessels; when the lungs expand the pulmonary vessels are pulled open and fill with blood, and diversion of this extra blood from its onward movement leads to a reduced flow into, and output from, the left ventricle. Occasionally in man when the breathing is purely abdominal in type (*i.e.*, mainly by the diaphragm), the blood pressure rises during inspiration and falls during expiration. This effect may possibly be explained by the flow of blood into the thorax. During inspiration blood is aspirated into the great veins and heart from extrathoracic structures, and the rise of intra-abdominal pressure produced by descent of the diaphragm forces blood from the abdomen into the chest; in this way the filling and output of the heart would be increased during inspiration. X-ray photography, after intravenous injection of an opaque substance, shows that during inspiration the flow through the superior vena cava is increased, but in the dog, cat and rabbit the inferior vena cava is constricted by contraction of the diaphragm; in these animals at least it is unlikely, therefore, that the flow through the inferior vena cava is increased during inspiration.

The pulse is accelerated during inspiration and slowed during expiration—a reflex effect which is abolished by section of the vagi.

The Liver and Portal System. The blood-flow through the liver is very large; about half the blood-flow through the inferior vena cava comes from this source. After leaving the intestinal capillaries the blood gathered into the portal vein traverses a second set of capillaries in the liver. Since the portal pressure in the dog is only about 8 cm. H_2O the resistance offered by the liver vessels must be very small. The liver is also supplied by the hepatic artery, which contributes about a quarter of the blood and 40 per cent. of the oxygen supplied to the organ. The liver, the portal vein and the territory it drains ordinarily accommodate about one-third, or more, of the total blood volume. Experiment suggests that a large proportion of this is expelled in the early stages of hæmorrhage. After the injection of adrenaline or stimulation of the sympathetic nerves the outflow from the liver exceeds its inflow, a large part of its blood being thus discharged into the great veins. It is likely, therefore, that the liver and portal system constitute a variable reservoir, whence blood is discharged to augment the inflow and output of the heart in conditions such as hæmorrhage, emotion and exercise.

A piece of dog's colon, transferred to the outer abdominal wall with its nerve and blood supply intact, blanches at the beginning of exercise, though, as exercise is continued, it slowly fills again with blood. This presumably illustrates what happens to the vessels of the whole gut in exercise.

The Spleen. The branches of the splenic artery open into venous sinuses, which unite to form the splenic vein. Along the course of the artery and vein are perforations communicating with the spleen pulp, which contains red and white blood corpuscles in its network. In the dog the spleen has been brought to the exterior through an incision on the abdominal wall and left there for many months. Its size at rest indicates that it may hold one-fifth of the total blood volume. During hæmorrhage, emotion, asphyxia and muscular exercise the muscular capsule of the spleen contracts, and its blood content, which is exceptionally rich in red cells, is expelled into the general circulation.

The Skeletal Muscle. At rest the circulation through skeletal muscle is very small, about 2 to 3 c.c. per 100 c.c. muscle per minute in man. After exercise the blood flow may rise to 20 c.c. or more, per 100 c.c. per minute and the increase in blood-flow slowly subsides during the 10 minutes or so following moderate exercise. The vaso-dilatation is evidently due to a vaso-dilator substance or substances released during exercise and there is some evidence that this may be histamine. Indian ink injected into the circulation enters only 10 per cent. of the muscle capillaries at rest but may enter all the capillaries when the muscle is active. Strong muscular contraction reduces the increased blood-flow produced by exercise, presumably because the blood vessels are compressed by the contracted muscle fibres. Paralysis of all the nerves supplying resting skeletal muscles doubles the blood-flow, an effect which is absent after sympathectomy. In a fainting attack, muscle blood-flow is increased, and this increase is prevented by paralysis of the nerves. In small doses adrenaline dilates the muscle vessels in man.

The Skin. The part played by the skin in the regulation of body temperature has already been mentioned, and in the normal animal the regulation of the skin circulation through the sympathetic nerves is very largely in the interests of the maintenance of body temperature. In this connection an important part is played by the arteriolo-venous communications, short wide connections between the arterioles and venules which, are very abundant in man in the nail beds, the skin covering the volar surfaces of the fingers and palm of the hand and in the corresponding sites of the foot. The changes in blood-flow through the fingers which may occur in response to changes in body temperature are very large, ranging from 1 c.c. per 100 c.c. per minute when the body is cool to 100 c.c. when the body is hot. The skin vessels also constrict readily when the maintenance of the arterial pressure is threatened as after hæmorrhage and in fainting attacks, as the coldness and pallor of the skin show. The skin vessels constrict reflexly and temporarily to any strong sensory stimulus, in emotion and in the initial stages of exercise.

The skin vessels possess unusual interest in that their behaviour to local disturbances is easily studied, and possibly typifies the behaviour of most vessels of the body, though the " flare " appears to be confined to the skin. The local reactions of the skin vessels are as follows :—

(a) **White Reaction.** If the skin of the forearm or back is lightly stroked with the end of a ruler, after about fifteen seconds the line of the stroke becomes sharply marked by pallor, which lasts about three minutes. The pallor is due to active constriction of the capillaries, for it occurs even when the circulation to the forearm has been arrested by inflating a sphygmomanometer cuff on the upper arm above systolic pressure. If adrenaline is pricked into the skin, pallor is also produced and persists even if the pressure in the vessels is raised to 100 mm .

Hg by inflating to this pressure an armlet placed proximally. The force that can be exerted by the capillaries in contracting is thus considerable.

(b) **Triple Response.** If the skin is injured by scratching, by lightly burning, by freezing or by pricking in injurious substances such as hydrochloric acid or caustic soda, the point of injury is marked by reddening of the skin, which later gives place to whealing as fluid passes out of the capillaries and distends the tissue spaces of the skin. Around the local reddening is a diffuse bright red mottled flush or " flare," which is due to the opening of the surrounding arterioles. The local redness due to widening of the minute vessels, the wheal due to their increased permeability and the flare are the components of the triple response of the vessels to injury. The whole response is independent of the central nervous system, being unchanged

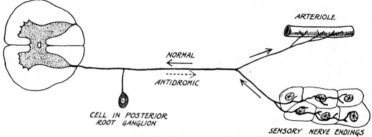

Fig. II. 30.   Diagram of the Nervous Connections concerned in the **Axon Reflex.**

immediately after section of all nerves to the skin. After all the nerves have degenerated, however, the flare is absent; if the sympathetic supply alone has degenerated the flare is unimpaired. The flare is an example of a local axon reflex through the sensory fibres. The fibres entering the posterior roots of the cord divide at their periphery into branches to the blood vessels and to the tissues. Injury to the skin stimulates the sensory branches, and the stimulus passes proximally to the point of bifurcation and back down the other branch to the arterioles (see Fig. II. 30). The whole of the triple response has been shown to be due to the release of a chemical substance from the injured skin, and this, from its resemblance to histamine, has been termed " H substance." The triple response is in the skin the vascular basis of the phenomenon of inflammation.

(c) **Reactive Hyperæmia.** If the circulation to a warm limb is arrested for a few minutes and then released, a bright flush, reactive hyperæmia, at once suffuses the skin and then slowly fades. After circulatory arrest lasting ten minutes the blood-flow to the forearm may be increased to ten or twenty times the normal (Fig. II. 31); both muscle and skin vessels share in

this vaso-dilatation. The intensity and duration of reactive
hyperæmia depend on the duration of circulatory arrest and on
the temperature of the limb. The flush represents a dilatation
of the minute vessels ; it is independent of any central or local
nervous mechanism and is due to the action of vaso-dilator
substances formed locally and normally removed by the
circulating blood. When, as is constantly happening, areas of
skin and of subcutaneous tissue are rendered bloodless by
supporting the weight of the body, they may be said to

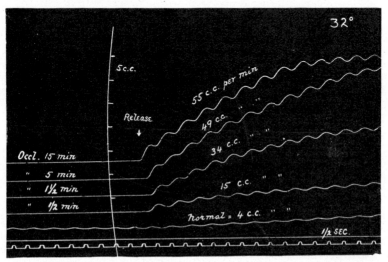

FIG. II, 31. Five **forearm volume curves** showing the normal rates of blood-
flow in c.c. per minute per 100 c.c. of arm, and the rates after periods
of circulatory arrest lasting ½, 1½, 5 and 15 minutes. These curves
were obtained with the plethysmograph shown in Fig. II. 15. The
normal blood-flow is given by the rate at which blood collects in the
forearm when its venous outlet is temporarily occluded by inflating a
pneumatic cuff on the upper arm to 70 mm. Hg. The blood-flow
after circulatory arrest is given by the rate at which blood collects
when the pressure in the cuff on the upper arm is suddenly dropped
from a value above systolic pressure (*e.g.*, 200 mm. Hg.) to a value
sufficient to impede the venous outflow (70 mm. Hg.). (Lewis and
Grant.)

accumulate a blood-flow debt ; reactive hyperæmia ensures
the discharge of this debt as soon as blood is free to enter the
tissues again. Reactive hyperæmia also provides an explanation of the more general problem of how the tissues regulate
their own blood supply ; for the tissues appear continuously
to release, at a rate proportional to their activity, vaso-dilator
substances which increase the blood-flow locally. It has
been shown in man that the histamine equivalent of the blood
issuing from the forearm during the early stages of reactive
hyperæmia is increased, but it is not known whether histamine
is the only or the chief substance concerned.

The Regulation of the Blood Supply to the Tissues

It has already been emphasised that the supply of blood to the individual tissues depends on two factors, the total cardiac output and the proportion of it distributed to the various organs. It will now have become evident that many tissues of the body (we cannot yet say all) are equipped with a local chemical mechanism which ensures that when the blood supply falls below the metabolic requirements of the tissues, or if the metabolic activity of the tissue rises, vaso-dilator substances are released which dilate the vessels of the tissue in question and thus secure a larger proportion of the cardiac output. As we have seen, there is some evidence that histamine may be one of the vaso-dilator substances concerned, but at least two others, acetyl choline (which is, however, rapidly destroyed in the body) and compounds of adenylic acid are known constituents of normal tissues ; nicotinic acid also has vaso-dilator properties, and a vaso-dilator substance " kallikrein " has been extracted from the pancreas and normal urine. It was long thought that the vaso-dilator substances were acid metabolites such as lactic acid and carbon dioxide which dilated the vessels by virtue of a change of hydrogen ion concentration. More careful experiments have shown that changes in hydrogen ion concentration of a magnitude reasonably to be expected in the body have little action on the vessels, although there is some evidence that lactic acid may play a part in dilating the muscle vessels during muscular contraction.

Local vaso-dilatation which accompanies the increased activity of an organ does not usually produce a fall of blood pressure, presumably because of vaso-constriction in inactive organs and increased cardiac output ; changes largely brought about through the carotid sinus and depressor reflexes and perhaps through the release into the circulation of substances such as adrenaline and renin. The maintenance of the arterial pressure secures at all times an adequate blood flow through the brain and heart.

Thus in spite of the complexity of the factors involved in the circulation and distribution of blood, arrangements are such that the various organs of the body are automatically supplied according to their varying needs.

The Circulatory Changes during Exercise

In concluding this chapter, it is instructive to view the circulation as a whole and to contrast its resting state with that of the most intense activity of which the organism is capable, namely severe muscular work.

When severe exercise is imminent, and before the skeletal muscles contract, the respiratory and circulatory systems are prepared by messages from the brain. The circulatory changes are produced by a general increase in sympathetic vaso-motor tone and by the output of adrenaline into the blood-stream. These result in increased frequency and force of beating of the heart, and in constriction of the vessels to the skin, alimentary canal and quiescent muscle. The peripheral resistance is increased and the arterial pressure rises. Blood is expelled from the great reservoirs, the spleen, the skin, and the liver and portal system, and augments the inflow to and thus the output from the heart. The augmented cardiac output is distributed mainly to the organs where vessels are least constricted or are actually dilated by sympathetic activity, namely to the brain, the heart and any active muscles.

When muscular exercise begins, the changes already described are accentuated, chiefly by an increase in the impulses from the brain, and perhaps in part through stimulation of the vaso-motor centre by the carbon dioxide produced in muscular contraction. But another factor which has a much greater effect on the output of the heart now comes into play, namely the increased circulation through the active muscles. When the skeletal muscles contract, their arteries, arterioles and capillaries dilate and receive a correspondingly large portion of the cardiac output. It might be supposed that in severe exercise this extensive vaso-dilatation would result in a profound fall of blood pressure due to lowered peripheral resistance, and in a reduced cardiac output due to increased capacity of the circulation. In fact the reverse is true, exercise augments the cardiac output and raises the arterial blood pressure, and the magnitude of these changes is proportional to the severity of the work. This result is thought to follow for two reasons. In the first place muscular vaso-dilatation is balanced to a large extent by vaso-constriction elsewhere ; most of the blood traverses dilated vessels, thus entering the veins at unusually high pressure and flowing rapidly to the heart. Secondly, during muscular contraction, blood is squeezed out of the muscles and is forced towards the heart. When the muscles relax, blood is free to enter only from the arterial side, because reflux through the veins is prevented by their valves. Muscular movements thus pump the blood through the muscles and so increase the venous return to the heart.

CHAPTER III

THE BLOOD AND THE OTHER BODY FLUIDS

THE BLOOD

THE blood, in its circulation, brings to the tissues the foodstuffs and oxygen necessary for their metabolism, and carries away the carbon dioxide and other waste products. The blood, however, is no mere indifferent circulating fluid, but has remarkable " buffering " properties ; these enable it to change its composition with respect to the most important substances—oxygen and carbon dioxide—without at the same time bringing about an equally large change in the composition of the fluids surrounding the tissue cells.

The Red Blood Corpuscles

We are all familiar with blood as a bright red, rather viscous and sticky liquid. If blood is left undisturbed it separates into two parts, the lower contains the cells, and is opaque and red, while the upper is a clear pale yellow liquid—the **plasma.** Under the microscope we see an enormous number of pale yellow discs, the **red blood corpuscles** (also called **erythrocytes** or **red cells**), floating in a clear colourless fluid. It is the settling of these red cells which brings about the separation of the blood into two parts ; although yellow when seen individually, they become red in bulk. They are described as biconcave discs, since they are thicker near the edge than in the middle. Their average diameter in human blood is about 8·6 μ, and their thickness about 2·6 μ. Their specific gravity is rather greater than that of the plasma (1·06 against 1·03), which accounts for their settling out—a process which can be hastened over a thousand-fold by centrifuging. The red colour is due to the presence of the important substance hæmoglobin, which is responsible for most of the " buffering " action mentioned in the first paragraph.

The estimation of the number of red cells per cubic millimetre of blood (the *Red Cell Count*) is important for both clinical and research purposes. The apparatus used is called a *hæmocytometer* (from the Greek for " blood-cell measurer ").

This consists of : (1) A small pipette in which a drop of blood is diluted two hundred-fold with a solution which " fixes " the corpuscles (in the histological sense) (Hayems' solution). (2) The counting slide ; a thick glass slide on which, demarcated by two deep grooves, is a polished surface lying exactly 1/10th mm. below the general level of the slide. When a flat cover-slip is placed on the slide to cover the polished surface, a chamber exactly 1/10th mm. deep is formed—the counting chamber. On the polished surface are engraved two sets of fine lines crossing at right angles to form a large number of squares, each with an area of 1/400th of a square millimetre. A drop of diluted blood, thoroughly mixed in the pipette, is applied to the edge of the counting chamber, into which it is drawn by capillarity. When the cells have settled down, they are counted under the microscope. To obtain the average number of cells per square, about 500 cells should be counted and divided by the number of squares they occupy.

$$\text{Red cell count per cubic millimetre} = \frac{\text{No. of cells}}{\text{No. of squares}} \times \text{dilution} \times \frac{1}{\text{area of a square}} \times \frac{1}{\text{depth of chamber}}$$

e.g., $\dfrac{480}{80} \times 200 \times 400 \times 10 = 4{,}800{,}000$ red cells per c.mm.

The red cell count in healthy men varies from $4\frac{1}{2}$ to 6 million per c.mm., the average being about $5\frac{1}{2}$ million. In women the count is even more variable, but on an average about 10 per cent. lower than in men. The uncertainty in the method of obtaining a blood count, as ordinarily performed, is likely to be at least $\pm$ 5 per cent.

The red blood corpuscles normally occupy 40 to 45 per cent. of the volume of the blood in man. This important ratio can be measured by means of the *hæmatocrit* (from the Greek for " blood-separator ") ; this is a graduated capillary tube of uniform bore, which is filled with blood (coagulation being prevented). This blood is centrifuged at high speed until the column of sedimented red cells shows no further shrinkage ; the volume of the tightly packed cells can then be read off and compared with that of the whole blood.

The microscopic examination of the blood cells is conveniently carried out on dried and stained smears of blood. On drying, the red cells shrink, so that their diameters are diminished by 8 to 16 per cent. In such dried preparations of normal human blood the average diameter of the red cells is only $7\cdot4 \pm 0\cdot3 \; \mu$. The shrinkage and distortion of the cells so prepared are of no great consequence in the clinical examination of the blood, because the characteristic changes in blood associated with different diseases are commonly described in terms of the changes which appear in the dried smears.

In the diagnosis of anæmias, considerable attention is paid to the average diameter of the red cells and to their individual variations of size and shape. In pernicious anæmia the average diameter of the red cells is usually greater than normal.

The White Blood Corpuscles

In addition to erythrocytes, the blood contains white blood corpuscles, or leucocytes, and platelets, or thrombocytes.

There are several varieties of **leucocyte,** but all have (*a*) a nucleus (in which respect they differ from mammalian red cells and platelets, which have no nuclei) ; (*b*) colourless cytoplasm (in the living state). Normal human blood contains 5,000 to 10,000 leucocytes per c.mm. When the number is lower than normal, a state of *leucopenia* is said to exist—as, for example, in typhoid and influenza. Most general infections, on the other hand, are accompanied by a striking increase in the number of circulating leucocytes, a condition known as *leucocytosis*.

For the estimation of the number of white blood corpuscles per cubic millimetre of blood (the *White Cell Count*) the hæmocytometer is used in much the same way as for the red cell-count, but with the following modifications : (1) Because the white cells are fewer than the red cells the blood is diluted only twenty times. (2) For the same reason, larger areas of the counting chamber must be used. At the corners of the ruled area will be found larger squares (1/16 sq. mm.) for use in white cell counts. (3) The dilution fluid contains acetic acid to dissolve the red cells and so secure an unobstructed view of the leucocytes.

The estimation of the proportion of each type of leucocyte in a particular sample of blood can be done on any properly stained blood smear, and is known as the *Differential White Count.*

The white blood corpuscles are usually classified into three groups, the granular cells (sometimes called *Polymorphs*, but now often called *Granulocytes*), the *Lymphocytes* and the *Monocytes.* The polymorphs (polymorpho-nuclear leucocytes) are so named because in stained smears their nuclei are lobulated in various ways. According to the staining reactions of their granules, the granulocytes are subdivided into *neutrophils, eosinophils* and *basophils.* The neutrophils are now sometimes called polymorphs.

Differential Cell Count

(1) Granulocytes	⎧ Neutrophils, 70 per cent. ⎫	
	⎨ Eosinophils, 1 ,, ,, ⎬ Of total white
	⎩ Basophils, 0·5 ,, ,, ⎭ cell count.
(2) Lymphocytes	24 ,, ,,	
(3) Monocytes	4 ,, ,,	

Neutrophils. Deep indentations divide their nuclei into two, three or four lobes. The number of lobes is believed to increase with the age of the cell. The cytoplasmic granules are very fine, and have no striking affinity for acidic or basic stains. Neutrophils probably play an important part in defending the body against infection. They gather in large numbers at the site of acute infections, where their proteolytic ferment breaks down dead tissue into the liquid known as pus. In the leuco-cytoses which accompany acute inflammatory diseases it is mainly the neutrophils that are increased.

Eosinophils resemble neutrophils, except that their granules are very coarse and are stained bright red by eosin, while the nucleus is nearly always bi-lobed. The proportion of eosinphils is increased in certain abnormal conditions, *e.g.*, asthma and various skin infections. Their function is obscure.

Basophils (sometimes called mast cells) also have lobed nuclei and coarse granules with an affinity for basic dyes, and hence are blue when stained by the stains ordinarily used for blood.

The red bone marrow is the normal site of production of granulocytes and in it can be recognised immature granular cells in two developmental stages. The younger are known as myeloblasts and the older as myelocytes. Myeloblasts have no granules, but myelocytes have granules in which the tendency to become eosinophilic, basophilic or neutrophilic can be easily seen. The nuclei of the myelocytes, however, are only slightly indented. These immature forms of granular blood cells may appear in the circulating blood in blood diseases, called *leukœmias*.

The *Lymphocytes* of normal blood are the smallest of the white blood cells, the small forms having about the same diameter as a red cell. They are characterised by an almost round, densely staining nucleus surrounded by a narrow zone of cytoplasm free from granules. The lymphocytes are produced in the lymphoid tissue from larger cells with pale nuclei. Lymphocytes gather in large numbers around the margins of tuberculous and other chronic lesions where, perhaps, they have some effect in checking the progress of these diseases.

The *Monocytes* (*transitional cells* or *large mononuclears*) have large oval or bean-shaped nuclei ; both nuclei and cytoplasm are pale staining. They are supposed to be derived from the cells of the reticulo-endo-thelial system (see below), chiefly because they also take up particulate matter from the circulating blood.

The Reticulo-endothelial System

The reticulo-endothelial system includes phagocytic cells, often called histiocytes, which are found in varying numbers in connective tissue and in the stroma of various organs. They all have the property of ingesting certain dyes, such as trypan blue or lithium carmine, and particulate matter such as indian ink, when these substances are intro-duced into their neighbourhood. When these dyes are injected intra-venously, they are taken up for the most part by the endothelial cells lining the sinusoids in the liver (Kupffer cells), the reticulum cells and cells lining the blood sinuses of the spleen and bone marrow and in the lymph sinuses of lymph glands.

Besides ingesting foreign matter, including bacteria, and dealing with fragmented red cells, the reticulo-endothelial system is concerned in the production of substances called antibodies ; these help to destroy invading micro-organisms and the poisons (toxins) which they elaborate (see below).

The Platelets and the Coagulation of the Blood

The smallest elements in the blood are the *platelets* or *thrombocytes*. These are round or oval disc-shaped bodies, 2 to 3 μ in diameter, with granular cytoplasm, but no nucleus. They are believed to be derived from the large multinuclear cells of the bone marrow called megakaryo-cytes. Cytoplasmic processes of these cells become pinched off and pass into the blood as platelets. Normal blood contains from 250,000 to 450,000 platelets per c.mm. Within a few seconds after blood is shed its platelets agglutinate, that is, clump together, and then, more slowly, disintegrate. Consequently, in smears of normal blood the platelets are to be seen only in clumps often consisting of as many as thirty or forty platelets. The clumping of platelets at the site of bleeding in small vessels tends to plug the wound in the vessel and thus helps to restrain hæmorrhage. This function is reinforced by the way in which platelets hasten blood clotting.

Shed blood normally sets to a jelly in the course of five or ten minutes. It is said then to have *clotted* or *coagulated*. If the clot is washed free from red cells, it is found to consist of an interlacing network of fine white fibres of protein material to which the name *fibrin* is given. If the early stages of clotting are observed by means of an ultramicroscope, it will be found that the needles of fibrin always begin to form in the immediate neighbourhood of clumps of disintegrating platelets, and to grow out from these centres till the whole of the blood is enmeshed in the network. This suggests that the platelets have an important function in the inception of blood clotting.

If a blood clot is allowed to stand, it slowly shrinks (retraction or syneræsis) and a pale yellow liquid called *serum* is squeezed out. Serum closely resembles plasma, but lacks a protein constituent which can be precipitated from plasma by half-saturation with sodium chloride. This protein is called *fibrinogen*, because it changes into fibrin during the process of clotting. If precipitated fibrinogen is redissolved in 2 per cent. sodium chloride, and a little fresh serum added, a clot is formed in much the same way as it is in plasma. Fresh serum therefore contains a substance which induces fibrinogen to clot; this substance is known as *thrombin*.

Thrombin is an enzyme, and can be isolated in a moderately pure state by extracting fresh serum or blood clots for some months with alcohol. Unclotted blood treated in the same way yields no thrombin, so that thrombin does not exist in circulating plasma, but is formed some time after the blood is shed. Plasma, therefore, must contain a substance—known as prothrombin—which can change into thrombin under the proper conditions. If calcium ions are removed from freshly shed blood by adding sufficient sodium or potassium oxalate (which precipitates the calcium), the change of prothrombin to thrombin is prevented and clotting does not occur. Once the thrombin is formed, however, it will clot fibrinogen even in the absence of calcium ions.

Since the blood does not normally clot in the circulation, we infer that the process of clotting is initiated by (1) the contamination with tissue juices which takes place as it flows from a wound, and (2) the contact with foreign surfaces such as the skin and the vessels in which it is collected.

(1) The addition of extract of most tissues, or of disintegrated platelets, to blood increases the rate of clotting, and it is supposed that this action is due to a substance apparently a second enzyme, called *thrombokinase* (or *cytozyme* or *thromboplastin*). *Cephalin* has the same action, and is believed by some to be a constituent of thrombokinase.

(2) Clotting is greatly delayed if the blood is shed through a cannula coated with paraffin wax into a vessel also coated with wax; all the foreign surfaces are thus chemically inert and are not wetted by the blood. Such treatment greatly delays the agglutination and disintegration of the platelets.

Blood clotting, therefore, may be schematised as follows :—

Calcium-Prothrombin Complex

(In presence of :
Disintegrated platelets ;
Tissue juices ;
Foreign surfaces.)

Thrombin

$$\text{Fibrinogen} \xrightarrow[\text{of Thrombin)}]{\text{(By action}} \text{Fibrin}$$

The mechanisms of the reactions in this scheme are still in dispute.

Most interest has been centred on the question of what keeps prothrombin in circulating plasma from changing into thrombin. This may very reasonably be attributed to the relative stability of the platelets ; but there is reason to believe that there may be a second line of defence by means of a substance which acts as an anti-prothrombin and prevents the formation of thrombin by thrombokinase. This substance is known as Heparin. It was originally isolated from the liver (hence the name), but has also been extracted from the blood vessels.

Measurements of Clotting Time. The clotting time of normal blood may vary from four to sixty minutes, depending on the method used to measure it. To get consistent results, the following conditions must be controlled : (1) *Temperature.* Clotting time increases as the temperature decreases. (2) *The manner of obtaining the blood.* Blood drawn from a vein clots more slowly than blood from a skin puncture, which allows more contamination by tissue juices. (3) *Agitation of the blood.* Agitation hastens clotting. (4) *Cleanliness of apparatus.* The cleaner the apparatus, the slower the clotting.

A simple method is to collect a few drops of blood from a puncture in the lobe of the ear on a clean watch glass, which is then covered by another watch glass to limit evaporation. The fluidity of the drop is tested from time to time by gently tipping the watch glass. The time from the shedding of the blood till the first signs of clotting appear under these conditions is about 4 to 8 minutes at 20° C., for normal human blood.

The chief clinical interest in blood clotting is in connection with the arrest of hæmorrhage and the development of clots in the blood vessels (thrombosis) under pathological conditions. Hæmophilia is an inborn disease in which blood clotting is so slow that hæmorrhage from a relatively trivial wound may be profuse enough to be dangerous ; it is an hereditary defect which is manifested almost exclusively in males, but inherited through the mother. The prolonged clotting of hæmophilic blood is apparently due to the unusually long time the platelets take to release adequate amounts of thrombokinase but other views have been put forward, and the matter is still in dispute.

Blood can be preserved in the fluid state in the following ways :—

(1) By defibrination. The blood while clotting is stirred vigorously with some object, *e.g.*, a bundle of feathers—to which fibrin will adhere. The fibrin is thus removed as it forms and the red cells are left suspended in serum.

(2) By removing the calcium salts by the addition of sodium or potassium oxalate (0·1 to 0·3 per cent.), which precipitates calcium oxalate.

(3) By inactivating calcium salts by the addition of sodium citrate or fluoride (e.g., 0·2 to 0·4 per cent. citrate), which results in the formation of an unionisable calcium salt.

Calcium ions seem to be necessary not only for the change of prothrombin to thrombin, but for the disintegration of platelets ; thus oxalate and citrate solutions can be used to preserve platelets intact.

(4) By cooling the blood to 0° C., which retards clotting almost indefinately and preserves the platelets.

(5) By preserving blood from contact with surfaces which it wets.

(6) By the addition of heparin, which acts as an antiprothrombin.

(7) By the addition of certain azo dyes, e.g., chlorazol fast pink, which are thought to act as antithrombokinases.

(8) By the addition of hirudin, a material obtained from leech heads, which acts as an antithrombin.

(9) By the addition of suitable concentrations of almost any neutral salt, e.g., one-seventh saturation with $MgSO_4$.

The Life History of the Red Blood Corpuscle

In post-natal life the red blood corpuscles are formed in the blood spaces of the red bone marrow. In the earlier stages of their development red cells possess nuclei. Two stages in the development of nucleated red cells from the mesenchymal parent cell are distinguished ; they are known successively as *erythroblasts* and *normoblasts*. The normoblast becomes an adult red cell when it loses its nucleus. For the first few days of its adult life, spots and threads of basophilic material can be demonstrated in the red cell by vital staining with cresyl blue. In this stage it is known as a *reticulocyte* or reticulated red cell. After the first week of life reticulocytes form only about 1 per cent. of the circulating red cells, but they form a larger proportion of the red cells found in bone marrow. The proportion of them in circulating blood rises considerably whenever the new formation of red cells is increased, as after a hæmorrhage.

The old red cells are continually being destroyed, probably by fragmentation, being smashed into erythrocyte dust in the circulation. The fragments are further acted upon by the reticulo-endothelial cells, which change the hæmoglobin into inorganic iron and the pigment *bilirubin*. The latter travels in the plasma to the liver, where it is slightly changed during its passage through the liver cells into the bile. In the bowel bilirubin is changed into *stercobilinogen* and *stercobilin*, which give the fæces their dark colour. Not all the bile pigment is excreted, however. Some is reabsorbed into the portal blood stream in the form of a colourless compound called *urobilinogen*, which is picked up by the liver, perhaps to be used in the production of new hæmoglobin. From the rate at which bilirubin is formed in the liver, it is calculated that the average life-time of a red cell is about four weeks. When large quantities of bilirubin are formed (as in hæmolytic jaundice), and consequently large amounts of urobilinogen absorbed, appreciable amounts of urobilinogen are excreted in the urine. (This is to be distinguished from the excretion of bilirubin in the urine which occurs when the bile passages are obstructed, for example, by a gall-stone (obstructive jaundice).) Urobilinogen is also found in the urine when the liver function is impaired, and thus unable to deal with the normal quantities carried to it in the portal blood stream.

The study of the disease, pernicious anæmia, has resulted in the discovery of at least one factor concerned in the normal development of red cells. In this disease megaloblasts, which are a special immature nucleated type of red cell found in this disease, become very numerous, while the normoblasts which are normally in the majority are very scarce. It appears that something is lacking which is necessary for the maturation of the megaloblast.

This missing factor is formed in the stomach out of some substance known as the *extrinsic factor*, contained in protein food ; this is acted on by another substance—known as the *intrinsic factor*—which is secreted by the walls of the stomach ; the intrinsic factor is also known as *hæmopoietin*, and is probably an enzyme. The substance so formed is stored in the liver. Pernicious anæmia is always fatal unless treated, and is due to the lack of the intrinsic factor ; its treatment by the administration of preparations of hog's stomach or liver extracts is one of the most striking advances in therapeutics.

Iron is necessary for the formation of red cells ; the anæmia which may occur in infants during the suckling period is attributed to the almost complete lack of iron in the milk, and can be cured by administration of salts of iron. The presence of a trace of copper is essential to the proper utilisation of the iron.

Hæmolysis

The hæmoglobin of the red cell does not normally pass into the plasma, because it is prevented from doing so by some kind of limiting membrane. When the red cells are injured in such a way as to allow the hæmoglobin to escape into the surrounding fluid, *hæmolysis* or *laking* is said to have occurred.

There are three general ways in which the red blood corpuscles can be made to discharge their hæmoglobin. In the first, the cells are burst by being placed in a solution of lower salt concentration than the plasma, whereupon they swell up by reason of the excess osmotic pressure within them and finally burst ; in the second, the cell membranes are disintegrated by means of a solution of ether, saponin, bile salts or certain other substances ; in the third, the blood is repeatedly frozen solid and thawed as rapidly as possible.

A solution is defined as being isotonic if it has the same osmotic pressure as the tissue fluids, hypertonic if it has a greater osmotic pressure, and hypotonic if it has a smaller. The magnitude of the osmotic pressure cannot be specified, however, except in relation to a definite membrane, and hence two solutions may be isotonic with respect to one membrane, but not with respect to another. If the membrane is permeable only to water, and impermeable to all the substances in solution, the osmotic pressure is determined by the concentration of the dissolved substances and their molecular weights. In membranes occurring in animals the concentration of all those substances to which the membrane is permeable must be left out of consideration. For example, the red blood corpuscles are impermeable to neutral salts, but permeable to urea, oxygen and carbon dioxide, so that the addition of, say, 1 per cent. of urea to 0·9 per cent. salt solution will not make a hypertonic solution with respect to the red blood corpuscles ; similarly, the ordinary collodion membrane (and the glomerular membrane in the kidney) is permeable to all crystalloids, so that only the concentration of the colloids need be considered. In physiology we often use the word " isotonic," without further specification, to mean " isotonic with respect to the red blood corpuscles." It must be remembered that most membranes are more permeable to water than to any solute, so that transient osmotic effects may be observed even with solutions that are, in the long run, isotonic with respect to those membranes. Such effects are important in the formation of lymph (p. 121), and possibly in the formation of urine. The withdrawal of fluid from the tissue spaces into the blood as a result of transient osmotic pressure of glucose is illustrated in Fig. VII. 8, p. 268.

The membrane of the red blood corpuscle is almost impermeable to cations (*e.g.*, Na^+ and K^+), but readily permeable to anions (*e.g.*, Cl^- and HCO_3^-). If, however, anions pass through the membrane, the electric charge on the cations which are left behind attracts other anions from the further side of the membrane to preserve electrical neutrality in the solution. Consequently, there can be interchange of particular anions between the red cells and the plasma, but no net movement of anions as a whole across the membrane. The membrane is effectively impermeable to electrolytes from the point of view of the osmotic balance between the interior of the cell and the plasma.

When hæmolysis takes place by swelling in a hypotonic salt solution, it is found that the amount of swelling which can take place without rupture of the membrane varies in different cells ; in normal human blood, while the great majority of cells are just hæmolysed in about 0·4 per cent. NaCl, a small proportion (5 to 10 per cent.) burst in stronger solutions, and about the same proportion are unaffected unless the concentration is reduced to less than to 0·4 per cent. In this way a *resistance* or *fragility curve* can be constructed, showing the proportion of corpuscles hæmolysed as ordinates, against the salt concentrations as abscissæ.

The proportion of cells with small resistance is greatly increased in the blood of patients suffering from certain diseases such as familial hæmolytic jaundice ; when these patients have their spleens removed, their red cells attain a resistance which is normal, or even greater than normal. During recovery from anæmia (*e.g.*, pernicious, or after hæmorrhage), on the other hand, the proportion with a large resistance is greatly increased. The resistance to hæmolysis of a given cell probably depends upon its age, the membrane becoming steadily weaker during its life in the circulation until it finally gives way altogether.

Immunity Reactions

Infectious diseases are transmitted from one animal to another by the transference of characteristic micro-organisms. Bacteria, for example, are concerned in many familiar diseases such as diphtheria, typhoid, tetanus and tuberculosis. Animals are not all liable to the same infections ; dogs, for example, are immune to typhoid, and man, fortunately, is immune to many diseases common in animals. Apart from such inborn immunity, immunity is often acquired ; it is well known that an attack of a certain disease will confer immunity to a later infection with the same disease. Such immunity is due to the development of *antibodies*, provoked by the original attack (which is due to the presence of the *antigen*) and outlasting it by many years ; these oppose a subsequent infection. Such antibodies can, in many cases, be prepared artificially, or the animal can be induced to develop them itself without having to undergo the full rigours of an actual attack of the disease ; their study has consequently become an important part of medical science, known as *Immunology*. It is only with a few aspects of the subject that we are here concerned.

Many substances, such as proteins, bacterial toxins and red cells, have the power to act as antigens ; these, when injected into an animal, lead to the production of antibodies, which are classified according to the way they react with their antigen. If they precipitate it they are called *precipitins ;* if they agglutinate it they are called *agglutinins ;* if they dissolve it, as they sometimes do in the case of red cells or bacteria, they are called *lysins,* or more specifically *hæmolysins* or *bacteriolysins ;* if they neutralise the poisonous effects of toxins they are called *antitoxins.* One of the most remarkable properties of these antigen-antibody reactions is their specificity. Serum proteins from different species, for example, which cannot be distinguished by chemical methods, can be distinguished by the way they react with an antibody prepared against one of them.

Suppose a specific hæmolysin has been produced in one animal by repeated injections of the red cells of another animal ; if serum containing the specific hæmolysin is heated to 56° C. its hæmolytic power is lost. The addition of fresh serum from almost any normal animal, however, restores the hæmolytic power. Since the added normal serum would not, by itself, have hæmolysed red cells, it is evident that two factors are concerned in this type of hæmolysis, (1) a specific antibody which is stable to heat (thermostable), and (2) a non-specific factor which is destroyed by heat (thermolabile), known as the *complement ;* this is present in any normal serum. Red cells which have been treated with *heated* serum (containing the antibody which would have hæmolysed them if the complement had not been destroyed) are said to be sensitised, because, if they are introduced into a solution containing the complement, hæmolysis follows immediately.

Not all types of reaction between antibodies and antigens require complement for their completion, but nearly all antigen-antibody compounds have the property of absorbing complement, and thus making it inactive or *fixed.* Complement fixation can be used as a test for the presence of either antibody or antigen. The most famous of these complement-fixation tests is the *Wassermann reaction,* which is a test for the presence of the syphilitic antibody in the blood of a patient suspected of suffering from syphilis. A standard amount of antigen and a standard amount of complement are added to the heated serum of the patient. If the syphilitic antibody is present, it reacts with the antigen ; complement is fixed, and sensitised red cells added subsequently are not hæmolysed. Curiously enough, the standard antigen used in the Wassermann test has nothing to do with syphilis, but is prepared from an alcoholic extract of heart muscle. Presumably this empirical antigen, unexpectedly discovered in the course of controls on the Wassermann reaction, has the same chemical configuration as some antigen in the causal organism of syphilis, for exhaustive tests have only confirmed the usefulness of the reaction in the diagnosis of syphilis.

The production of antibodies is one of the mechanisms by which the body defends itself against infectious diseases, but some antigen-antibody reactions, far from being a benefit to a person, are definitely dangerous. *Anaphylactic shock,* for example, is produced in an animal if a single injection of an antigen is followed after an interval of about ten to fourteen days by an injection of a second dose of the same antigen. The second dose results in profound, and often fatal, collapse, due to a very low blood pressure resulting from dilatation and increased permeability of the capillaries ; in some animals, asphyxia is induced by intense constriction of the bronchi. The first dose of the antigen clearly rendered the animal hypersensitive, instead of immune, the hypersensitivity being associated with a *low* content of antibodies in the blood. A widely supported view of the mechanism of anaphylactic shock supposes that the circulating antibodies due to the first injection are sufficient to " neutralise " only a part of the second dose of antigen ; the remainder of the antigen reacts with antibodies, which are attached to tissue cells. This reaction damages the tissue cells in some way, leading to the production of histamine, which is known to produce, when injected intravenously, a train of events very like anaphylactic shock. If the animal in the hypersensitive state is given a series of injections of the antigen, each too small to produce shock, it will, in time, become desensitised, presumably because an adequate supply of circulating antibodies is developed.

On rare occasions a condition resembling anaphylactic shock results from an intravenous injection of an antitoxin. This is usually due to the patient being hypersensitive to the horse serum from which most antitoxins are prepared. Less violent manifestations of hypersensitivity, which are also antigen-antibody reactions, and which are often called *allergic reactions*, are seen in many skin diseases, hay fever, food idiosyncrasies and some forms of asthma.

Blood Groups. It is well known that the effects of severe loss of blood are usually best countered by transfusion of blood from another individual. Early attempts at such transfusion often had disastrous results, owing to the fact that the injected red cells may clump together (agglutinate) in large masses which block certain of the capillaries in the body (Fig. III. 1) ; the cells then hæmolyse, and the liberated hæmoglobin is in part converted to bilirubin, with consequent jaundice, and in part excreted by the kidneys ; the secretion of urine is impaired, or may even stop. When such effects follow the transfusion, the blood of the donor is said to be " incompatible " with that of the recipient. This incompatibility was explained when it was discovered that human serum can normally contain agglutinins, and even lysins, which act on the red cells of certain other subjects by making the cells stick together or by bursting them. To be susceptible to the agglutinins, these red cells must contain agglutinogens (*i.e.*, antigens) with which the agglutinins react. The experimental facts were found to be explicable by the hypothesis that two kinds of agglutinogen, A and B, are to be found in human red cells. In some bloods the red cells contain agglutinogen A, in others they contain B, in others both A and B together, and in still others they contain neither. Thus blood can be classified into four groups according as their cells contain the agglutinogens, A, B, AB or O. Similarly, it is postulated that there are in human sera two agglutinins, α and β, which react respectively with agglutinogens A and B. Obviously, in any normal blood, the corresponding agglutinins and agglutinogens which would react with each other cannot be present at the same time. Consequently, only in O blood are α and β agglutinins to be found together. In A blood only β agglutinin is present, in B blood only α, while in AB blood neither α nor β is present (Table I.).

Two other systems of designating the human blood groups are in common use ; in these the different groups are denoted by numbers. The systems are named after their respective originators, Jansky and Moss, and while both, fortunately, applied the numbers II. and III. to the same groups, they unfortunately used the numbers I. and IV. in opposite senses. Table I. gives the relation between all three systems of nomenclature :—

TABLE III. 1

Jansky numbering.	Moss numbering.	International designation.	Agglutinogens in the cells.	Agglutinins in the serum.
I.	IV.	O	—	α and β
II.	II.	A	A	β
III.	III.	B	B	α
IV.	I.	AB	A and B	—

In blood transfusion it is always desirable to use a donor of the same group as the recipient, but in dire emergency it is considered allowable to use any donor whose cells are not agglutinated by the serum of the recipient. The donor's cells are exposed to the full effect of the recipient's serum, whereas the donor's serum is diluted by the greater volume of the recipient's blood, and hence is not likely to harm the recipient's cells. Fig. III. 1 shows the effect of serum from each group on cells of each of the other groups.

It can be seen from Fig. III. 1 that cells of group O are not agglutinated by any type of serum. Hence people with blood of group O are called *universal donors*. Similarly, serum from group AB will not agglutinate cells of any group ; people with blood of this group are called *universal recipients*.

The blood of a particular man can be easily assigned to its proper group if samples of serum from blood of groups A and B are available. A large drop of each of the two known sera is placed on a glass slide, and to each is added a small drop of the unknown blood. If agglutination occurs in neither serum, the blood is of group O ; if it occurs in A serum, the blood is of group B ; if in B serum of group A ; and if in both, it is of group AB (Fig. III. 1).

In addition to grouping the donor and recipient, it is advisable before transfusion to test directly the donor's cells against the recipient's serum, and the recipient's cells against the donor's serum, a procedure known as the *cross agglutination* test. This is a precaution not only against errors in grouping, but also against anomalous agglutinations which occasionally happen.

Among the Western European races, and their American descendants, groups O and A are most common, each occurring in about 40 per cent. of the population. Blood groups are inherited according to Mendelian laws ; they are, therefore, available to prove non-paternity in law suits concerning the paternity of illegitimate children. The chance of getting positive evidence is increased by the fact that, in addition to the agglutinogens A and B, human red cells contain one or other or both of two other inheritable agglutinogens, called M and N. These are of no consequence in transfusions, since normal human sera do not contain the corresponding agglutinins. They can, however, be developed in rabbits.

Rouleaux Formation and Sedimentation Velocity

Red blood corpuscles in plasma nearly always show a tendency to come together with their broad surfaces in apposition, thus forming aggregates which look like rolls of coins, and hence have been named *rouleaux*. In practice it is never difficult to distinguish these orderly rouleaux of ten or twenty cells from the disorderly clumps of thousands of cells found in the agglutination reactions. The tendency to form rouleaux varies among different individuals and different species, and largely determines the suspension stability of the blood, *i.e.*, the time required for the red cells to sediment down completely in blood allowed to stand. This is due to the fact that the rate at which a system of suspended particles settles increases with the size of the particles, other factors remaining constant. Now rouleaux are formed more readily

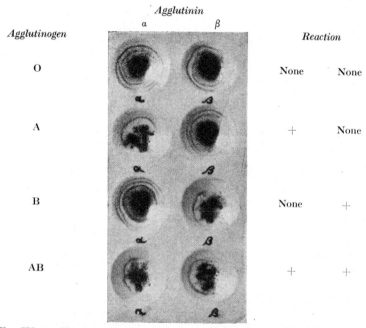

Fig. III. 1.   The **Agglutination of Red Blood Corpuscles,** and the **Four Blood Groups** in Man.

Four large drops of serum of group B (containing agglutinin *a*) and four large drops of serum of group A (containing agglutinin *β*) were placed on the slide. To each of the top two drops was added a small drop of blood of group O ; to the second two, a drop of blood of group A ; to the third two, a drop of blood of group B ; and to the bottom two, a drop of blood of group AB. Agglutination only occurred when the agglutinogens on the corpuscles met the corresponding agglutinins in the serum.   (Lattes' " Individuality of the Blood.")

when the content of either fibrinogen or globulin in the plasma is increased ; since this occurs in certain conditions, such as pregnancy and most inflammatory diseases, the measurement of the sedimentation velocity—and hence the tendency to rouleaux formation—is of medical interest.

Sedimentation sometimes occurs so rapidly that a clear layer of plasma is left before coagulation begins ; the clot is thus partly free from corpuscles and forms what is known as the *buffy coat* on the surface of the corpuscular mass. This fact has been known since the days of the Greeks, and very largely formed the basis of the practice of blood-letting as a cure for all diseases. It was thought that the buffy coat was formed by the foul matter in the blood that was responsible for the disease ; the more blood one could remove, therefore, the quicker would the patient recover. Accidents sometimes happened, however, through the physician mistaking the normal effect of pregnancy for evidence of a pathological condition.

The Viscosity of Blood

Poiseuille performed experiments on horses with a view to discovering the relations between blood pressure and flow in the circulation. He found his observations so bewilderingly variable that he turned his attention to the simpler problems concerned with the flow of pure liquids like water through glass tubes. For our purposes, the results of his experiments may be summarised by the statements (*a*) that the rate of flow of a liquid through a tube is proportional to the pressure driving it ; (*b*) that if water and another liquid are successively driven through a given tube by the same pressure the ratio of the rate of outflow of water to the rate of outflow of the other liquid is a characteristic property of the other liquid known as the *relative viscosity* (*i.e.*, viscosity relative to that of water) ; and (*c*) that the relative viscosity so measured is the same even if the length or diameter of the tube, or the applied pressure, is varied over wide limits.

The relative viscosity of blood can be measured in the same way, by comparing its rate of flow through a tube with that of water, the same pressure being applied in each case. Unlike that of " perfect " liquids, the value of the viscosity of blood, so obtained, depends on the pressure chosen, and on the dimensions of the tube. The idea of viscosity as a " constant " property of a liquid is therefore inapplicable to blood, and the term *apparent viscosity* is used for the value obtained when its flow is compared with that of water under a particular set of conditions (pressure, size of tube), which should be specified. The value of the apparent viscosity of a given sample of normal dog's blood (defibrinated) may vary from about two to twenty times that of water, according to the way in which these specific conditions are chosen.

Of the conditions which affect the apparent viscosity of blood, but do not affect the viscosity of " perfect " liquids, the most important are (*a*) the diameter of the tube in which it is measured, and (*b*) the velocity of the flow (which depends on the pressure applied) chosen for the comparison with water.

(*a*) For diameters of less than about 0·2 mm., the smaller the tube the lower is the apparent viscosity of blood. Although the viscosity is independent of the diameter of the tube in tubes larger than 0·2 mm., and such larger tubes are commonly used for measurements of viscosity, it is with very small tubes, namely, the arterioles, that we are mainly concerned as physiologists ; it was shown in Fig. II. 22 that the main pressure fall between arteries and veins occurs in the small blood vessels. In tubes of such a size (about 0·02 mm. diameter) the apparent viscosity would be only about one-half of what it is in larger tubes.

Halving the apparent viscosity of blood would be an important economy in the circulation, for it should halve the work done by the heart in maintaining a given circulation rate ; for a given maximum output of work of the heart it would about double the amount of work a man could perform in violent exercise. The question arises : is it fair to infer anything about the viscosity of blood in the circulation from experiments on glass capillaries ? Direct experiment on the circulation itself justifies this inference. In experiments on the hind limb of a dog, for example the value of the apparent viscosity of blood circulating through the vascular bed is found to be one-half of that of the same blood passing through a relatively large glass capillary tube (Fig. III. 2).

(*b*) If the flows of blood and water are compared when pushed through a tube by a fairly high pressure (50–200 mm. Hg.), the apparent viscosity of blood usually comes out to about 4·5. So long as the pressure does not fall too low, or rise high enough to disturb the normal stream-line motion, the value obtained will not be very different ; but if the pressure chosen is low, the apparent viscosity will be high ; at the lowest pressures at which measurements have been taken the apparent viscosity is about 20. This effect is of some importance in the clinical measurements of viscosity, for this has till recently been usually performed in a sort of pipette, known as an Ostwald viscometer. In such instruments the movement of the blood is so slow

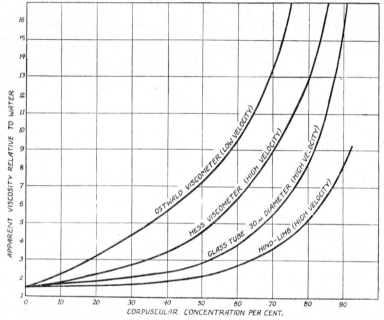

Fig. III. 2. **The Influence of the Corpuscular Concentration** (measured with a hæmatocrit) on the **Apparent Viscosity of Blood.**

Measurements were made on dog's blood, defibrinated, with four different types of viscometer: (1) the Ostwald (low velocity), (2) the Hess (high velocity), (3) a glass tube of very small diameter, and (4) the dog's hind limb. If the glass tube used had had an even smaller diameter, the apparent viscosities would have been still lower. (After Whittaker and Winton, and L. E. Bayliss.)

that the apparent viscosity is largely affected by the velocity of the blood—a matter depending on the exact design of the instrument. Fig. III. 2 shows the apparent viscosity obtained with such an instrument, and how it compares with that obtained in a viscometer, consisting of a straight glass capillary tube through which the blood is pumped at a velocity so high that small variations do not affect the apparent viscosity. The normal velocity of the blood in circulation is sufficiently high for the apparent viscosity to be independent of the rate of flow.

These remarkable properties of blood, in virtue of which its apparent viscosity may vary over so wide a range, are due to the presence of the corpuscles. Fig. III. 2 shows the influence of corpuscular concentration on the apparent viscosity as determined in three different ways. In blood of normal concentration (just under 50 per cent.), the relative viscosity of the serum

(1·5) is increased by the corpuscles about fivefold in the Ostwald viscometer, threefold in the Hess viscometer, but only 50 per cent. in the hind limb. If blood flowing in small tubes or blood vessels be observed under the microscope, the corpuscles appear to be largely confined to the region near the axis of the tube, while the peripheral zone consists of plasma almost free from corpuscles. Clearly, blood would have a lower viscosity if a solid core of corpuscles were floating in a stream of plasma—the internal friction being located in the liquid of low viscosity—than if the corpuscles were evenly distributed. It seems likely that the curious variations of the apparent viscosity of blood are largely due to the extent to which this axial concentration of corpuscles proceeds under various conditions.

General Chemical Properties of the Blood

A full and exact description of the chemical constitution of the blood cannot yet be given. In the table below, the concentrations are given of those substances which are present in easily analysable quantities, but there are many others, equally important physiologically, whose concentration is too low for accurate estimation ; among them are amino-acids of various kinds, creatine, salts of nucleic acid, cholesterol, lecithin, fats and salts of fatty acids. Besides these, again, are those substances whose presence can only be inferred from their activities, many of them not having been isolated or even chemically identified; these belong to the two groups of substances known as enzymes and hormones, and in the blood we find, for example, lipase belonging to the first group and insulin and adrenaline to the second.

It may be well to remind the reader that, although concentrations are often expressed in grams per 100 c.c., it is necessary to express concentrations in terms of gram-molecules rather than of grams when considering the chemical properties and equilibria of a solution, since its components react in molecules at a time, and not grams (a millimol of any substance is 1/1000 of the molecular weight expressed in grams, *i.e.*, 1/1000 of a gram-molecule). It is necessary, also, to express the concentrations as gram-molecules per litre of water, rather than per litre of solution. This is of particular importance in colloidal solutions, such as plasma or the contents of blood corpuscles, which contain only about 90 per cent. and 65 per cent. of water, respectively. In Table II, below, the concentrations are given in terms of a unit volume of plasma or corpuscles as the case may be, and not in terms of a unit volume of blood. The latter can easily be calculated if one remembers that the corpuscles make up about 45 per cent. of the blood, so that 1,000 c.c. of blood contains 450 c.c. of corpuscles and 550 c.c. of plasma.

Inspection of the table shows that there are several peculiarities in the chemical composition of the blood that require special consideration. Amongst the **electrolytes** we notice that the concentration of sodium, potassium and calcium is quite different in the plasma from that in the corpuscles. Moreover, the ratio of the molar concentrations of sodium and potassium in the plasma is very different from that in the corpuscles, and these ratios vary greatly in different animals, as is indicated in the table below :—

	Man.*	Dog.†	Sheep.†
Molar Ratio Na/K in corpuscles .	0·17	17	5
Molar Ratio Na/K in plasma .	30	30	29

* From Gram. † From Abderhalden.

TABLE III. 2

Composition of Normal Human Blood

	Concentration in	
	Plasma g./100 c.c.	Corpuscles. g./100 c.c.
Water	93	71
Sodium	0·310	0·042
Potassium	0·020	0·315
Calcium	0·012	0
Chloride	0·370	0·185
Bicarbonate	0·160	0·115
Phosphate (inorganic HPO_4^{--}) .	0·02	0·02
Sulphate (inorganic) . . .	0·01	—
Lactate { normal	0·02	0·012 }
{ maximum . . .	0·2	0·12 }
Protein	7·5	33
Total " lipids "	0·67	—
Lecithin	0·2	0·4
Cholesterol	0·22	0·19
Urea	0·02–0·04	0·03
Glucose	0·07	0·05
Total weight . . .	103	105·5

Total molecular concentration 160 millimols per litre of water,
$\equiv$ 0·93 per cent. NaCl.

	c.c./100 c.c.	c.c./100 c.c.
Carbon dioxide { arterial { dissolved .	2·55	1·90 }
{ combined	60	29·5 }
venous { dissolved .	3·15	2·25 }
{ combined	64·5	36·5 }
Oxygen { arterial	0·3	47 }
{ venous	0·1	26·5 }
Nitrogen.	1·0	0·9

This is one of the pieces of evidence in favour of the conclusion expressed earlier in the chapter that the membrane of the red cell is impermeable to cations.

The **proteins** of the plasma and of the cells differ not only quantitatively, but qualitatively. In the cells nearly the whole of the protein is hæmoglobin. The small amount of other protein probably forms a part of the framework (stroma) of the red cell. Hæmoglobin is of such importance that a special section will be devoted to it later.

Of the 7 to 8 g. of protein in each 100 c.c. of plasma, about 0·3 to 0·4 g. is fibrinogen, which was mentioned in the section on the coagulation of the blood. The remainder can be split into many fractions, but, for most purposes, it is sufficient to consider it as being composed of two parts, serum globulin and serum albumin, accounting for 2 g. and 5 g. per 100 c.c. plasma respectively. Serum globulin is particularly interesting, because, combined with it, or adsorbed on it, are several of the substances discussed earlier in the chapter, such as prothrombin, complement and antibodies in general. It was mentioned, also, that the concentration of globulin is increased in many diseases, and that this is responsible for an increased sedimentation velocity of the red

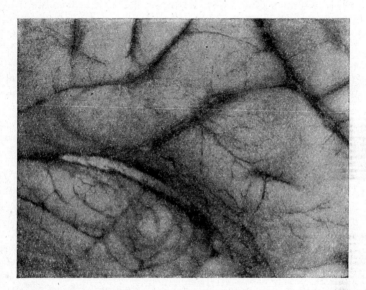

Fig. III. 3. **Gas Bubbles** in the inferior superficial cerebral veins of the right temporal lobe of the brain of a *Macacus rhesus* monkey decompressed instantaneously from atmospheric pressure to 120 mm. Hg. Magnification × 3. (From Eggleton, Elsden, Figler and Hebb.)

cells. The urea concentration in the blood depends on the amount of protein in the diet. In people on very restricted diets, which, as we shall see in Chapter VI, contain a minimum quantity of protein, the blood urea concentration is markedly lower than the figures usually given ; these are mostly derived from well-fed people on nineteenth century diets.

A word must be said, also, with regard to the amount of **Gases** in solution. Both oxygen and carbon dioxide exist in two forms in the blood : (*a*) in physical solution ; and (*b*) in chemical combination. Carbon dioxide is present in both forms, in both the plasma and the corpuscles ; there is, however, no combined oxygen in the plasma, and the amount in direct solution in the corpuscles is so small in relation to that combined with hæmoglobin that it is negligible.

The amount of nitrogen in solution becomes of importance only in special circumstances. In common with all gases, its concentration in physical solution depends upon its partial pressure in the gas mixture with which the solution is in equilibrium, in this case atmospheric air. If the pressure of the air in which a man is working is raised, as is the case with divers or men working in caissons under the water, the concentration of nitrogen in solution in the blood is raised, sometimes very considerably. When the air pressure is lowered again, as when emerging from the caisson, this excess nitrogen comes out of solution, and if the pressure is allowed to fall too quickly, bubbles are formed in the blood, which may block the capillaries, so that areas in the nervous system and elsewhere become asphyxiated. This results in paralysis and severe pains, particularly in the limbs. In extreme cases the whole heart becomes filled with a mass of froth and the circulation ceases. Prevention of these symptoms is easy, since it is only necessary to lower the atmospheric pressure slowly, and to give the excess nitrogen time to be removed by the lungs before becoming so supersaturated in the blood as to form bubbles. The symptoms can be relieved, also, by recompressing the patient to a pressure as high as, or higher than, he was in before, so that the excess nitrogen is redissolved ; the pressure is then lowered gradually. This prevention and cure of Caisson disease, as it is called, is a good example of the value of applying purely physical principles to physiological processes.

Gas bubbles are similarly released in the blood vessels when a subject, initially exposed to a normal atmospheric pressure, is suddenly exposed to a low pressure (Fig. III. 3). This would occur, for example, if the occupants of an aircraft with a pressurised cabin were compelled to bail out at a very high altitude, or, of course, if the walls of the cabin were suddenly destroyed.

Hæmoglobin

This substance has such striking properties, both physiological and chemical, that it merits special attention. If we consider the primary functions of the blood to be the carriage of oxygen from the lungs to the tissues and the regulation of the neutrality of the organism as a whole (which involves also the carriage of carbon dioxide from the tissues to the lungs), then it would be no exaggeration to say that the exercise of these functions would be impossible without some substance possessing the chemical and physical properties of hæmoglobin.

In this section we shall consider mainly the first of these functions, the carriage of oxygen, and shall defer the question of neutrality regulation and carbon dioxide transport to subsequent sections.

Hæmoglobin acts as an oxygen carrier by combining with oxygen to form a scarlet red compound, oxy-hæmoglobin, the absorption spectrum of which shows two well-defined bands, one in the yellow, the other in the green. The oxygen can be completely removed again by shaking the solution repeatedly *in vacuo*, or with gas containing no oxygen, such as hydrogen or nitrogen. The colour of the solution changes to purple when the oxygen is removed, and the hæmoglobin is then said to be reduced. Reduced hæmoglobin shows only one band in the visible spectrum. This is broad and dim, and is in the yellow-green region. Hæmoglobin thus has the power of reacting chemically with oxygen to form what is generally believed to be a chemical compound, oxy-hæmoglobin, *i.e.*, $Hb + O_2 \rightleftharpoons O_2Hb$, (Hb being the symbol generally used for hæmoglobin).

In the blood of lower animals there are found other respiratory pigments, such as *hæmocyanin*, the copper-containing pigment of molluscs and some arthropods (this changes from colourless to blue on oxygenation), and *chlorocruorin*, the iron-containing pigment of certain marine worms. The respiratory function of these bloods has, however, not been developed to nearly as high a degree as has that of the blood of the higher vertebrates.

It is understandable, therefore, that a knowledge of the concentration of hæmoglobin in the blood should be of importance in many cases where the respiratory function appears to be inadequately performed. A man may become unduly distressed by going upstairs or running for a bus, not only because his heart or lungs are inadequate, but also because his blood is unable to carry enough oxygen or is unable to prevent his tissues from becoming too acid. A blood count, of course, will indicate whether he has the normal number of red cells, but these may not contain the normal amount of hæmoglobin, so that it is essential also to measure the hæmoglobin directly. This, fortunately, is easily done colorimetrically, since hæmoglobin has so strong a red colour.

In actual practice, the colorimetric comparison is usually made with the hæmoglobin in the form of carboxy-hæmoglobin, although acid hæmatin and reduced hæmoglobin are also used ; these substances are more stable than oxy-hæmoglobin. The *Haldane Hæmoglobinometer* is most commonly used. The appropriate volume of the blood under test (20 c.mm.) is treated with coal gas, so as to convert the hæmoglobin to carboxy-hæmoglobin, and is then diluted in a special tube, of the proper size, until it has the same depth of colour as has an arbitrary standard ; this may either be a solution of carboxy-hæmoglobin in a sealed tube, or better, a solid rod of suitably coloured glass. The final volume of the diluted unknown blood is then read on special graduations on the tube, which give the hæmoglobin concentration as per cent. of that of the standard. This value, sometimes known as the " hæmoglobin concentration," does *not* give the actual hæmoglobin concentration, or the oxygen capacity, of the blood, but only the relation to the standard. This latter is conventionally adjusted in Great Britain to contain 13·8 g.Hb per 100 c.c. blood, which is equivalent to an oxygen capacity of 18·5 c.c. O_2 per 100 c.c. blood, These figures, therefore, will also apply to any blood which has " 100 per cent. hæmoglobin." It was originally believed that this figure corresponded to the average hæmoglobin concentration in the blood of a normal man ; more recent evidence, however, shows that a more correct figure for the normal hæmoglobin concentration is 15·6 g. per 100 c.c., or 21 c.c. O_2 per 100 c.c. blood.

The hæmoglobin concentration of the average red blood cell is known as the *Colour Index*, and is obtained by dividing the per cent. hæmoglobin by the number of red cells in millions per cubic millimetre multiplied by 20 (since the normal count is taken as five millions). It is ordinarily about unity in healthy persons, but is decreased considerably in secondary anæmia (*e.g.*, after repeated hæmorrhage), in which the hæmoglobin concentration may fall to 50 per cent., and it is often increased in pernicious anæmia, in which the red cell count may fall to one million or less.

Chemically, hæmoglobin consists of an iron-porphyrin complex, known as reduced hæmatin, or *hæm*, united with a protein, *globin*. Hæm is closely related chemically to the prosthetic groups of many enzymes concerned in the oxidation of the foodstuffs, notably the cytochromes, and peroxidase. Hæm can unite with a number of nitrogen-containing substances, forming *hæmochromogens* ; hæmoglobin is a special case of a hæmochromogen.

Hæm, and the hæmochromogens contain iron in the *ferrous* state. If treated with a suitable oxidising agent, the iron is oxidised to the *ferric* state, with the formation of *hæmatin* from hæm, and *methæmoglobin* from hæmoglobin.

Hæmatin unites with hydrochloric acid to form the hydrochloride *hæmin* ; this substance crystallises readily from solution, and the character of the crystals is sufficiently distinct to be used as a chemical test for blood pigments. Hæmoglobin itself only crystallises easily when derived from certain species, *e.g.*, the horse, rat or guinea-pig, The shape of the hæmoglobin crystals varies with the species of blood used.

Of the hæmochromogens, hæmoglobin and myoglobin alone will unite with oxygen in a reversible manner, to form *oxy-hæmoglobin*, and will give up the oxygen again to a vacuum, or to a gas mixture which contains no oxygen. The iron in oxy-hæmoglobin is in the ferrous state, and the uptake of oxygen is thus referred to as an *oxygenation* and not an oxidation. Hæmoglobin is the only compound known which undergoes such a reaction, and this shows the peculiar importance of the protein, globin. If oxy-hæmoglobin is treated with ferricyanide, the reduced hæmoglobin which is always present in small quantities is converted into methæmoglobin, so that the equilibrium between oxy-hæmoglobin and reduced hæmoglobin is upset (see next section) ; in an attempt to restore equilibrium, oxy-hæmoglobin gives up its oxygen, and more reduced hæmoglobin is formed ; this is again removed by the ferricyanide, and more oxy-hæmoglobin decomposes, and so on. In this way, the whole of the oxygen in reversible combination can be driven off under suitable conditions, and hence the *oxygen capacity* of the oxy-hæmoglobin solution determined.

For further information as to the chemical relations of hæmoglobin, reference should be made to a text-book of Biochemistry. All the compounds concerned have characteristic absorption spectra, which are invaluable for their identification.

The Combination of Hæmoglobin with Oxygen. We must now consider this chemical reaction in greater detail.

The amount of oxygen, which combines chemically with hæmoglobin, depends on the partial pressure of oxygen in the gas with which the solution is in equilibrium. There is a limit, however, to the amount of oxygen which can be combined (as contrasted with that which can be physically dissolved) ; the solution is then saturated, and the amount of oxygen chemically combined in a unit volume is its oxygen capacity. The amount of oxygen combined with hæmoglobin is usually expressed as a percentage of the amount when it is fully saturated.

The partial pressure of a gas in a mixture of several gases is that fraction of the total pressure which can be considered as being contributed by that gas. This is considered in more detail in the next chapter (p. 134), where examples are given of the partial pressures of the gases in gas mixtures under various conditions.

The exact relation between the percentage saturation and the partial pressure of oxygen in blood is shown in Fig. III. 4. The points on these curves are determined by shaking a sample of blood gently with oxygen at various partial pressures until equilibrium is reached (thirty to forty-five minutes), then measuring the percentage saturation of the blood and the percentage of oxygen in the gas. The apparatus used for this purpose is called a *tonometer* and generally consists of a cylindrical glass vessel of about 300 c.c. capacity, with a stopper at one end and a two-way stop-cock at the other. The various partial pressures of oxygen are usually obtained, not by altering the total pressure in the tonometer, but by keeping this at atmospheric pressure and using mixtures of air and nitrogen, which are analysed after equilibration with the blood in an ordinary gas analysis apparatus.

The type of gas analysis apparatus most generally used is that devised by Haldane. A sample of the gas to be analysed is taken into a water-jacketed burette, previously completely filled with mercury, and its volume measured. Carbon dioxide is then absorbed by transferring the gas into a vessel from which it displaces a strong solution of caustic potash ; it is then brought back into the burette and its volume measured again. Oxygen is absorbed by transferring it in a similar manner into a vessel previously filled with an alkaline solution of pyrogallol, and the residual volume measured once more. Absorption of the carbon dioxide and oxygen is hastened by passing the gas to and from the appropriate absorbing vessels and the burette by raising and lowering the reservoir of mercury connected with the lower end of the burette.

The percentage saturation of the hæmoglobin is estimated by driving off the oxygen from the blood, either : (1) by boiling *in vacuo* ; or (2) by adding ferricyanide ; or (3) by both together.

(1) The first was the method used by the earliest workers, who evacuated a large vessel by means of a mercury pump, for example, a Töpler pump, and ran a known volume of blood, previously warmed to 40°, into it. The gas liberated was then pumped off and delivered to a gas analysis apparatus, where its total volume and composition were determined.

(2) When the reaction of ferricyanide with oxy-hæmoglobin was discovered, it seemed that this would be a much easier way of determining the oxygen combined with hæmoglobin than the vacuum pump methods previously used. Haldane, indeed, at once adopted the principle in his blood gas apparatus. In this oxy-hæmoglobin is mixed with *alkaline* ferricyanide (the alkalinity prevents the escape from the solution of any carbon dioxide gas) and the only gas evolved is oxygen,

which is measured directly in a burette over water. The same principle is also used in the Barcroft differential apparatus. Much work has been done by these two methods, but doubt has been cast on their general applicability by the finding that the evolved oxygen is sometimes in part reabsorbed owing to a secondary reaction with the blood in presence of ferricyanide. This can be overcome by taking adequate precautions.

(3) This error is avoided by combination of vacuum extraction and ferricyanide. This principle has been developed by van Slyke to a high pitch of perfection in recent years, and his apparatus has been applied to numerous other estimations besides that of oxygen and carbon dioxide in blood.

An acid ferricyanide solution and a known volume of the blood under examination, are run into an evacuated vessel ; the gases given off are extracted by shaking, and the residual solution is discharged by means of a two-way tap at the bottom of the extraction vessel. The volume of the extracted gases is determined either by transferring them to a burette, over mercury, and measuring the volume occupied at atmospheric pressure (constant pressure apparatus), or by compressing them to a known volume over mercury, and measuring the pressure exerted, with a mercury manometer (constant volume apparatus). This is the more accurate method, since the scale on which the measurements are made is a great deal longer, and no errors can arise from faulty adjustment of the pressure of the gas in the burette. Carbon dioxide is absorbed from the extracted gases by adding a caustic soda solution, and oxygen by adding a solution of pyrogallol or sodium hyposulphite ; the contraction in volume (or reduction in pressure) is measured at each stage, and represents the volume of the respective gas present in the extracted mixture.

Curves connecting the per cent. saturation with the partial pressure of oxygen shown in Fig. III. 4 are known as *dissociation curves* : their shape depends on many factors, such as the animal from which the hæmoglobin was obtained, the electrolyte composition of the solution, the temperature and the acidity. Increase of either temperature or acidity decreases the per cent. saturation at a given oxygen pressure, *i.e.*, decreases the affinity of hæmoglobin for oxygen. Increased carbon dioxide pressure increases the acidity and hence has the same effect. It is possible that carbon dioxide also exerts a specific effect due to its combining directly with hæmoglobin to a slight extent (see p. 117). Fig. III. 4 shows a family of curves at different carbon dioxide pressures.

The dissociation curve of whole mammalian blood is always found to be S-shaped, as in Fig. III. 4. This shape is of distinct physiological service, since it enables a large amount of oxygen to dissociate from the hæmoglobin without too severe a drop in the oxygen pressure with which it is in equilibrium. This is an important point as regards supply of oxygen to the tissues, for it is the partial pressure of oxygen in the blood, and not the amount of combined oxygen, that determines the rate of diffusion of oxygen from the blood to the tissues. A curve of the rectangular hyperbola type (*v.* dotted curve in Fig. III. 4) would, from this point of view, be obviously unserviceable.

The effect of carbon dioxide and acidity is also of some importance in the organism in enabling the blood to unload oxygen more readily into the tissues. Thus, for example, it can be seen from the curves that at an oxygen partial pressure of 32 mm. the per cent. saturation is 64 when the carbon dioxide pressure is 40 mm., and only 58 when the carbon dioxide pressure is increased to 50 mm. Now the partial pressure of carbon dioxide is about 40 mm. Hg in the arterial blood, and about 50 mm. Hg in the venous blood, so that it can be seen that $\dfrac{64-58}{100} \times 18$, *i.e.*, roughly 1 c.c. of extra oxygen is obtained by the tissues from each

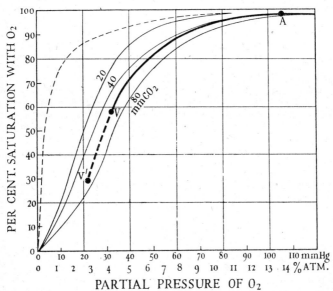

Fɪɢ. III. 4.   **Oxygen Dissociation Curves** of Blood at various Partial Pressures of Carbon Dioxide.

AVV' is the " physiological oxygen dissociation curve," A being the arterial point, V the venous point at rest, and V' the venous point during exercise.   Compare Fig. III, 6.

The dotted curve is a rectangular hyperbola, as given by myoglobin ; note how little oxygen is given off until the partial pressure of oxygen is reduced to very low values, but that oxygen is readily accepted from hæmoglobin in the conditions of venous blood.   (After Bock, Field and Adair, and R. Hill.)

100 c.c. of blood, owing to this displacing action of acid, without lowering the partial pressure of oxygen within them.

Since carbon dioxide is blown off in the lungs, and taken up in the tissues, none of the family of curves shown in Fig. III. 4 accurately represents the " physiological oxygen dissociation curve." This passes from a point A, corresponding to the conditions met with in the lungs, *i.e.*, 98 per cent. saturation with oxygen at a partial pressure of 108 mm. of oxygen and 40 mm. of carbon dioxide, to a point V, corresponding to the conditions met with in the tissues, *i.e.*, 58 per cent. saturation with oxygen at a partial pressure of 32 mm. of oxygen and 50 mm. of carbon dioxide.

It will be observed that the whole of the oxygen is never removed from the blood. This is due, first, to the fact that a small, but definite partial pressure of oxygen must exist in the tissue cells, and secondly, to the fact that oxygen must diffuse from the blood capillaries to the tissue cells, sometimes over quite a long distance. A considerable head of pressure is thus needed to drive the oxygen across at the requisite rate.

In exercise, the rate at which oxygen is needed by the muscles is greatly increased, and the amount of oxygen taken from each cubic centimetre of blood is also increased, with the result that the partial pressure of oxygen in the venous blood is decreased (point V' in Fig. III. 4). There is thus a smaller head of pressure available for an increased rate of diffusion. This apparent contradiction is resolved by the observation that the number of capillaries carrying blood, per unit volume of muscle, is enormously increased when the muscle becomes active—possibly becoming 100 times greater. Consequently, not only is the distance decreased over which the oxygen must diffuse, but also the surface is increased over which oxygen can leave the blood.

Many attempts have been made to explain the shape of the dissociation curve by applying the Law of Mass Action to the equilibrium between oxygen and hæmoglobin. Direct chemical analysis of the oxygen and iron content of purified hæmoglobin shows that when fully saturated with oxygen there is just one molecule of oxygen for each atom of iron, and that the weight of hæmoglobin containing 1 atomic weight of iron, *i.e.*, 56 g., is 16,700 g. The minimum molecular weight of reduced hæmoglobin is therefore 16,700 ; the actual molecular weight is some multiple of this, so that reduced hæmoglobin may be written Hb_n and oxy-hæmoglobin $(HbO_2)_n$—the symbol Hb being used for the minimum molecular weight.

This suggests the equation $Hb_n + nO_2 \rightleftharpoons (HbO_2)_n$, which leads, by the Law of Mass Action, to what is known as Hill's equation, viz.,

$$\frac{\text{per cent. saturation}}{100} = \frac{K[O_2]^n}{1 + K.[O_2]^n}$$

K being the equilibrium constant of the reaction.

If $n = 1$, this equation gives a rectangular hyperbola. It can, however, be made to fit the S-shaped curve of blood satisfactorily over most of its course, if a value of n between 2 and 3 is chosen.

Unfortunately, however, direct determinations of the molecular weight of hæmoglobin from mammalian blood by osmotic pressure determinations or by the ultra-centrifuge give a value of 68,000, which implies that n must be 4. This, if substituted in Hill's equation, gives a curve with a much greater inflection near the origin than is ever observed.

The present tendency is to assume that the four molecules of oxygen combine with the Hb_4 molecule in discrete stages, forming intermediate compounds Hb_4O_2, Hb_4O_4, Hb_4O_6, all of which can exist contemporaneously with Hb_4 and Hb_4O_8. On this basis a complicated equation can be derived, which can be made to fit the observed curve beautifully ; but since this equation contains *four* unknown constants and since, moreover, the postulated intermediate compounds have never been observed directly the matter cannot yet be regarded as settled.

The Fœtal Blood. The hæmoglobin in the blood of the fœtus has a greater affinity for oxygen than has that in the maternal blood. Its dissociation curve, even at relatively high partial pressures of carbon dioxide, would lie to the left, in Fig. III. 4, even of that drawn for 20 mm. of carbon dioxide. When the maternal blood, therefore, is, say, 50 per cent. saturated with oxygen, the fœtal blood will be, perhaps, 80 per cent. saturated. Oxygen will consequently pass readily from the mother to the fœtus in the placenta. There is, of course, a corresponding disadvantage, in that the partial pressure of oxygen in the fœtal tissues must be small before the fœtal hæmoglobin will part with its oxygen.

Myoglobin. Most mammalian muscles contain a pigment which is closely related chemically to hæmoglobin, and is known as *myo-hæmoglobin*, or *myoglobin*. It differs from hæmoglobin in having an oxygen dissociation curve which is a rectangular hyperbola (dotted curve in Fig. III. 4). Myoglobin will become nearly fully saturated with oxygen at partial pressures normally found in the tissues, and at which hæmoglobin has parted with most of its oxygen. It is known, also, that the tissue oxidation enzymes will function at oxygen pressures down to 5 mm. Hg or a little less, and at these pressures, myoglobin will part with about 40 per cent. of its oxygen. Myoglobin, therefore, can act as an effective reservoir of oxygen in the muscles.

The uptake and loss of oxygen by myoglobin in a living muscle has been studied by observation of the absorption spectrum of the whole muscle. Appreciable loss of oxygen from the myoglobin occurs in 0·2 sec. after the beginning of a tetanus, and 60 per cent. saturation is reached in less than 1 sec. even when the blood supply is intact. The reserve of oxygen, therefore, is exhausted during the first second or so, of the tetanus, after which myoglobin can play no part in the supply of oxygen. In intermittent short contractions of individual fibres at relatively long intervals, as occurs in tonic contractions, for example, the myoglobin may well be able to supply the heavy demand for oxygen which follows each contraction (*cf.* Chap. IX), and so enable the tonic contraction to be maintained without the production of even a temporary oxygen debt.

Speed of the Reactions. The combination of oxygen with hæmoglobin and the dissociation therefrom are both very rapid chemical reactions and cannot be timed by the ordinary methods—they require the special methods of Hartridge and Roughton for measurement of their rates. To determine the speed of combination, for instance, a solution of reduced hæmoglobin and a solution of oxygen in water are driven through separate leads into a small chamber where they mix in less than 1/1,000 second and travel thence into an observation tube. The percentage oxy-hæmoglobin in the streaming fluid at various positions along the observation tube is measured spectroscopically, the fluid being kept in motion whilst the readings are taken. From the rate of flow of the liquid and the distance of the point of observation from the mixing chamber, the time taken by the reaction to reach the oxy-hæmoglobin percentage recorded by the spectroscope is simply calculated, and hence the velocity of the reaction can be determined.

Under physiological conditions both chemical reactions only take about 1/100 second, and are thus too rapid to limit the rate of exchange of oxygen between the circulating blood in the capillaries (which each corpuscle takes a second at least to traverse) and the lungs or tissues. Diffusion seems to be the main factor which limits the rapidity of oxygen exchange in the animal.

The Combination of Hæmoglobin with Carbon Monoxide. Carbon monoxide also combines reversibly with hæmoglobin, but the affinity is much greater than in the case of oxygen, *i.e.*, about 250 times ; blood can be completely saturated at a partial pressure of only 0·5 per cent. of an atmosphere at 37° C., whereas it requires at least 15 per cent. of oxygen before even approximate saturation is reached. In other respects the reaction between carbon monoxide and hæmoglobin is very like the oxygen-hæmoglobin reaction : thus the dissociation curve is also S-shaped, and is similarly affected by acidity and temperature. The volume of carbon monoxide combined at maximum saturation is the same as that of oxygen. The greater affinity of carbon monoxide for hæmoglobin is due to the fact that the compound of carbon monoxide with hæmoglobin (usually known as *carboxy-hæmoglobin* and often written COHb) dissociates 1,000 or more times more slowly than oxy-hæmoglobin. In a mixture of oxygen (partial pressure pO_2) and carbon monoxide (partial pressure pCO) hæmoglobin distributes itself between the two gases according to the equation :

$$\frac{COHb}{O_2Hb} = K\frac{p \cdot CO}{p \cdot O_2} \text{ where K is about 250.}$$

The high affinity of carbon monoxide for hæmoglobin accounts for the danger attending inhalation of small amounts of carbon monoxide or a mixture of gases containing it, *e.g.*, coal gas ; since the whole of the available hæmoglobin becomes saturated with carbon monoxide, no oxygen can be carried and the animal is asphyxiated.

No marked symptoms are detectable until about 30 per cent. of all the hæmoglobin in the body is saturated with carbon monoxide. Vision, hearing and intelligence become impaired when the carbon monoxide saturation reaches 50 per cent., and death has been known to occur at 60 per cent. saturation ; 80 per cent. saturation is almost invariably fatal. The average dissociation curve of carboxy-hæmoglobin shows that with most people the first symptoms would be observed when the air they were breathing contained about 0·03 per cent. (1 part in 3,000) of carbon monoxide, while 0·4 per cent. (1 part in 250) would be fatal ; different people, however, have somewhat different susceptibilities.

If an ordinary gas leak occurs in an ordinary room (a gas fire is turned on and not lighted, for example), it is very unlikely that there will ever be more than 2·5 per cent. of gas in the room, owing to leakage up the chimney and through the cracks of the window and diffusion through the walls and the ceiling to adjacent rooms (this would probably not apply to the case of a large gas cooker in a small kitchenette). Coal gas contains, as a rule, not more than 10 per cent. of carbon monoxide, although there may occasionally be as much as 15 per cent. if the gas company mixes it with much water gas ; there might thus be 0·2 per cent. and perhaps 0·4 per cent. of carbon monoxide in the room, so that it is unlikely that any ordinary leak in an ordinary room not hermetically sealed would have fatal consequences, although the symptoms might be very serious. Coal gas, it must be remembered, is lighter than air, and hence rises to the ceiling ; a tall man may thus notice symptoms of anoxæmia before a short man.

Tobacco smoke contains appreciable quantities of carbon monoxide, and the deleterious effects of over-smoking have been attributed to a chronic anoxæmia produced by the continuous presence of carboxy-hæmoglobin in the blood ; it is, indeed, quite easy to detect the presence of this compound in the blood of a heavy smoker. The exhaust gas of motor cars also contains considerable amounts of carbon monoxide.

The treatment in all cases of carbon monoxide poisoning should be the administration of oxygen, to which about 7 per cent. carbon dioxide has been added so as to stimulate the respiration of the patient. The high pressure of oxygen not only facilitates the eventual dissociation of the carboxy-hæmoglobin, but also enables an appreciable amount of oxygen to be carried in simple solution in the blood.

Carboxy-hæmoglobin is cherry pink in colour rather than scarlet, like oxy-hæmoglobin. Its absorption spectrum shows two bands in the visible spectrum, one in the yellow, the other in the green. These resemble the corresponding bands of oxy-hæmoglobin, except that they are not quite so distinct and are nearer to the blue end of the spectrum. Unlike oxy-hæmoglobin, carboxy-hæmoglobin is very readily dissociated by exposure to strong light.

The estimation of carbon monoxide in blood is of importance both from the medico-legal and from the physiological points of view (*cf.* estimation of blood volume, Chapter II) ; a variety of methods have been used :—

(1) *Optical.* (*a*) Depending on the difference in colour between carboxy-hæmoglobin and oxy-hæmoglobin (*cf.* Haldane's carmine titration method).

(*b*) Depending on the difference in position between the absorption bands of carboxy-hæmoglobin and of oxy-hæmoglobin (*cf.* Hartridge's reversion spectroscope).

(2) *Chemical.* Depending on the colour of the precipitate formed by COHb with tannic acid.

(3) *Gasometric.* Depending on an adaptation of van Slyke's methods for oxygen and carbon dioxide estimation in blood.

Where sufficient blood is available, the gasometric method is the most accurate and reliable. For further details the student should consult the writings of Barcroft, Haldane and van Slyke.

The Regulation of the Hydrogen Ion Concentration

When oxygen is shaken with water, it merely goes into physical solution, and does not form any chemical compound, unless there be added to the water some substance like hæmoglobin, which is specially capable of combining with the oxygen. Carbon dioxide, on the other hand, not only dissolves readily in water (or any watery fluid), but also reacts chemically with the water to form carbonic acid, H_2CO_3 ; this being a weak acid, splits up to some extent into hydrogen ions and bicarbonate ions. Bicarbonate ions are also capable of splitting up further into hydrogen ions and carbonate ions, but this second ionisation only occurs appreciably at more alkaline reactions than those found in the body fluids.

The first ionisation, viz., the formation of H^+ and HCO_3^- ions, is, however, very marked under the conditions in the body and hence the blood would go markedly acid when it takes up carbon dioxide in the tissues, were there not present some chemical mechanism to counteract such changes, namely, the buffer mechanism explained later. The presence of the latter is hardly to be wondered at, for many processes in living organisms, such as the velocity of enzyme actions, and the stability of proteins, are greatly affected by changes in acidity and to *different extents ;* hence any marked change in acidity would tend to throw the whole organism out of gear.

Carbon dioxide transport and maintenance of neutrality are both

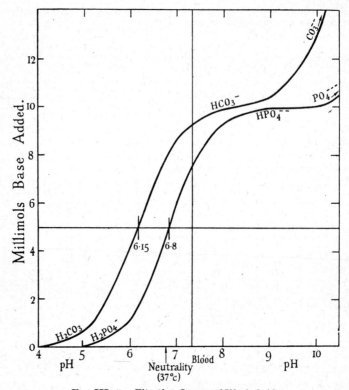

Fig. III. 5. **Titration Curves of Weak Acids.**

H_2CO_3 and NaH_2PO_4 in 10 mM. solution are titrated with NaOH. The value of pK' is given by the pH at which the acid is half titrated. This value varies with the nature and concentration of the other ions in the solution ; the curves are drawn approximately for the conditions in plasma. The vertical line is drawn at the pH of blood, (After L. J. Henderson.)

important, and both closely interconnected : for a clear understanding of them some knowledge of the general physical chemistry of buffer systems and of ionic equilibria in solution is needed. The reader is recommended to consult a suitable text-book of Biochemistry or Physical Chemistry.

Buffer Action. If we titrate a weak acid, such as carbonic acid, with a strong base, such as sodium hydroxide, and plot the pH of the solution against the number of gram-molecules of base added, we get a curve such as that shown in Fig. III. 5. Clearly, the steeper is the titration curve, the more base (or, of course, acid) must be added in order to produce a given change in *p*H, and the more strongly is the solution said to be *buffered*. The salt of the weak acid is very nearly completely ionised, while the free acid is almost completely un-ionised ; we can thus regard the variation with *p*H of the amount of base added, as equivalent to the variation with *p*H of the degree of ionisation of the acid. The maximum slope, and the strongest buffer action occurs when the weak acid is exactly half titrated, *i.e.*, when the hydrogen ion concentration is equal to the apparent dissociation constant of the weak acid. In practice, the region of hydrogen ion concentration over which the buffering power is reasonably large is taken to be ten times greater to ten times less than the value of the dissociation constant. Alternatively, we can say that the *p*H must be within one unit on either side of the value of *p*K′. The buffering power of a given solution is also, of course, directly proportional to the concentration of those buffer substances whose *p*K′ is within one unit of the *p*H of the solution. Exactly similar arguments can be used in connection with weak bases, when titrated with strong acids ; they also act as buffers, but are not met with in any appreciable concentration in solutions of physiological interest.

The reader may perhaps be reminded that the *p*H is a convenient measure of the hydrogen ion concentration, which is usually extremely small. The *p*H is defined as the negative logarithm of the hydrogen ion concentration ; so that a hydrogen ion concentration of, say, 5×10^{-8}, or $10^{-7.3}$ g. ions per litre corresponds to a *p*H of 7·3.

The shape of the titration curves may be deduced from the Law of Mass Action. If we have a weak acid HA which dissociates into H^+ and A^-, the following reaction will be in equilibrium.

$$HA \rightleftharpoons H^+ + A^-$$

whence

$$[H^+] = K_a . \frac{[HA]}{[A^-]}$$

or

$$pH = pK_a - \log . \frac{HA}{A^=}$$

square brackets denoting concentrations. These equations indicate that so long as the H^+ ion concentration is of the same order of magnitude as the dissociation constant K_a, the greater is the H^+ concentration, the less is the acid ionised.

The buffer substances present in blood are (*a*) bicarbonate, (*b*) hæmoglobin, (*c*) the plasma proteins, and (*d*) phosphates. From Fig. III. 5 we see that the bicarbonate system is not, by itself, a very effective buffer at the normal *p*H of blood—its *p*K value is 1·2 units from the *p*H of blood. It is present, however, in relatively high concentration, so that its effect is quite appreciable. The $Na_2HPO_4 - NaH_2PO_4$ system, on the contrary, is effective as far as buffer power is concerned, but the concentration of phosphates is so low that they play little part in buffering the blood. In the urine, phosphates provide the greater part of the buffering in normal circumstances. The most important buffering substance in the blood is undoubtedly hæmoglobin ; this, in the corpuscles, exists as a mixture of the potassium salt KHb, which may be regarded as ionised into K^+ and Hb^-, and the free acid HHb, which is un-ionised. Hæmoglobin is a complex polybasic acid, and its titration curve consists of a large number of the S-shaped curves of Fig. III. 5 on top of one another, and overlapping. The general conception of buffer action is nevertheless still applicable. The plasma proteins behave in a similar way, but are present in much smaller concentration. If, then, we add a small quantity of an acid to some blood, the hydrogen ion concentration will be increased. This, however, will lead to a reduction in the ionisation of both hæmoglobin and carbonic acid, and many of the extra hydrogen ions will be absorbed and tucked away in the undissociated acids. Conversely, if an alkali be added, the extra hydroxyl ions will combine with hydrogen ions to form water, and the effect will be exactly the opposite of that which occurs when acid is added. Hæmoglobin and carbonic acid will dissociate more completely, and provide extra hydrogen ions to replace those which were removed by the alkali. All this is, of course, but a verbal description of the fact illustrated in the titration curves, that in a buffered system, the pH changes only slowly with the addition of acid or alkali.

The efficiency of the buffering process in the blood is indicated by the following calculation. If we take blood at a pH 7·4 and add acid until it has a pH 7·2, the increase in free hydrogen ion concentration is $10^{-7·2} - 10^{-7·4}$ or $2·3 \times 10^{-8}$ g.-ions per litre. During the course of this change in pH, however, the hæmoglobin absorbs, by buffer action, no less than $660,000 \times 10^{-8}$ g.-ions per litre, while the carbonic acid absorbs $70,000 \times 10^{-8}$ g.-ions per litre. The total amount of hydrogen ions which must be added to produce this change in pH is thus $730,000 \times 10^{-8}$ per litre of blood, of which only $2·3 \times 10^{-8}$ remain free. If we remove hydrogen ions from normal blood (or add hydroxyl ions) until the pH is 7·6, the decrease in free hydrogen ion concentration is $1·5 \times 10^{-8}$ g.-ions per litre, while hæmoglobin releases again $660,000 \times 10^{-8}$ g.-ions per litre and carbonic acid releases $44,000 \times 10^{-8}$ g.-ions per litre. These figures indicate the relative importance of carbonic acid and hæmoglobin in buffering the blood. Roughly, 90 per cent. of the hydrogen ions added or removed are absorbed or released by hæmoglobin, and 10 per cent. by the carbonic acid-bicarbonate system.

The above calculations are based on the following equations : (1) The buffering power of hæmoglobin is represented by the empirical equation
$$[HbO_2^-] = 0·22 \, [HbO_2] \, (pH - 6·60)$$
$[HbO_2^-]$ is expressed in mg. equivalents per litre and $[HbO_2]$ in g. per litre.
(2) The buffering power of carbonic acid-bicarbonate system is represented by the well-known Henderson-Hasselbalch equation
$$pH = 6·12 + \log [HCO_3^-] - \log [H_2CO_3]$$
The values taken are :

$[HbO_2]$ 150 g./litre.
Total $CO_2 = [H_2CO_3] + [HCO_3^-] = 24·8$ millimols/litre.
Total base $= [HCO_3^-] + [HbO_2^-]$ at pH 7·4 $= 50$ millimols/litre.

In this example, we have imagined that no carbon dioxide is lost or gained by the blood when the pH is changed. This approximates to the conditions in the capillaries when, say, lactic acid is formed in the muscles and diffuses into the blood stream. If we consider the body as a whole, however, the conditions are different, since carbon dioxide can be blown off in the lungs and acid or base can be excreted by the kidneys. As we shall see in later chapters, the respiratory centre and the kidneys adjust the ventilation rate and pH of the urine, respectively, in such a way as to keep the pH of the blood constant. The buffering is thus perfect. Confining ourselves for the moment to the actions of the respiratory centre, we see that the buffering results, in the end, entirely from the increased loss, or retention, of carbon dioxide in the lungs. The extra hydrogen ions are entirely absorbed, or released, by the bicarbonate system, and hæmoglobin in the long run plays no part. There are thus three lines of defence against changes in hydrogen ion concentration : (1) direct buffering in the blood, mainly by hæmoglobin ; (2) indirect buffering by the action of the respiratory centre in controlling the free carbon dioxide concentration in the blood ; and (3) indirect buffering by the kidneys, which excrete the excess acid or base, as the case may be.

The Carriage of Carbon Dioxide

Blood loses oxygen and gains carbon dioxide in its passage through the tissues and undergoes the reverse changes during its passage through the lungs. In the tissues and lungs the changes are roughly equal and opposite, so that it will only be necessary to describe one of them. For convenience, we shall consider the uptake of carbon dioxide by the blood in the tissues. The partial pressure of carbon dioxide in arterial blood is usually about 40 mm. Hg, and the total carbon dioxide content (as estimated by vacuum extraction with acid) is about 50 c.c. (at N.T.P.), per 100 c.c. The partial pressure of carbon dioxide in the tissues is higher than that in the arterial blood, hence carbon dioxide diffuses from the tissues into the blood capillaries. The amount of carbon dioxide taken up by the blood is some 20 times greater than the amount taken up by water under like conditions of carbon dioxide pressure, hence only about 5 per cent. of the carbon dioxide uptake by the blood is by simple solution, the remaining 95 per cent. being through chemical combination.

The problem then, as in the case of oxygen, is to discover the means whereby each unit volume of blood takes up in the tissues, and gives out in the lungs, so much more carbon dioxide than would water in similar circumstances. We now know that there are two chief means by which this is done ; one resulting from the combination of carbon dioxide with water, to form carbonic acid, which is buffered just as is any other acid ; and the other resulting from a direct combination of carbon dioxide with hæmoglobin.

In forming our ideas as to the transport of carbon dioxide, we must distinguish between the results of experiments in which blood is shaken outside the body with various gas mixtures, and the behaviour of the blood in the circulation. The former usually takes about fifteen minutes or longer ; in the latter, the blood is often only in contact with the tissues (where it takes up carbon dioxide) and with the lungs (where it gives up carbon dioxide) for times of the order of one second. Attention must therefore be paid to the speed of the various processes, and this has revealed the presence of important factors which would otherwise have been missed.

Carbon Dioxide as an Acid. We have already discussed, in the previous section, how carbon dioxide combines with the water in which it is dissolved, to form carbonic acid ; and how the buffer substances in the blood (chiefly hæmoglobin) prevent the acidity from changing to any serious extent. The reactions involved may be written :

$$CO_2 + H_2O \rightleftharpoons H_2CO_3$$
$$H_2CO_3 \rightleftharpoons H^+ + HCO_3^-$$
$$H^+ + Hb^- \rightleftharpoons HHb$$

These reactions can be combined into the one equation :

$$CO_2 + H_2O + Hb^- \rightleftharpoons HCO_3^- + HHb$$

The net result of the series of reactions therefore is that almost all the extra carbon dioxide is carried in the blood in the form of HCO_3^- ions, the negative charges being supplied by the Hb^- ions. By this means the amount of carbon dioxide that can be carried in a given volume of blood is increased enormously over that which would be carried at the same partial pressure, in simple solution.

This does not, strictly, express the whole story. There must be some increase in hydrogen ion concentration, otherwise there would be no reason why the ionisation of the hæmoglobin should be depressed. This rise in hydrogen ion concentration has the effect of preventing some of the added carbon dioxide from being converted into bicarbonate ions. A little, therefore, remains as carbonic acid (the partial pressure of the carbon dioxide in venous blood is greater than that of arterial blood) ; the majority forms hydrogen and bicarbonate ions, and most of the hydrogen ions are absorbed by the hæmoglobin.

The reaction of carbon dioxide with the plasma proteins may be expressed in a similar way, *viz. :*

$$H_2CO_3 + Pr^- \rightleftharpoons HCO_3^- + HPr$$

and with phosphates by the equation.

$$H_2CO_3 + HPO_4^{--} \rightleftharpoons HCO_3^- + H_2PO_4^-$$

The plasma proteins contribute only about 7 per cent., and the phosphates less than 3 per cent. of the total buffering and carbon dioxide carrying power of the blood. They are, therefore, of minor importance as compared with hæmoglobin.

Oxy-hæmoglobin and Reduced Hæmoglobin as Acids. This superior efficiency of hæmoglobin over the plasma proteins is in part due to its higher concentration and the nature of its titration curve in the physiological pH range ; but it is, in the main, due to a much more important factor which has not yet been mentioned. In the body, when blood takes up carbon dioxide it also loses oxygen from combination with hæmoglobin, so that the latter is left in the reduced form. Now it has been definitely shown that reduced hæmoglobin is a *weaker acid* than oxy-hæmoglobin, *i.e.*, at a given pH, reduced hæmoglobin is less ionised than oxy-hæmoglobin. This means that the reaction

$$H_2CO_3 + Hb^- \rightleftharpoons HCO_3^- + HHb$$

must proceed further to the right at a given partial pressure of carbon dioxide, than does the reaction

$$H_2CO_3 + HbO_2^- \rightleftharpoons HCO_3^- + H.HbO_2$$

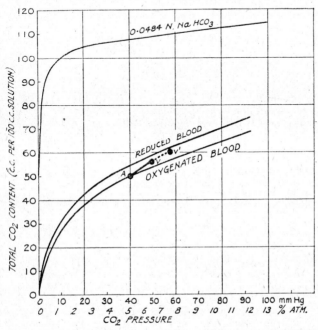

Fig. III, 6. **Carbon Dioxide Dissociation Curves** of Oxygenated and Reduced Blood, and of a Solution of Sodium Bicarbonate of the same concentration of Total Available Base as the Blood.

AVV′ is the " physiological carbon dioxide dissociation curve," A being the arterial point, V the venous point at rest, and V′ the venous point during exercise. Compare Fig. III. 4. (After Parsons.)

i.e., the reduced hæmoglobin ions do not hold on to their negative charges so firmly as do the oxy-hæmoglobin ions, and so transfer them more readily to the bicarbonate ions. Reduced blood, therefore, takes up carbon dioxide in the tissues more readily than does oxygenated blood. Conversely, in the lungs when oxy-hæmoglobin is reformed from reduced hæmoglobin the carbon dioxide will be liberated from the blood more readily.

These relationships are well shown by a comparison of the CO_2 dissociation curves of oxygenated and reduced blood. In curves of this kind the total concentration of carbon dioxide (chemically combined and dissolved) is plotted against the partial pressure of carbon dioxide in the gas phase when equilibrium has been reached with the blood.   In Fig. III. 6 the point A represents the average condition of the arterial blood, V the average condition of the mixed venous blood at rest, V' the condition of the venous blood in exercise.   V and V' are both situated between the oxygenated and reduced blood curves, since in the circulation the venous blood is only partially reduced.   It will be seen that the line AV is about twice as steep as the carbon dioxide dissociation curve of oxygenated or reduced blood.   This means that the change from fully oxygenated to partially reduced blood enables the blood to take up about twice as much carbon dioxide for a given increase of CO_2 pressure as it could take up if the change from oxy- to reduced hæmoglobin did not alter the buffer power or acid strength.

The whole difference in CO_2 carrying power of oxygenated and reduced blood must not be attributed to the difference in acid strengths of oxy- and reduced hæmoglobin.   The formation of carbamino compounds (see p. 117) is also partly responsible.

The explanation of how reduced hæmoglobin comes to be a weaker acid than oxy-hæmoglobin is probably that one of the $-NH_2$ groups in the molecule, which takes up H^+ ions, is close to the hæmatin nucleus, and that when O_2 combines with the latter, it reduces, perhaps by " steric hindrance," the ease of binding of the H^+ ion at this neighbouring $-NH_2$ group.   Oxy-hæmoglobin, being thus less able to bind H ions, behaves as a stronger acid.

The fact that loss of oxygen from the blood, as it passes through the tissues, renders it *ipso facto* more competent to take up carbon dioxide, just where such extra power is needed, is a beautiful example of the way in which divers chemical phenomena are co-ordinated into a harmonious physiological process.   Another example of the same principle is to be found in the so-called " chloride shift."

The Chloride Shift.   This phenomenon consists of a migration of chloride ions from the plasma to the interior of the corpuscle when the carbon dioxide content of the blood is raised, and in a reverse migration when the carbon dioxide content is lowered.   The explanation is roughly as follows :

When carbon dioxide enters the blood from the tissues, some stays in the plasma, and the rest passes into the corpuscles.   In both media the carbon dioxide combines with water to form carbonic acid, which dissociates into hydrogen ions and bicarbonate ions.   Owing to the far greater buffering power of the corpuscle contents, this dissociation will proceed much more extensively in the corpuscle than in the plasma. Consequently, there will be a concentration gradient propelling carbon dioxide (undissociated) from plasma to corpuscle, and another gradient propelling bicarbonate ions from corpuscles to plasma.   But, as described earlier in this chapter, the membrane of the corpuscle has the peculiar property (shared by some other cell membranes) of being permeable to anions such as Cl^- or HCO_3^-, but of being impermeable or only very slightly permeable to cations such as Na^+ or K^+ under normal conditions. A few HCO_3^- ions will diffuse out under the influence of the concentration gradient, but since they cannot be accompanied by ions of the opposite charge, the corpuscle will thereby be left no longer electrically neutral, but with a net positive charge. Hence, by the ordinary laws of electricity, the positively charged corpuscle will tend to suck back negative ions of all kinds from the plasma. Chloride ions, being the most readily available, will be the chief species of ion to migrate inwards from the plasma : the process will continue until finally an equilibrium is reached at which

$$\frac{[HCO_3^-] \text{ in corpuscle}}{[HCO_3^-] \text{ in plasma}} = \frac{[Cl^-] \text{ in corpuscle}}{[Cl^-] \text{ in plasma}}$$

this being a case in which the physico-chemical principle known as the Donnan membrane equilibrium applies. The net result is that there is an exchange of bicarbonate ions from the corpuscle with chloride ions from the plasma. The carbon dioxide carrying power of the plasma is thus brought up to the level, or even beyond that, of the corpuscles. Since the plasma hydrogen ion concentration is determined by the ratio of the carbon dioxide pressure to the concentration of bicarbonate ions, the transfer of bicarbonate ions from the corpuscles will assist in preventing the hydrogen ion concentration of the plasma from rising. On this account, the chloride shift may be regarded as a process of sharing out the superior buffering power of the corpuscles with the inferior buffer power of the plasma—it is often spoken of as " secondary buffering " of the plasma.

If the plasma is replaced by isotonic NaCl solution, the chloride shift again occurs when the blood corpuscle suspension in NaCl is shaken with carbon dioxide, and for the same reasons as above. If, however, isotonic sugar solution is used, there is now no ion in the outside fluid to exchange with HCO_3^- from the corpuscle, so that when the corpuscle suspension is shaken with carbon dioxide, the outside sugar solution cannot be secondarily buffered, and, since it contains no intrinsic buffer, it therefore goes very acid.

The chloride shift is mainly responsible for the difference between the carbon dioxide dissociation curve of " separated plasma " and that of " true plasma." The curve for " *separated plasma* " is obtained by centrifuging the blood, removing the supernatant fluid, shaking the latter with various pressures of carbon dioxide and then estimating the total CO_2 content at each CO_2 pressure. Over the physiological range of carbon dioxide pressure the curve is almost as flat as the CO_2 dissociation curve of a solution of sodium bicarbonate (Fig. III. 6) : such a curve would be of little physiological service, since the extra amount of carbon dioxide which would be taken up when its pressure is raised from 40 to 50 mm. Hg would be so small. The dissociation curve of " *true plasma* " is obtained by equilibrating the *whole* blood with various pressures of carbon dioxide, and then transferring the blood to a centrifuge cup (the escape of carbon dioxide into the air is prevented by a layer of liquid paraffin) ; the supernatant fluid, separated by centrifuging, is estimated for total CO_2, and the latter plotted against CO_2 pressure. Each sample of plasma thus is in equilibrium, not only with each different pressure of CO_2, but also with the corpuscles—whereas all the samples of separated plasma were in equilibrium with the corpuscles at one particular CO_2 pressure, namely, that which happened to obtain in the blood at the time when the plasma was centrifuged off. The true plasma dissociation curve is clearly quite different from the separated plasma curve : it is, indeed, of the same type as that of whole blood, and like the latter is of a serviceable shape as regards carbon dioxide transport.

As a result of all these mechanisms, the hydrogen ion concentration of the plasma is kept remarkably constant in the neighbourhood of *p*H 7·4 when the body is at rest. The difference in *p*H between arterial and venous blood is only about 0·03, but in work it is rather greater, viz., about 0·08.

The Speed of the Processes involved in Carbon Dioxide Transport. This important question was first taken up seriously by Henriques in 1928. Most of the individual chemical reactions we have described as occurring in the uptake or output of carbon dioxide are of an ionic type, *e.g.*,

$$H_2CO_3 \rightleftharpoons H^+ + HCO_3^-,$$
$$H_2Po_4^- \rightleftharpoons H^+ + HPo_4^{--},$$

HPr (protein molecule) $\rightleftharpoons H^+ + Pr^-.$

Simple ionic reactions of this type have been generally supposed to be very rapid—experiments have, indeed, shown that all these reactions reach to within 1 per cent. of equilibrium within 1/1,000 second (from whichever side of it they start) ; they must therefore be too fast to limit the rate of output or uptake of carbon dioxide by the blood. The final chemical reaction, which, on the bicarbonate hypothesis, comes just before the evolution of carbon dioxide into the expired air is, however, a non-ionic one, viz., the formation of CO_2 from H_2CO_3.

By the Law of Mass Action the speed of this reaction is equal to $k[H_2CO_3]$, where k is the velocity constant of the reaction : $H_2CO_3 \rightarrow CO_2 + H_2O.$

Now we have seen that $[H_2CO_3] = [H^+] [HCO_3^-]/K$ and therefore the speed of CO_2 formation $= k[H^+] . [HCO_3^-]/K.$

The value of the velocity constant k has been measured by several physical chemists : it can thence be calculated that at body *p*H and temperature, and with the usual $[HCO_3^-]$ in the blood, carbon dioxide could only be evolved in the lungs at about 1/200th the rate at which it actually escapes into the expired air. Either, then, there must be some other mechanism for the transport of carbon dioxide in the blood besides the bicarbonate one, or else there must exist in the blood some catalyst to speed up the reaction $H_2CO_3 \rightleftharpoons CO_2 + H_2O.$

Meldrum and Roughton have separated from the red blood corpuscles a substance which catalyses the reaction $H_2CO_3 \rightleftharpoons CO_2 + H_2O$ strongly. This substance has all the properties of an enzyme, and has been given the name *carbonic anhydrase :* it is not present in the plasma, but the amount in the corpuscles, if it is as efficient there as in solution, is enough to accelerate the formation of CO_2 from H_2CO_3 about 600 times under body conditions. Presumably during the short time the circulating blood is in the capillaries, the change from CO_2 to bicarbonate and *vice versa* must occur chiefly in the red corpuscles.

Carbamino-hæmoglobin. Blood can still react *rapidly* with a small amount of carbon dioxide even when carbonic anhydrase is absent or incapacitated by addition of some enzyme poison, *e.g.*, KCN ; this residual rapid reaction cannot be bicarbonate formation or the reverse (since both these processes, in absence of carbonic anhydrase, only proceed slowly). There is chemical evidence that it is due to a direct reaction of CO_2 with the —NH_2 groups of hæmoglobin to form compounds of a carbamino type, *e.g.*,

$$Hb—NH_2 + CO_2 \longrightarrow Hb\ NHCOOH.$$

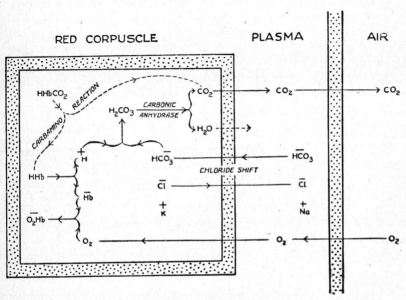

Fig. III, 7.   Scheme showing the Most Important Changes involved in the Liberation of Carbon Dioxide from Blood into Air.

This type of reaction is well known in the case of simpler —NH_2 containing compounds, such as ammonia and glycine, and is a very rapid one even in the absence of special catalysts.

Carbamino bound carbon dioxide plays an appreciable *rôle* in carbon dioxide transport, even though the absolute amounts of such compounds under physiological conditions form only a small fraction of the total amount of carbon dioxide present in the blood (in the neighbourhood of 2 per cent.) Reduced hæmoglobin takes up carbon dioxide in the carbamino form more readily than does oxy-hæmoglobin ; and of the total quantity of carbon dioxide carried from the tissues to the lungs— *i.e.*, of the difference between the carbon dioxide contents of venous and arterial blood—it is estimated that about 15 per cent. is in the carbamino form.

Other evidence, of a more physico-chemical type, suggests that some carbon dioxide combines directly with hæmoglobin, not only in the carbamino form, but possibly in some other form.

Summary. The uptake of carbon dioxide by the blood in the tissues is believed to occur as follows :—

(1) CO_2 diffuses from the tissues into the blood plasma.

(2) Some of the CO_2 hydrates slowly in the plasma to form H_2CO_3 ; the latter then yields its H^+ ions to the plasma proteins and phosphates and forms bicarbonate ions.

(3) Most of the CO_2, however, passes into the red corpuscles :

(*a*) Some combines directly with hæmoglobin to form compounds of a carbamino type—this combination is increased as the hæmoglobin loses oxygen in the blood capillary.

(*b*) By far the greater part changes over rapidly into H_2CO_3 under the influence of the enzyme carbonic anhydrase ; the H_2CO_3 then yields its H^+ ions to the hæmoglobin, forming bicarbonate ions. The latter process is much increased as the hæmoglobin changes from the oxy- to the reduced form, since reduced hæmoglobin, being a weaker acid than oxy-hæmoglobin, absorbs H^+ ions more readily and thereby allows H_2CO_3 to become more completely ionised.

(4) A small amount of HCO_3^- then diffuses out from the corpuscle into the plasma ; this sets up an electric field which draws Cl^- ions into the corpuscle from the plasma in place of the HCO_3^- ions, which have diffused out (the chloride shift). The twin process goes on until an equilibrium is reached. The CO_2 carrying power and buffer efficiency of the plasma are thereby brought up to the level of the red corpuscle.

In the lung carbon dioxide is formed and evolved by a reversal of all these processes, as indicated in Fig. III, 7.

The Effect of Exercise

The changes that take place in the blood as a result of exercise, or of increased activity of any kind, are quantitative rather than qualitative, and their magnitude depends largely upon the magnitude of the simultaneous changes in the respiratory and circulatory systems.

The first result of an increased activity in any group of cells is that more oxygen is used and more carbon dioxide evolved ; the partial pressure of oxygen around them falls, and that of carbon dioxide rises. This effect is passed on to the blood capillaries, so that the quantities defining the venous points on our dissociation curves are altered, taking up, for example, values somewhat as shown in Figs. III, 4 and III, 6 by the points marked V', *i.e.*, the oxygen pressure falls to 22 mm., the carbon dioxide pressure rises to 58 mm., the per cent. saturation with oxygen falls to 30, and the total carbon dioxide concentration rises to 60 c.c. per 100 c.c. The extra carbon dioxide is thus carried away, and the extra oxygen provided, simply by allowing the partial pressure in the blood of the one to rise and of the other to fall. We have seen that this does not necessarily involve similar changes in the tissue cells, owing to the opening up of extra capillaries and the reduction in the distance that has to be traversed by the gases between the blood and the tissue cells. The increased blood flow required is provided for by the vasomotor reflexes and local chemical mechanisms as described in Chapter II.

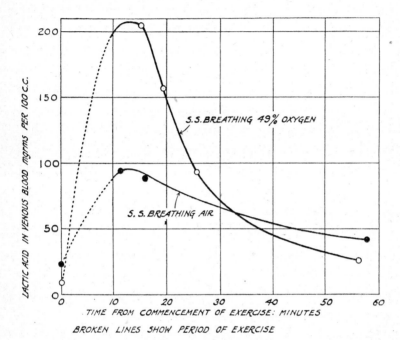

FIG. III, 8. The **Lactic Acid** concentration in the blood during and after severe muscular exercise (standing-running). The subject was able to perform more work when breathing 49 per cent. oxygen than when breathing air. *Note.*—(1) The greater accumulation of lactic acid associated with this greater effort, and (2) the effect of breathing 49 per cent. oxygen in lowering the " resting " lactic acid concentration (before starting the exercise), and in hastening the removal of the lactic acid after the exercise. (After Hill, Long, and Lupton.)

A limit must come to this, however, and if the activity continues to become greater, the oxygen pressure in the tissue cells begins to fall, and the oxygen supply to be deficient. The cells go into oxygen debt, and, if this is severe enough, begin to liberate lactic acid. This addition of extra hydrogen ions drives the equilibrium reaction,

$$H_2CO_3 \rightleftharpoons H^+ + HCO_3^-$$

from right to left. The carbonic acid so formed is converted to carbon dioxide and blown off in the lungs (the respiratory centre adjusts the rate of ventilation so as to ensure this). The buffering power of the tissues is reduced, nevertheless, since the buffer salt, bicarbonate, is replaced by the fully ionised lactate, which has no buffer action ; the hydrogen ion concentration of the tissues rises. If the exercise continues, there may be so much lactic acid produced that the hydrogen ion concentration of the arterial blood is affected to a significant extent. We shall see in the next chapter that the carbon dioxide pressure in the lungs may rise also, and these two effects may so alter the oxygen dissociation curve that the per cent. saturation of the arterial blood falls. The oxygen and carbon dioxide transport system has now got into a vicious circle, and the exercise must stop. It is, indeed, sometimes terminated by unconsciousness.

It should be remarked that the whole of the body is affected by the changes that result in the blood from one group of muscles going into oxygen debt ; the lactic acid, indeed, diffuses into all the wet tissues of the body, and may be oxidised in them—and particularly in the liver and heart—as well as in the muscles in which it was formed. The blood buffers play somewhat the part of a bank which allows one of its clients to overdraw his account at the expense of the rest, but if the overdraft is allowed to increase until it is comparable in size with the whole of the negotiable securities of the bank—and this in spite of the activities of the other clients to redeem it—the bank's failure is inevitable.

TISSUE FLUID AND LYMPH

The production of tissue fluid is essentially a matter of filtration. The walls of the capillaries are permeable to all the constituents of the plasma except the proteins ; if, therefore, the capillary pressure exceeds the osmotic pressure of the proteins, fluid will pass out from the capillaries into the tissues. The pressure at the arterial ends of the capillaries is high enough for this to occur, but not that at the venous ends, and here fluid will pass in again.

This filtration and reabsorption can be seen in the capillaries of the frog's mesentery. The mesentery is observed under a binocular microscope ; a capillary with a rapid circulation is chosen and blocked by pressing a fine blunt glass rod on it by means of a micro-manipulator. In some cases the mass of corpuscles remaining in the capillary moves towards the block, indicating that filtration is taking place, and in some cases they move away from the block, indicating reabsorption. A very fine glass pipette is now inserted into the capillary, connected with a water manometer, and the capillary pressure is measured, the block being still in place. The results of a large number of such experiments are shown in Fig. III. 9, in which the rate of passage of fluid through the capillary wall is plotted against the capillary pressure. It will be seen that, on the average, fluid passes out when the pressure is greater than 11·5 cm. of water, and in when it is less than this ; independent measurements of the osmotic pressure of frog's plasma indicate that it normally lies between 10 and 12 cm. of water.

The walls of the capillaries are not always completely impermeable to the plasma proteins, and tissue fluid may, in some conditions, contain up to 2 or 3 per cent. of protein. This implies that fluid can pass out of some of the capillaries even when the capillary pressure is less than the osmotic pressure of the proteins.   Only a few capillaries are normally permeable to protein, however, and in the majority only crystalloids can pass back into the blood circulation in regions of low capillary pressure ; the excess fluid left in the tissues thus has a higher concentration of protein than has the fluid filtered off by the capillaries.

This excess fluid—which is known as **Lymph**—is carried off by the lymphatic system.   This consists of very thin-walled vessels

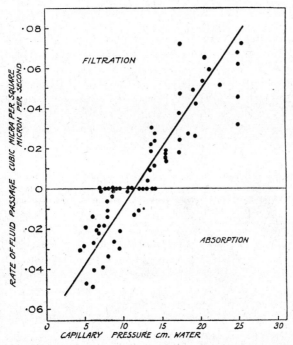

FIG. III. 9.   The effect of the Pressure within a Capillary on the Passage of Fluid through its Walls.

Positive values of the rate of fluid passage indicate filtration of fluid ; negative values indicate absorption.

The observations were made on several different frogs, and the straight line, representing the average, passes through the line of zero flow at a hydrostatic pressure of 11·5 cm. of water (about equal to the colloid osmotic pressure of the blood) ; fluid passes neither in nor out at this pressure, and the rate of flow is directly proportional to the pressure both above and below it.   (Landis.)

provided with valves, which all run towards the thorax, those from the hind limbs, abdomen, left side of chest and left arm all joining together to form the *thoracic duct*, which empties into the venous system at the junction of the left internal jugular vein with the left subclavian vein. Fluid is propelled along the lymphatics partly by means of the pumping action of muscular movement, as in the veins, and partly by reason of the negative pressure in the thorax.

The protein concentration of the lymph is very variable (1 to 6 per cent.), and lymph from the intestines and liver has a higher protein concentration (6 per cent.) than that from the muscles (2 per cent.). Otherwise lymph contains the same substances as does the plasma, and in about the same concentrations. It usually clots if left to stand, but not so rapidly as the blood, owing to the absence of platelets. After a meal there is often a considerable quantity of fat present, giving it a milky appearance ; we shall see in Chapter V that the lymphatic system is the chief route for the absorption of fats from the alimentary canal. It normally contains, also, considerable numbers of lymphocytes.

Factors influencing the Flow of Lymph. These are, of course, those which influence the difference between the rate of filtration and the rate of reabsorption, and may be grouped under three headings : (1) the capillary pressure ; (2) the difference between the osmotic pressure of the plasma and that of the tissue fluid ; and (3) the permeability of the capillary wall.

(1) Any rise in capillary *pressure* occasioned either by dilatation of the arterioles or obstruction of the veins increases the flow of lymph. Such a rise is the usual accompaniment of activity in any organ, and the increased production of tissue fluid is of great value in bringing in substances for combustion and removing the waste products.

(2) Two factors come into the consideration of the *osmotic pressure :* (*a*) the concentration of the colloids, and (*b*) the concentration of crystalloids.

(*a*) The concentration of the plasma proteins, and hence the colloid osmotic pressure, can be reduced to a very low value by a process known as *plasmaphorœsis*. This consists in repeatedly bleeding an animal and re-injecting the blood corpuscles suspended in physiological salt solution ; the plasma proteins are thus removed, but not the corpuscles, so that the blood can still carry oxygen and carbon dioxide in a more or less normal manner. This process leads to a large increase in the rate of formation of lymph.

(*b*) If the concentration of crystalloids is increased by injecting a hypertonic solution intravenously, the reabsorption of tissue fluid is increased owing to the increased osmotic pressure of the plasma, so that in a short time the total volume of the blood is increased sufficiently to render it once more isotonic (the simultaneous diffusion of the excess salt through the walls of the capillaries assists in this, of course). The flow of lymph practically ceases during this time. This transient osmotic action of the crystalloids has now reduced the colloid osmotic pressure, the rate of filtration is increased, the lymph flow starts again and continues at a rate larger than normal until the excess fluid has been removed. The net result, therefore, of introducing a hypertonic salt solution is the same as that of plasmaphoræsis ; both act as *lymphagogues* (from " lymph," and the Greek word for " to lead "). The excess fluid is not all returned to the blood by the lymph, however, but mainly stays in the tissues until it is excreted by the kidneys.

The action of the crystalloid osmotic pressure is of importance, also, during the activity of any organ. Activity results in the production of metabolites, which are mainly of smaller molecular weight than the parent substances from which they are derived. These diffuse out into the tissue spaces, raise the osmotic pressure, and draw fluid from the capillaries. They may also increase the permeability of the capillary walls.

(3) When a capillary dilates excessively, it allows more fluid to pass through its walls at a given filtration pressure (difference in hydrostatic pressure between inside and outside, less the osmotic pressure) and holds back protein less completely. Whether the physiological dilatation that occurs during activity of the organ supplied by them plays a part in the increased flow of lymph, is disputed, but it is of importance in connection with certain abnormalities. Histamine is one of the most powerful capillary dilators known, and, moreover, it injures the capillary endothelium, making it more permeable to large molecules. Histamine, therefore, increases the rate of formation of tissue fluid and of lymph. Its introduction below the surface of the skin through a needle prick results also in the formation of a wheal, just as if the skin had been burnt. Now there is a type of mild anaphylactic response known as an " allergic " response, which produces nettle-rash or urticaria, *i.e.*, the eruption of wheals on the skin, or congestion of the mucous membranes of the nose and pharynx. This follows the consumption of mussels, lobsters, strawberries or several common foodstuffs by certain persons who are said to be " sensitive." Similar reactions result from contact with the skin, of the leaves of the poison ivy, or the stings of stinging nettles or jelly-fish ; " sensitive " persons may also get such reactions from the pollen of certain grasses (hay fever), the hairs of certain animals, or even the close presence of these animals. Taking into consideration also the similarity between the symptoms of the generalised anaphylactic response and those of the administration of histamine, it seems possible that such localised urticaria is one of the symptoms of a histamine production. Substances such as histamine and peptone, therefore, which dilate the capillaries and increase their permeability by injuring their endothelium also act as lymphagogues.

The increased permeability of damaged capillaries has been observed by the method described above (Fig. III. 9). When alcohol or mercuric chloride was added to the blood flowing through them, fluid passed out much more rapidly, and there was practically no reabsorption except at very low pressures; they had thus become almost completely permeable to proteins.

When the rate of production of tissue fluid in any organ is in excess of its removal, either by reabsorption or by the lymphatics, the organ swells, becomes puffy, and *œdematous*. *Œdema or dropsy* occurs physiologically to a very mild degree in the muscles after exercise, and pathologically in heart failure owing to the rise in venous pressure, and also in certain types of nephritis. The œdema fluid appears to be free to pass from one part of the body to another with great readiness, since in cases of dropsy the fluid collects in the legs during the day, when the patient is standing up, and becomes more evenly distributed during the night.

THE PERITONEAL, PLEURAL AND PERICARDIAL FLUIDS

These all have much the same composition as the tissue fluid, and, in all probability, originate in the same manner. Their function is very largely one of lubrication, enabling the intestines, lungs and heart to move freely in their respective enclosures.

THE INTRA-OCULAR FLUIDS

There are two of these, the *aqueous humour* in front of the lens, and the *vitreous humour* behind the lens. In many respects, the composition and rate of formation of the aqueous humour are consistent with its being formed by a process of filtration from the blood ; the membrane through which it is filtered being impermeable to proteins, and less permeable to large non-electrolyte molecules than to small. There are, however, a number of well-founded observations which appear to be inconsistent with this simple conception, and it may prove necessary to postulate some active secretory process, both in respect of the fluid as a whole, and of certain of the individual solutes contained in it. The vitreous contains, in addition to the constituents of the aqueous, protein which sets to a gel even in the very low concentrations (0·025 per cent.) present in the eye.

The aqueous humour is chiefly derived from the blood vessels of the ciliary processes, and is removed (1) by reabsorption into the veins of the iris, (2) by passing through the spaces of Fontana in the filtration angle into the canal of Schlemm, and so into the ciliary veins, and (3) by passing through the vitreous and flowing down the lymphatics of the sheath of the optic nerve. The rate of formation of the aqueous humour is probably small under normal conditions. But after withdrawal of a considerable fraction of the amount normally present, the rate of formation is increased, and the amount withdrawn will be replaced in man, in about 1 hour.

THE CEREBRO-SPINAL FLUID

There are four membranes covering the central nervous system. They are (1) the pia mater, which closely invests the nervous substance and carries the blood vessels to it ; (2) the arachnoid, separated from the pia by the sub-arachnoid space, which contains the *cerebro-spinal fluid ;* (3) the meningeal layer of the dura mater ; and (4) the periosteal layer of the dura mater. The venous sinuses are situated between the two layers of the dura, and delicate processes known as the *arachnoid villi* arise from the arachnoid and penetrate into the venous sinuses. The relations between these structures are essentially similar in the skull and in the spinal column ; but since the pia ends, with the spinal cord, at the first lumbar vertebra, and the dura and arachnoid extend as far as the second sacral vertebra, the sub-arachnoid space is of considerable size in this region. Cerebro-spinal fluid can, therefore, be readily obtained by inserting a hollow needle (usually between the fourth and fifth lumbar vertebræ) into this space; this is called *lumbar puncture*, and the fluid usually emerges at a rate of about one drop per second.

The cerebro-spinal fluid is formed mainly by the plexuses of blood capillaries, known as the *choroid plexuses*, in the ventricles of the brain. This can be shown by the facts that (*a*) fluid can be collected from a tube inserted into either of the ventricles; (*b*) blocking the outflow of a ventricle leads to its distension (hydrocephalus); and (*c*) if the choroid plexus is first removed, subsequent blocking of the outflow no longer leads to a distension of the ventricle. A second important source of cerebro-spinal fluid is the system of perivascular spaces, which replaces the lymphatic system in the central nervous system; these perivascular spaces are minute extensions of the sub-arachnoid space, which ensheath the blood vessels and end in the tissue spaces around the nerve cells. Fluid emerges from the blood capillaries into the perivascular space, much as does lymph, and such of it as is not re-absorbed into the capillaries finds its way into the sub-arachnoid space to mix there with the fluid from the ventricles. Most of the cerebro-spinal fluid is absorbed into the venous sinuses through the arachnoid villi.

The composition of the cerebro-spinal fluid is, like that of lymph, practically that of an ultra-filtrate of plasma containing a little protein (0·02 per cent.). The contribution of the perivascular spaces to the fluid has exactly such a composition; the fluid that can be collected from the ventricles, on the other hand, differs appreciably from plasma in the concentration of some of its constituents. This difference is sufficient to make it necessary to regard the choroid plexuses as secretory organs, and not merely as membranes which act as simple physical filters impermeable to proteins. Nevertheless, most of the diffusible constituents of the plasma are present in the cerebro-spinal fluid in about the same concentration as in the blood; changes, for example, in the urea or glucose content of the blood are followed by similar changes in the fluid, while alcohol in the blood diffuses freely into the fluid. The total volume of cerebro-spinal fluid, in man, is about 120 c.c., and its rate of formation is about 0·5 c.c. per minute. The pressure, measured in the enlargement of the sub-arachnoid space at the base of the brain, known as the *cisterna magna*, is about 90 mm. water when the subject is lying down, and may fall to atmospheric pressure when he is standing up. All these measurements may vary within wide limits.

Lumbar puncture is a procedure of considerable medical importance, for not only may it relieve increased intra-cranial pressure by providing an escape for excessive cerebro-spinal fluid, but it may yield valuable information enabling a distinction to be made between those diseases which exhibit characteristic changes in the nature and amount of the fluid. Inflammation of the membranes of the brain (meningitis), for example, is accompanied by an abnormally high rate of production of the fluid, by an increase in its protein content (which may be tenfold), by a reduction of the glucose and chloride concentration, and by an enormous increase in the cell content (normal fluid contains about 1 to 5 lymphocytes per cubic millimetre; meningitic fluid contains hundreds of cells per cubic millimetre, which are mainly polymorphonuclear leucocytes or lymphocytes, according as the infection is septic or tuberculous).

Lumbar puncture is also of value when local anæsthetics are to be injected into the nervous system to produce spinal anæsthesia. The injection of lipiodol (a heavy liquid opaque to X-rays) into the cisterna magna results normally in its flowing down the spinal column in virtue of its weight ; if the flow is obstructed by a tumour or inflammatory adhesion, the exact site of the lesion can so be discovered.

If the volume of the brain increases, as by the formation of a cerebral tumour, the intra-cranial pressure rises. This is transmitted to all points within the rigid brain-case by the cerebro-spinal fluid, with the result that the veins are compressed and the capillary pressure rises. The first structure to suffer is the optic nerve, and the obstruction of the veins running along it causes œdema of the optic disc, which can be observed with an ophthalmoscope ; this condition is known as *papillœdema*. The intra-cranial pressure is also increased in the condition known as *hydrocephalus*, which results from an excessive accumulation of cerebro-spinal fluid. This may be caused by obstruction to the fluid pathway from ventricles to sub-arachnoid space, or by blocking or maldevelopment of the arachnoid villi.

Rise in the pressure of the cerebro-spinal fluid is also caused by injections of isotonic or hypotonic saline into the blood, showing that its production does depend to some extent upon physico-chemical factors. Injections of hypertonic saline, on the other hand, cause a fall in the pressure, probably due chiefly to an osmotic withdrawal of fluid from the brain itself, with consequent diminution in volume. This is a procedure commonly used in brain surgery, where it is often advisable to reduce the volume of the brain before the skull is opened.

CHAPTER IV

RESPIRATION

CONTINUED vital activity of tissues demands the appropriate inter-change of the gases, oxygen and carbon dioxide, between the tissues and the atmosphere. In its more usual sense, respiration means the opera-tion of the special apparatus concerned with the absorption of oxygen by, and the removal of carbon dioxide from, the body as a whole ; this is termed external respiration. Internal, or tissue respiration, on the other hand, is the local process of utilisation of oxygen and production of carbon dioxide by the tissue cells, and will be considered in a later chapter on Metabolism. In the present chapter we are mainly concerned with the processes of external respiration.

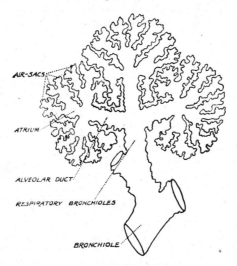

FIG. IV. 1. Sectional Diagram of a Structural Unit of the Lungs.
(After Miller.)

The Structure and Movements of the Respiratory Mechanism

Air enters and leaves the lungs by traversing, first the nasal passages (and also the buccal cavities when the mouth is open), where the vascular mucous membrane warms and moistens the incoming air ; next the pharynx, the larynx, and lastly the trachea into the bronchi. The final branching network of the bronchial tree opens into the terminal air sacs with their alveolar saccules, or alveoli (see Fig. IV. 1). It is in the alveoli that the respiratory gases, oxygen and carbon dioxide, are able to make close contact with the blood in the capillaries.

The tubes of the trachea and bronchi are kept permanently open by a series of cartilaginous rings embedded in their walls. These are partly made up of a dense fibro-elastic membrane. The whole of the bronchial tree is richly supplied with elastic fibres, mainly disposed in a longitudinal direction. These fibres, along with the elastic tissues in the lungs, account for the recoil of the lungs and the bronchial tree which takes place on expiration. (See Fig. IV. 2).

The respiratory passages are lined with ciliated and with mucus-secreting cells. The cilia produce a constant wave-like motion in the direction of the nasal and buccal cavities and are very efficient in expelling any foreign material that may come to rest on their surfaces.

The pharynx is a common pathway for air and food. In order to prevent the food going down the " wrong way," the aperture of the larynx is guarded by the epiglottis. During the process of swallowing, the arytenoid cartilages are closely approximated and pulled forwards

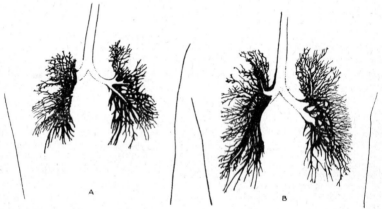

FIG. IV. 2. X-ray Photographs (retouched) of the **Bronchial Tree** of a Young Woman : (A) in full expiration, (B) in full inspiration. (Macklin.)

towards the epiglottis, and at the same time breathing is inhibited (deglutition apnœa).

The lungs are so constructed that an almost instantaneous exchange of gases can take place between the air within them and the blood passing through them. The pulmonary capillaries, although individually only about a millimetre in length, may altogether expose a surface area to the lung gases of approximately 70 sq. metres ; the blood in these capillaries is exposed for no more than a second. Interposed between the blood and the air in the alveoli are two delicate membranes each of one cell thickness, namely the epithelium forming the alveolar wall and the endothelium of the capillary. Across such a membrane the respiratory gases can readily diffuse.

Only a portion of the lungs is normally used in quiet breathing. A patient who had four out of his six lobes removed did not suffer from respiratory embarrassment as long as he did not indulge in too severe exercise.

The Bronchial Muscles

The walls of the smaller bronchi and the bronchioles contain strips of plain muscle which run spirally round them. Contraction of this muscle, therefore, both narrows the bore and decreases the length of these tubes, and consequently reduces the volume of air contained in the lungs at any given value of the intra-pleural pressure, *i.e.*, increases the elastic recoil. It also increases the resistance to the passage of the air in and out of the lungs and causes laboured breathing when the contraction is excessive. The bronchial muscles contract when fibres in the vagi nerves are stimulated or when acted on by para-sympatho-mimetic drugs, *e.g.*, acetylcholine or pilocarpine, and they relax when nerve fibres from the sympathetic system are stimulated and by the action of sympatho-mimetic drugs, *e.g.*, adrenaline. There is some evidence that they contract on each expiration and relax on each inspiration, thereby assisting the diaphragm and the intercostal muscles in renewing the air in the lungs. Apart from this, there does not appear to be any evidence that they are in any way essential to the normal functioning of the lungs.

Nerve Supply of the Bronchial Tree. The *efferent* nerve supply is derived entirely from the autonomic nervous system, and supplies the bronchial muscles as just described.

Afferent. The laryngeal mucosa is supplied by the superior laryngeal nerve, which when its nerve endings are irritated by the presence of a foreign body, or as a result of disease, reflexly causes coughing. From the bronchial tree and the lung, afferent fibres run up in the vagus nerve trunk ; their chief function is to indicate to the respiratory centre, the degree of expansion of the lungs. We will return to this later.

Asthma. Under certain conditions the efferent vagal fibres supplying the muscles in the bronchioles are stimulated reflexly by irritation in various parts of the body, especially the nose and the air passages themselves, and produce a spasmodic contraction in these muscles. This results in the condition known as asthma, in which great difficulty is experienced in breathing, particularly in expiration, since this is normally a passive movement. Bronchial asthma is associated also with hypersensitivity to certain proteins, notably those in the pollens of certain grasses, analogous to the sensitivity of an anaphylactic type responsible for urticaria and hay fever. Anaphylaxis in general appears to be associated with the production of a histamine-like substance, and it is significant in this connection that histamine has a powerful constricting action on the bronchial muscles. Relief is rapidly obtained on administration of adrenaline or ephedrine, both of which bring about relaxation of the bronchial muscles. Atropine may alleviate the condition by paralysing the motor endings of the vagus nerve, and so blocking the reflex excitation which is constricting the bronchioles.

The Pleura and the Pleural Cavities

The lungs are enveloped in a closed membranous sac. The outer wall of the sac lines the chest wall and is called the parietal pleura. This is reflected at the roots of the lungs, where it is continuous with the visceral layer which covers the lungs. The potential space between the layers is spoken of as the pleural cavity. It contains a small amount of fluid which acts as a lubricant. When the chest wall expands and contracts during the phases of respiration, the parietal and the visceral layers of the pleuræ normally maintain contact with each other. If air is introduced between the layers of the pleuræ, either artificially, or during disease, they can now separate, with expansion of the air, and the elastic tissue of the lungs and bronchi will make the lungs collapse. The tendency of the lungs to collapse subjects the contents of the thorax—such as the great veins, but not, of course, the alveoli and air passages of the lungs—to a pressure which is less than that of the atmosphere ; this pressure is measured by thrusting a hypodermic needle, connected to a manometer, through the chest wall. The small quantity of air which enters does not appreciably affect the pressure. In man, this *intra-pleural pressure* is about –5 mm. Hg in expiration, and –10 mm. Hg in inspiration, although in a forced inspiration it may fall to –30 mm. Hg. If much air is allowed to enter the pleural cavity, the oscillations of the intra-pleural pressure become more violent, since the respiratory efforts are largely wasted in expanding the air in the pleural cavity. Eventually the lungs will not move at all, even with the most violent inspiratory efforts possible. The condition where gases are present in the pleural cavity is called a *pneumothorax*. These gases are eventually absorbed and contact once more established between the pleuræ.

Pneumothorax. In the treatment of pulmonary tuberculosis, it has been found beneficial to immobilise the affected lung. This is achieved by inserting a needle through the chest wall and admitting air to the space between the lung and the thorax, so forming an artificial pneumothorax. If 500 c.c. of air be so admitted, and pain be avoided by skilful insertion of the needle, there need be no disturbance of the normal frequency or depth of the respiration. There is fairly rapid interchange of gases between the gas injected and the surface of the lungs. The equilibrium composition of the gas in the intra-pleural space is much the same as that of gas placed in the abdominal cavity, or injected subcutaneously, and corresponds to the partial pressure of oxygen and carbon dioxide in the tissue fluids. The 500 c.c. is almost completely absorbed through the pleura in the course of a week, unless the pleura is thickened by inflammation (pleurisy), in which case there is often an effusion of liquid into the intrapleural space (hydrothorax). If a series of injections of air be given, so that in the course of a fortnight one lung is completely immobilised—involving a pneumothorax containing, say, 3 litres of air—there is rapid adaptation and respiratory function is adequate for the needs of the body, even during exercise, such as an active game of tennis. Despite the collapse of the one lung, there is no arterial anoxæmia, such as would be inevitable if blood continued to circulate through a collapsed lung. It is clear that collapse of a lung results, after quite a short while, in the arrest of the pulmonary circulation through that lung; the bronchial circulation presumably persists, and provides for the survival of the tissues.

The Respiratory Movements

There are two phases in the respiratory cycle.

Inspiration. This is achieved, first, by the lifting and expansion of the bony cage which forms the outer wall of the thorax. This is carried out by the elevation of the sternum and the movement of the ribs on the vertebral column. Thus the size of the chest is increased in its lateral and antero-posterior diameters. Secondly, the chest is enlarged from above downwards by the descent of the diaphragm. The diaphragm is the chief muscle of respiration. During deep breathing it may be responsible for as much as 65 per cent. of the total volume of air inhaled. The diaphragm is innervated by the phrenic nerves.

Expiration. The muscles relax, the thoracic cage through its own elasticity contracts and the walls of the chest are brought closer together assisted by the recoil of the bronchial tree and the lung tissues (see Fig. IV. 2). In *quiet* breathing, expiration is probably entirely passive. A forced expiration is assisted by the contraction of the abdominal muscles, which press the contents of the abdomen against the diaphragm and force it to ascend. The internal intercostal muscles contract and increase the extent of the depression of the ribs.

If a subject is observed in the supine position, it will be noticed that the abdominal wall rises and falls in each respiratory cycle. This is due to the movements of the diaphragm displacing the abdominal contents, and is sometimes referred to as " abdominal respiration."

Fœtal Respiration and Expansion of the Lungs at Birth

The lungs of the fœtus are airless and unexpanded and contain a small amount of amniotic fluid. The pulmonary circulation is small, the greater part of the blood having been short-circuited by a direct opening between the two auricles (the foramen ovale) and an opening between the pulmonary artery and the aorta (the ductus arteriosus). It is probable that small respiratory movements are made *in utero* in an effort to dilate the future air passages. At birth these movements are greatly increased in amplitude. The diaphragm descends, the intercostal muscles contract, and the pulmonary circulation is established. Full expansion of the chest takes some days.

The fœtuses of animals show marked respiratory movements when the mother is given gas mixtures containing little oxygen or much carbon dioxide or when the placental circulation is interfered with. It is perhaps a similar mechanism which promotes breathing at birth. " The respiratory mechanism seems to be a dormant system charged with potentialities long in advance of the time it can be of any use to the fœtus." (Windle.)

Sounds Associated with the Movements of the Lungs

There are two distinct sounds associated with the movement of air into and out of the normal lungs, both of which may be heard by placing the ear on the chest or, better, by using a stethoscope. The first of these is a fine rustling noise, occurring during inspiration and the beginning of expiration, known as *vesicular breathing* ; the second, heard only when the stethoscope is placed over one of the larger air passages, is louder and rougher, like a whispered " hah," and is known as *bronchial breathing*.

The Volume of Air in the Lungs

The diagrammatic representation of a tracing of respiratory movements shown in Fig. IV. 3 was taken from a subject who, after a few normal quiet respirations, took the deepest inspiration that he could and then expired to the limits of his ability. The upward stroke represents inspiratory and the downward stroke expiratory movements. The extent of the volumes involved is shown on the scale at the side of the figure.

These figures are obtained by breathing into and out of a *spirometer*. This is a volume recorder made on the lines of a gasometer; a cylindrical bell,

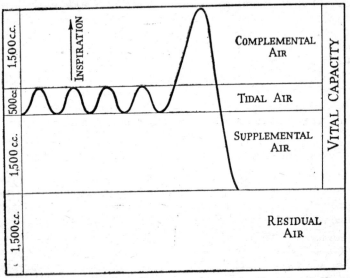

Fig. IV. 3. Diagrammatic Representation of a Tracing of **Normal** Respiratory Movements, and the Measurement of **Vital Capacity, etc.**

closed at the upper end, is immersed in a tank of water, and counterbalanced. Air blown in through a pipe passing through the water seal, raises the bell; and the distance traversed, and hence the volume of air introduced, can be read on a scale.

The volume that is inspired and expired during quiet breathing is referred to as the **tidal air** and varies from 350 to 600 c.c. The volume of the tidal air multiplied by the frequency of the respirations per minute gives the total volume of air breathed per minute; this is known as the **ventilation rate**. At rest this is usually 4 to 8 litres per minute. The volume of the deepest inhalation that can be taken at the end of a normal inspiration is called the **complemental air** and is about 1,500 c.c. The deepest exhalation possible at the end of a normal expiration is called the **supplemental** or **reserve air** and is about 1,500 c.c.

The Vital Capacity. When a subject after the deepest inspiration expires the largest volume that he can into a spirometer, the volume of air that he expires is termed his *vital capacity*.   Reference to the diagram in Fig. **IV**. 3 shows that this volume is the sum of his complemental, tidal and reserve airs, and in this instance is 3·5 litres.   This amount is not an expression of the total volume of air in his lungs, since when he has completed his forced expiration there still remain about 1,500 c.c. of the *residual air*, which could only be expelled by opening the chest wall and allowing the lungs to collapse.   To determine the total capacity of the lungs this residual air must be estimated and added to the vital capacity. Even in the collapsed lung a small volume of the residual air is trapped ; it is this which gives the collapsed lungs their buoyancy in water and is used in medico-legal investigations to ascertain whether the lungs have ever expanded and so determine whether a child breathed after birth.

In the past, vital capacity has been taken as a measure of respiratory function, but it is now thought that a single measurement gives little useful information, whereas a change in the vital capacity may be significant.   Thus, the vital capacity of a patient suffering from active lung disease, falls as the disease progresses.

The vital capacity is affected by the volume of blood in the pulmonary circulation.   The vital capacity is smaller when the subject is supine than it is when he is standing, the larger volume of blood in the pulmonary vessels presumably encroaching on the air capacity of the lungs.   In certain forms of heart failure, also, particularly in left ventricular failure where the pulmonary vessels are congested, there is a reduction in vital capacity.   The respiratory distress (dyspnœa) of these conditions is proportional to the reduction of the vital capacity, and this cardiac asthma, as it is termed, probably results from continued stimulation of the afferent vagal nerve endings in the lungs (see " Nervous Control of Breathing ").

The Expired Air.   A sample of the expired air is obtained by making the subject breathe through valves so arranged that he breathes in from the atmosphere and out into an air-tight bag, known as a *Douglas bag*, from the name of its first user.   The total volume of air expired in a given time is measured by subsequently pressing out the contents of the Douglas bag through a gas meter, and its composition is determined by analysing a sample in a gas-analysis apparatus.

The Composition of the Gases in the Lungs

Alveolar Air.   The gases in the depths of the lungs are referred to as alveolar air.   A sample can be collected by forcibly expiring down a short length of 1 inch bore rubber tubing and collecting a sample at the end of the expiratory effort.   Haldane recommended the collection of two samples ; the first at the end of a forced expiration immediately after a normal expiration, which he called the " end expiration " sample ; the second at the end of a forced expiration immediately after inspiration, the " end inspiration sample."

The significance of the composition of alveolar air will be better understood by reference to Fig. IV. 4 (see also section on "Chemical Control"). This is a diagrammatic representation of what happens to the pressure of the carbon dioxide and oxygen in the alveolar air and in the blood as it circulates through the lungs. Let us suppose that a sample of the venous blood entering the lungs by the pulmonary artery contains carbon dioxide at a pressure of 44 mm. Hg. As this sample circulates through the pulmonary capillaries some of the carbon dioxide will diffuse out into the air in the alveoli and will continue to diffuse until there is no further pressure difference between blood and alveoli. If the pressure of carbon dioxide in the alveolar air is 38 mm. Hg, the pressure of carbon dioxide in the arterial blood in the lung circulation will also reach this value. This means that the carbon dioxide pressure in the alveolar air is the same as that of the arterial blood

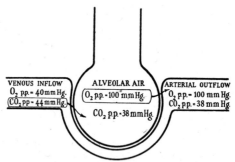

Fig. IV. 4. Diagrammatic Representation of **Alveolar Air** (see text).

leaving the lungs. Some workers in order to divorce the term alveolar air from its anatomical conception, prefer to use the term, "arterial pulmonary air," which lays emphasis on the fact that the partial pressures of the gases in the "alveolar air" are in equilibrium with the pressures of the gases in the arterial blood, leaving the lungs in the pulmonary veins. The evidence that such an equilibrium exists will be considered in a later section.

It may be as well, at this point, to state briefly the physical laws which govern the passage of gases from one point to another, and to illustrate some of the consequences which follow the operation of these laws. The partial pressure exerted by the gas concerned is always the most important quantity, and is that fraction of the total pressure which can be considered as being contributed by that gas ; it is calculated from the percentage composition of the gas mixture and the total pressure (very often, the barometric pressure). Every gas will diffuse from a point where its partial pressure is greater to any other point where its partial pressure is less, and this applies both to free gases and to gases in solution. Consequently, if a solution is in equilibrium with a mixture of gases, the partial pressures of all these gases will be the same in the solution as in the gas mixture. Further, the molar concentration of any gas in solution is directly proportional to its partial pressure, the constant of proportionality being the solubility. Thus, as has been shown in the previous chapter, the acidity (hydrogen ion concentration) of the blood is directly proportional to the concentration of carbonic acid, and thus to the partial pressure of carbon dioxide in the blood, or, as just stated, to the partial pressure of carbon dioxide in the alveolar air. Lastly, if one of the gases in the mixture is the vapour of a liquid, such as water, then so long as the gas mixture is in equilibrium with that liquid, *e.g.*, with a watery solution, the partial pressure of that vapour is independent of the total pressure, and of the composition of the gas mixture, and is determined only by the temperature.

To illustrate these points, we will take a few examples.

At sea-level the total atmospheric pressure is approximately 760 mm. Hg. (760 mm. Hg. has been adopted for standard purposes). Thus, the partial pressure of oxygen in ordinary damp air is 20·71 per cent. of 760 mm. Hg. which is 157 mm. Hg. ; that of carbon dioxide similarly is 0·3 mm. Hg. ; of nitrogen is 593 mm. Hg. ; and of water vapour is 9·5 mm. Hg. (see Table I). If a subject descends in a diving bell, the pressure in the bell will rise to, say, 1,000 mm. Hg. but the percentage composition of the air will still be the same. There will still be 20·71 per cent. oxygen, but its partial pressure will now be 20·71 per cent. of 1000 mm. Hg. or 207 mm. Hg. and the partial pressure of the other gases will show similar rises—that of carbon dioxide becomes 0·4 mm. Hg. ; of water vapour becomes 12·5 mm. Hg.; of nitrogen becomes 780 mm. Hg. (The partial pressure of water vapour can rise, in this case, because the air is not saturated—*i.e.*, in equilibrium with liquid water.)

Or let us see what happens to an aviator flying at 21,000 feet, where the total atmospheric pressure is 335 mm. Hg. He is instructed to breathe oxygen from a cylinder. Let us assume that this is pure dry oxygen, so that 100 per cent. of the atmosphere that he is breathing is made up of oxygen. The oxygen partial pressure will therefore be equal to the total atmospheric pressure, that is, 335 mm. Hg. Examination of the dissociation curve for oxygen on p. 103 shows that a partial pressure of 100 mm. Hg. or more will saturate his blood with oxygen ; so that as long as this pilot breathes from the oxygen cylinder his blood will be fully oxygenated. If the pilot failed to apply his oxygen mask, at 21,000 feet the partial pressure of oxygen in his alveolar air would be only 39 mm. Hg. (this would correspond to 5·1 per cent. at sea-level, and he would rapidly lose consciousness from oxygen lack (see later, p. 156). Further illustrations of these points will be found in a later section.

Table IV. 1 gives the composition in volumes per cent. of the inspired air, the expired air and the alveolar air of a normal subject at rest, together with the partial pressures exerted by the constituent gases in the inspired and the alveolar air at a normal barometric pressure (760 mm. Hg). Figures are given both for the dry air at room temperature (18° C.) and for the air in its natural conditions, *i.e.*, the inspired air at 18° C. and 60 per cent. saturation with water vapour, and expired and alveolar air at 37° C. and 100 per cent. saturation with water vapour.

TABLE **IV.** 1

Composition of the Respiratory Gases

	Inspired Air.			Expired Air		Alveolar Air.		
	Dry. p.c.	Wet. p.c.	Wet. Pressure. mm.Hg.	Dry. p.c.	Wet. p.c.	Dry. p.c.	Wet. p.c.	Wet. Pressure. mm.Hg.
Oxygen . .	20·96	20·71	157	15·8	14·6	14·0	13·2	100
Carbon dioxide .	0·04	0·04	0·3	4·0	3·8	5·3	5·0	38·0
Water vapour .	0	1·25	9·5	0	6·2	0	6·2	47·1
Nitrogen . .	79·00	78·00	593	80·2	75·4	80·7	75·6	575

Roughly, then, expired air contains 15 per cent. oxygen and 4 per cent. carbon dioxide, while alveolar air contains 13 per cent. oxygen and 5 per cent. carbon dioxide. The exact figures will vary from one subject to another, even at rest, and will vary in any one subject according to circumstances ; the normal range of alveolar carbon dioxide pressures in different subjects being 32 to 44 mm. Hg. Only one point in this table needs special mention. It will be observed that there is a higher percentage of nitrogen in the dry expired air than there is in the dry inspired air ; this does not indicate an excretion of nitrogen, but is an expression of the fact, discussed in Chapter VI (p. 194), that the volume of carbon dioxide given out in any period is less than the volume of oxygen taken in. This results from the fact that some of the oxygen is used to oxidise the hydrogen contained in the foodstuffs to water, and its implications will be considered in a later chapter.

The Dead Space. The space of these parts of the respiratory tissues— the trachea, bronchi, bronchioles, etc.—which act as a conduit for the passage of gases to the pulmonary tissues is referred to as the *dead space* of the lungs. It is those parts of the respiratory passages which at the commencement of an expiration are filled with inspired air. Here there is no gaseous exchange. In quiet breathing it is approximately 150 c.c.

The volume of the dead space cannot be measured directly, but can easily be calculated. From Table IV. 1, we can take the following representative figures : (1) CO_2 in alveolar air ; 5·3 per cent. : (2) CO_2 in expired air ; 4·0 per cent. We will take the volume of tidal air as 600 c.c. (all measured dry and at room temperature). Then the total quantity of carbon dioxide expired in each breath is $\dfrac{600 \times 4 \cdot 0}{100} = 24$ c.c. But this quantity of carbon dioxide is contained in $24 \times \dfrac{100}{5 \cdot 3} = 450$ c.c. of alveolar air ; so that the 600 c.c. of expired air has the same composition as 450 c.c. of alveolar air mixed with 150 c.c. of inspired air, containing no carbon dioxide. The dead space consequently would have a volume of 150 c.c. It must be remembered that this is the volume of the gas in the dead space measured dry and at a lower temperature than that at which it was when in the body. But since we wish to measure the volume of a cavity within the body, we must correct this gas volume to body temperature (37° C.) and saturate with water vapour (47 mm. Hg). (For details see textbooks of practical human physiology.)

During deep breathing, a larger volume of air is hurried over some of the tissues which are normally concerned with gaseous exchange, and the dead space may rise to as much as 600 c.c. Thus the volume of the dead space as measured above, must not be regarded as constant either for all individuals, or even for one individual at different times. We have already remarked also that bronchial walls contain plain muscle which may be induced to contract and relax by a variety of agents and thus alter the capacity of the bronchial tree.

Methods of Recording the Respiration. Ideally, the record of the respiratory movements should allow us to discover (*a*) the frequency of respiration, (*b*) the depth of respiration and (*c*) the degree of expansion of the lungs at any moment, even if respiratory movements have stopped. There are only two ways in which this can be done. The first is to connect the mouth of the subject (or the tracheal cannula of an animal) with a spirometer, to remove continuously the carbon dioxide from the expired air, and to add oxygen to make up for that used in the metabolism—to make use, in fact, of exactly the same apparatus as is used for determining the metabolism, as will be described in a later chapter. The other way is to enclose the whole body, with the exception of the head, in an airtight box; the hole through which the head protrudes being sealed by a rubber collar around the neck. A spirometer connected with the box then records the respirations completely. An " iron lung " (p. 161) could be used for this purpose.

The simpler forms of apparatus for recording the respiration in man do not give accurate measurements of the total ventilation, but are useful, nevertheless, for many purposes. The *stethograph*, as now commonly used, consists of a piece of large diameter rubber tubing stoppered at both ends and connected with a tambour by a side tube at the centre; this is tied round the chest or abdomen, the movements of which distort it, and drive air into or out of the tambour. Many other devices for recording the movements of the chest or abdomen have also been described.

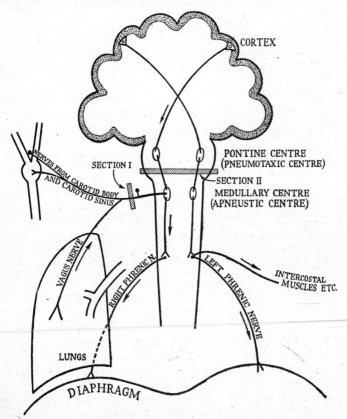

Fig. IV. 5. Diagrammatic Representation of the **Nervous Control of Breathing.**

The Nervous Control of Breathing

The nervous system controls and co-ordinates the activity of the respiratory muscles. In *quiet breathing* the respiratory centre sends impulses to the muscles responsible for inspiration. When these contract, expansion of the thorax and lungs takes place. Expiration in quiet breathing is largely a passive process during which the centre is quiescent and the inspiratory muscles relax. The rhythmic activity of the respiratory centre is an intrinsic property but it is influenced by afferent nervous mechanisms.

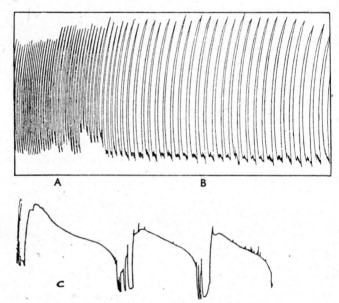

FIG. IV. 6. Respiratory Movements of a Cat, showing the **Different Types of Respiration.**

A. **Normal** respiratory movements (inspiration upwards).
B. The same after **Section of the Vagi.**
C. The **Apneustic** type, with prolonged inspiratory tonus.
Similar results are obtained after making sections across the brain stem, as indicated in Fig. IV. 5. (A and B after Taylor, C after Lumsden.)

The Respiratory Centre. This is not a discrete node but is built up mainly of two bilateral groups of neurones distributed in the pons and medulla. Breathing (in the dog and cat) may be unaffected by removal of nervous tissue above the pons, but respiratory activity ceases when all but the last third of the medulla is removed, and there is evidence that in man, also, the essential parts of the respiratory centre lie in the pons and upper two-thirds of the medulla.

Functionally, again, the respiratory centre has been shown to consist of two parts. The medullary centre (or apneustic centre) is mainly concerned with inspiratory activity, while the pontine centre (or pneumo-taxic centre (rhythmically inhibits this inspiratory activity and thus confers on the respiratory centre its intrinsic rhythmic activity.

The activity of the respiratory centre has been investigated by serial sections made from above the pons and continued below the medulla. Reflexes from the lungs themselves are first excluded by cutting the vagi nerves (see Fig. IV, 5 Section, I). Then the medullary centre was isolated from the pontine centre by a section below the pons (see Fig. IV. 5, Section II). These procedures isolated the medullary centre from all afferent inhibitory activity and resulted in the unimpeded domination of the inspiratory activity of the medullary group of neurones ; thus breathing became predominantly inspiratory in type. This mode of breathing is called apneustic breathing, and is characterised by long sustained periods in which the inspiratory position of the chest is maintained (see Fig. IV. 6). Apneustic breathing is due to the activity of the medullary centre and is not a reflex phenomenon.

Further attempts have been made to discover the exact localisation of the inspiratory and expiratory groups of cells. Pitts and his co-workers defined a small region in which carefully localised electrical stimulation produced maximum inspiration involving the thorax and diaphragm, which remained fixed in the position of maximum inspiration, and rhythmic breathing ceased. Comroe showed, in addition, that localised injections of a carbon dioxide—bicarbonate buffer solution at suitable points led to a normal hyperpnœa ; he was unable to produce maintained inspiration in this way.

For the sake of convenience, one often speaks of a centre in a certain portion of the brain stem when removal of that portion, or localised stimulation, alters the behaviour of the animal in a certain characteristic and uniform way. It may be that certain nerve cells are removed, or stimulated, but it may also be that a certain nerve tract is attacked, or that the normal flow of blood or cerebro-spinal fluid is interfered with, and it is often very difficult to get evidence that will decide which is the true explanation. These remarks apply as much to the vaso-motor " centre " and to the temperature regulating " centre " as to the respiratory " centre."

Descending pathways from the respiratory centre to the motor neurones of the respiratory muscles lie in the anterior and in the ventral part of the lateral columns. The centres are bilateral and inter-connected, but a mid-line section does not destroy respiratory movements, since each side then develops its own independent rhythm.

Afferent Nervous Mechanisms Influencing the Activity of the Respiratory Centre

There are four important afferent nervous mechanisms :

(1) The vagus nerves which carry impulses from stretch receptors in the lungs.

(2) The nerves which transmit impulses from chemo-receptor mechanisms of the carotid and aortic bodies.

(3) The nerves which transmit impulses from the pressor receptors in the carotid sinus and aorta.

(4) Afferent fibres carrying impulses from the limbs (see later).

The Part Played by Afferents from the Lungs in the Control of Breathing. Vagal afferent nerve endings are present in the bronchi and bronchioles. These nerve endings are sensitive to distension of the lungs, but are insensitive to changes in the partial pressures of oxygen and carbon dioxide.

In 1868 Hering and Breuer showed that interruption of breathing by blocking the respiratory passages during inspiration and expiration had marked effects upon the pattern of breathing, but that when the vagi nerves were cut, these effects were completely absent. A few years later in 1889, Head again demonstrated this reflex (now known as

A

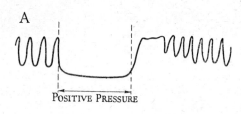

POSITIVE PRESSURE

B

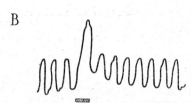

SUCTION OR NEGATIVE PRESSURE

FIG. IV. 7. Recordings of Contractions of a slip from the Diaphragm of a Rabbit.

A. Between the arrows a positive pressure was applied to the lungs. The contractions of the slip, and inspiratory movements, were inhibited.

B. A "momentary" diminution in the volume of the lungs (suction) was produced during normal respiration, as indicated. An increased contraction of the slip, *i.e.*, an increased inspiratory effort, resulted. (After Head.)

the Hering-Breuer reflex), by observing the effect of inflation of the lungs on the movements of the diaphragm in the rabbit. The rabbit is unique in that its diaphragm is so arranged that it is possible to separate that part which is attached to the ensiform cartilage from the remainder, without damaging the blood supply or nervous connections. The active movements of this strip follow exactly those of the remainder of the diaphragm, and can easily be recorded without interference from movements of the chest or diaphragm as a whole, whether active or passive. The essence of Head's results is shown in the accompanying Fig. IV. 7.

In the first tracing (A) a positive inflating pressure has been applied to the trachea, and it can be seen that while the pressure is applied the activity of the diaphragm is inhibited. In the lower figure (B) suction applied for a very short period causes an immediate contraction of the strip of the diaphragm. These effects were abolished when the vagus nerve connections were blocked.

In 1933 Adrian observed in the cat that action currents were set up in the vagus nerve by inflating the lungs, and that the rate of discharge of the impulses was roughly proportional to the degree of inflation (see Fig. IV. 8). When he recorded the impulses in a single vagal fibre from a cat during normal breathing, he observed that the frequency waxed and waned in rhythm with the inspiratory and expiratory phases of breathing (see Fig. IV. 9). The impulses from the lungs fell to zero at the

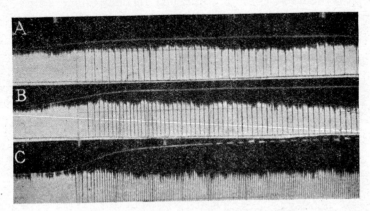

Fig. IV. 8.   Oscillograph Record of the **Action Potentials in the Vagus Nerve of a Spinal Cat.**

The nerve was cut high up in the neck, and subdivided with fine needles, after removal of the sheath, until only one active fibre remained.

At the top of the record are marks made by a time-signal every quarter second ; below this is a white line indicating the position of the lungs, a rise denoting inspiration ; at the bottom is the oscillograph record of the action potentials.

The lungs were inflated by a pump, and the frequency of the discharge of the sense organ increases as the inflation increases.

A. Inflation 65 c.c.   Maximum frequency of discharge 80 per sec.
B.   ,,   115 c.c.   ,,   ,,   ,,   120 ,,   ,,
C.   ,,   230 c.c.   ,,   ,,   ,,   250 ,,   ,,

(Adrian.)

completion of expiration. He also observed that no impulses were recorded when the lungs were deflated (except when such a deflation was far greater than could occur during any normal respiratory movements).

In 1914, the Hering-Breuer reflex was investigated in human subjects by Haldane during which the use of anæsthetics, with their depressing effects, was avoided. A subject breathed from a mouthpiece to which either a positive or a negative pressure could be applied, and the respiratory movements were recorded with a stethograph. The accompanying Fig. IV. 10 summarises the results of the experiments. When the lungs are distended with a positive pressure, expiratory activity takes place ; deflation, on the other hand, leads to inspiratory activity.

The function of these afferent impulses in the vagus nerve in normal breathing is to signal the depth of inspiration to the respiratory centre and allow expiration to take place, after an adequate tidal volume has ventilated the lungs. Double vagotomy in an otherwise intact animal removes this signal and thus the inspiratory phase is prolonged, and breathing becomes slower and deeper (see Fig. IV. 6); a normal ventilation rate, however, is maintained. Thus when the medullary inspiratory centre transmits its impulses to the inspiratory muscles, it is subjected to an afferent discharge from the lungs which progressively increases in intensity until it inhibits the inspiratory activity and initiates the expiratory phase, allowing the chest wall to collapse in a passive manner. Thus a cycle of (*a*) inspiratory activity and (*b*)

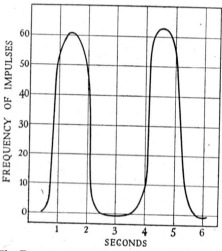

FIG. IV. 9. The **Frequency of the Impulses** in a single fibre of the Vagus nerve of a decerebrate cat during Normal Breathing. (Adrian.)

inspiratory inhibitory activity takes place during normal quiet breathing. It has already been pointed out that apneustic breathing occurs, and that rhythmic breathing ceases, when connections between the pontine and medullary centres are cut, together with section of the vagi nerves. If such a brain stem section is made when the vagi nerves are intact, rhythmic breathing will continue, due to the part the vagus nerve plays in the cycle of events just described.

To summarise : In *quiet breathing*, the respiratory centre initiates inspiratory activity. Afferent impulses in the vagus nerve signal the degree of expansion of the lungs. This afferent vagal discharge (which increases as inspiration progresses), inhibits the central inspiratory activity and thus the respiratory muscles relax and expiration takes place.

Afferent Nerves from the Chemoreceptors. The chemoreceptors are the carotid and aortic bodies, of which the carotid bodies are by far the more important. They are sensitive to changes in the partial pressures of oxygen and carbon dioxide in the blood, and play an important part in the regulation of the respiration. This will be considered in a later section (pp. 152 to 153).

The Influence of Changes in Blood Pressure on Breathing. These have been shown to be largely due to changes of blood pressure within the carotid sinus and aorta. By cross-circulation to an isolated carotid sinus with its nerve supply intact, it was found that a rise in pressure in the sinus inhibited breathing in the perfused animal and a fall stimulated breathing. Denervation of the sinus abolished these effects.

The accompanying tracing by Heymans, Fig. IV. 11, records the inhibitory effect of a rise in blood pressure on the movements of respiration. The recording of the respiratory movements (line A) are taken from the larnyx, since the head of the animal is united to the body only by the vagodepressor nerves. The blood pressure (line B) was recorded from the femoral

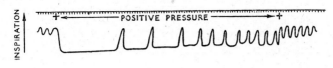

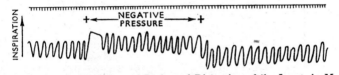

Fig. IV. 10.   A. The Effect of **Prolonged Distension of the Lungs** in Man by positive pressure.
B. The Effects of **Partial Deflation of the Lungs** in Man by negative pressure.   (Christiansen and Haldane.)

artery of the same animal. An arrow on the tracing records the point where an injection of adrenaline was given; this was followed by a rise in blood pressure and an inhibition of respiratory movements. This phenomenon could not have been due to a central effect since the blood supply to the head came from another source, *i.e.*, the donor animal. These pressor effects probably play a very minor *rôle* in the nervous control of breathing in the normal animal; they must not be confused with the very important part played by the carotid sinuses in the reflex regulation of the blood pressure (Chapter II). Students during the practical course in physiology will have observed the hyperpnœa that follows the inhalation of amyl nitrite. This is due in part to the depressing effect that this drug has on blood pressure.

Other Afferent Mechanisms in the Nervous Control of Breathing. Cutaneous sensation may play a part. Most of us have observed how a cold shower " takes our breath away."

Sneezing occurs as a result of irritation of the mucous membranes of the nasal passages by foreign bodies (*e.g.*, snuff), or by disease. The sensory nerve endings of the trigeminal nerve are involved.

Coughing occurs as a result of similar irritation of the mucous membranes of the pharynx, larynx, trachea and bronchi. The afferent pathway is in the glossopharyngeal nerve from the pharynx, and in the vagus nerve from the larynx, trachea and bronchi. The explosive quality of the act of coughing is the result of the initial closure of the vocal cords, which only open after the commencement of the expiratory phase.

The Mechanism of Gaseous Exchange between the Lungs and the Blood

In the lungs, carbon dioxide leaves the blood stream and enters the air in the lung alveoli, and oxygen leaves the alveoli, and enters the blood. In doing so, the gases have to pass through two membranes, the walls of the alveoli and the walls of the capillaries. The question

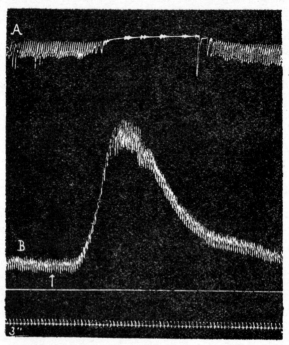

Fig. IV. 11. Inhibition of Respiration by a Rise in Blood Pressure.

A shows the respiratory movements (movements of the larynx) in the head of a dog ; this is united with the trunk only by the vagi nerves, and is perfused with blood from a second (donor) dog. (*Cf.* cross circulation experiments, Fig. II. 26, p. 67.)

B shows the blood pressure in the trunk of the dog with the isolated head. At the moment indicated by the arrow, 0·04 mg. adrenaline were injected.

The rise in blood pressure occurred in the aorta and peripheral circulation only, and not in the respiratory centre itself. The inhibition of the respiratory movements that occurred must have resulted from a reflex action through the vagi nerves. A similar result would be obtained if the changes in blood pressure occurred in the carotid sinus only. (Heymans and Heymans.)

before us at the moment is whether these membranes play an active part in promoting the passage of the gases through them (secretion), or whether they play only a passive part such as might be played by a non-living membrane (diffusion).

There is very little doubt that the partial pressure gradients of carbon dioxide and of oxygen between the incoming venous blood and the alveolar air, are such that carbon dioxide will diffuse from blood to air, and oxygen from air to blood. Representative values of the partial pressures concerned have already been given in Fig. **IV. 4** (p. **184**). If, however, it can be shown that, in any particular circumstances, the partial pressure gradients are reversed, then we must suppose that active secretion is taking place. Thus, if it can be shown that the partial pressure of oxygen in the alveoli is ever less than that in the arterial blood the oxygen must be carried from the one to the other by a process of secretion. The converse observation, that the partial pressure of oxygen in the alveoli is greater than that in the arterial blood, is not conclusive evidence in favour of diffusion, but it renders the hypothesis of secretion unnecessary.

The rate at which a gas will pass through a membrane by diffusion depends not only upon the difference in pressure on the two sides, but also on the solubility of the gas in the substance of the membrane. The solubility of carbon dioxide in watery solutions (and tissues), is very much greater than that of oxygen, and since it will be shown that diffusion is probably adequate to account for the passage of oxygen from the alveoli to the capillaries, it is even more probable that the same factor will account for the passage of carbon dioxide in the reverse direction, even though the pressure difference is less.

The partial pressure of oxygen in the arterial blood may be estimated in three ways, the principles of which are briefly as follows.

(1) The *Aerotonometer*. A very small volume of air is brought into equilibrium with a relatively large volume of blood, which has been withdrawn from the subject and made incoagulable without being allowed to come into contact with the air. The small bubble of air is then analysed, and since the actual amount of gas that has been exchanged with the blood is very small, the partial pressures of the gases in the bubble are sensibly the same as those originally in the blood.

(2) The percentage saturation of the blood with oxygen is determined on one portion of a sample withdrawn from the subject, and an oxygen dissociation curve is constructed on another portion ; the partial pressure of oxygen corresponding to the percentage saturation of the first portion can then be read off. Care must be taken, of course, that the dissociation curve is made at the same partial pressure of carbon dioxide as that in the first portion of the sample.

(3) The subject is made to breathe a gas mixture containing known partial pressures of oxygen and of carbon monoxide. The ratio of the concentrations of oxyhæmoglobin and of carboxy-hæmoglobin in the subject's arterial blood is determined either by the reversion spectroscope (Hartridge) or by comparison with mixtures of oxyhæmoglobin and carmine in dilute solution (Haldane). It is then assumed that no secretion of carbon monoxide can occur, and that the following relation holds in the blood.

$$\frac{[O_2Hb]}{[COHb]} = K \cdot \frac{p.O_2}{p.CO}$$

square brackets indicating concentrations. The value of the constant K can be determined *in vitro*, we know the value of p.CO and the value of the ratio on the left side of the equation ; we can thus calculate the value of p.O_2.

The results of the determinations made on man under normal conditions all showed that the partial pressure of oxygen in the arterial blood is very close to that in the alveolar air, and left the question more or less undecided. The next step was to make similar measurements under conditions of diminishing oxygen supply to the lungs, by ascending to high altitudes, for example, or breathing mixtures of air and nitrogen, on the assumption that if the alveolar walls were at all capable of secreting oxygen they would do so most vigorously when oxygen was relatively scarce. The earlier work of the Oxford school (Haldane and co-workers) on the summit of Pike's Peak (14,000 ft.), indicated quite clearly that the arterial oxygen pressure (as measured by the carbon monoxide method and carmine titration), could exceed the alveolar oxygen pressure, so that secretion must have been taking place. Later work of Barcroft and his co-workers at Cambridge in an atmosphere corresponding to that at a height of 18,000 feet, and using arterial puncture and an ærotonometer, failed to confirm this. Barcroft's views have since been confirmed by Dill and his collaborators, the average of a series of analyses in ten subjects at 17,500 feet showing no significant difference between the pressure of the oxygen in the lungs and that in the arterial blood (see Table IV. 2). In the mountains of the Andes, moreover, there are natives who for many generations have lived all their lives at a high altitude, but whose arterial blood has a low saturation with oxygen. Even they, apparently, have not been able to secrete oxygen in their lungs very effectively, if at all.

TABLE IV. 2

Partial Pressures of Oxygen in Alveolar Air and in Arterial Blood at a Height of 17,500 feet

Subject.	Alveolar.	Arterial.	Difference.
	mm. Hg.	mm. Hg.	mm. Hg.
B	41·5	43·0	− 1·5
C	45·7	41·7	+ 4·0
D	37·4	37·6	− 0·2
E	41·3	39·9	+ 1·4
F	42·6	44·1	− 1·5
H	43·1	43·4	− 0·3
K	44·7	43·7	+ 1·0
M	41·6	43·7	− 2·1
Mc	47·5	50·4	− 2·9
T	37·8	43·7	− 5·9
Average	42·3	43·1	− 0·8

It must be admitted, however, that no definite source of error has been found which will account for the observations of the Oxford school ; they may yet be shown to be correct. Indeed, an apparent secretion of oxygen has also been observed by Killick, using the carbon monoxide method, in conditions of negligible oxygen lack. It would appear that breathing carbon monoxide may have effects which are not entirely explained.

One further point requires consideration in this connection. It is clear that the amount of oxygen which will diffuse through the alveolar walls in a given time under a given pressure head (difference between alveolar oxygen pressure and blood oxygen pressure) will depend upon the total area available for diffusion, the thickness of the walls, and other factors, all of which are grouped together under the term " diffusion constant." Several attempts have been made to estimate the value of this constant, but none of them is entirely free from objection on technical grounds. It is likely, however, that the figures arrived at are too low, and since they are just large enough, even as they stand, to allow the requisite quantity of oxygen to be carried across by diffusion, except in the case of a few of the experiments carried out at high altitudes, there does not appear to be any necessity to assume the presence of secretory activity on this ground.

The Regulation of Breathing

The Chemical Control. The predominant factor in the chemical control of breathing is the sensitivity of the respiratory centre to changes in the carbon dioxide pressure of its blood supply. Normal breathing in the resting subject continues its even tenor so long as the carbon dioxide pressure in the alveolar air and so in the arterial blood leaving the lungs, remains constant. If the carbon dioxide pressure falls below this level breathing is inhibited, until carbon dioxide accumulation once more restores it to the normal value. On the other hand, a rise in the partial pressure of the alveolar carbon dioxide acts as a respiratory stimulant and once more the pulmonary ventilation is so organised that the normal alveolar partial pressure of carbon dioxide is maintained. The part played by oxygen in the chemical control of breathing is, at sea level, a relatively minor one.

The Maintenance of a Constant Partial Pressure of Carbon Dioxide in the Alveolar Air. The manner in which the respiratory centre responds to carbon dioxide and maintains a constant partial pressure of carbon dioxide in the alveolar air can be demonstrated by the addition of small supplements of carbon dioxide to the inspired air. The results of one such experiment are given below.

Examination of this table shows that in the particular subject investigated, the breathing of a mixture containing as much as 3·07 per cent. carbon dioxide failed to cause the alveolar carbon dioxide percentage to rise measurably ; the ventilation rate, however, was trebled. However, when he breathed mixtures containing 5·14 per cent. carbon dioxide and over, the mechanism whereby the alveolar carbon dioxide pressure was maintained constant was overwhelmed, and the carbon dioxide percentage in the alveolar air rose. According to Haldane, a rise of 0·2 per cent. of an atmosphere, or 1·5 mm. Hg, in the alveolar

Table IV. 3

Effect of Carbon Dioxide in Inspired Air on Pulmonary Ventilation and Composition of Alveolar Air.

CO_2 inspired, p.c.	Pulm. Vent. in litres per min.	CO_2 in alveolar air. p.c.
0·04	9·4	5·6
0·79	10·3	5·5
2·02	13·0	5·6
3·07	19·2	5·5
5·14	33·6	6·2
6·02	56·8	6·6

carbon dioxide pressure, normally causes an increase of 100 per cent. in the alveolar ventilation.

That carbon dioxide is of greater importance than oxygen in the control of breathing can be demonstrated by rebreathing air from a small rubber bag. The results of one such experiment were as follows. The rebreathing was carried out until marked hyperpnœa was experienced. At this point the bag was found to contain 5·5 per cent. carbon dioxide and 14·5 per cent. oxygen. The rebreathing was now repeated and the accumulation of carbon dioxide was prevented by its absorption in soda lime. The rebreathing in this second instance was continued until the

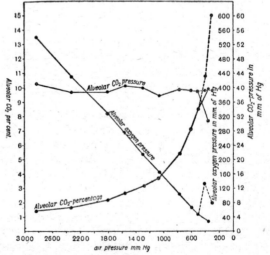

Fig. IV. 12. The effect of Alterations in the Barometric Pressure on the Pressure of Carbon Dioxide, the percentage of Carbon Dioxide, and the pressure of Oxygen in the Alveolar Air of a Man.

Note the constancy of the carbon dioxide pressure, and that the excitant effects of oxygen lack are not seen until the atmospheric pressure falls below 500 mm. Hg. (Boycott and Haldane.)

subject was cyanosed. It was found that the percentage of oxygen had fallen to 8 and yet no very marked increase in pulmonary ventilation had developed.

The importance of the *partial pressure* of carbon dioxide rather than its percentage, already mentioned on p. 134, can be seen by examination of Fig. IV. 12. Here can be seen the effect of alterations in the barometric pressure both above and below the normal value, on the alveolar pressure

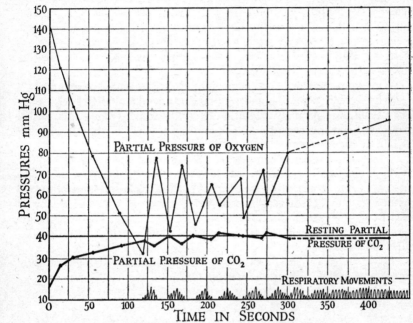

FIG. IV. 13. The effect of **Voluntary Hyperpnœa** on the Composition of the Alveolar Air and on the Frequency and Depth of Respiration.

Voluntary hyperpnœa was carried out for two minutes before the beginning of the record. Note that the first group of respirations begins at a moment when the alveolar carbon dioxide pressure is definitely less than the normal value, owing to the low value of the alveolar oxygen pressure. Similarly, respirations cease before the alveolar oxygen pressure has reached the normal value, owing to the low alveolar carbon dioxide pressure, the result being the production of **Periodic (Cheyne-Stokes) Respiration.** (Douglas and Haldane.)

and percentage of carbon dioxide, and on the alveolar pressure of oxygen It will be observed that while the alveolar oxygen pressure falls steadily as the atmospheric pressure falls, as might be expected, the percentage of carbon dioxide rises steadily and in such a way as to maintain the alveolar carbon dioxide pressure constant. This relation breaks down when the atmospheric pressure falls below 500 mm. Hg (corresponding to an altitude of about 10,000 feet and an oxygen pressure of 14 per cent. of an atmosphere), owing to the stimulating action of oxygen lack.

The Effect on Breathing of a Reduction in the Partial Pressure of the Carbon Dioxide in the Alveolar Air. A fall in the carbon dioxide partial

pressure in the lungs can be brought about by forced breathing. If the
subject is suitable a tracing of his respiratory movements will follow a
pattern similar to that in Fig. IV. 13. In this figure, there are three
graphs. The lowest is a tracing of the respiratory movements; the
upper and middle curves represent the pressures of the oxygen and
the carbon dioxide in the alveolar air. The heavy line represents the
resting alveolar carbon dioxide pressure. It can be seen from examination of the respiratory tracing that the period of forced breathing was
followed by cessation of breathing (apnœa). Then followed a period
during which a few breaths were taken, and then a second apnœic
period. This " periodic breathing " continued with shortening periods
of apnœa until normal breathing was resumed. Amongst the interesting
questions which we have to answer are :—

Why are respiratory movements inhibited after forced breathing ?

Why is there a waxing and waning rhythm or periodicity ?

The period of respiratory inhibition or apnœa which followed the period
of forced breathing was due to the inhibitory effect of the low alveolar
carbon dioxide pressure, for the following reasons.

(1) During the forced breathing, the carbon dioxide was washed out
of the lungs and its pressure was lowered. Examination of the curve
in Fig. IV. 13, representing the changes in the alveolar pressure of carbon
dioxide, demonstrates that in this subject after the period of forced
breathing, the carbon dioxide pressure fell to 15 mm. Hg—well below
his normal pressure of 40 mm. Hg—and thus exerted an inhibitory
effect on breathing.

(2) If such a subject repeats the forced breathing with a gas mixture
containing carbon dioxide (approximately 4·5 per cent.), apnœa will
not develop since the alveolar carbon dioxide pressure remains at
approximately the resting value.

(3) It can be shown that the rise in alveolar oxygen pressure is not
to blame, since gas mixtures containing a high percentage of oxygen
have no inhibitory effect on breathing.

The explanation of the " periodic breathing " is as follows. (For
further notes on " periodic breathing " see later, p. 154.) During the
first period of apnœa, the oxygen pressure fell to a level where it acted as
a respiratory stimulus, despite the fact that the carbon dioxide pressure
was still below normal, and would thus have exerted an inhibitory
influence. It was to satisfy this oxygen want that the subject began to
breathe again. (The student will have no doubt about the part that
oxygen lack plays, when he carries out the experiment himself, for if
he watches a subject in whom apnœa has lasted over half a minute,
he may observe the development of cyanosis—blueing of lips, etc., due
to an increase in the amount of reduced hæmoglobin). A few breaths
sufficed to satisfy the oxygen requirements, so that once again the low
alveolar carbon dioxide pressure could exert its inhibitory influence,
and thus a second apnœic period followed. This periodicity continued
until the alveolar pressures of oxygen and carbon dioxide returned to
normal.

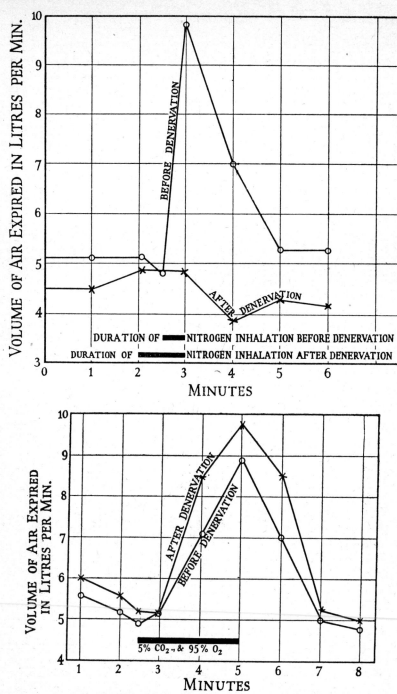

Fig. IV. 14. The effect of **Denervation of the Carotid Sinuses** on the **Respiratory Response** of an unanæsthetised dog to inhalation of Nitrogen and of Carbon Dioxide. Both experiments were on the same animal. (Germill and Reeves.)

The Part Played by the Sino-Aortic Reflex Mechanisms in the Control of the Respiration. The respiratory response of an animal to the administration of carbon dioxide in the inspired air is sensibly unchanged by denervation of the reflex mechanisms in the carotid and aortic bodies, as is indicated in Fig. IV. 14. The reflex mechanisms, therefore, play only a small part in the control of the respiration by changes in the carbon dioxide pressure. More refined studies, however, both of the action potentials in the nerves supplying the carotid bodies, and on the effects of perfusion with blood containing various partial pressures of carbon dioxide, have shown that the reflex mechanisms are, in fact, active even under normal conditions. They thus add appreciably to the response of the respiratory centre when the changes in the carbon dioxide pressure are relatively small, but become " saturated," as it were, and have proportionately little effect, when these changes are large.

Administration of gas mixtures containing less oxygen than atmospheric air, only increases the ventilation rate so long as functioning reflex mechanisms are present (Fig. IV. 14) ; indeed, lack of oxygen has mainly a depressant action on the respiratory centre itself, although some stimulation action has been observed in special circumstances. In the absence of carotid and aortic bodies, therefore, lack of oxygen results in a reduction of the ventilation rate. Careful study, again, has indicated that in experimental animals, the reflex mechanisms are just active under normal conditions of oxygen pressure in the blood. Breathing gas mixtures containing 40 per cent. oxygen suppresses this activity, and breathing mixtures containing 18 per cent. oxygen increases it. There is some doubt as to whether this is true in man ; some individuals respond to moderate reductions in the alveolar oxygen pressure, and others do not. There may, therefore, be individual variations in the relative magnitudes of the reflex excitation and the central depression, produced by lack of oxygen in the blood.

It is important to remember that the central and reflex mechanisms for regulating the respiration are integrated with one another in such a way as to remove just so much carbon dioxide as is being produced in the body, and to supply just so much oxygen as is being used. Removal of the reflex mechanisms will not necessarily produce an obvious change in the ventilation rate ; but the absence of the additional stimulus due to the presence of carbon dioxide, or to a deficit of oxygen, in the carotid bodies, may result merely in a small rise in the alveolar carbon dioxide pressure, which acts as an increased stimulus to the respiratory centre itself.

The Mode of Action of Carbon Dioxide and Oxygen on the Respiratory Centre. The delicacy of the response of the respiratory centre to a change in the carbon dioxide pressure in the alveolar air was demonstrated many years ago by Haldane and his co-workers. Winterstein, later, suggested that the stimulating effect was not due to the presence of carbon dioxide as such, but to the associated rise in hydrogen ion concentration. Mellanby and others, however, found that in animals, injection of lactic acid and sodium bicarbonate caused considerable changes in the acidity of the blood and relatively small changes in breathing, while inhalation of carbon dioxide caused a large increase in pulmonary ventilation and little effect on the hydrogen ion concentration of the blood. In man, also, it has been found that ingestion of ammonium chloride results in a smaller increase in ventilation for a given change in blood acidity than does inhalation of carbon dioxide. In order to account for these, and other, observations, Gesell pointed out that it was probably the hydrogen ion concentration of the cell interior which was responsible for the control of the activity of the respiratory centre, rather than that of the blood ; it is known that the two may differ appreciably, not only as a result of the metabolism of the cell itself, but also as a result of the presence of indiffusible electrolytes within the cell (this latter point was discussed in connection with the red blood cell in Chapter III, p. 88).

Now carbon dioxide is known to penetrate cell membranes very rapidly, whereas ions such as HCO_3^- and H^+ pass through some hundreds, or even thousands, of times more slowly, and may, indeed, be incapable of penetrating at all. A change in the partial pressure of carbon dioxide in the blood, therefore, would change the conditions within the neurones of the respiratory centre or the carotid body very rapidly ; whereas a change in the concentration of HCO_3^- or H^+ ions would only gradually reach the cell interior. A complete study of the problem, however, cannot be made without quantitative data, much of which is not yet available. It can be stated as reasonably certain at the moment, that the activity of the respiratory centre is determined by a combination of the partial pressure of carbon dioxide, and of the concentration of either bicarbonate or hydrogen ions (the two are interrelated), within the neurones or in their close vicinity. The problem is one of great complexity, particularly since it has been shown that acetyl-choline undoubtedly plays some part in the excitation of the respiratory centre, as it does in the excitation of so many other neurones ; but its exact relation to the pressure of carbon dioxide is not known.

The mode of action of oxygen is even more speculative. Its depressant action on the respiratory centre might be due to a reduction in the oxidative metabolism, and hence of carbon dioxide production, by the neurones themselves. Alternatively, it is well known that the semipermeable properties of the cell membranes are only maintained in the presence of an adequate oxygen supply ; isolated nerves, for example, lose their excitability in the absence of oxygen, although a much more complete lack of oxygen is needed than that which is sufficient to affect the respiratory centre. The stimulating action of oxygen lack on the carotid bodies might be due to the production of lactic acid by sensitive cells, instead of carbon dioxide. The lactate ions would diffuse out very much more slowly than the corresponding amount of carbon dioxide, and the hydrogen ion concentration of the cells would thus be increased.

The Effects of Low Pressures of Oxygen

Reduction of the partial pressure of oxygen in the inspired air may result from the addition of an inert gas such as nitrogen or hydrogen or to a fall in the total atmospheric pressure such as occurs when a subject ascends to a high altitude. Whatever the cause, it will produce a fall in the partial pressure of oxygen in the alveolar air and in the arterial blood so that the tissues will suffer from lack of oxygen, or anoxia. The physiological effects produced by anoxia are important both for the mountaineer and for the aviator.

Acclimatisation to Oxygen Lack. (The mountain climber.) When a mountaineer climbs slowly to a high altitude, changes take place, both in his respiration and in his blood circulation, which are directed towards ensuring an adequate delivery of oxygen to the tissues. This process of adaptation is called *acclimatisation*. Signs of oxygen want appear at a height of about 10,000 feet, and the limit which has been reached by man, without additional oxygen, even after acclimatisation, is about 28,000 feet (close to the summit of Mount Everest). We shall first examine the changes in hæmo-respiratory functions and the process of acclimatisation in a subject who climbs to an altitude of at least 14,000 feet and remains there.

External respiration. The first line of defence against oxygen lack at high altitudes is an increase in pulmonary ventilation, and this increase remains even after acclimatisation is complete. The result of this is that the pressure of oxygen in the alveolar air is kept as high as possible. It is those subjects who can produce the greatest increase in pulmonary ventilation, who suffer least from anoxia and altitude sickness. One of the effects of this hyperpnœa is a fall in the alveolar carbon dioxide pressure, as is shown in Figs. IV. 12 and IV. 16.

The results of a series of investigations made on persons who were permanently resident at high altitudes, indicate that the alveolar oxygen pressure falls in proportion to the increase in height, and judging from these results, the oxygen partial pressure at 28,000 feet in an acclimatised subject would be approximately 25 mm. Hg. A sample of alveolar air collected at 22,700 feet had a carbon dioxide pressure of 19·3 mm. Hg, and an oxygen pressure of 38·8 mm. Hg. These figures may be compared with those given for unacclimatised persons in Fig. IV. 16 ; it will be noted that acclimatisation results in an appreciable increase in the oxygen pressure, but in little change in the carbon dioxide pressure. The fall in carbon dioxide pressure will disturb the normal ratio $H_2CO_3/BHCO_3$ in the blood (see Chapter III) and so increase its alkalinity. This alkalæmia is compensated by an excretion of less acid in the urine so that a stable and normal alkalinity of the blood is maintained.

The low carbon dioxide pressure exerts an inhibitory effect on breathing. The low oxygen pressure, however, acts as a stimulus, and the combination produces a " periodic " type of breathing, which disappears when acclimatisation is complete. It should be added that Haldane considered that part of the mechanism responsible for acclimatisation was oxygen secretion. This has already been dealt with (see p. 150).

The circulation. The circulatory system assists in the process of acclimatisation to high altitudes, mainly by an increase in the oxygen carrying power of the blood. There is also the possibility of a redistribution of the circulating blood, so that the more vital tissues will receive a priority of supply ; some workers consider this an important factor, although evidence for it is lacking. *The cardiac output* increases during the initial period of acclimatisation, but returns to its sea-level value as the hæmoglobin concentration rises. The increase in the oxygen carrying power of the blood is achieved by a parallel increase in the concen-

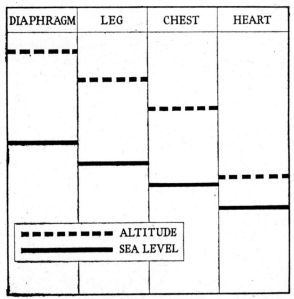

Fɪɢ. IV. 15.   Muscle Hæmoglobin **(Myoglobin)** Concentration in various tissues of the dog at sea level and **at high altitudes.**   (Hurtado and others.)

trations of hæmoglobin and of red blood cells.   Permanent residents at high altitudes have counts of 6,000,000 to 8,000,000 cells per cu. mm. and a total oxygen content which may be higher than that of dwellers at sea level, in spite of the fact that the hæmoglobin is not fully saturated. The increase in red cell count is an indication of the increase in oxygen capacity of the blood.

The hæmoglobin is not modified in any way to facilitate the transport of oxygen ; even under the conditions obtaining within the body, hæmoglobin obtained from a dweller at 20,000 feet cannot be distinguished from that of a subject living at sea level.

Changes in internal respiration.   As we shall see in Chapter IX, mammalian skeletal muscle contains a respiratory pigment, myoglobin, which transfers oxygen from the tissue fluids to the cellular oxidative enzymes, in the same way as the hæmoglobin in the blood transfers oxygen from the alveolar air to the tissue fluids. Myoglobin, however, is specially suited to operating at low partial pressures of oxygen, as is indicated in Fig. III. 4. Just as in the blood, the concentration of hæmoglobin is increased during acclimatisation to low barometric pressures, so also is the concentration of myoglobin in the muscles. The same quantity of oxygen can thus be carried even though the maximum saturation is less. It can be seen from Fig. IV. 15 that the myoglobin concentration in the diaphragm of a dog born and brought up at high altitudes is almost double that in the diaphragm of a dog living at sea level.

The oxygen saturation of the venous blood of subjects suffering from sub-acute mountain sickness is higher than that of the acclimatised dweller. This is due to the fact that the tissues of the mountain-sick subject fail to take up as much oxygen from the blood as those of the native, so that the latter may have an arterio-venous oxygen difference of 60 mm. Hg while that of the former may be only 40 mm. Hg. The mechanism responsible is not known, but may possibly be related to an increase in myoglobin concentration.

Acute Oxygen Lack in the Aviator. It has already been pointed out that the climber who ascends slowly and has time in which to become acclimatised has been able to reach heights of 28,000 feet (Everest). When an aircraft pilot climbs rapidly, there is no time for these processes to take place and it is, therefore, impossible for him to reach such altitudes without the use of oxygen. Should he expose himself to the atmosphere at 25,000 feet for as long as 10 minutes, he is likely to die.

The effects of oxygen want in the aviator first show themselves at about 5,000 feet, by increased breathing. Above 12,000 feet, mental and physical functions are impaired and over-confidence develops. At 18,000 feet, circulatory changes occur, producing an increase in pulse rate and blood pressure. The senses of touch, pain, vision and hearing are impaired. At these altitudes the flyer may observe how much brighter the day appears and how much louder the engines sound when he breathes from his oxygen mask. Between the heights of 18,000 and 30,000 feet, unconsciousness—which is sudden in onset and without warning—followed by paralysis and death, may occur.

The effects of oxygen lack are affected by bodily activity. During quiet walking oxygen consumption may be three times that of the resting individual, and the pilot should, therefore, reduce his movements to a minimum. It is a common complaint by the captain of a bomber aircraft who orders one of his men to walk to the tail of the aircraft that the mental effects of oxygen lack result in the messenger, when half way there, forgetting entirely the nature of his mission and failing to carry it out. It is always advisable for a pilot to remain connected with an oxygen supply when above 10,000 feet. At very high altitudes, failure to breathe oxygen may cause irreparable damage to the central nervous system. Brain cells exposed to oxygen lack for one minute may be permanently damaged.

The changes that occur in the pressures of the lung gases in the high altitude flyer can be seen in Fig. IV. 16. The alveolar air pressures shown were taken at heights up to 25,000 feet, under conditions where oxygen was not inhaled; 25,000 feet is the highest altitude to which a subject can fly without the use of oxygen. The top curve represents the partial pressure of oxygen in the atmosphere; the next curve represents the oxygen saturation of the blood in the lungs; and the third curve represents the partial pressure of oxygen in the alveoli. This last curve does not follow a parallel course to that of the atmospheric

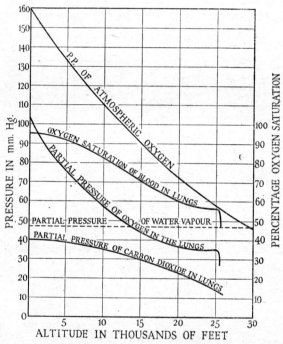

Fig. IV. 16. Curves showing the partial pressure of the atmospheric oxygen; the oxygen saturation of the blood passing through the lungs; the partial pressure of the oxygen in the lungs; and the partial pressure of the carbon dioxide in the lungs; at all altitudes between sea level and 30,000 feet. (After Grow and Armstrong, from "Fit to Fly.")

oxygen pressure because of the hyperventilation caused by the low oxygen pressure; for the same reason the carbon dioxide pressure (bottom curve), falls, instead of remaining constant. The horizontal parallel line represents the water vapour pressure in the lungs which remains constant at 47 mm. Hg (compare the remarks on p. 135 above). Consequently, if an altitude were reached at which the total atmospheric pressure was 47 mm. Hg, the body fluids would boil. This altitude is about 63,000 feet, and the lung gases would then consist solely of steam. The constancy of the lung water vapour pressure causes it to be an increasing handicap and obstacle to normal respiratory function, as the pilot ascends. At a height of approximately 50,000 feet the lungs would be entirely filled with carbon dioxide and water vapour and the altitude record for a pilot in an open cockpit, and breathing oxygen from a mask, is 47,358 feet. An altitude of 33,000 feet is the limit to which a pilot who is breathing oxygen can fly and still maintain a normal pressure of oxygen in his lungs.

The influence of the inhalation of oxygen on its pressure in the lungs and its saturation in the blood may be seen in Fig. IV. 17, where one line represents the partial pressure of oxygen in the lungs, and the

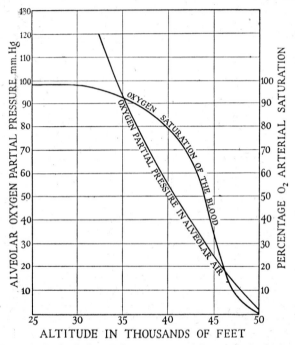

Fig. IV. 17. The variation of the oxygen partial pressure in the lungs and the oxygen saturation of the blood with altitude, during ascent from 33,000 feet to 50,000 feet while breathing pure oxygen.
(After Grow and Armstrong, from " Fit to Fly.")

other, the oxygen saturation of the blood. (The shape of this curve is due to the nature of the dissociation curve.)

The rarefied atmosphere at high altitudes produces certain mechanical effects upon the body (apart from the respiratory effects due to the low oxygen pressure). The necessary hyperventilation is easy because of the low pressure on the chest wall. Speech has a nasal quality, which is partly due to the inability of the rarefied atmosphere to vibrate the vocal chords. Foreign bodies can only be expelled with difficulty, and a cough fails to dislodge particles from the respiratory mucous membranes, so that the cause of the coughing remains and pilots under these circumstances are subjected to continuous irritation. The low barometric pressure causes distension of abdominal organs, which contain gas ; this may cause pain and discomfort. Severe frontal sinus pain may develop for the same reason.

The Effects of High Pressures of Oxygen

Gas mixtures containing up to 60 per cent. of oxygen may be inhaled without danger. Pure oxygen at four atmospheres pressure produces signs and symptoms of oxygen poisoning which include convulsions and a fall of blood pressure. These may be due to the increased amount of oxygen dissolved in the blood, so that when the blood passes through the tissues, less oxygen is lost from combination with hæmoglobin. As we have seen in Chapter II, hæmoglobin becomes more acid when it combines with oxygen and is, therefore, less ready to surrender base for carbon dioxide combination. This results in a reduction in the amount of carbon dioxide removed from the tissues so that the effects of oxygen excess may be due to accumulation of carbon dioxide in the tissues. On the other hand, if this is the correct explanation, the carbon dioxide pressure should rise in the venous blood ; this has not yet been demonstrated. Again, it is well-known that high concentrations of carbon dioxide exert a narcotic effect, and are, therefore, unlikely to lead to convulsions. The explanation of the phenomenon of oxygen poisoning has yet to be elucidated.

Conditions under which the Lungs Fail to Oxygenate the Blood

There are two important ways in which the supply of oxygen from the atmosphere to the blood in the body may become inadequate : first, the circulation of blood through the alveoli may be reduced, and, secondly, the passage of oxygen from the air in the alveoli to the blood flowing in their walls may become obstructed.

The circulation of blood through the lungs will be retarded if the cardiac output is diminished by failure of the heart (see p. 42) ; if so, the blood leaves the lungs fully oxygenated (there is no " arterial anoxæmia "), but the yield of oxygen by the scanty blood supply to the organs may not be enough to meet their requirements, and the oxygen content of the venous blood will be abnormally low. Inhalation of oxygen instead of air can only increase the quantity of oxygen in the blood by increasing the quantity in physical solution. Since this normally only represents about 2 per cent. of the total, it is clear that no marked increase in the supply of oxygen to the tissues is to be expected. The circulation of blood through the lungs may be retarded even with a normal output of the heart, if some of that output does not pass through the alveoli ; in congenital disease of the heart, some of the blood may pass direct from one side of the heart to the other by way of a defective interventricular septum, or a patent foramen ovale, and thereby escape passage through the lungs altogether (see p. 302). The arterial supply to the body is thus derived only in part from blood that has been oxygenated in the lungs, so that the mixed arterial blood will be deficient in oxygen. This condition of arterial anoxæmia, due to a " venous short circuit," cannot be appreciably mitigated by inhalation of oxygen, because that part of the blood which passes through the lungs is, as we have seen, practically fully oxygenated when the partial pressure of oxygen in the alveoli is only that of the atmosphere. A functional venous short circuit occurs also at certain stages of some pulmonary diseases. In the early stages of lobar pneumonia, for example, exudate may prevent access of air to the alveoli, though blood is still flowing through the capillaries in their walls. In pulmonary tuberculosis, on the other hand, the blood clots in the vessels leading to the affected regions, and there is no venous short circuit and no arterial anoxæmia, since the reserves of the lungs are so great that a considerable proportion of lung tissue can cease to function without detectable impairment of respiration. We may mention, in passing, that the occlusion of the blood vessels leading to the affected regions is not necessarily followed by the death of the tissue, because it still receives its blood supply from the bronchial arteries (derived from the systemic, not the pulmonary, circulation).

The second class of failure of respiratory function of the lung includes those conditions in which there is an adequate pulmonary circulation, but the blood is inadequately oxygenated. This is commonly due to œdema of the lungs, to the thickening of the alveolar walls associated with inflammatory processes, and to the reduction of the diffusion surface, characteristic, for example, of emphysema. If the gas in the alveoli is separated from the blood by an abnormally thick wall or by œdema fluid, it will diffuse more slowly than usual ; but since the rate of diffusion depends on the gradient of oxygen pressure, it can be very considerably increased by inhalation of oxygen instead of air. If an arterial anoxæmia is due to such circumstances, therefore, it can be remedied by administration of pure oxygen. The beneficial effect of breathing oxygen in pneumonia, for example, is attributed to the increased uptake of oxygen in those parts of the lungs which, though not consolidated, are impaired by the presence of œdema and thickened alveolar walls. Similarly, failure of the left heart leads to a rise in pulmonary venous pressure, and hence to the formation of œdema fluid and often to a thickening of the alveolar walls ; this condition can also be alleviated by the administration of oxygen.

Shallow Breathing. The resistance of the lungs to distension is not uniform throughout, and the parts around the roots where the bronchi and the large blood vessels enter, are more easily distended than are the more distal parts in contact with the pleura. The lungs, therefore, do not expand uniformly and simultaneously all over, but open up lobe by lobe ; their motion has been likened to the opening of a Japanese fan, rather than to the distension of a toy balloon. If, for any reason, such as asthma or adhesions of the lungs to the chest walls, the act of breathing gives rise to severe discomfort, or even pain, the depth is voluntarily made as small as possible. In extreme cases of such " shallow breathing " some parts of the lungs may be inadequately ventilated. The blood flow appears to become redistributed, however, and anoxæmia does not always occur. Administration of carbon dioxide assists in reducing the anoxæmia, if it is present, owing to its effect in increasing the depth of the respirations.

Asphyxia

The behaviour of an animal when its normal respiratory exchange is seriously interfered with, as by closing the respiratory passages by clamping the trachea or other means (throttling), or by making it rebreathe its own expired air (suffocation), is of some importance. At first, the effect is to produce hypernœa of the normal type, but as the alveolar carbon dioxide pressure rises and the oxygen pressure falls, the respiratory efforts become more and more violent, especially during expiration, and the animal loses consciousness. The second stage is reached when these efforts spread throughout the body ; there is a general excitation of the sympathetic system, the blood pressure rises owing to cardiac acceleration and vaso-constriction, and practically every muscle in the body takes part in the fight for breath. Soon, however, this gives way to the third stage, that of exhaustion, the medullary centres are *in extremis*, the respiration is reduced to a series of violent inspiratory gasps, the blood pressure falls, mainly due to failure of the asphyxiated heart, the pupils become dilated, and no reflexes can be elicited. Four or five minutes later, the heart stops and the animal is dead.

Artificial Respiration

There are many circumstances in which respiratory movements cease temporarily. Death will follow from asphyxia unless fresh oxygen can be supplied, and the excess carbon dioxide washed out, by some means of artificial ventilation of the lungs. The cause of the respiratory failure can often be removed in this way, and complete recovery results. Common instances of such circumstances are drowning, electric shock, asphyxia from smoke, etc., in fires, carbon monoxide poisoning, certain diseases of the central nervous system which result in paralysis of the respiratory muscles, and the failure to breathe of the new-born.

Artificial respiration may be performed (1) by blowing air into the lungs, (2) by distending the thoracic cavity by applying suction to the outside of the thorax or abdomen, or both, and (3) by compressing the thoracic cavity, either directly by pressure on the ribs, or indirectly by pressure on the abdominal contents and so on the diaphragm. Respiration may sometimes be induced, also, as a result of the nervous reflex set up by pulling out the tongue or applying some other painful stimulus.

The first method is now generally used for animal experiments, and, sometimes, as mouth to mouth breathing, in the new-born. The second method is the most physiological, since inspiration is the active muscular phase of normal respiration, and the expiratory position is the position of rest ; it requires comparatively complicated apparatus such as that of Drinker and Shaw (the " Iron Lung ").

The Drinker and Shaw apparatus consists of a large cylindrical chamber with a lid at one end. The patient is placed in the chamber with his head protruding through a hole in the lid, a tight seal being made around his neck by means of a rubber ring. A powerful pump creates a partial vacuum within the chamber, and a valve releases it every ten seconds or so ; the chest is thus rhythmically expanded, and the lungs ventilated.

The third method is effective by reason of the fact that, as we have seen, the lungs, in the normal expiratory position, still contain a considerable quantity of air ; some of this can be expelled by pressure on the abdomen. This compresses the abdominal contents against the diaphragm, which is pressed into the thoracic cavity. Inspiration is due, partly to the recoil of the ligaments and cartilages, and partly to the nervous reflex set up by the expiration. This method is largely used in emergencies, as it has the greatest combination of simplicity and safety.

The *Schafer method* is applied in the following manner. The patient is placed face downwards on the ground, his head turned slightly sideways, so that his mouth and nose are free, and his tongue pulled well forwards so that it does not obstruct the air passages. The operator then kneels astride the patient or to one side and, placing his hands over, or just below the lowest ribs, throws his weight forwards, so as to press downwards and towards the head. Pressure is maintained for two seconds, released for two seconds, applied again for two seconds, and so on. This method has the defect that no assistance is given to inspiration. The efficiency can be considerably increased if a second operator raises the patient's arms to assist inspiration, while the first operator is relaxing his pressure on the patient's back (Drinker combined method).

The *pulsator* of Bragg and Paul performs a somewhat similar operation mechanically ; the pressure is applied to the outside of the thoracic cavity, and inspiration is effected by the elastic recoil of the walls of the thorax. A rubber bag is wrapped round the chest and fastened by a broad canvas band (the cuff of a sphygmomanometer can be used for babies). This bag (or the cuff) is rhythmically inflated at any desired frequency and to any desired pressure by means of a bellows driven by an electric motor, or other means. This method has the advantage over that of Drinker and Shaw in that the patient can adopt any desired posture, and even move about within limits. The whole apparatus is also very much more portable.

Whenever it is available, it is a great advantage to give the patient a mixture of 7 per cent. carbon dioxide in oxygen to breathe. Even a relatively inadequate ventilation rate will thus maintain a reasonably high alveolar oxygen pressure, and the excess carbon dioxide stimulates the respiratory centre as it recovers from the effects of the oxygen want.

The Respiration During and After Exercise

It will be clear from what has been said already that the increased carbon dioxide production during exercise by its effect on the respiratory centre will automatically increase the total ventilation without the intervention of any special reflex mechanism. Where the exercise is anticipated, however, it is often preceded by an increase in respiration, in much the same way as the circulatory adjustments are made in advance, *i.e.*, by an irradiation of nerve impulses from the motor centres. During the performance of the exercise, there is evidence that reflex excitation of the respiratory centre occurs, presumably from the proprioceptive nerve endings ; such reflex stimulation can be obtained in man even if the limbs are moved passively by an observer. In relatively mild exercise, the combined nervous stimulation—by irradiation and reflex—may override the chemical stimulation, and the alveolar carbon dioxide pressure may actually fall.

During severe exercise, as we shall see in Chapter IX, lactic acid is released into the blood stream. The consequent reduction in bicarbonate concentration, and increase in hydrogen ion concentration, will in itself act as a stimulus to the respiratory centre, over and above that resulting from the increased rate of production of carbon dioxide. Immediately after the end of severe exercise, therefore, the alveolar carbon dioxide pressure is usually lower than it was initially.

The Action of Drugs on Respiration

(1) *Morphine.* The most important actions of morphine are a depression of the sensitivity to pain and a weakening of the respiration, which becomes very much slower and consequently deeper, although the increase in depth does not fully compensate for the decrease in frequency, and the total ventilation is reduced. Large doses often induce periodic (Cheyne-Stokes) respiration.

(2) *The general anæsthetics, chloroform and ether,* both depress the respiration if given in large doses, but the medullary centres in general are not affected until the whole of the rest of the central nervous system has become paralysed. Chloroform depresses the heart very much more readily than does ether, so that while death often occurs from heart failure after an overdose of chloroform, respiratory failure occurs first after an overdose of ether. Artificial respiration, therefore, almost invariably brings about recovery when ether is used, but not so often when chloroform is used.

The barbiturates, in large doses, reduce the sensitivity of the respiratory centre. This reduction, particularly when combined with that due to morphine, may be so great that respiration is maintained only by the sino-aortic reflex mechanism. In these circumstances, administration of oxygen may have the unexpected, and undesirable, effect of stopping the respiration altogether, the reflex system being no longer stimulated by a slight oxygen lack.

(3) *Caffeine,* on the other hand, stimulates the respiration, which becomes more rapid and shallower, so that the total ventilation is increased. It is often used as an antidote to morphine. Medullary stimulants, *e.g.,* leptazol, nikethamide and picrotoxin are powerful respiratory stimulants, particularly in barbiturate poisoning.

(4) *Adrenaline* in some animals may cause a temporary apnœa, or a decrease in the depth of respiration, coincident with the maximum rise in blood pressure. Whether this is a part of the reflex response of the carotid sinuses to the rise in pressure, or is also due to a cerebral anæmia resulting from an intense vaso-constriction, has not been definitely settled.

CHAPTER V

DIGESTION

Most of the food we eat is unsuitable for direct use by the cells of the body, either because it is solid or colloidal and therefore cannot pass through the wall of the intestine into the blood, or because although diffusible, it is in some form which the cells cannot at once assimilate.

The effect of digestion is to resolve the different foodstuffs into simple components, which will pass easily through the intestinal mucosa into the circulation, and from there into the cells which are to make use of them. Polysaccharides must be broken down into monosaccharides, fats into fatty acids and glycerol, and proteins into their constituent amino-acids. A few substances, such as the fat-soluble vitamins, which have no value as a source of energy, but are of vital importance to the body, may have to be rendered soluble in water before they can be absorbed.

This necessary and radical transformation of the food is effected by the enzymes contained in the digestive juices which are poured into the gut by the various glands situated in or near it, whenever food is eaten. It is noteworthy that all these enzymes are *hydrolytic* in their action, and the minimum of energy is wasted during the process of digestion. Absorption of the products of digestion, which proceeds coincidently with their liberation throughout the small intestine, is also a highly efficient process ; the material which is finally collected in the colon for excretion has little food value and consists largely of cellulose, bacteria, and débris from the intestinal mucosa.

Besides the products of digestion, the water, salts and organic constituents of the juices themselves must be absorbed. The total volume of digestive juices secreted daily is not known, but it is certainly not less than several litres in man, *i.e.*, of the same order as the volume of circulating blood. There is thus a very large daily " turnover " of water and salts between the blood and intestinal lumen, and if anything prevents re-absorption of the fluids (*e.g.*, their loss through vomiting or diarrhœa) *dehydration* of the body tissues quickly ensues, fluid being withdrawn from these into the blood to maintain its volume.

Saliva. The prompt response of the salivary glands to the sight, smell, or even the anticipation of appetising food, is familiar to everyone as "watering of the mouth." This is a "conditioned" reflex (page 440), *i.e.*, one which has become established by training and experience and in which the cerebral centres play an important part. The stimuli received by the special sense organs are conveyed to the cerebral cortex ; from there they are relayed to the cells forming the " salivatory nuclei " in the region of the medulla, and from these cells fibres run to the various glands. Salivation is also brought about when food is actually eaten, by direct stimulation of sensory end-organs in the mucosa of the mouth, tongue and pharynx, from which impulses are transmitted to the salivatory nuclei. This reflex is " unconditioned " ; it is present from birth and does not involve the higher cerebral centres. Thus, reflex salivation is readily produced in a decerebrate cat (p. 416), by introducing acid, alcohol, etc., into the mouth.

Saliva has a pH of about 6·8, is fairly well buffered and contains a lubricant *mucin* and (in man) the enzyme *ptyalin* which breaks down starch into a mixture of dextrins and maltose. The main function of saliva is to moisten and lubricate the food, thus preparing it for swallowing, and also to dissolve its soluble constituents, so that the flavour is appreciated and the secretion of saliva itself and of other digestive glands is stimulated.

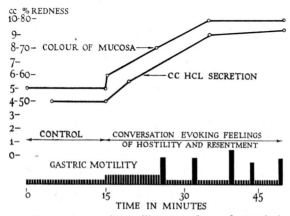

Fig. V. 1. Changes in gastric motility, secretion and vascularity of the human stomach accompanying feelings of hostility and resentment aroused by conversation. The subject was a man (" Tom ") who had a large gastric fistula. The vascularity of the mucosa was estimated as the intensity of the red colour, and was expressed in arbitrary units. (Wolf and Wolff, " Human Gastric Function.")

Innervation of the Digestive Glands. The existence of "secretory" nerves was discovered by Carl Ludwig (1851) who stimulated the lingual nerve, a branch of which (the *chorda tympani*) supplies the submaxillary gland, and found that it caused the secretion of saliva. It has since become abundantly clear that all the digestive glands receive a dual innervation from the autonomic nervous system, namely, vasodilator and " secretory " fibres from the parasympathetic division, and vasoconstrictor and (in some cases) inhibitory fibres from the sympathetic division. The former are distributed to the abdomen in the vagus and pelvic visceral nerves (colon), the latter for the most part run to the viscera from the autonomic ganglia along the walls of the large arteries.

There is a similar dual nerve supply to the smooth muscle of the alimentary tract, the parasympathetic fibres increasing the motor activity, and the sympathetic fibres depressing it, so that in general the state of activity of an organ may be said to represent the resultant of the influence of the two systems. However, the extent to which the motor and secretory functions of the digestive tract are normally controlled by these nerves remains problematical ; for instance, complete denervation of an intestinal loop produces a striking increase in tone, motility and spontaneous secretion, but a rapid recovery occurs and in a few days the behaviour of this denervated loop is almost indistinguishable from normal.

In addition to the motor or efferent autonomic fibres mentioned, *afferent* fibres carry sensory impulses from all parts of the tract to the central nervous system ; and the reflex arcs formed by these with the autonomics play an important part in the activities of the gut.

The ultimate " centre " in the brain for visceral afferents and efferents appears to be the *hypothalamus* (p 422) which thus exerts a general influence over the motor, secretory and vascular reactions of the entire alimentary tract ; damage to or experimental interference with this region of the brain produces changes in secretion and motility of the stomach and intestines.

The hypothalamus has connections with the thalamus and cerebral cortex ; and the thalamus is well known to be concerned with the perception of the painful or pleasurable quality of sensations. Means thus exist by which disagreeable or pleasant emotions may influence the working of the digestive tract. A good example of this is afforded by the experiment depicted

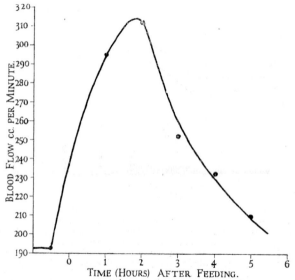

Fig. V. 2. The blood-flow in the superior mesenteric artery of a conscious dog during the digestion of a meal, recorded by a Rein flowmeter which was attached to the artery at an aseptic operation some days previously. (Herrick *et al.*)

in Fig. V. 1, which is taken from the study by Wolf and Wolff of the daily variations in gastric function of a laboratory technician (" Tom ") ; this man had had from childhood a large gastric fistula, permitting inspection of the interior, withdrawal of contents, etc. It is common everyday experience that pain, fear, anger, resentment or worry are potent causes of " indigestion," and similar upsets of the gastro-intestinal tract.

The Secretory Work of the Digestive Glands. Vasodilatation occurs in all the digestive glands when they are active, so that during the digestion of a meal there is a great increase in the blood-flow through the portal circulation (Fig. V. 2). A ready supply of water and salts is thus assured for the production of secretions ; but the enzymes and other organic constituents, *e.g.*, mucin, are probably prepared from " raw materials " in the blood by the gland-cells themselves. Many of the cells in the digestive glands contain granules or droplets which are apparently antecedents of organic constituents of the juice. These accumulate during inactivity and are discharged during secretion, particularly if this is prolonged ; these cellular changes can be correlated to some extent with the amounts of enzyme, mucin or other organic material found in the juice (Fig. V. 3).

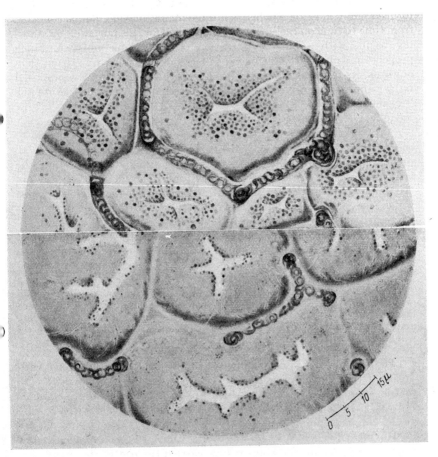

FIG. V. 3. Portions of the unstained living pancreas of a white mouse (*a*) after twenty-four hours fast ; the cells contain plenty of zymogen granules, and (*b*) after 3 hours stimulation of secretion. Most of the intracellular material has been discharged. (Hirsch.)

The act of secretion is not merely a washing-out of preformed constituents from the cell by fluid filtered off from the blood ; the submaxillary gland can produce saliva against a pressure much higher than that in the arteries (Ludwig) and during secretion its usage of oxygen and sugar is increased (Barcroft).

Apart from the synthesis of organic materials by gland-cells *osmotic* work may be done during secretion ; for instance, the parietal cells of the gastric glands concentrate the H ion about three million times in preparing the acid of the gastric juice from blood.

Swallowing

Each mouthful of food is chewed and mixed with saliva until it forms a pulpy mass or " bolus " suitable for swallowing, and is collected from time to time on the surface of the tongue for this purpose. Swallowing begins with a quick contraction of the tongue muscles, which propels the bolus past the faucial pillars into the pharynx ; from then onwards, its progress is beyond voluntary control, and is accomplished by a rapid and complicated series of movements which constitute the " swallowing reflex " and are co-ordinated by a " centre " in the medulla.

As the bolus enters the pharynx, the soft palate is approximated to the posterior pharyngeal wall by contraction of its muscles, so as to prevent entry of food into the nasal passages. At the same time the larynx is brought upwards and forwards under the shelter of the base of the tongue, raising and opening the upper end of the relaxed œsophagus, which the bolus now enters. Whether or not the epiglottis turns backwards to guard the entrance of the larynx is uncertain ; but the risk of food entering the air-passages is lessened by the reflex approximation of the vocal cords and momentary inhibition of respiration, which also form part of the reflex.

The passage of the bolus from the mouth to the upper part of the œsophagus is so rapid, and the reflex movements so easily disturbed by experimental procedures, that it has proved very difficult so far to elucidate many of the details of the act, and in particular the nature of the forces which transport the bolus so rapidly.

The swallowing reflex is touched off by contact of the food with areas on the fauces, pharynx and tonsils which are very sensitive to tactile stimulation, and from which impulses travel to the medullary centre ; if these areas are anæsthetised by painting them with cocaine, swallowing is impossible.

Having travelled through the upper third of the œsophagus in a fraction of a second, the bolus is now carried the rest of the way much more slowly, by an advancing ring-like contraction of the smooth muscle of the œsophagus. If the bolus is soft and well-lubricated, it reaches the cardiac sphincter at the entrance to the stomach in a few seconds ; but if dry, it may take a minute or so, and *secondary waves* (which give rise to a painful sensation in the chest) may arise in the œsophagus and force it along.

Liquids, owing to the impetus given them by the act of swallowing and the effect of gravity, outstrip the œsophageal wave and arrive at the cardiac sphincter in a second or two, where they wait for the arrival of the œsophageal wave. When this approaches the cardiac sphincter the latter relaxes before it and the food enters the stomach.

Gastric Digestion

X-ray examination of the human stomach after eating meals made radio-opaque by the addition of barium sulphate shows that there are wide variations among apparently normal persons in the position, shape and motility of the stomach. An ordinary meal may begin to leave the stomach less than 30 minutes after it is eaten, and although the rate of gastric emptying varies with the size of the meal and its consistency and composition, gastric emptying is usually completed in 4-5 hours.

While the food remains in the stomach it becomes mixed with the gastric juice, the secretion of which from the millions of tubular glands buried in the mucosa starts within a few minutes of eating.

Composition of Gastric Juice. The juice is really a mixture in variable proportions of the individual secretions of the various types of cell present in the glands. Heidenhain (1878) first recognised the *chief cells*, which contain pepsinogen, and the *parietal cells*, which secrete HCl. Both are absent from the pyloric region of the stomach ; the glands there contain *mucoid cells*, which produce mucus, and between the pyloric region and the rest of the stomach there is a transitional zone where pyloric mucoid cells are mingled with chief and parietal cells. Besides the pyloric glands, mucus is secreted by cells in the necks of the glands elsewhere and also by the cells of the surface columnar epithelium.

The parietal cells are believed to secrete a fluid which is isotonic with blood, contains most of the water of the gastric juice, and is a practically pure solution of hydrochloric acid, the strength of which as secreted (0·58 per cent.), is constant whatever the rate of its formation. However, the acidity of the gastric juice is generally much lower than this maximal value, owing to neutralisation by the bicarbonate of the mucous secretion and by the proteins, peptones and polypeptides of the gastric contents.

A large amount of the enzyme *carbonic anhydrase* (p. 116) is found in the parietal cell ; it is possible that the formation of HCl involves ionic exchanges very similar to those which take place in the red blood corpuscles during the carriage of carbon dioxide, but the part played by carbonic anhydrase is not yet settled.

It is interesting to note that carbonic anhydrase is also found in the renal tubules, where the glomerular filtrate undergoes acidification, and in the pancreas, where bicarbonate is secreted in higher concentration than in the blood.

The chief cells probably contribute a scanty non-acid secretion ; it contains *pepsinogen*, which is activated by acid, forming the proteolytic enzyme *pepsin*. The mucous cells produce a jelly-like fluid which contains much mucus and is faintly alkaline owing to the presence of bicarbonate (0·28 per cent.).

Although stimulation of the vagus causes the secretion of a juice containing acid, enzyme and mucus indicating that the cells concerned all have a secretory innervation from the vagus, they can respond to some extent independently of one another to other forms of stimulation (mechanical or chemical) so that the final composition of the gastric juice may show wide variations. Thus the drug *histamine* is a powerful and almost exclusive stimulant of the parietal cells, providing a juice of high acidity and containing little pepsin or mucus (its effect on the stomach of the subject " Tom " previously referred to, is shown in

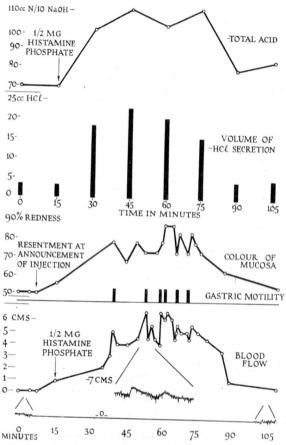

Fig. V. 4); while mechanical or chemical irritation of the mucous membrane causes a profuse flow of mucus, with comparative little acid or pepsin. No selective stimulus for the chief cells is yet known.

Pepsin in acid solution breaks down proteins into peptones and

Fig. V. 4. The effect of a hypodermic injection of histamine on gastric secretion, mobility, vascularity and blood flow in a human subject.

The vascularity was estimated as the redness, in arbitrary units, of the mucosa. The presence of large gastric contractions only, is recorded. The blood flow was measured by a thermal method, and is expressed in arbitrary units from an arbitrary zero ; the inset in this record is a sample of the actual record from which the chart above it has been plotted. (Wolf and Wolff, " Human Gastric Function.")

proteoses, which are fairly large fractions of the original molecule ; some amino-acids are liberated, but the further breakdown of proteins and the above derivatives is accomplished later by the enzymes of the pancreatic and intestinal juices.

Stimulation of Gastric Secretion. Pavlov (1902) and his pupils were the first to show clearly that the secretion of gastric juice which starts within a few minutes of eating a meal occurs whether the food actually enters the stomach or not, and is due to a combination of " conditioned " and " unconditioned " reflexes similiar to those causing the flow of saliva under the same conditions. A dog was provided by a previous surgical operation with a gastric fistula for the collection of gastric juice,

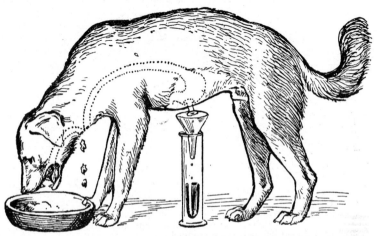

FIG. V. 5.   A Dog with Œsophageal and Gastric Fistulæ.

The food consumed is seen dropping out of the open end of the anterior portion of the œsophagus ; the animal is fed through the opening in the posterior portion.   The gastric fistula consists simply of a tube flanged at each end, stitched into the wall of the stomach at one end, and into the abdominal wall at the other.   (Hober.)

and an œsophageal fistula, so that the food which was swallowed never entered the stomach but fell out of the opening in the neck (Fig. V. 5). A few minutes after the animal was thus " sham-fed " there began a flow of gastric juice, which could be stopped by cutting the gastric branches of the vagus, or paralysing them by the injection of the drug atropine.   Sham-feeding was not always necessary to elicit secretion ; in intelligent animals, the mere sight, smell, or sounds associated with the arrival of food, were sufficient.

These findings have been confirmed and extended by experiments on human subjects who have become accustomed by training to swallow and retain without discomfort a stomach-tube for withdrawal of the gastric juice ; and occasional opportunities have also arisen of making similar and more extensive experiments on patients who, usually on account of an œsophageal stricture, have been provided by means of an operation with a gastric fistula for feeding.   The classical example is that of Alexis St. Martin, an Indian

" runner " at a trading station in Michigan, U.S.A., who was left as the result of a gunshot wound with a large gastric fistula. The observations and experiments made upon him (1825–33) by his physician, William Beaumont, have become famous. More elaborate studies of a similar kind have since been made by Carlson (1916) and Wolf and Wolff (1943).

The reflex response to a " sham " meal gradually ceases in about an hour ; but if the swallowed food is allowed to enter the stomach in the usual way, to be digested by this juice (and later by the pancreatic and intestinal enzymes) gastric secretion is augmented and prolonged for 3 hours or more, in fact, long after the meal has been forgotten.

The cause of this continued secretion resulting from digestion of the food was first investigated by Pavlov by means of the famous " Pavlov

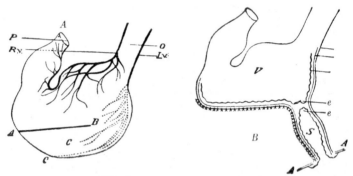

FIG. V. 6.   The Pavlov Pouch.

The left diagram (A) shows the line of the incision, A—B, into the gastric wall. O, œsophagus ; R. v. L.v., right and left vagus nerves ; P, pylorus ; C, cardiac portion of stomach.

The right diagram (B) shows the operation completed (part sectional). V, main portion of stomach ; S, cardiac *cul-de-sac* (pouch) ; e, e, mucous membrane reflected to form a diaphragm between the two cavities. (From Starling's " Principles of Human Physiology.")

pouch " (Fig. V. 6). The secretion from this " miniature stomach " always runs closely parallel with that of the remainder, so that it becomes possible to follow the course of secretion in the main stomach during digestion, without interfering with it in any way.

Using dogs with such a pouch, and also a gastric fistula, Pavlov showed that placing meat in the animal's stomach without its knowledge (no reflex stimulation) caused little or no secretion, and digestion of the food took many hours ; but if the meat was first partly digested with " reflex " juice (obtained by sham-feeding another dog) the mixture stimulated gastric secretion strongly when introduced, and digestion was rapidly completed. Not only does this experiment illustrate the importance of the " reflex " juice in gastric digestion, but it also indicates that digestion products are responsible for the later stimulation of gastric secretion.

Similarly, the introduction of food or its digestion products directly into the small intestine stimulates gastric secretion. The existence of this " intestinal phase " of gastric stimulation has been proved in dogs, by Ivy, by making the entire stomach into a pouch at an aseptic operation, joining the œsophagus directly to the duodenum. After recovery from the operation, when the animal eats a meal, this passes straight into the small intestine and is there digested ; a considerable secretion of gastric juice from the pouch occurs (Fig. V. 7).

How the products of protein digestion thus stimulate gastric secretion is still the subject of controversy. There is no doubt that a stimulating substance of some sort does enter the blood from the small intestine during digestion of protein there ; but whether it is a hormone is uncertain. It has also been asserted that under similar conditions a hormone " Gastrin " is liberated from the mucosa of the pyloric region and excites gastric secretion. There is no conclusive evidence of this.

Gastric Inhibition. Besides the stimulation of gastric secretion from the intestine, inhibition may be brought about by the presence there of fats, fatty acids and other substances. Since the last century, physicians have employed fat in the form of olive oil or cream, to depress gastric secretion in the condition of peptic ulcer, in order to promote healing; and these substances have been shown to liberate from the duodenal

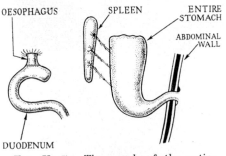

Fig. V. 7.   The pouch of the entire stomach (Ivy.)

mucosa into the circulation a hormone *Enterogastrone*, which inhibits gastric secretion and motility. This is the physiological basis for the view that fatty meat such as pork is " indigestible " ; it takes a longer time to be digested and leave the stomach.

Movements of the Stomach

The normal human stomach some hours after a meal is empty apart from a small and variable quantity of gastric juice, saliva, mucus, etc., and its walls are in a state of tonic contraction. When the swallowed food enters it, a *receptive relaxation* occurs as the result of a nervous reflex and the food slides down into the most dependent portion. Soon, as indicated in Fig. V. 8, ring-like contractions appear in the body of the stomach and slowly move towards the pyloric sphincter, becoming deeper as they pass into this region where the muscle is stronger (W. B. Cannon, 1898). As digestion and emptying proceed, the strength and frequency of the contractions increase to a maximum which varies with the size and nature of the meal, and then gradually decline. Each wave occupies the stomach for about half a minute, and as many as four may be seen at the same time during the height of digestion. These contractions serve to mix the food with the gastric juice, and—particularly in the pyloric antrum—provide the propulsive force for the passage of gastric contents at intervals into the duodenum.

Although the stomach relaxes when food enters, the tone is gradually regained, so that by the time most of the food has left the stomach a high tone is again present, with small regular fluctuations, termed a "tonus rhythm." This continues for a few hours after the stomach has emptied ; and then if the next meal is not forthcoming, gives place to contractions similar in type to those normally seen in the filled stomach, but much more powerful. These occur in groups, lasting for about half an hour, and at intervals of two to three hours. Their incidence coincides with a sensation of hunger ; and as they become stronger, definite pain—" pangs of hunger "—is felt with each contraction (Carlson, 1919).

Emptying of the Stomach. For many years it was believed that gastric emptying was chiefly controlled by the pyloric sphincter (Fig. V. 9), which was supposed to remain closed for most of the time in the face of the gastric contractions, opening briefly at intervals to allow exit of some of the gastric contents. However, direct observations of the behaviour of the stomach and pyloric sphincter in human subjects by means of X-rays and the gastroscope, and experiments on trained conscious animals in which the regions concerned have been made accessible by the surgical preparation of fistulæ, show that the sphincter is *relaxed* for the greater part of the time during gastric emptying, behaving like the pyloric antrum of which it is anatomically a part. In fact, the three regions, pyloric antrum, sphincter, and duodenal cap act as a single co-ordinated physiological unit. As a gastric wave passes over each in turn, the antral contraction expels food through the still relaxed sphincter into the duodenal cap ; but this is brought to an end by the closely following contraction of the sphincter, and before the antrum and sphincter have relaxed, the contraction of the duodenal cap occurs, expelling the food down the duodenum. The effect is that of a " gastric pump " (Quigley, 1943), regurgitation from the duodenum to stomach being prevented by the slightly persistent contraction of antrum and sphincter ; not every gastric wave results in this complete cycle of contractions, so that only

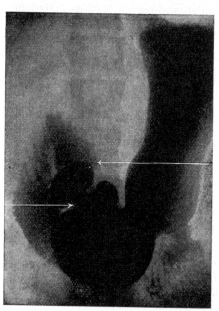

Fig. V. 8. Radiograph of a human stomach after a " barium meal " showing peristaltic waves. (F. Haenisch.)

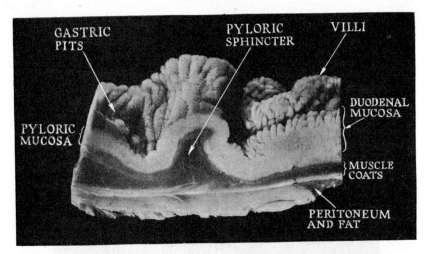

Fig. V. 9. The pyloro-duodenal junction of the monkey, showing surface textures of the mucous membranes, and the thickness of the mucosal and muscular coats. (From a preparation by K. C. Richardson.)

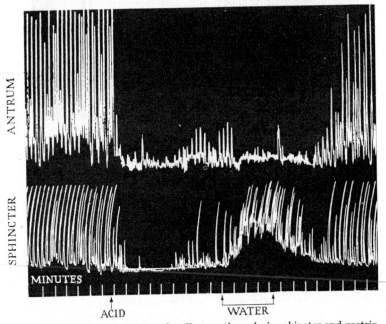

Fig. V. 10.—Record showing the effect on the pyloric sphincter and gastric peristalsis in a conscious dog of : (a) injecting acid into the duodenum (20 c.c. N/10 HCl) ; and (b) distending the duodenum with water under 30 cm. pressure.
Gastric peristalsis was recorded by a balloon in the antrum, and contractions of the sphincter by a second balloon in the sphincter. (Thomas, Crider and Mogan.)

a proportion of the waves which arrive at the pyloric antrum cause the exit of gastric contents.

Gastric emptying thus depends fundamentally upon the propulsive activity of the gastric muscle and the co-ordination of the three regions mainly concerned ; and both these factors are controlled to a large extent from the duodenum. Enterogastrone has already been mentioned (p. 173) ; but there are many substances, such as acid, sugars, hypertonic solutions and protein digestion-products, which retard gastric emptying when they are introduced into the duodenum, and this they do by causing reflex inhibition of the gastric musculature, including the pyloric sphincter (*the enterogastric reflex*) as shown in Fig. V. 10. In

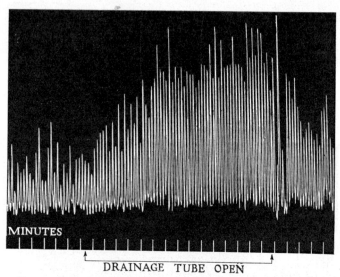

FIG. V. 11. Record showing the effect of duodenal drainage on gastric peristalsis in a conscious dog (exclusion of enterogastric reflex). (Thomas, Crider and Mogan.)

fact, by means of this reflex a constant restraining influence is normally exercised from the duodenum on gastric tone and motility ; if the reflex is prevented from operating during gastric emptying, gastric motility is greatly increased and the stomach empties abnormally rapidly (Fig. V. 11).

Towards the end of gastric emptying, particularly of a fatty meal, the contraction cycles are weak, the pressures in antrum, sphincter and duodenum are nearly equal, and the sphincter is open most of the time ; such conditions are favourable for the regurgitation of intestinal juices and bile into the stomach, and evidence of this is afforded by the presence of these in samples of the gastric contents withdrawn by a stomach-tube.

Vomiting. This is a reflex act involving the muscles of the diaphragm and abdominal wall and those of the stomach and œsophagus. It is co-

ordinated by a " centre " in the medulla, which may be stimulated by irritation of any part of the digestive tract, by impulses from the semicircular
canals (sea-sickness) or by disturbance of the centre itself (*e.g.*, by cerebral
tumours or the action of drugs such as apomophine). A more or less prolonged sensation of *nausea* usually precedes retching and vomiting ; it is
marked by pallor, sweating, salivation and partial or complete inhibition of
the gastric musculature ; antiperistalsis in the small intestine has been
observed radiographically in human subjects. Nausea may culminate in
retching, which consists of a series of inspiratory-like efforts accompanied by
closure of the glottis, the stomach becoming compressed between the diaphragm and the contracted abdominal muscles ; the gastric contents are
finally ejected through the relaxed cardiac sphincter and œsophagus. The
larynx is drawn up as in swallowing and elevation of the soft palate also
occurs ; this largely prevents egress of the vomitus by the nose.

Intestinal Digestion

As the stomach contents pass at intervals into the duodenum, they
meet and mix with secretions from the pancreas, liver and intestinal
glands, which complete the digestion of proteins, fats and carbohydrates,
as the food passes down the intestine. The products are absorbed
simultaneously into the portal and lymphatic circulations.

Pancreatic Juice. The acinar cells, which secrete the pancreatic juice,
are apparently all of the same type ; they produce a secretion containing a
number of enzymes and having a pH of 8–8·4 with a bicarbonate content
which is approximately 1–5 times that in the blood, increasing with the rate
of secretion. The amount of chloride present is approximately inversely
proportional to the rate of secretion, so that the sum of the concentrations of
the two ions HCO_3 and Cl remains about the same. The pancreas contains
the enzyme *carbonic anhydrase* which is presumably concerned in the formation of the bicarbonate in the juice.

Secretion of Pancreatic Juice. The collection of pancreatic juice
from a conscious dog by means of a cannula tied into the pancreatic
duct, was first carried out by Regnier de Graaf (1664) and the method
was revived nearly 200 years later by Claude Bernard, who gave the first
description of the properties of the juice. Animals provided by a
previous surgical operation with such pancreatic fistulæ remain in
excellent health indefinitely, provided the juice is returned to the
intestine daily, and not lost to the animal. For some purposes, however,
collection of the juice for a few hours after cannulation of the duct in an
anæsthetised animal is more suitable.

As in the case of the saliva and gastric juice, a reflex mechanism
exists for the provision of pancreatic juice when a meal is eaten, and
again it is the vagus which carries the secretory fibres to the gland ;
the secretion is scanty, but rich in enzymes. A much greater flow of
juice occurs, however, as the gastric contents are passed on into the
duodenum. The agent chiefly responsible is the *acid*, although fats, bile
and protein digestion-products are also effective ; these substances
cause the liberation from the intestinal mucosa into the circulation of a
hormone *Secretin*, which excites a copious and watery secretion from
the pancreas ; the flow of hepatic bile and of juice from Brunner's
glands in the duodenum is also excited to a small extent.

Fig. V. 12 shows the effect of an injection of secretin on the flow of pancreatic juice in a human subject ; the juice was withdrawn by means of a stomach tube which was swallowed and allowed to pass into the duodenum.

Secretin was the first hormone to be discovered. The fact that the entry of the acid gastric contents into the duodenum excited pancreatic secretion was well known to Pavlov and his contemporaries, but was ascribed to a reflex. However, in 1902, Bayliss and Starling showed that dilute acid still excited pancreatic secretion when placed in a *denervated* loop of small intestine, so that the effect must be mediated by way of the circulation. Intravenous injection of acid was without result ; but the injection of a neutralised acid extract of the intestinal mucosa caused a copious secretion of pancreatic juice; and the active principle, Secretin, has since been crystallised and identified as a polypeptide.

The copious flow of "secretin juice" flushes out from the gland the enzymes "mobilised" by the initial nervous stimulation ; secretin itself does not excite the secretion of enzyme. Although this is true for *crystalline* secretin it has frequently been shown in the past that cruder concentrates of the hormone stimulate the production of enzymes as well as of water and salts ; and an interesting explanation has recently been provided by Harper and Raper (1944). They showed that such secretin extracts contain another substance, *Pancreozymin*, which can be separated from secretin and which stimulates the output of enzymes by the pancreas when injected intravenously. This would indicate that the continued production of enzymes by the pancreas during duodenal digestion is ensured by a second hormonal mechanism, namely, the liberation of pancreozymin from the duodenal mucosa by the intestinal contents.

Fig. V. 12. Human pancreatic secretion evoked by secretin administration. The volume-rate and bicarbonate concentration is increased ; the concentrations of diastase and trypsin are decreased by dilution. (Agren and Lagerlof.)

Actions of Pancreatic Juice. The pure juice is almost without action on most varieties of protein, the powerful proteolytic enzyme it contains being present in an inactive form *trypsinogen*. This is rapidly converted into the enzyme *trypsin* when the juice mixes with the intestinal juice which contains an enzyme-like activator *enterokinase*. Thus formed, trypsin acts upon all proteins and their digestion products, converting them finally into amino-acids and polypeptides. Pancreatic *diastase* breaks down starch into maltose, while the *lipase* also present hydrolyses the fats into fatty acids and glycerol.

The Bile

The entry of the gastric contents into the duodenum provides the stimulus for the appearance there of the bile, whose importance for digestion lies chiefly in the fact that the bile salts and lecithin it contains are valuable aids in the emulsification, digestion and absorption of the fats of a meal. It is also necessary for the efficient absorption of iron and of the fat-soluble vitamins.

Hepatic bile, a neutral golden-yellow slightly syrupy fluid, is secreted by the hepatic cells, and there is little evidence that its production is normally under nervous control. Between meals, the tone of the sphincter-like muscle around the duodenal end of the common bile duct is relatively high, and the bile flows into the relaxed gall-bladder where it is rapidly concentrated by the activity of the mucosa, becoming very

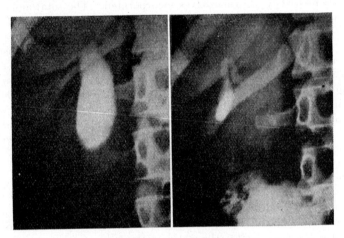

Fig. V. 13. X-ray Photographs of the **Gall-Bladder of a Man** before and after a meal of fat.

Tetra-iodo-phenolphthalein was injected intravenously fourteen hours before the first photograph was taken (Graham-Cole test). The second photograph was taken twenty minutes after the meal of fat. The discharge of the contents of the gall-bladder in response to the presence of fat in the duodenum has filled the cystic and common ducts with dye, and they can be seen, in the second photograph, forming a loop above the gall-bladder ; in some cases the hepatic duct becomes filled also. (Ivy.)

dark and thicker and slightly acid. When a meal is eaten, a little bile is sometimes reflexly expelled from the gall-bladder into the duodenum ; but the main emptying occurs later when the contact with the duodenal mucosa of the gastric contents excites the liberation into the circulation of the hormone *Cholecystokinin,* which causes slow contractions and emptying of the gall-bladder. Fat is particularly effective in liberating the hormone and hence stimulating emptying of the gall-bladder (Fig. V. 13).

After the gall-bladder has emptied, hepatic bile may flow directly into the duodenum for a time, until digestion there is over ; gradually the tone of the sphincter increases and the bile is once more diverted into the gall-bladder until the next meal.

Cholecystography. This clinical test of gall-bladder function depends on the fact that tetrabromphenolphthalein and similar compounds are opaque to X-rays and are excreted in the bile after oral or intravenous administation. They are concentrated in the gall-bladder and so enable it to be visualised by X-rays. If a meal rich in fat is then fed, the emptying of the gall-bladder may be recorded by serial radiographs (Fig. V. 13).

The increase in the rate of flow of bile from the liver, which occurs during the digestion of a meal is to some extent due to the passage through the liver of the products of digestion ; but the chief stimulus is supplied by the bile-salts themselves. Returning to the liver after absorption from the small intestine they stimulate the secretion of more bile, in which they are themselves incorporated. The total amount of bile salts thus circulating between liver, gall-bladder and intestine (*entero-hepatic circulation*), appears to be maintained at an approximately constant level by the liver ; if extra bile salts are administered to an animal, they are destroyed in a few days and the original circulating total is soon restored. If all the bile is drained from an animal having a biliary fistula and not returned to it, the rate of bile salt secretion falls to a low " basal " level ; it represents the rate of new bile salt formation by the liver, presumably in response to a maximal stimulus (the fall to zero of the quantity in circulation). When the return of bile is once more instituted, the quantity circulating rises in a few days to the original value (Berman and Ivy).

The bile salts are derivatives of the sterol cholic acid, and are thus allied structurally to cholesterol and the sex and adrenal-cortical hormones. A number of different bile acids exist, but only a few are present in the bile of a particular species. A small amount only is present as the acid itself ; the rest is in the form of a compound of the bile acid with the base taurine, or the amino-acid glycine. Taurocholic and glycocholic acids are present in human and ox bile : the dog, sheep and goat have only the former, the hog only the latter. How the liver synthesises the bile acids is still unknown.

The bile pigments. The hæmoglobin of worn-out red blood corpuscles is broken down by the cells of the reticulo-endothelial system, notably those of the liver (Kupffer cells), spleen and bone marrow, through the stages of hæmochromogens (p. 100), which still contain the iron and globin of the original hæmoglobin molecule, to the *bile pigment biliverdin*, and its reduction product *bilirubin*, which are iron and protein-free. The latter is set free into the blood, contributing to the yellow colour of normal plasma, and taken up from it by the liver, to be excreted in the bile. Under some circumstances, *e.g.*, in starving dogs, biliverdin is excreted by the liver in place of bilirubin.

The Intestinal Juices. The digestive juices contributed by the glands present in the wall of the small intestine come from *Brunner's glands* in the first inch or so of the duodenum, and *Lieberkuhn's glands*, which are found throughout the small and large intestines. Both secretions are alkaline and contain a good deal of mucus ; the stimulus for their appearance seems to be local mechanical and chemical excitation of the mucosa by digesting food.

The juice as ordinarily obtained—*e.g.*, by distension with a balloon of an isolated loop of intestine (Thiry-Vella loop, Fig. V. 14), contains small amounts of a variety of enzymes ; but similar enzyme activity is also demonstrable in extracts of the intestinal mucous membrane, and the invariable presence, in such samples of juice, of cast-off mucosal cells, leucocytes, etc., has given rise to the suspicion that most of its varied digestive properties may be due to *intracellular* enzymes liberated from the débris.   If this material is rapidly removed from cat's intestinal juice by centrifuging it immediately after collection, the only enzymes found in appreciable amounts are lipase, amylase, and enterokinase (Florey).

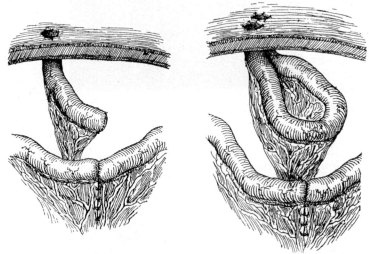

FIG. V. 14.   The Thiry and Thiry-Vella intestinal loops.   (From Markowitz, " Text-book of Experimental Surgery.")

The Movements of the Intestines

The mixing of the food with the intestinal secretions, and its passage through the alimentary canal is accomplished by the intestinal move-ments ; these are nicely co-ordinated with the progress of digestion and absorption, so that both are virtually completed by the time the colon is reached.

A good way to gain some idea of the normal pattern of the intestinal movements (and incidentally, to study them experimentally), is to open under warm saline the abdomen of a decerebrate or lightly anæsthetised animal at the height of digestion.   The inhibition caused by cold and drying is thus avoided ; and the movements of the coils of intestine, as they float outside the abdominal cavity, may be recorded by attaching them to levers writing on a smoked drum, or by taking moving pictures which are analysed later ; or balloons may be inserted into the intestine and connected to volume or pressure recorders.

Many other methods have been used for study of the intestinal move-ments ; the more fruitful are probably those which utilise as a subject a conscious trained animal previously operated upon to render accessible the required region of the intestine (*e.g.*, the Thiry-Vella loop).

Three types of movement can often be distinguished. The " pendular movements " are a rhythmical lengthening and shortening of a
segment of intestine and are probably caused by gentle waves of contraction which travel down the intestine for a short distance at about
2–5 cm. per second and occur about 10–12 times a minute. Besides these

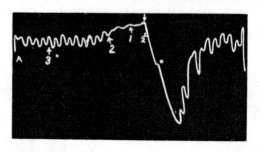

Fɪɢ. V. 15. The passage of a Bolus along the **Small Intestine.** Contractions of the Longitudinal Coat as recorded by an Enterograph.

The bolus (of soap and cotton wool) was inserted into the intestine
4 in. above the recorded spot at the moment indicated by A. At subsequent
moments it was 3 in., 2 in., 1 in. and ½ in. from the recorded spot as
indicated below the tracing. As the bolus arrives 2 in. above the levers,
there is cessation of the rhythmic contractions and inhibition of the tone of
the muscle. This is followed, as the bolus is forced past, by a strong
contraction on the rear of the bolus. (Bayliss and Starling.)

one occasionally sees a portion of the gut which is the seat of a much
stronger contraction of the circular muscle. This contraction obliterates
the vessels and the lumen of the gut blanching the intestine. It travels
very slowly down the gut, about 0·1–0·5 cm. per minute, preceded by a
less obvious but equally circumscribed region of inhibition. The double
wave is known as a *peristaltic wave* (Bayliss and Starling, 1899), and is

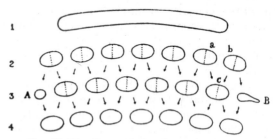

Fɪɢ. V. 16. Segmentation in small intestine.

elicited by distending or stimulating the intestine strongly at any point.
Such a response of the intestine (contraction above, inhibition below,
as shown in Fig. V. 15), is probably due to a local reflex in the nerve-
plexuses of the intestine, and has for this reason been termed the
" Myenteric Reflex " (Cannon).

A third type of movement often seen is " segmentation " ; a portion
of intestine, frequently the jejunum, becomes occupied by several

simultaneous localised contractions. After a few seconds these all disappear and are replaced by exactly similar contractions in the intervening regions, so that the intestine is divided into a fresh set of segments (Fig. V. 16). By this means the food is mixed with the digestive juices and brought into intimate contact with the mucous membrane.

The movements just described, and variations of them, are the groundwork from which is built up the normal complicated pattern of intestinal activity. But we do not yet understand very well how they are co-ordinated ; for instance, what determines the appearance of a given type of movement in some region of the gut, its intensity and

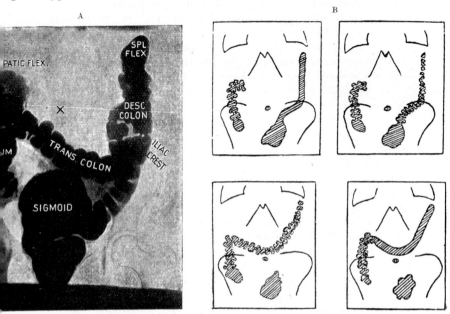

A   B

Fig. V. 17. (A) Radiograph of the human colon after a barium enema, showing haustra, and (B) a diagram (Holtzknecht) of a " mass movement." (From A. B. Barclay, " The Digestive Tract," 2nd edition, 1933.)

range of influence, why it gives place to some other movement after a time, and finally how the movements as a whole are kept in step with the progress of digestion, so that the food moves along neither too quickly nor too slowly.

The intestine as a whole shows a descending gradient of activity throughout its length. After a meal, the duodenum and jejunum show great and varied activity ; but as the ileum is approached, the bowel becomes more and more quiescent, the terminal ileum making only occasional movements as it gradually fills with the residue of digestion.

Filling and Emptying of the Colon. As the stomach empties, the ileum is stimulated reflexly (*gastro-ileal reflex* of Hurst), to pass on its semi-fluid contents into the cæcum by sustained " stripping " contractions which occur every few minutes and persist while food remains in the stomach. All movement of the cæcum is inhibited and it relaxes to receive the ileal contents. Gradually the cæcum, ascending and transverse colons are filled, without obvious peristalsis or other movement, the general appearance being one of " impressive immobility." There is a wide range of variation among normal persons in the time taken for different regions of the colon to become filled ; but as soon as cæcum and ascending colon are well filled, the saccular folds known as haustra appear (Fig. V. 17), and by their slow filling and emptying knead the contents and aid the absorption of salts and water.

This slow and irregular process of filling is interrupted two or three times a day by a "mass movement" (Fig. V. 17). Starting usually about the middle of the colon, the haustra disappear and the colon becomes shortened and flattened by a rapidly advancing powerful contraction, and its contents are moved on bodily into the descending and pelvic colons in a few seconds usually without any subjective sensations whatever.

In most people, the rectum is empty until just before the urge to defæcate, or " call to stool " comes (usually after breakfast) which is caused by a mass movement distending the rectum with fæces. The attainment in this way of a certain degree of distension of the rectum reflexly excites contractions of its walls and a reciprocal relaxation of the anal sphincters, which is augmented and prolonged by the passage of the fæces along the rectum and anal canal. The expulsion of fæces is assisted by " straining," *i.e.*, raising the intra-abdominal pressure by expiring against a closed glottis and contracting the abdominal muscles ; emptying of the anal canal is completed by contracting the levator ani muscles, which also restores the everted mucous membrane.

Colonic secretion. The colonic mucosa contains very large numbers of mucous cells ; and Florey has shown that a secretion of mucus, accompanied by vasodilatation and contractions of the muscle, is produced by stimulation of the parasympathetic nerve supply, the pelvic visceral nerves. Stimulation of the sympathetic supply causes vasoconstriction and inhibition of movements without secretion.

Absorption of the Digestion Products

The Villi. The columnar epithelium of the small intestine is specially adapted for absorption of the products of digestion by the presence of the villi. These are finger-like projections of the surface, about 0·5 mm. long and containing a strand of muscle from the muscularis mucosæ, blood-vessels, nerves, and a central lymph vessel termed a lacteal ; the surface available for absorption is thus greatly increased. Between the villi open the mouths of the intestinal glands.

During fasting, the villi are shrunken and motionless ; but during digestion they swell up, due to the increased blood and lymph-flow through them, and contract rhythmically and independently of each other (Fig. V. 18). These movements are probably of value in maintaining a good circulation through each villus and ensuring that this is constantly brought into contact with fresh portions of the intestinal contents. The water-soluble products of digestion, such as the amino-acids and sugars, are absorbed into the portal venous blood-stream and so pass through the liver before gaining the general circulation.

The pressure in the portal vein is about 20 mm. Hg., which is higher than the hydrostatic pressure of the intestinal contents. The intestinal wall, however, is impermeable to colloids, so that unless there is an appreciable colloid osmotic pressure within the intestine, water may well be absorbed as a result of the colloid osmotic pressure of the plasma proteins. The end result of the digestive processes is the breakdown of all colloidal material into crystalloidal ; finally, the intestinal contents will exert no colloid osmotic pressure. But in the intermediate stages there may well be a substantial colloid concentration, and water may be drawn in from the blood. Similarly, any substances which can diffuse through the intestinal wall will do so if their concentrations within the intestine are greater than those in the blood ; if there is no such concentration gradient in either direction, they will be carried through with the water. There is reason to believe that some sub-

Fig. V. 18. Portion of a Cinematograph Film following the **Movements of the Villi** in the Living Intestine of the Dog.

The interval between each frame is approximately one second. Note that the villus indicated by the arrow in the right-hand frame becomes progressively shorter until it can only just be seen in the third and fourth frames from the right ; it then becomes longer again, and is only a little shorter in the last frame than it is in the first. (Kokas and Ludàny.)

stances of relatively small molecular weight normally leave the intestine in this way. On the other hand, other substances are transferred from the intestine to the blood proportionately more rapidly when in low concentration than in high, and sometimes appear to move against the concentration gradient ; some unknown secretory process must be involved in these cases. As examples, we may mention urea, xylose and erythritol, which appear to be absorbed by diffusion only, while glucose and most amino-acids seem to be assisted through the intestinal wall by active participation of the mucosal cells ; mannitol, a homologue of erythritol of greater molecular weight, and the disaccharides, are hardly absorbed at all. Similarly, chlorides are absorbed rapidly, but sulphates are only absorbed very slowly.

Such feats on the part of the intestinal epithelium are reminiscent of those performed by the kidney tubule cells in producing urine from the glomerular filtrate ; and the intracellular mechanisms involved are no doubt similar.

Absorption of Fat. During the absorption of a fatty meal, the lymphatics draining the intestine can be seen to be filled with a creamy fluid *chyle* which consists of lymph loaded with globules of neutral fat. This very early observation (Asellius, 1622) gave rise to the natural assumption that the emulsified fat in the intestine was absorbed unchanged, much as oil soaks through paper ; but Claude Bernard's discovery (1846) of the powerful lipase present in the pancreatic juice originated the view which is generally accepted to-day, that the greater

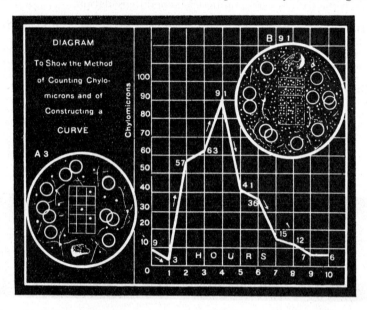

FIG. V. 19. Chylomicron curve and two microscopic fields : (A) before and (B) after a meal of fat. (From S. H. Gage and P. A. Fish.)

part of the fat is hydrolysed in the small intestine before absorption ; the liberated fatty acids enter the mucosal cells and are there resynthesised into neutral fat, which passes into the central lacteal of the

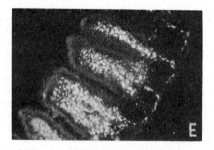

FIG. V. 20. A fluorescence photograph of the small intestine of a rat during the absorption of fat containing vitamin A. The fluorescent material is visible in the epithelium, central lacteal of the villus and submucosal lymphatics. (Popper and Greenberg.)

villus and is ultimately discharged into the systemic venous blood via the thoracic duct. Most of the fat in the blood after a meal is in the form of minute droplets 0·5–1·0 μ in diameter—the *chylomicrons*—which consist of neutral fat covered with a thin film of protein (Fig. V. 19).

Fig. **V. 20** shows a photomicrograph taken by ultraviolet radiation of the intestine of a rat during absorption of fat containing vitamin A ; the fluorescent fatty material is seen in the intestinal epithelium, central lacteal of the villus and in the submucosal lymphatics.

Bernard also showed that the presence of the bile was necessary for the absorption of fat, as indicated by the appearance of chyle in the intestinal lymphatics ; the fatty acids liberated by lipolysis in the small intestine do not form soaps but are kept in solution and rendered absorbable by the bile salts.

Besides the lymphatic pathway for the absorption of fat, there is an alternative route—the portal venous blood. It has been suggested that some of the fatty acids pass in this way directly to the liver, without participating in resynthesis, but the evidence is conflicting. Again, the possibility that intestinal lipolysis is normally incomplete and that some of the emulsified fat is absorbed unchanged, as was once assumed, cannot at present be excluded.

CHAPTER VI

METABOLISM AND NUTRITION

ONE of the outstanding characteristics of the living animal is its ability to maintain itself as an individual, separate from its surroundings. The tissues forming the animal body are composed of chemical substances all of which are derived from its environment, and in the course of the animal's life these substances are returned to that environment many times over. In spite of this dynamic equilibrium the living animal maintains its individuality and indeed life is the continuity of this individuality. At death the continuity is broken, and the elements which composed the animal body become once more part of the environment. This maintenance of the individual depends on an elaborate series of chemical processes and the combination of all these reactions is called metabolism. These chemical reactions can be regarded mainly as of two kinds. The first of these is concerned with the building up of the complex substances of the body tissues out of simpler substances. These processes are responsible for the maintenance of the tissues by replacement of the loss due to wear and tear, and in addition to this, in the young animal they are responsible for growth and development. These synthesising reactions (sometimes grouped together under the term anabolism) do not supply the energy which the body needs for carrying out its functions ; indeed, they themselves require a certain amount of energy from some other source. The source of this energy, and also of the energy which the body needs for its other activities, is provided by a second set of chemical reactions which are grouped together under the term catabolism. In these reactions more complex chemical substances are broken down into simpler ones, and this disintegration, which is mostly of an oxidative nature, is accompanied by liberation of energy. The complex substances, capable of yielding energy on oxidation are taken into the body as food, and it has already been seen how the breaking-down process begins in the intestine. The digestion, however, is not an oxidative process, and is not accompanied by liberation of an appreciable amount of energy. This takes place after the food has been absorbed into the blood stream, and it is to those changes subsequent to absorption that the term metabolism is generally applied.

The general aim of metabolic studies is to determine how the chemical energy of the food substances is used for carrying out contraction of muscles, secretion of glands, transmission of impulses along nerves, growth of tissues and the other activities characteristic of the living animal. The present position of the problem is that a very great deal is known about the chemical reactions which occur and the amount of energy made available, but relatively little is known about how this energy is used by the tissues for their purposes. Consequently most of this chapter is devoted to an account of the chemical processes occuring in metabolism, the methods used for their study, the end products produced and the energy relations involved in these processes.

GENERAL METHODS OF METABOLIC STUDIES

The actual oxidative processes take place in the separate cells which compose the body, but the provision of the metabolic fuel, and the utilisation of the energy liberated, is only possible when the cells are organised into tissues, organs, individuals and indeed societies of individuals. On the other hand many of the chemical reactions cannot easily be studied in the whole animal, but only on isolated organs or tissues. Hence it is necessary to study metabolic problems at a series of different levels of biological organisation, *i.e.*, to study the metabolism of individual cells, of isolated tissues, of organs and of individuals. From the disconnected pieces of information obtained from these different sources we try to form a composite picture of the whole process of metabolism. Each type of metabolic experiment has its own special use. In the case of the whole animal we can administer substances by mouth, intravenously, intraperitoneally or subcutaneously, collect the waste products in the urine, estimate chemically the changes in the blood, measure the gaseous metabolism, and thus study the energy relationships under physiological conditions. In particular, studies on the whole animal are essential for investigation of the effect of hormones on metabolism and the total nutritional requirement of the individual. Under this heading must also be placed the mass of clinical observation which has contributed greatly to our knowledge of physiological processes in the field of metabolism. Experiments with isolated organs make possible a rather fuller study of the chemical changes undergone by the food substances, and also bring the oxidative processes into relationship with the special activity of each particular organ. The use of isolated tissues has made possible a very detailed study of the enzyme systems of the body and of the chemical changes brought about by these, even although the tissues in the experiments are not working under physiological conditions. The study of the individual cells has shown that at least some of the enzymes can be located in definite cells, and even possibly in definite positions in the cell.

The Respiratory Quotient

Whatever method we use to investigate metabolism we consider the amount of oxygen used, the amount of carbon dioxide formed, the nature and amount of the foodstuff oxidised and the energy liberated, and all these must bear a strict relationship to each other. Since of these quantities the amounts of carbon dioxide and of oxygen are often the simplest to measure, and also because they give easily obtainable quantitative information about metabolism, it is of great importance to understand their full significance.

If the food substance being oxidised is glucose, the reaction (or rather the sum total of a large number of intermediate reactions) is as follows :

$$C_6H_{12}O_6 + 6O_2 = 6CO_2 + 6H_2O$$

Since the volumes of gases are proportional to the numbers of molecules present, the volume of carbon dioxide formed will be exactly equal to the volume of oxygen used. The ratio of carbon dioxide produced to oxygen used is called the respiratory quotient, and in this case is equal to one. In a similar way if equations for the oxidation of fats are written down the respiratory quotient can be calculated for each case ; thus for triolein

$$C_{57}H_{104}O_6 + 80\ O_2 \rightarrow 57\ CO_2 + 52\ H_2O$$

The respiratory quotient in this case is 57/80 or 0·71. In the case of proteins, it is not possible to work out the respiratory quotient in this simple way, but from a knowledge of the percentage composition of the protein, and the products of oxidation in the body, it is possible to calculate that the respiratory quotient is about 0·8.

The respiratory quotient for all forms of carbohydrate is 1·0. The exact value of the respiratory quotient will vary for different fats and proteins, but by taking a mean value for those normally present in the food it can be determined that the respiratory quotient for a diet consisting of fat would be 0·71 and for protein 0·81. A knowledge of the respiratory quotient therefore gives us information about the type of food which is actually being oxidised, and since the energy liberated by a certain amount of oxygen depends on the nature of the substance oxidised, it is evident that from the amount of oxygen used and from the respiratory quotient much information can be obtained about metabolic activities. The significance of the respiratory quotient will be considered more fully later in connection with the metabolism of the whole animal.

Tissue Metabolism

Under suitable conditions the cells and tissues of the body will continue to respire and metabolise even after they have been removed from their normal environment and are no longer in their physiological relationship as parts of a living animal. The requisites for respiration in isolated tissues are a supply of available oxygen, the maintenance of normal body temperature, and the provision of a suitable medium. Provided these are present, tissues, finely minced or cut into thin slices, can use oxygen, carry out oxidative reactions, and produce carbon dioxide. To measure these respiratory activities, microrespirometers are used, the usual type being that developed by Warburg.

The tissue, either minced or sliced, is put into a glass vessel which can be attached to a manometer. The manometer is fixed on a stand so that it, together with the attached cup, can be shaken continuously with the cup immersed in a water bath of constant temperature. A centre compartment in the cup contains a small piece of filter paper soaked in caustic soda, and this absorbs the carbon dioxide produced. After introducing the tissue suspended in a suitable saline medium, the whole apparatus is filled with oxygen, and the shaking apparatus is then set in motion. Readings are taken at regular intervals, and the consumption of oxygen is indicated by the change of pressure in the manometer. The manometer cups are usually provided with one or two side arms into which reagents can be put which are to be added during the course of the experiment. Analysis of the contents of the cups can also be made at the end of the experiment and the products of metabolism estimated. There are many modifications of the manometers and cups and it is possible by various techniques to measure the respiratory quotient or the changes taking place anaerobically.

It is important to appreciate the value of the results obtained from these tissue respiration experiments, and this can be done by realising the possibilities of the method and at the same time recognising its limitations. All the reactions which can be demonstrated by such a technique do not necessarily take place in the tissues under physiological conditions, and furthermore, we derive no information about how the tissues utilise the energy liberated by the reactions which occur. At the same time the method is invaluable for studying the various enzyme systems present in the cells, and for seeing what substances do actually take part in the chemical reactions in the tissues. From the study of minced and sliced tissues it has been found that the respiration of the cells depends on a large number of complex substances, which are called " carriers." These are substances existing in oxidised and reduced forms which are mutually interconvertible by oxidation and reduction. By alternate oxidation and reduction they can transport hydrogen by accepting it from one substance and giving it up to another. As a result of a chain of carriers, the hydrogen of the food-substance (in experiments of this type, called " substrate ") is brought into contact with the oxygen in the tissues in a series of reactions, and at each stage there is liberation of a fraction of the energy. The ultimate fuel of the tissues is thus seen to be hydrogen, and during the series of reactions, carbon dioxide is split off at some stage by a process of decarboxylation, a type of reaction not itself associated with a large energy production. Among the substances which may take part in these " carrying " processes are the pyridine nucleotides (coenzymes I and II) the flavoproteins, the cytochromes, the four-carbon atom dicarboxylic acids, glutathione, ascorbic acid (vitamin C), and various oxidases and dehydrogenases. The microrespirometer technique also lends itself to the study of substances which stimulate or depress metabolism, and the study of inhibiting substances is particularly valuable. If the inhibiting substance interferes with some particular stage in metabolism, it may lead to the accumulation of intermediate products of metabolism which would not otherwise be detected.

Metabolism of Isolated Organs

It is often desired to study the metabolism of some particular organ in relation to its functional activity, *e.g.*, to study kidney metabolism in relation to the formation of urine or cardiac metabolism in relation to the pumping activity of the heart. For such purposes it is necessary to use whole organs instead of isolated tissues, but it is also necessary to separate in some way the metabolism of the organ being investigated from the metabolism of the animal as a whole.

Perfusion Experiments. One method of attacking such a problem is to supply the organ with nutrient material and oxygen by an artificial perfusing system instead of by its own circulation. Defibrinated blood or heparinised blood is usually employed for the purpose, and this is saturated with oxygen, either by passing it through the lungs or through an oxygenator, and is then pumped through the vessels of the organ to be studied. By such a system organs can be kept " alive " for a number of hours after complete isolation from the rest of the body. The metabolism of heart, lungs, liver, kidney, brain and limbs have all been studied in this way. The gaseous metabolism is measured by estimating the volume of oxygen taken up by the blood and the volume of carbon dioxide given off, or alternatively it may be measured by estimating the contents of oxygen and carbon dioxide in the blood supplying and leaving the organ and also the rate of blood flow. In some cases, *e.g.*, heart and voluntary muscle, the physical work done can be measured and compared with the rate of metabolism, in other cases, *e.g.*, the kidney, the osmotic work can be studied. In some organs, however, such as the brain, it is very difficult to get any clear idea of the relation between functional activity and metabolism.

Metabolism of Organs in Situ. Another method of studying the metabolism of individual organs is to leave the organ *in situ*, and measure the oxygen and carbon dioxide content of the arterial and venous blood together with the rate of blood flow. For this purpose it is very useful to have an apparatus which will register continuously the amount of oxygen in the arterial and venous blood.

The amount of oxygen in the blood can be registered by applying to the blood vessel a small instrument consisting of a source of light which is directed through the blood in the artery and then falls on a suitable colour filter and photo-electric cell. Since the colour of the blood is altered when oxygen is taken up or given off the amount of light falling on the photo-cell will also vary with the degree of oxygenation of the blood. As the variation in the illumination of the photo-cell can be electrically recorded the apparatus can be arranged to register the oxygen content of the arterial and venous blood.

The Metabolism of the Intact Animal

When the metabolism of the whole animal is considered it is usually not in terms of the intermediate products of metabolism but rather of the sum total of the metabolic reactions, *i.e.*, the amount of food and of oxygen used and the amount of carbon dioxide and waste products formed. It is also possible to measure the total heat production of the animal and the amount of physical work carried out, so that balance sheets can be prepared of the total intake and output of energy in all its various forms, thermal, chemical, mechanical, etc. Very careful measurements of these energy relations have shown that the animal body behaves exactly like all other chemical or mechanical systems as regards the law of the conservation of energy, in that the total energy produced is equal to the total energy supplied. The vital activities of the body are in no way a creation of energy but simply a transference of energy from one form to another. The particularly " vital " part of the process is that some of these energy transformations can only take place in living tissues and so far have not been imitated in non-biological systems.

The Energy Value of the Foods. In order to prepare our complete balance sheet we require to know the energy values of the foods taken. For this purpose we assume that oxygen is freely available and therefore consider the amount of energy capable of liberation by oxidation of the food. This can be determined outside the body by means of the bomb calorimeter.

This consists of a strong steel chamber, which can be sealed by a tightly fitting lid. Into the chamber a measured quantity of the food substance is introduced and the whole apparatus filled with oxygen at high pressure. The bomb calorimeter is now placed in a known volume of water at a certain temperature. Combustion of the contained substance is initiated electrically and the amount of heat produced is estimated from measurement of the rise in temperature of the surrounding water.

By means of the bomb calorimeter it is found that 1 g. of carbohydrate produces 4·1 kilocalories, 1 g. of fat 9·2 kilocalories, and 1 g. of protein 5·3 kilocalories. These are the energy values when combustion is complete. In the body this is not the case, though with fat and carbohydrate the loss is a negligible one and occurs only in the alimentary tract. In the case of protein the end product, urea, is still capable of further oxidation though not inside the body, and hence the energy value of the urea must be subtracted from that of the protein. Making these corrections the values for the three types of food are : carbohydrate and protein each 4·1 kilocalories per g. and fat 9·2 kilocalories per g. Knowing these values and also the amount of each food substance in the diet we can calculate the total energy provided by the food. This knowledge of the energy content of food is essential in making up diets for people under various conditions.

Energy Production from Oxygen Intake. The food taken into the body gives the total energy intake but it does not tell us the rate of metabolism at any one time, since the food is not all used immediately but may in part be stored. The rate of metabolism is derived from the oxygen intake, for we know the oxygen intake only keeps pace with the immediate metabolic needs. The oxygen intake alone, however, does not give the desired information since different foods will yield a different energy production on combustion with the same amount of oxygen. It is essential to have information about the type of food being metabolised at the particular time, and such knowledge, as we have seen, can be obtained from the respiratory quotient.

Respiratory Quotient in Man. Since the respiratory quotient varies with the type of food taken, the problem is to determine what combination of *three* food substances will give a particular observed respiratory quotient. This is done as follows. The total nitrogen in the urine is estimated over a known time. By multiplying this value by 6·25 one can calculate the total amount of protein metabolised during that period. (The average amount of nitrogen in dietary proteins is 16 per cent.) We can further calculate the amount of oxygen needed to oxidise this protein in the body and the amount of carbon dioxide produced. These amounts of oxygen and carbon dioxide are now subtracted from the total amounts of the oxygen and carbon dioxide involved in metabolism, and the resultant figures give the oxygen used and the carbon dioxide produced in non-protein metabolism. Since there are now only two substances to be dealt with, fat and carbohydrate, and since we know the respiratory quotient corresponding to each, we can calculate the proportions of each necessary to give the respiratory quotient of the non-protein metabolism. In practice one gets the result from tables already worked out for each possible respiratory quotient. (Table VI. 1). Such tables also give the energy production per litre of oxygen for each respiratory quotient so that the total energy production can readily be calculated once the total oxygen consumption and the non-protein respiratory quotient are known.

Since the respiratory quotient for protein is intermediate between that for fat and for carbohydrate it is often considered sufficiently accurate to neglect altogether protein metabolism, and treating the whole metabolism of the animal as non-protein metabolism, to make the calculations accordingly.

TABLE VI. 1

The relation between the Respiratory Quotient, the relative amounts of fat and carbohydrate oxidised, and the energy production of the non-protein metabolism.

Non-protein Respiratory Quotient		1·00	0·95	0·90	0·85	0·80	0·75	0·718
Per cent total O_2 consumed by carbohydrate		100	82	65	47	29	11	0
Grams Foodstuff per litre O_2	Carbohydrate	1·23	1·01	0·80	0·58	0·36	0·14	0
	Fat	0	0·09	0·18	0·27	0·36	0·45	0·50
	Total	1·23	1·10	0·98	0·83	0·72	0·59	0·50
Kilocalories per litre O_2		5·05	4·99	4·94	4·88	4·83	4·77	4·74

Methods of Determining Metabolism in Man

These methods depend on the estimation of the gaseous metabolism, and while many techniques are used, they mostly fall into two groups, the open methods and the closed methods, the difference between these being that in the former the subject breathes freely from the atmosphere and only the expired air is collected while in the latter there is a closed system into and out of which the subject breathes.

Open Methods. The subject breathes through a mouthpiece containing valves so that the expired air can be collected in a Douglas bag. This is a large flexible bag of material impermeable to the respiratory gases. The volume of the expired air in a given time can thus be

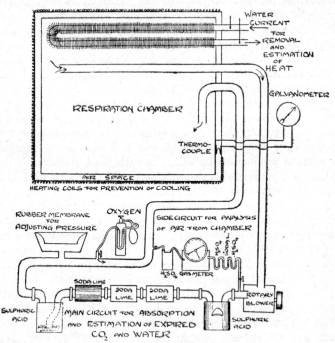

Fig. VI. 1.   Diagram to Illustrate the Principle of the **Atwater-Benedict Respiration Calorimeter.**

The upper part represents the calorimeter, in which the subject is placed, and his heat production measured in terms of the rise in temperature and rate of flow of the cooling water (in practice the cooling pipes are carried right round the chamber).

The lower part represents the **Benedict Respiration Apparatus,** in which the carbon dioxide produced by the subject is absorbed by the soda-lime, and the oxygen used is replaced from the cylinder through a meter (not shown) at such a rate as to keep the rubber membrane of the pressure equaliser in a constant position. The gas is dried in the sulphuric acid bottles before entering the carbon dioxide absorbers, since soda-lime absorbs water as well as carbon dioxide. Any water that may be evolved from the soda-lime in its reaction with carbon dioxide is absorbed in the second sulphuric acid bottle.

When the respiration apparatus is used for indirect calorimetry only, the tubes leading to the calorimeter are connected to a mouth-piece, which is held between the subject's teeth, his nose being closed by a clip. (Parson's "Fundamentals of Biochemistry.")

measured, and by analysis of a sample from the bag the composition can be obtained. From this information the oxygen consumption, carbon dioxide production and respiratory quotient can be calculated, and hence the metabolism worked out. This method has the advantage of great mobility, as the bag can be fixed on to the subject's back and metabolic studies can be made during the performance of various kinds of work.

Closed Methods. These in general require a less mobile equipment and hence are limited in their use. In the simpler types of apparatus for the human subject the expired air, collected from a mouthpiece supplied with valves, passes over soda lime which absorbs the carbon dioxide. The soda lime is usually contained in a recording spirometer, and from this the subject rebreathes his own expired air freed from carbon dioxide. During this process the volume of the air in the circuit diminishes at a rate equal to the consumption of oxygen, and by recording the volume change by means of the spirometer the rate of oxygen consumption can be measured. It will be noted that in such a method no account is taken of the respiratory quotient, and the metabolism is calculated by assuming an average value for the respiratory quotient.

By means of more elaborate circuits it is possible to measure the carbon dioxide production as well. In such cases the air is circulated by a pump and passes through containers with sulphuric acid to absorb moisture, and with soda lime to absorb carbon dioxide. These can be weighed periodically and hence the production of water and carbon dioxide measured. In these systems, the oxygen consumption is measured by adding oxygen at a known rate so as to replace the amount used. This is most conveniently done by having in the circuit at some point, a sensitive rubber membrane, which will indicate alterations in the total pressure and hence in the volume of the system. Such circuits are often used for small animals. For application to man, Benedict's apparatus is employed. For more complete metabolic estimations in man, this system may be combined with a large respiration chamber, in which the subject can remain for a number of days if necessary, the Atwater-Benedict Respiration Calorimeter. This chamber is thermally insulated, and the heat production of the subject is determined by careful measurement of the temperature of a current of water circulated through the respiration chamber. The arrangement of the apparatus is shown diagrammatically in Fig. VI. 1.

By means of such apparatus a complete balance sheet of the energy exchanges in man can be made, and since much can be learned from the study of this, the results of one such experiment are given in Table VI. 2.

The Basal Metabolic Rate

The rate of metabolism depends on the amount of physical work which the body does, and therefore can be reduced by the subject remaining at complete rest. But even when all unnecessary movements are stopped a certain amount of energy is used in maintaining the body temperature and in providing for the needs of circulation, respiration and other vegetative processes, and this cannot be further reduced without damage to the tissues. This amount of metabolism is considered the basal level, on which extra metabolic activities are superimposed when the body undertakes more work. It is called the basal metabolic rate or more usually the B.M.R. One of the functions

TABLE VI. 2

Energy Balance Sheet for Human Subject.

I.—Indirect Calorimetry

Food Ingested.[1]		Class of food.	Food Oxidised.[2]	
Weight, g.	Energy, kcal.		Weight, g.	Energy, kcal.
79·2	448	Protein	64·8	366
59·6	569	Fat	117·8	1,124
201·0	842	Carbohydrate	226·3	948
339·8	1,859	Total	408·9	2,438
69·1	579	From body stores (*i.e.*, excess of food oxidised over food ingested).		
408·9	2,438	Total	408·9	2,438

II.—Direct Calorimetry

Heat produced, as measured .   .   .   .   2,334 kcal.
Potential energy of urine   .   .   .   .   90 ,,

Total heat produced .   .   .   .   .   2,424 ,,

III.—Test of Law of Conservation of Energy

Heat production as calculated from results of
   indirect calorimetry .   .   .   .   .   2,438 kcal.
Heat production as observed by direct calorimetry   2,424 ,,

            Difference .   .   .   14 ,,
                     i.e., 0·6 per cent.

[1] Corrected for losses in digestion and absorption.
[2] Calculated from respiratory exchange.

of this basal metabolism in warm blooded animals is to keep the body temperature above that of its surroundings, and since the loss of heat from the body takes place from the surface exposed to the atmosphere it is not surprising to find that the B.M.R. is more closely related to the body surface than to the body weight. This is well illustrated in Table VI. 3. which gives the B.M.R. for animals of different sizes expressed per unit weight and per unit body surface.

TABLE VI. 3

The Basal Metabolic Rates of Various Animals.

Animal	Weight in kg.	Kilocalories produced per day	
		per kg. of weight.	per sq. m. of surface.
Horse . . .	441	11·3	948
Pig . . .	128	19·1	1,078
Man . . .	64·3	32·1	1,042
Dog . . .	15·2	51·5	1,039
Mouse . . .	0·018	212	1,188

The area of the body surface is not an easy quantity to measure directly, but it is usually obtained from the height and weight by means of the following formula of Du Bois,

$$S = 0 \cdot 007184 \times W^{0 \cdot 425} \times H^{0 \cdot 725}$$

where S is the body surface in sq. metres, W the weight in kilograms

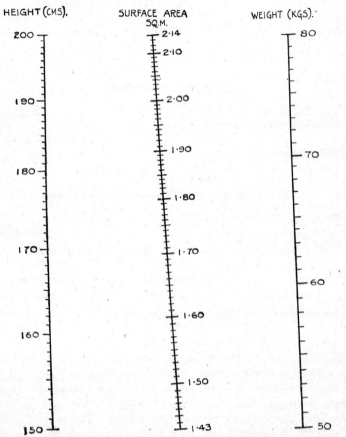

Fɪɢ. VI. 2.　Alignment Chart for calculation of the area of the body surface from the height and weight.　(W. A. M. Smart).

and H the height in centimetres. It can be obtained more easily from nomograms based on this formula (Fig. VI. 2).

In a well-nourished man the B.M.R. has been found to be about 1,800 kilocalories per day. This is equivalent to about 40 kilocalories per square metre body surface per hour or to about 1 kilocalorie per kg. body weight per hour. It varies with sex and with age, being higher in males and young people. In expressing the B.M.R. of an individual, it is usual to express it as a percentage increase or decrease above or below these standard values. Normal individuals vary within about 15 per cent from the standard values.

Since the metabolic activities of the body can be increased by taking food or by performance of work, it is very important in measuring the B.M.R. that the subject should be at complete mental and physical rest and should be in a condition of fasting for about 12 hours. Extremes of temperature, previous diet, previous exercise, emotion or menstruation may all have some effect on the result.

The Thyroid Gland and the Basal Metabolic Rate. Of the pathological causes of alteration in the B.M.R. the commonest is abnormal activity of the thyroid gland. In diseases where there is thyroid deficiency as in cretinism and myxœdema, there is a low B.M.R. and this can be increased by administration of thyroid extract. In exophthalmic goitre there is hyperthyroidism and here the B.M.R. is considerably increased. Surgical removal of part of the thyroid gland leads to a fall in the B.M.R. along with alleviation of the other symptoms. The active principle in the thyroid which is responsible for the effect on metabolism is thyroxine and is discussed in Chapter XV. The stimulating effect of this and related compounds on metabolism has been used for their biological assay. Since pure thyroxine is administered in quantities of the order of milligrams, which may increase the metabolic rate by some 200 kilocalories per day, its action is clearly independent of any specific dynamic action it may have as an amino-acid. This could not amount to more than a small fraction of a calorie.

Specific Dynamic Action

Under basal conditions a certain amount of metabolism is going on at the expense of the body tissues and stores, resulting in a certain rate of energy production. If food is given to a fasting animal it is found that not only is it used to replace the body tissues as metabolic fuel, but it also causes an increase in the metabolism. If sufficient protein is given to liberate 100 kilocalories during metabolism, then the basal metabolism is increased by 30 kilocalories. This effect is called the specific dynamic action. It is shown by fat and carbohydrate also, but to a lesser extent. If sufficient fat or carbohydrate is given to liberate 100 kilocalories then the extra metabolism is 4 kilocalories in the case of fat, and 6 in the case of carbohydrate. The exact cause of the specific dynamic action is uncertain, but is thought to be due to chemical changes carried out by the body on the food substances preparatory to oxidation. The specific dynamic action of protein has been most studied on account of its greater magnitude. If certain amino-acids are injected into the blood stream, they produce a specific dynamic action equal to that of the corresponding amount of protein, so that the effect cannot be due to digestion. The specific dynamic action of protein is prevented by previous removal of the liver, and this would suggest that the effect is probably concerned with deamination of the amino-acids or formation of urea rather than with stimulation of cellular metabolism generally.

The Use of Isotopes in Metabolism

A new phase in the study of metabolism commenced with the introduction of isotopes as a means of following the chemical changes which take place in the body. Besides the ordinary forms in which the elements are usually known there are isotopes. The different isotopes of an element are chemically indistinguishable from each other, although they can be separated by certain physical measurements. If compounds be prepared containing these isotopes, many experiments have shown that the body does not treat them in any respect differently from the corresponding compounds containing the ordinary forms of the element. For example, amino-acids containing nitrogen of atomic weight 15 (N^{15}) follow the same course of chemical changes as do those containing ordinary nitrogen of atomic weight 14. Two kinds of isotope are available for metabolic studies. There are first the naturally occurring isotopes of hydrogen, oxygen, nitrogen, carbon and sulphur. Of these deuterium (the isotope of hydrogen H^2), N^{15} and C^{13} have been extensively used. The great reactivity of oxygen limits very much the value of experiments with O^{18}. In addition to these there are the radioactive isotopes which can be produced for very many elements, and can be used for those elements, e.g., phosphorus, iodine, iron, etc., which are of great interest in metabolic processes, but of which no naturally occurring isotope exists. Both kinds of isotope are extensively used. It is of interest to note that the first experiments of this kind were done with radium D which is a radioactive isotope of lead, in order to investigate the changes undergone by lead in the animal body. The use of isotopes enables certain substances, or even parts of the molecule of the substance to be " labelled," so that they can be again recognised after passing through various chemical transformations. Sometimes two isotopes are introduced into one molecule, e.g., the carbon chain of an amino-acid may be labelled with C^{13}, while the amino group may be labelled with N^{15} or one of the hydrogen atoms replaced by deuterium. One of the great advantages of isotope studies is that chemical reactions can be investigated on whole animals in natural physiological conditions which previously could only be investigated on isolated tissues or organs, or under abnormal conditions where substances not normally metabolised by the body were used, or where inhibitors had to be used to stop metabolic processes at some particular stage. Some examples of how isotopes have been used in metabolic research will be given in later parts of this chapter.

THE METABOLIC HISTORY OF THE FOOD SUBSTANCES

In the preceding section the general methods of metabolic studies have been discussed, and we can now turn to the special problems of protein, fat, carbohydrate and mineral metabolism. This subject is now so large as to constitute almost a separate science belonging more properly to the domain of biochemistry, and the account given here must necessarily be extremely brief. For a more complete account of the chemical changes undergone by the food substances, the reader is referred to textbooks in biochemistry.

Protein Metabolism

The protein taken in the food is absorbed from the intestine as amino-acids. Some of these amino-acids are subsequently resynthesised to protein to help to replace the worn tissues of the body, or to produce hormones or enzymes. The remaining amino-acids are used to supply energy. The replacement of the worn tissues can be carried out only by protein supplied in the food, whereas the energy supplying function of the protein can be replaced by fat or carbohydrate. Since protein is the most expensive part of the diet, and under many conditions the part most likely to be in short supply, it is important to determine precisely how far it can be replaced by the other food substances, and what is the minimum protein intake. This can be seen by studying the nitrogen balance of the body.

Nitrogen Equilibrium. When an animal is living on an adequate diet and maintaining its weight at a constant level, it takes in a certain amount of nitrogen with the protein of the food, and loses the same amount of nitrogen in the excreta. Such an animal is said to be in

TABLE VI. 4

Establishment of Nitrogen Equilibrium in a Dog after Starvation.

Food.	Nitrogen in Food.	Nitrogen in Excreta.	Difference.
	g.	g.	g.
Starvation	0	4·00	— 4·00
100 g. Meat	4·10	5·56	— 1·46
140 g. Meat	5·74	6·50	— 0·76
165 g. Meat	6·77	7·22	— 0·45
185 g. Meat	7·59	7·80	— 0·21
200 g. Meat	8·20	8·73	— 0·53
230 g. Meat	10·24	10·58	— 0·34
360 g. Meat	11·99	12·05	— 0·06
410 g. Meat	15·58	14·31	+ 1·27
360 g. Meat	13·68	13·62	+ 0·06
Starvation 3rd day	0	4·03	— 4·03

nitrogen equilibrium. The nitrogen in the excreta is coming partly from the nitrogen of the food, and partly from the breakdown of protein in the animal's own tissues, this being replaced again from the food. If now the animal be given a diet with ample fat and carbohydrate, but completely lacking in protein, it continues to excrete some nitrogen from its own tissues, and since this is not replaced it loses weight and ultimately dies. If after a short period of nitrogen starvation protein be added to the food in known amounts and at the same time the nitrogen loss estimated, it can readily be determined how much nitrogen must be given in the food to bring the animal back to nitrogen equilibrium. The result of such an experiment is given in Table VI. 4.

From such an experiment two important conclusions can be drawn. First, the minimum protein requirement for the particular animal can be seen. In the example given, an intake of about 360 g. of meat is required to make the intake of protein balance the loss. But another important result appears. The amount of protein which a starving animal excretes is not the amount which is needed to maintain it in nitrogen equilibrium, for it can be seen that by the time it has reached nitrogen equilibrium it is taking in and excreting about four times the amount excreted in the starvation state. The principal reason for this is the following. The protein given in the food does not supply the amino-acids in the proportion required by the body, so that food containing a considerable excess of some may have to be given to supply a sufficient quantity of others. The amount of protein needed to maintain nitrogen equilibrium depends, therefore, on the type of proteins supplied ; and the value of proteins is estimated from the amounts they contain of certain of the amino-acids, which the body cannot manufacture for itself, and which are, therefore, regarded as essential in the diet. If an animal be fed on a protein deficient in any one of these it cannot be kept in nitrogen equilibrium no matter how much of the protein is supplied. An essential amino-acid has been defined as one which cannot be synthesised by the organism out of materials ordinarily available at a speed commensurable with the demands for normal growth. The essential amino-acids as determined for the rat are ; lysine, valine, tryptophan, methionine, histidine, phenylalanine, leucine, isoleucine, threonine and arginine. While there is evidence that this list applies to other animals, it is by no means certain how far it applies to human nutrition.

From the practical aspect the important point is that proteins can be divided into those of high biological value (first-class proteins) and low biological value (second-class proteins), the first group containing the essential amino-acids in proportions approaching those required by the body. Usually by first-class proteins is meant proteins of animal origin (proteins of milk, cheese, meat, eggs, etc.).

The Break-down of Protein. The amino-acids not used for synthesis of body tissues are oxidised with liberation of energy. The first stage in the process is deamination *i.e.*, the removal of the nitrogen-containing group from the rest of the molecule. If amino-acids are injected into the blood stream they are rapidly removed and can be partly recovered from various tissues. Of these the liver has been found to take up the largest quantity. It can further be shown that the amino-acids taken up by the liver gradually disappear, suggesting that they undergo some transformation. At the same time as the amino-acids disappear from the blood there is a rise in the concentration of blood urea. It is possible to keep an animal alive for some time after removal of the liver, and if in such a preparation amino-acids be injected they are only removed slowly from the blood, and there is no increased formation of urea. These experiments together with much other evidence show that the liver plays a very important part in the formation of urea from amino-acids. Urea is one of the end products of protein metabolism. It does not undergo further change and is excreted in the urine. A small fraction of the amino groups is not excreted in this form, but as ammonia, which is formed largely in the kidney itself, the amount being related to the acidity of the urine.

Formation of Urea. If ammonia containing N^{15} be fed to animals the isotope appears in the urea, so that formation of ammonia is probably a preliminary process in the formation of urea. The method of formation of urea from ammonia is still a matter of discussion, but it seems very likely that it depends on a cyclical series of reactions involving ornithine, citrulline and arginine. Ornithine combining with carbon dioxide and ammonia forms first citrulline and then arginine, which is hydrolysed by the enzyme arginase to form urea and ornithine.

Fate of the Non-nitrogenous Residues. The non-nitrogenous part of the amino-acid left after deamination undergoes oxidation, the ultimate products being carbon dioxide and water. In carnivorous animals much of the energy needed by the body is obtained from this source, but in man the amount obtained is relatively small, depending on the excess protein in the diet over the protein minimum. The immediate product of deamination is a keto-acid but the type of keto-acid will vary according to the amino-acid from which it is derived. Some of these keto-acids, *e.g.*, pyruvic acid, are known to be intermediaries in carbohydrate breakdown and could thus provide a route by which the further breakdown of protein might follow the line of carbohydrate metabolism, or by which proteins could cause formation of carbohydrates. It can be shown that this does actually happen under certain conditions. In a diabetic animal or in an animal poisoned with phlorizin, there is a great loss of sugar from the body. (Phlorizin is a drug which causes elimination of sugar through the kidneys without any increase in the blood sugar concentration). In such an animal, the carbohydrate stores are rapidly depleted. If now carbohydrates be withheld from the diet but protein be given it is found that the excretion of glucose continues, and this must have been derived from protein.

The amino-acids which can give rise to glucose during metabolism are glycine, alanine, serine, cysteine, ornithine, proline, oxyproline, aspartic acid and glutamic acid. Some amino-acids, *e.g.*, leucine, phenylalanine and tyrosine do not give rise to glucose, but on perfusion through the liver can be shown to give rise to acetoacetic acid. This is a product of fat metabolism, which under certain conditions accumulates in large quantities in the blood, and gives rise to a condition called ketosis. (See sections on fat and carbohydrate metabolism.) For this reason, leucine, phenylalanine and tyrosine are said to be ketogenic, while those amino-acids which give rise to glucose are said to be anti-ketogenic. A few amino-acids, lysine, valine and tryptophan form neither glucose nor acetoacetic acid.

While the formation of glucose or of acetoacetic acid suggests that these particular amino-acid residues in their further breakdown follow the metabolic pathway of carbohydrates and fats, the exact course followed by each amino-acid is not known with certainty.

Creatinine. This is another end product of protein metabolism. It is formed from creatine (methyl guanidine acetic acid) of which it is the anhydride. Creatine is present in the tissues in the form of creatine phosphate and, in this form, it plays a part in the chemical processes responsible for muscular contraction. Creatinine is regarded as a waste product of muscle metabolism, and is always a normal constituent of the urine. Creatine is not normally present in the urine, but in some cases for reasons not understood it may be a urinary constituent. It often appears in the urine of women, but is apparently not related to the menstrual cycle.

Nucleo-proteins. These are proteins found especially in the nuclei of cells, and they form a small part of the dietary protein. They consist of a protein conjugated with nucleic acid, this latter substance being a combination of a purine or pyrimidine base with phosphoric acid and a pentose. The purines present are adenine and guanine, the pyrimidines, thymine and cytosine. The nucleoproteins are broken down during digestion, and among the products are the purine and pyrimidine bases. The latter after absorption are completely oxidised. The purine bases undergo deamination and partial oxidation to uric acid. In man, this is an end product of nucleoprotein metabolism and is excreted in the urine, but in most mammals it undergoes a further stage of oxidation to allantoin.

Exogenous and Endogenous Metabolism. The main end products of protein metabolism differ considerably in different states of nutrition. The urea output of the body is fairly closely dependent on the amount of protein in the diet. On the other hand the amount of creatinine excreted is almost constant, even during large fluctuations of dietary protein. Uric acid occupies an intermediate position as regards the relation between the amount excreted and the protein intake. The different behaviour of these substances suggested that protein metabolism could be divided into the metabolism of the protein fuel supplied by the diet, and the metabolism of that supplied by the tissues. Since the amount of creatinine did not vary with the diet it was thought to be an index of tissue metabolism, or " endogenous " metabolism, while urea was thought to be an index of " exogenous " metabolism. Recent experiments with isotopes have shown, however, that protein metabolism cannot be divided in this way. Animals were fed with leucine and glycine containing deuterium attached to the carbon chain and N^{15} in the amino group of the molecule. When the excreta were collected and examined, it was found that only a small amount, about one-third, of the isotope had been eliminated from the body. An examination of the different tissues showed that the proteins of the blood, and the proteins of most of the organs contained isotopic leucine and glycine. Since deuterium as well as N^{15} was present in the tissue proteins it proved that not only the amino-group but the whole molecule of the amino-acids given in the food had been incorporated in the tissue proteins. The animals had not gained weight during the process, so that it was not a question of retention of amino-acids to build up extra body tissues. The only possible conclusion was that the amino-acids given had replaced some of the leucine and glycine previously present in the body proteins. This showed that there is a constant synthesis and breakdown of body protein with replacement of the amino-acid molecules by new ones derived from the dietary protein. It is thus not possible to separate the exogenous and the endogenous metabolism, as there is a dynamic equilibrium between the amino-acids in the body tissues and those in the blood stream. Further investigation showed that the replacement of the tissue proteins applied not only to the isotopic amino-acids given in the diet. When isotopic leucine or glycine was fed, other amino-acids isolated from the tissues contained the N^{15}. This indicated that the N^{15} supplied in the leucine and glycine had been used for the synthesis of other amino-acids to supply new units for the tissue protein. Even when abundant quantities of some particular amino-acid are supplied in the diet synthesis of this amino-acid still occurs.

Lipoid Metabolism

The term lipoid is applied to a number of different classes of substances which occur in the animal body and in the diet. These are ; (1) the simple triglycerides of fatty acids (the fats proper), ; (2) the sterols and their esters with fatty acids, and (3) the more complex phospholipoids and cerebrosides. Of these the fats proper form the greatest bulk of the tissue and dietary lipoid and most of this section will be devoted to them.

The Sterols. The sterols are mono-atomic alcohols characterised by the presence in the molecule of the cholane ring. Among the sterols which have biological significance the most important is cholesterol, which is very widely distributed in living tissues. Coprosterol is a product of cholesterol metabolism, which occurs in the fæces. Ergosterol has great interest as a precursor of vitamin D. A number of other substances of great biological importance are closely related chemically to cholesterol. These include the bile acids, the sex hormones, and the adrenal cortical hormones.

Cholesterol is found in the body both free and in the form of waxes, *i.e.*, in combination with fatty acids. These are the only waxes occurring in the higher animals. Little is known about their metabolism.

Phospholipoids. The important phospholipoids are lecithin, cephalin and sphingomyelin. These substances consist of glycerol, fatty acids, phosphoric acid and certain nitrogenous bases, choline in the case of lecithin and sphingomyelin, and cholamine in the case of cephalin. Sphingomyelin contains also the base sphingosine. The phospholipoids are concerned in fat transport in the body.

Cerebrosides. These are substances containing the base sphingosine, fatty acids and galactose. Little is known about their function and metabolism. The important representatives are phrenosine and kerasine.

Fats. The fatty acids present in the body fat are restricted to those with even numbers of carbon atoms in the molecule. Of these all members of the series from acetic acid (2 carbon atoms) to stearic acid (18 carbon atoms) have been found, but by far the most important quantitatively are the 16 and 18 carbon atom fatty acids, palmitic $C_{15}H_{31}COOH$ and stearic $C_{17}H_{35}COOH$, together with the unsaturated oleic acid $C_{17}H_{33}COOH$. These three in the form of their glycerol esters make up most of the body fats.

Unsaturated Fatty Acids. More highly unsaturated fatty acids, linoleic and linolenic, occur in the body, and play an important though unknown part in metabolism. They cannot be synthesised in the body, and if not supplied in the diet of rats symptoms of deficiency appear in the form of skin disturbances.

The physical properties of the body fat depend on the varying proportions of the constituent fatty acids, and are more or less characterisitic for each species. This constancy of body fat is, however, dependent on dietary habit and if an animal be starved so as to reduce its fat stores and then fed with an unusual type of fat, it is quite easy to alter the nature of its body fat as regards physical and chemical properties, *e.g.*, melting point, iodine number, saponification value, etc.

The Storage of Fat. There are certain parts of the body where the fat content can be greatly altered, and such parts like the omentum and the subcutaneous tissues can act as fat depots. When an animal is putting on weight fat is laid down in these stores, and when it is living on its reserves the fat in these parts diminishes before other parts of the body are called on to contribute their share of metabolic fuel. The source of this depot fat we have just seen is the dietary fat, of which a part is used directly for oxidation and part is laid down as storage in the fat depots. Recent experiments, in which fat containing deuterium has been fed to animals, have shown that the depots do not consist of a static deposit of storage fat, but that the fat laid down is constantly being used and replaced.

It has also been well established that the non-fat part of the diet can contribute to the fat stores. This was demonstrated by the classical experiments of Lawes and Gilbert in 1852. Young pigs were fed on a diet of barley containing very little fat, and it was found that the amount of body fat present when the animals were killed was greater than could have been obtained from the fat supplied or even the fat and protein together, thus proving that carbohydrate can be converted into fat. Whether or not fat can be derived in the body from protein is uncertain.

Interconversion of Fat and Carbohydrate. Possible chemical reactions have been suggested which may be concerned in this conversion.

Glycerol is known to be produced in small quantities during fermentation of glucose by yeast, and it is possible that a similar production can occur in the body. The formation of fatty acids probably takes place from pyruvic acid, which is an intermediary product of carbohydrate metabolism. Various schemes, mostly involving acetaldehyde, have been proposed to explain the formation of the long carbon chain, but definite evidence is lacking that acetaldehyde can be formed from pyruvic acid by animal carboxylases, and the details of the synthesis must be regarded as unknown. The fatty acid thus produced combines with glycerol to form neutral fat. The process of fat production from carbohydrate requires the participation of certain vitamins of the B group. Besides aneurin (vitamin B_1) probably riboflavin and pantothenic acid are essential.

One important aspect of the interconversion of fat and carbohydrate in the body is the effect on the gaseous exchanges. While the respiratory quotient usually depends only on the type of food being oxidised it will also be affected by the interconversion of fat and carbohydrate. Inspection of the formula of glucose and a typical fat shows that the latter contains fewer atoms of oxygen per carbon atom than the former, and hence when fat is being formed from carbohydrate, oxygen will be freed for use in general metabolism and so less will be taken into the body from the lungs. Since the carbon dioxide production and excretion remains unchanged the respiratory quotient will be abnormally high. An example of this process is seen in the behaviour of those animals which hibernate. At the end of summer when they are building up large reserves of fat from carbohydrate to last over the winter, the respiratory quotient is abnormally high, and may reach a value of 1·5.

The Oxidation of Fat. The fats utilised by the body normally undergo complete oxidation with formation of carbon dioxide and water. Since the fatty acid molecules have a chain of 16 or 18 carbon atoms, there must be a large number of intermediate products formed during the oxidation, but as these are rapidly further oxidised, it is not possible by isolating them to determine the complete course of fat oxidation. Evidence as to how oxidation might proceed was obtained by Knoop's method of feeding to animals fatty acids containing a benzene ring attached to the carbon chain.

If benzoic acid is fed to animals it is found to be conjugated with glycine to form hippuric acid, and this is excreted in the urine.

$$C_6H_5.COOH + NH_2.CH_2.COOH = C_6H_5CONH.CH_2.COOH$$

If phenylacetic acid is fed, the excretory product is phenaceturic acid, which again represents a conjugation with glycine.

$$C_6H_5.CH_2.COOH + NH_2.CH_2.COOH = C_6H_5CH_2.CONH.CH_2.COOH$$

If phenyl derivatives of higher fatty acids are fed, it is found that the product of excretion is always either hippuric acid or phenaceturic acid, depending on whether there is an even or odd number of carbon atoms in the side chain. Thus hippuric acid was produced from $C_6H_5.COOH, C_6H_5.CH_2.CH_2.COOH$ and $C_6H_5.CH_2.CH_2CH_2.CH_2.$ COOH, while phenaceturic acid was given by $C_6H_5.CH_2COOH$, C_6H_5 .$CH_2.CH_2.CH_2.COOH$., and $C_6H_5.CH_2.CH_2.CH_2.CH_2.CH_2COOH$. These findings suggested that during the course of oxidation of the fatty acid chain the carbon atoms are split off in pairs, or in other words, oxidation takes place at the β-carbon atom. Hence this suggested method of fat oxidation was called β-oxidation.

Ketosis. In certain conditions the oxidation of fat is incomplete and certain products appear in the urine, β-hydroxybutyric acid, acetoacetic acid and acetone. These substances are called " ketone bodies," and the condition in which they appear is called ketosis. It occurs typically in diabetes mellitus, but it also occurs in less serious disturbances such as fasting, and severe vomiting. Of these ketone bodies it is known that acetone is formed from acetoacetic acid, and that the primary substances are the four-carbon atom substances, β-hydroxybutyric acid and acetoacetic acid. Probably acetoacetic acid is formed first, but the two substances are known to be interconvertible in the liver. The appearance of ketone bodies in fat metabolism is always related to a lowered oxidation of carbohydrate by the tissues, and this may be brought about either by lack of carbohydrate as in fasting, or by inability of the tissues to oxidise carbohydrate as in diabetes. In the diabetic, the appearance of ketone bodies can always be prevented by administration of insulin with or without carbohydrate (see p. 216); in the non-diabetic, ketosis is prevented by supplying carbohydrate. When the formation of ketone bodies is very great it may be sufficient to lower the alkali reserve of the blood and produce a condition of acidæmia (movement of pH of blood towards the acid side). Note that the term ketosis does not mean the formation of ketone bodies, but only their formation in such amounts as to appear in the urine.

Theories of Ketone Body Formation. According to the β-oxidation theory, the ketone bodies are formed because the oxidation of the carbon chain stops when there are still four carbon atoms remaining, instead of going on to complete combustion. This implies that each molecule of fatty acid could only form one molecule of a ketone body. Actually it has been shown that the amount of ketone bodies formed from fatty acids by the liver is much greater than this, and therefore, other theories of fat oxidation have been put forward. According to the multiple-alternate-oxidation theory the fatty acid molecule is not broken down by successive splitting off of two carbon atom units, but it divides into four-carbon-atom units, and each of these units can give rise to ketone bodies. According to another theory, the β-oxidation-condensation theory, the breakdown of the fatty acid molecules proceeds by successive splitting off of two carbon atom units, and these are then synthesised to form ketone bodies.

Since the experimental evidence in favour of this last view presents a very good illustration of how isotopes may be used in metabolic problems it is given in some detail. The production of ketone bodies is known to take place in the liver. Liver slices are incubated with octanoic acid containing C^{13} in the carboxyl group of the molecule, $(CH_3.(CH_2)_5.CH_2.C^{13}OOH)$. The acetoacetic acid produced is converted into acetone and carbon dioxide, and the acetone treated with iodine to form iodoform. The isotope C^{13} is sought in these products of metabolism and is found to be present in equal amounts in the acetone and in the carbon dioxide formed from acetoacetic acid. When the acetone is decomposed to produce iodoform it is found that there is no isotope in the iodoform. The iodoform is known to be formed from the methyl groups of the acetone, and therefore the isotope in the acetone must be in the carbonyl group. Reference to Fig. VI. 3. will show that the isotope in the acetoacetic acid must therefore have been equally distributed between the carboxyl and the carbonyl groups.

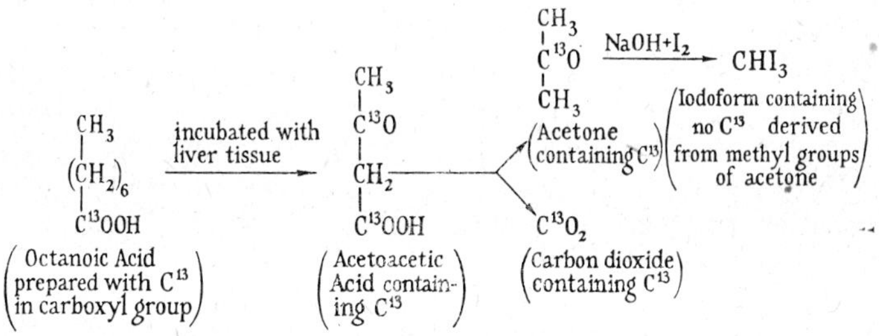

FIG. VI. 3. Method of localisation of C^{13} in the molecule of acetoacetic acid by examination of its breakdown products. The presence of C^{13} in the carbon dioxide and in the acetone, and its absence from the iodoform prove that it was originally present in the carboxyl and carbonyl groups of the acetoacetic acid.

All the isotope in the original octanoic acid was present in the carboxyl group only, so that this carboxyl group must have entered into formation of both halves of the acetoacetic acid molecule. This means that in some molecules it entered into formation of one half, in others into formation of the other half, while into many other molecules it did not enter at all. The formation of acetoacetic acid must therefore have been a random coupling of two carbon atom units derived from the breakdown of the fatty acid. According to the original β-oxidation theory there should have been no C^{13} in the acetoacetic acid, since this would have been derived from the other end of the fatty acid chain. According to the multiple-alternate oxidation theory all the C^{13} in the acetoacetic acid would be present only in the carboxyl group. The distribution of the C^{13} in the final products of reaction is compatible only with the β-oxidation condensation theory.

Ketone Bodies in Metabolism. Until recently ketone bodies were considered merely to be the noxious end-products of disordered metabolism—useless and dangerous substances—which were rapidly excreted from the body. This view is no longer tenable. Many experiments have shown that ketone bodies can be oxidised in tissues such as muscle (both skeletal and cardiac) and that under some conditions their combustion can supply the major part of the energy released by oxidative processes in some organs. Now although ketone bodies may be formed from fatty acids during normal metabolic processes in tissues—the evidence on this point is still incomplete—it is fairly certain that the liver is the only organ which ever produces ketone bodies at such a rate as to liberate them into the blood stream in appreciable amounts. It is probable that such liberation of ketone bodies by the liver occurs at a significant rate only when carbohydrate oxidation in the tissues of the body is for any reason diminished. Ketone liberation by the liver may be regarded as the secretion of an emergency fuel for utilisation in the muscular and other tissues when their supply of carbohydrate is diminished, for example in starvation or when the animal consumes a low-carbohydrate diet, or when the tissues are unable to utilise the carbohydrate available to them at a satisfactory rate, for example, in diabetes. When the liberation of ketone bodies by the liver becomes an important factor in the economy of the animal it usually happens that the rate at which these substances are liberated into the blood stream exceeds the rate at which they are utilised in the tissues in general. Under these conditions ketone bodies tend to accumulate in the blood and, since the renal threshold for them is low, they appear in the urine ; a condition of ketosis and ketonuria is thus established in which a toxic effect of the ketone bodies makes itself manifest, while the acid-base balance is disturbed because of the accumulation of acid in the body and withdrawal of fixed base into the urine. It is clear therefore, that liberation of ketone bodies as emergency fuel into the circulation by the liver is attended by undesirable effects. When the metabolism of carbohydrate is proceeding at a satisfactory rate, it seems very probable that ketone bodies are not formed at such a rate as to lead to their liberation into the circulation in significant amounts. When, however, the rate at which carbohydrate is made available to the body becomes less than the rate at which the tissues need to oxidise carbohydrate or other suitable fuel, the liver glycogen content falls and the liver begins to liberate ketone bodies in place of its diminished supplies of carbohydrate. It may be that the fall in the glycogen content of the liver is the stimulus to ketone body liberation by the liver though this is not certain at present. It is very likely, however, that the hormones of the anterior pituitary gland are concerned in the control of these metabolic changes.

Carbohydrate Metabolism

The greater part of the carbohydrate in the body consists of the glycogen stored in the tissues, principally in the liver and in the muscles, and of the glucose in the blood and tissue fluids. The total amount of carbohydrate present in a well-nourished human body, of which about one-half is present in the liver as glycogen, is equivalent to less than one day's supply at the normal rate of consumption. To this observation we can relate the important fact that carbohydrate can be formed in the body from non-carbohydrate sources.

The carbohydrate absorbed from the small intestine from a normal diet consists largely of three monosaccharides—glucose, fructose and galactose. They are all convertible to glycogen in the liver, and the glycogen so formed breaks down, either by acid hydrolysis *in vitro* or under the influence of the enzyme systems present in liver, to give glucose and no other monosaccharide. In the enzymic formation and hydrolysis of glycogen, phosphoric esters of sugars and of certain other compounds play an essential intermediary role.

The Equilibrium between Glycogen and Glucose. Many years ago Claude Bernard showed that the glycogen of the liver, but not that of the muscles, could break down in the body to give glucose, and that, except after a recent meal containing carbohydrate, the blood leaving the liver contained more sugar than that entering the organ. Other organs of the body, and in particular the muscular tissues, appeared to be continuously absorbing glucose from the blood flowing through them. These important observations established the fact that although the concentration of the sugar in the blood falls only slightly during post-absorptive conditions or even during a long fast, this was not because the tissues ceased to absorb sugar from the blood under these conditions. The relative constancy of the blood sugar concentration in the absence of exogenous carbohydrate was to be ascribed to the fact that the amount of sugar withdrawn from the blood by the tissues in general was counterbalanced by the amount of sugar liberated into the circulation by the liver under these conditions. The importance of this power of the liver to secrete sugar was dramatically emphasised by Mann and his colleagues in 1921, who showed that if the liver is removed from a dog the blood sugar concentration falls rapidly, and death ensues within a few hours unless glucose is administered in large amounts. Undoubtedly some part of the sugar secreted by the liver comes from the glycogen present therein but the stored liver glycogen is quite insufficient to supply the body's needs for very long. We shall take up the question of the source of the sugar secreted by the liver later.

After the ingestion of carbohydrate food the blood sugar concentration rises from its normal post-absorptive value of 0·08–0·1 per cent. to a value in the neighbourhood of 0·15 per cent. As the blood sugar concentration rises the liver secretes less and less sugar until, when the concentration reaches about 0·12 per cent., the liberation of sugar by the liver ceases altogether. At blood sugar concentrations above this, the liver begins to absorb sugar from the blood stream and the liver glycogen content begins to rise. It is clear, therefore, that the glycogen in the liver represents, in part at least, a storehouse for carbohydrate coming from the food. The sugar which is thus stored during the temporary period of plenty is liberated by the liver during the lean period of post-absorptive conditions. The ability of the liver to adjust its output of sugar to the requirements of the body is sometimes described as its " homeostatic mechanism."

Although the skeletal muscles also absorb more glucose when the blood sugar concentration rises after carbohydrate food, the glycogen which accumulates in these tissues is not reconverted to blood glucose during post-absorptive conditions. The glycogen of muscle may be oxidised or it may be converted to lactic acid, but it never forms glucose in the body ; this contrast with events in the liver is to be ascribed to differences between the enzyme systems of liver and muscle tissues.

The process of the formation of lactic acid from glycogen in skeletal muscle is one which does not involve the addition of oxygen nor the elimination of hydrogen from the system. It is accordingly not an oxidation process and can take place under the largely anaerobic conditions which initially obtain in skeletal muscles during exercise. If the exercise is light, any lactic acid formed may be in part reconverted to glycogen in the muscles themselves, but if the exercise is severe most of the lactic acid may escape into the blood stream and is then converted to glycogen in the liver. Therefore, in the presence of the liver, muscle glycogen can give rise to blood glucose indirectly. These relationships will be clear from the diagram.

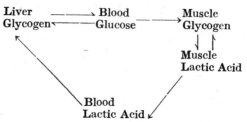

It should be noted that since the formation of lactic acid from glycogen in the muscles liberates energy, the reformation of glycogen from lactic acid requires the addition of energy to the system. In the muscles any energy thus required can be provided, under aerobic conditions, by oxidation of part of the lactic acid formed or equivalent glucose or glycogen. In the liver the source of the energy required for the formation of glycogen from lactic acid is not known with certainty.

Recent investigations with carbon dioxide containing C^{13} suggest that the formation of glycogen in the liver from lactic acid, and even from glucose, may involve the linking up of carbon dioxide with intermediate substances formed, so that the carbon skeleton of the glycogen which accumulates contains a significant proportion of carbon atoms originating from carbon dioxide. This complex subject is one for further research.

Gluconeogenesis. The question now arises : from what sources, other than glycogen stored as the result of the ingestion of carbohydrate-containing food, is sugar formed by the liver ? We have seen in a previous section (p. 203) that proteins can be converted into carbohydrate in the body. Most of the sugar formed in the liver under post-absorptive conditions comes from protein, though a part may be formed from the glycerol portion of natural fats ; according to some though not all investigators, carbohydrate may also be formed from natural fatty acids in the liver. The process of formation of glucose from non-carbohydrate sources, which is conveniently described by the ugly word " gluconeogenesis," is responsible for the maintenance of the blood sugar concentration when carbohydrate is not being ingested at a rate sufficient to supply the needs of the body ; that is during post-absorptive conditions, starvation, and when the animal receives a low-carbohydrate diet. It is under such conditions that ketosis and ketonuria tend to develop (see p. 208).

During starvation or deprivation of carbohydrate, the utilisation of carbohydrate by the muscles and other tissues is diminished and some part of their energy requirements is met by oxidation of ketone bodies. It seems probable, however, that nervous tissue is peculiarly dependent on a constant supply of carbohydrate or similar substances for integrity of function and that hepatic gluconeogenesis is of particular importance in providing the nervous system with one of its requisite metabolites. It should be mentioned that the brain (and the heart also) can oxidise lactic acid as well as glucose and thus can utilise the lactic acid formed anaerobically in skeletal muscle during vigorous exercise.

The Regulation of the Blood-Sugar Concentration. The accurate control of the blood sugar concentration is of the utmost importance in the economy of the human body. If the concentration rises above about 0·18 per cent.—the renal threshold—the re-absorption of sugar from the renal tubules is incomplete and glucose is lost to the body in the urine. If, on the other hand, the concentration falls below about 0·04 per cent., the central nervous system becomes disturbed. In man there is at first extreme hunger and fatigue, with general sweating ; later, delirium and profound coma are produced. In rabbits and certain other mammals, severe convulsions occur in addition just before the coma and death from respiratory failure ; these are known as " *hypoglycæmic convulsions.*" If the condition is not relieved by the administration of glucose, death may ensue. Even if death does not occur as the result of a temporary lowering of the blood sugar concentration, lesions may appear in the brain which involve permanent functional damage.

The mechanism which ensures that the blood sugar concentration normally moves only within the relatively narrow range of 0·08 per cent. to 0·16 per cent., is largely hormonal in character, the chief hormones concerned being adrenaline, insulin and anterior pituitary factors.

(*a*) *Adrenaline.* When the blood sugar concentration falls below about 0·07 per cent., the excitation of nervous centres in the lower part of the brain causes sympathetic stimulation and a release of adrenaline from the adrenal glands. The adrenaline so released stimulates a breakdown of liver glycogen to glucose, the liberation of which tends to arrest the fall of blood sugar concentration. The general sympathetic stimulation may assist this process. Under the influence of adrenaline, muscle glycogen breaks down to lactic acid which may be carried to the liver for reconversion to glycogen and glucose. These several processes tend to prevent a fall in the blood sugar concentration by rapidly mobilising the glycogen stores of the body.

During muscular exercise there is a general stimulation of all the sympathico-adrenal system, so that the rate of breakdown of glycogen in the liver is accelerated on just those occasions when glucose is being used most rapidly by the muscles. As far as we know, however, adrenaline does not directly affect gluconeogenesis in the liver, but can only bring about the breakdown of glycogen which has been stored in that organ.

It was shown many years ago by Claude Bernard that puncture of the floor of the fourth ventricle in the rabbit results in hyperglycæmia and glycosuria ; this is known as " *diabetic puncture*." The hyperglycæmia is due to the excitation of fibres that run into the sympathetic system, with a consequent outpouring of adrenaline.

(*b*) *Insulin*. As we have seen above, when the blood sugar concentration rises as the result of the ingestion of carbohydrate food the liver responds by first diminishing and then abolishing the liberation of sugar into the blood stream, and then proceeds to absorb part of the excess sugar in the blood stream, simultaneously increasing its glycogen content. The ability of the liver to suspend the production of sugar and inhibit gluconeogenesis, and to promote glycogen storage at the expense of the excess glucose in the blood, is dependent on the presence of insulin, the hormone secreted by the islets of Langerhans of the pancreas.

When the blood sugar concentration rises after a carbohydrate meal the excess glucose is stored as glycogen in the muscles as well as in the liver, while in the muscles the rate at which sugar is oxidised may increase under these conditions. All these processes for the storage and utilisation of glucose depend on the availability of insulin, and there is good evidence that the secretion of insulin by the pancreas is stimulated by a rise in the concentration of sugar in the blood ; the controlling action appears to be the direct effect of the excess sugar concentration on the cells of the pancreas, although it is possible that a nervous reflex is also involved. Apart from the formation of glycogen a further process for the storage of energy from excess ingested carbohydrate is the conversion of glucose to fat (glycerides) which are then stored in the fat depots. In general, therefore, insulin may be said to promote those metabolic processes which cause glucose to leave the blood stream (conversion to glycogen or fat, or promotion of carbohydrate oxidation) and to inhibit gluconeogenesis. All these processes tend to lead to a fall of the blood sugar concentration and if a large dose of insulin is given to a normal person in a post-absorptive state, fatal hypoglycæmia may develop.

(*c*) *Anterior pituitary hormones*. An animal from which the anterior pituitary gland is removed becomes abnormally sensitive to the hypoglycæmic action of insulin. Conversely, a normal animal to which anterior pituitary extract is administered becomes highly insensitive to the action of a small dose of insulin in lowering the blood sugar concentration. These observations show that in some respects anterior-pituitary secretion and insulin act antagonistically.

It seems possible that anterior pituitary secretions exert two separate actions on carbohydrate metabolism. The first, attributed to the action of pituitary adrenocorticotropin, stimulates the liberation of adrenalcortical hormones from the adrenal gland, and thus promotes gluconeogenesis, with consequent accumulation of glycogen in the liver. The second action possibly associated with the growth-promoting principle of anterior-pituitary extracts, depresses carbohydrate oxidation in the skeletal muscles with the accumulation of muscle glycogen stores.

Recent experiments by Cori and his colleagues (1945) have shown that anterior-pituitary secretions inhibit the action of the enzyme (muscle hexo-kinase) which catalyses the formation of glucose-6-phosphate from glucose in the muscles. The utilisation of glucose for almost any purpose in the body is probably initiated by the formation of glucose-6-phosphate, so these *in vitro* experiments are of importance as an indication of the possible mecha-nism of action of anterior-pituitary secretions in the inhibition of the utilisa-tion of carbohydrate. Cori and his colleagues have also shown that the

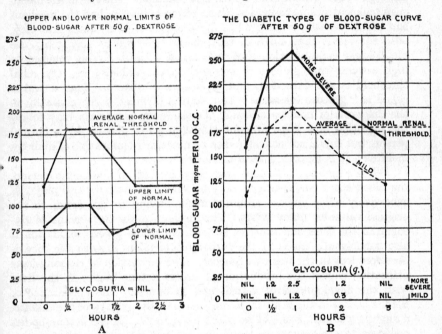

FIG. VI. 4. The Effect of the Ingestion of 50 g. Glucose on the **Concentra-tion of Sugar in the Blood.**

A. Normal Subjects. The concentration is not increased excessively and returns to the initial value within two hours. No sugar is excreted in the urine.

B. *Diabetic Subjects.* The concentration rises to a considerably higher value and takes three hours to return to the initial value. Considerable quantities of sugar are excreted in the urine.

The figures under " glycosuria " indicate the total quantity of sugar excreted in the sample of urine collected at that time. (Harrison's " Chemical Methods in Clinical Medicine.")

inhibition of the muscle hexokinase activity by anterior-pituitary extract is released by insulin acting *in vitro*. The antagonism of anterior-pituitary secretions and insulin has thus been directly demonstrated. Although these observations are of the greatest importance it is clear that they cannot provide a complete explanation of the manifold actions of insulin. For instance, they do not provide an explanation for the hypersensitivity to the hypo-glycæmic action of administered insulin of an animal from which the pituitary gland has been completely removed.

It is clear that the end-result of the various actions of anterior-pituitary secretions on carbohydrate metabolism is in opposition to those processes which lead to a fall of the blood sugar concentration, with a tendency for the blood sugar concentration to rise as the result of increased gluconeogenesis under those conditions in which the sugar thus formed cannot easily be utilised.

Diabetes in Man. If a normal man takes 50 g. of glucose by mouth and the blood sugar concentration is determined at intervals afterwards, the type of curve shown in Fig. VI. 4. is obtained. The rise of the blood-sugar concentration stimulates the secretion of insulin, and the mechanism which we have considered in the previous section comes into play, with the result that much of the glucose is stored as glycogen ; the blood-sugar concentration thus falls again without having reached so high a value that glucose is excreted by the kidneys, *i.e.*, the renal threshold is not exceeded, and glycosuria is absent. Such a test is called a " **glucose tolerance** " test, and is of much value clinically in the diagnosis of *diabetes mellitus*. Occasionally glycosuria may follow the ingestion of a large amount (150–200 g.) of glucose by a normal person, but this is not considered to be necessarily indicative of diabetes mellitus ; it is described as *alimentary glycosuria*.

When a glucose tolerance test is performed on a diabetic person, the blood sugar concentration may be very high initially and may rise excessively after glucose administration, failing to fall again to the original value for many hours. The mechanism for the storage of glycogen in the liver and muscles is defective, while glucose oxidation is also subnormal ; much of the carbohydrate taken in with the food is therefore lost in the urine as glucose. The depression of carbohydrate utilisation causes the production of excess ketone bodies in the liver with the development of ketosis and ketonuria. The appearance of ketone bodies in the urine is an indication of the gravity of the disease, a slight glycosuria being of no great importance. If the ketone bodies continue to accumulate in the body, the patient ultimately dies in a coma, if he has not already succumbed to infection, to which he becomes very sensitive. Daily subcutaneous injections of insulin, however, clear up the symptoms completely, and the patient can lead a normal life ; omission of the insulin is rapidly followed by a reversion to the diabetic condition. Excess insulin, as we have seen, leads to hypoglycæmia and serious consequences, so that doses must be carefully controlled ; immediate subcutaneous injection of glucose, or a large quantity given by mouth, quickly alleviates the symptoms should an overdose be given accidentally.

In severe cases where carbohydrate metabolism has been in abeyance for some time, and ketosis is rampant, insulin is sometimes found to have little effect. These cases are said to be " insulin resistant," but their resistance may be broken down by administration of carbohydrate food. This foodstuff appears to " sensitise " the tissues to the action of insulin, even in the normal individual.

The Aetiology of Diabetes Mellitus. It is extremely probable that *diabetes mellitus* is not a single syndrome with one origin ; it must consist of a number of different conditions arising from various causes but with the majority of symptoms in common. Accordingly, it is most unlikely that one causative agent can be assigned to this disease.

Experimentally a condition resembling human *diabetes mellitus* in some important respects can be induced in certain animals by surgical removal of the pancreas. The fact that degenerative lesions in the cells of the islets of Langerhans of the pancreas are sometimes found in human diabetes, together with the presence of subnormal amounts of insulin in the pancreas, suggests that pancreatic islet lesions are to be regarded as one direct cause of *diabetes mellitus*. Nevertheless, in a substantial proportion of human diabetics no obvious pancreatic islet lesions are demonstrable, and even where these exist we still have to seek the reason for their development. Abnormally high secretory activity of the anterior pituitary gland can obviously be regarded as one possible extra-pancreatic cause of clinical *diabetes mellitus*. Experimentally, a diabetic condition can be induced in intact cats and dogs by repeated injections of anterior pituitary extract, and such treatment may cause the appearance of lesions of the pancreatic islets of such severity that they remain after the pituitary treatment ceases, so that a persistently diabetic condition is seen. After the daily injections of anterior pituitary extract have ceased the persistent diabetes is easily controlled by the administration of insulin, but during the period of pituitary treatment the diabetic condition shows a remarkable insensitivity to control by insulin. It seems possible that continued overactivity of the anterior pituitary lobe may account in part for the " insulin insensitive " type of diabetes that is met with clinically, while a short period of pituitary overaction might be responsible for permanent islet lesions associated with a persistent clinical diabetes which is not abnormally unresponsive to control by insulin.

Over-activity of the secretory function of the adrenal cortex, either primary or secondary to pituitary overaction, can initiate or exacerbate clinical diabetes if adrenal steroids of the corticosterone type are produced in excessive amount, while abnormally high thyroid activity might also contribute to the development or maintenance of a diabetic condition. Thus a number of endocrine glands may be considered as possible extra-pancreatic factors concerned in the appearance of the symptoms of human *diabetes mellitus*, though dysfunction of the islets of Langerhans is, in a substantial proportion of cases, the direct, though perhaps only the secondary, cause of the condition.

NUTRITION

The natural stimuli that lead to the choice of appropriate foods are hunger, thirst and appetite, guided by the sensations of sight, taste and smell. Under the conditions of twentieth-century civilisation where food is, in general, not produced in the place where it is consumed, and where for one reason or another adequate supplies of food are likely to be periodically restricted, it is necessary to replace to some extent the operation of natural desires by carefully calculated allocation of the different food constituents. Nutrition is the science on which such attempts are based and embraces a very wide field of study. In deciding a nutritional policy for a population the following factors would have to be considered ; (1) the amounts of the different food constituents required by the human body in different working and climatic conditions ; (2) the amounts of these food constituents in the different food materials used ; (3) the availability of food in terms of labour and space required for production, bulk and value of food in relation to transport, cost of food in relation to wages level, ability to import and export, etc. ; (4) the storage and preparation of food so that the highest nutritive value is maintained and (5) general propaganda and education in regard to the preparation and use of foods. Of these aspects of nutrition, only the first two belong to the province of physiology, and accordingly only these will be considered here.

The six essential classes of substances required in the diet are proteins, fats, carbohydrates, vitamins, mineral salts and water. The first problem is to know the amounts of each of these required by the body under different conditions, and the second, to know the amounts of each of these in the food materials, or more accurately to know the amounts of these absorbed from the intestine. Substances originally present in the food but destroyed by cooking or not absorbed from the intestine will have no food value. In thinking of the food requirements we can divide these into foods supplying energy for bodily activity, and foods necessary for some other purpose. In the first case we are concerned with making up a certain number of calories which are required for metabolism, and in this respect the different calorie-providing foods are within certain limits interchangeable. In the second case we have to think of specific functions of food constituents which cannot be replaced by giving other types of food. To the energy-providing foods belong proteins, fats and carbohydrates and the only other dietary constituent likely to be a source of energy is alcohol. The mineral salts, the vitamins, and water belong to the group of food substances with specific functions, but to these we must also add the proteins and fats, as these in addition to supplying energy have other roles, which cannot be taken over by any other food constituent.

The Calorie Requirements

It has been seen that when the body is at rest it requires an energy production of about 40 kcal. per sq. metre per hour, which for an average adult amounts to about 1,800 kilocalories in 24 hours. When any physical activity is undertaken the energy consumption increases and the greater the physical work carried out the greater will be the need for calories. While mental work can cause a feeling of great fatigue and even hunger, it does not cause an increase in energy consumption apart from any physical movements accompanying it. Calorie requirements are, therefore, dictated by physical effort. From careful studies of the work done in different occupations it has been possible to lay down standards of the calorie requirements of the diet in each case. The following examples, taken from figures compiled by the Ministry of Food, give the daily calorie requirement in various occupations :—

Men	Kcal.	Women.	Kcal.
Light engineering .	2,700	Light engineering . .	2,300
Shipbuilding . .	3,300	Cotton spinners . .	2,400
Steel rollermen .	4,000	Railway goods loaders .	3,200
Coal miners . .	3,500–4,500		

Another way in which the calorie needs can be stated is in terms of hourly consumption, and the following examples show the range of needs in different activities.

	Kcal. per hour above Basal Metabolism.
Standing at rest	15
Sedentary work (writing, typing)	20–25
Walking slowly	120
Walking moderately fast	180–200
Moderately active work (carpentering) . . .	90–140
Active work (heavy metal work)	180–300
Very active work (mining)	320–380

The calorie requirements for the 24 hours for an active man might be made up in some such way as the following :—

8 hours sleeping. Basal rate of 70 kcal./hour . .	560 kcal.
8 hours awake but not working actively (basal of 70 + 25 kcal./hour).	760 kcal.
8 hours moderately active work (basal of 70 + 130 kcal./hour)	1,600 kcal.
Total .	2,920 kcal.

Sometimes it is necessary to think in terms of calorie needs of whole populations rather than of different occupations. In these cases the figures usually employed are 3,000 kcal. daily for men and 2,500 for women.

The calorie requirements of children though absolutely smaller than those of adults are in proportion to their weight, much greater. The greatest absolute requirement of calories is for youths. Table VI. 5. illustrates these points and shows the requirements of calories by different age groups.

The energy is supplied by the oxidation of proteins, fats and carbohydrates at the rate of 4·1, 9·2 and 4·1 kcal./g. respectively. It is usual to find that by far the greatest part of the calorie supply in the human diet is provided by carbohydrate, as this is usually the cheapest and most plentiful source. When food is scarce, the aim is to supply sufficient protein and fat dictated by other needs (see following sections),

[1] *Recommended Dietary Allowanc*
(*Food and Nutrition Boar*

	Kilocalories.	Protein grams.	Calcium grams.	Iron mg.
Man (70 kg.) :				
Sedentary	2,500		0·80	12
Moderately Active	3,000	70	(0·56)	
Very Active	4,500			(8·5)
Woman (56 kg.) :				
Sedentary	2,100		0·80	12
Moderately Active	2,500	60	(0·56)	
Very Active	3,000			(8·5)
Pregnancy (latter half)	2,500	85	1·5	15
Lactation	3,000	100	2·0	15
Children up to 12 years				
Under 1 year[4]	100/kg.	3 to 4/kg.	1·0	6
1–3 years[5]	1,200	40	1·0	7
4–6 years	1,600	50	1·0	8
7–9 years	2,000	60	1·0	10
10–12 years	2,500	70	1·2	12
Children over 12 years				
Girls, 13–15 years	2,800	80	1·3	15
16–20 years	2,400	75	1·0	15
Boys, 13–15 years	3,200	85	1·4	15
16 –20 years	3,800	100	1·4	15

[1] Tentative goal towards which to aim in planning practical dietaries ; can be met b a good diet of natural foods. Such a diet will also provide other minerals and vitamin the requirements for which are less well known. The restricted allowances are probabl adequate for adults other than nursing or expectant mothers.

[2] Requirements may be less if provided as vitamin A ; greater if provided chiefly a the pro-vitamin, carotene.

[3] 1 mg. thiamin equals 333 I.U. ; 1 mg. ascorbic acid equals 20 I.U.

[4] Needs of infants increase from month to month. The amounts given are for approx imately 6–8 months. The amounts of protein and calcium needed are less if derived fron milk.

[5] Allowances are based on needs for the middle year in each gronp (as 2, 5, 8 etc. and for moderate activity.

[6] Vitamin D is undoubtedly necessary for older children and adults. When not availabl

I. 5

Restricted Allowances in Brackets.)

ational Research Council.)

tamin A². I.U	Thiamin² (B¹) mg.	Riboflavin mg.	Nicotinic Acid mg.	Ascorbic Acid² mg.	Vitamin D I.U.
5,000 ⎫ (3,500) ⎬	1·5 (1·1) 1·8 (1·3) 2·3 (1·6)	2·2 (1·5) 2·7 (1·9) 3·3 (2·3)	15 (10·5) 18 (13) 23 (16)	75 (52)	6
5,000 ⎫ (3,500) ⎬	1·2 (0·8) 1·5 (1·1) 1·8 (1·3)	1·8 (1·3) 2·2 (1·5) 2·7 (1·9)	12 (8) 15 (10) 18 (13)	70 (49)	6
6,000	1·8	2·5	18	100	400 to 800
8,000	2·3	3·0	23	150	400 to 800
1,500	0·4	0·6	4	30	400 to 800
2,000	0·6	0·9	6	35	6
2,500	0·8	1·2	8	50	
3,500	1·0	1·5	10	60	
4,500	1·2	1·8	12	75	
5,000	1·4	2·0	14	80	6
5,000	1·2	1·8	12	80	6
5,000	1·6	2·4	16	90	6
6,000	2·0	3·0	20	100	

rom sunshine, it should be provided probably up to the minimum amounts recommended or infants.

Further Recommendations. The requirement for iodine is small; probably about ·002 to 0·004 mg. per day for each kg. of body weight. This amounts to about 0·15 to ·30 mg. daily for the adult, which is easily met by the regular use of iodised salt; the use f this salt is especially important in adolescence and pregnancy.

The requirement for copper for adults is in the neighbourhood of 1·0 to 2·0 mg. per day. Infants and children require about 0·05 mg. per kg. body weight. The requirement or copper is approximately one-tenth of that for iron.

The requirement for vitamin K is usually satisfied by any good diet. Special considera- ion needs to be given to new-born infants. Physicians commonly give vitamin K either o the mother before delivery or to the infant immediately after birth.

to calculate the calories provided by this, and to make up the rest of the calories with carbohydrate. A good average peace-time diet, *e.g.*, as recommended by the British Medical Association report in 1933, might make up the calories as follows :—

100 g. protein . . . . 410 kcal.
100 g. fat . . . . 920 kcal.
500 g. carbohydrate . . . . 2,050 kcal.

European diets since 1940 have certainly made up a greater proportion of the calories with carbohydrate than indicated by these figures. The general rule is that the cheaper the diet, the more carbohydrate it contains.

Specific Requirements

In the following paragraphs are discussed the specific requirements for different food substances. Figures are given in Table VI. 5 of the amounts of the various constituents which are regarded as desirable in the diet. In considering these figures it must be borne in mind that they are somewhat arbitrary, and often more in the nature of a generous guess rather than an accurate knowledge of the amounts which are required. Since the effects of deprivation of certain food constituents, particularly the vitamins, may not become apparent for a long time, it is obvious that the difficulties of assessing accurately the minimum requirements of the human subject for any one food factor are very great. It is easier to be sure that a certain intake is adequate, than to know what is the threshold requirement for health and probably for this reason figures tend to be somewhat too high. They must be interpreted as something to be aimed at, rather than as a carefully determined minimum need.

Protein in the Diet. In addition to supplying energy, protein is necessary for the building up of new tissues and replacing of used ones. We have already seen how the minimum protein requirement can be determined experimentally, and that, in addition to supplying a certain amount of protein we must also supply proteins containing certain essential amino-acids. The values of different proteins are conditioned by the amounts of those amino-acids which they contain. Those which contain amino-acids in a proportion approaching that required by the body are called first-class proteins. By judicious selection it is possible to supply most of the amino-acids required by a diet containing a high proportion of vegetable proteins, but for ordinary purposes, we must regard as first-class proteins those of animal origin and especially those of milk, cheese, eggs, meat and fish. It is generally considered that the aim should be to supply about 70 g. of protein daily, and of this about one-half should be first-class protein. The following figures show recommendations of protein to be supplied and the amounts of first-class protein :—

TABLE VI. 6

		Daily Requirement in grams.	
		Total Protein.	First-class Protein.
Children	0–5 years	15–45	15–25
	5–14 ,,	45–75	25–40
Adolescents	14–18 ,,	75–90	40
Adults		60–70	25
Pregnant women		85	40–50
Lactating women		100	50–75

Fat in the Diet. The fat of the diet is used like the carbohydrate and part of the protein to supply energy by oxidation, but in this respect, it has certain advantages over the other types of food. One gram of fat on oxidation will yield more than twice as much energy as the same amount of carbohydrate or protein, and furthermore the fat is taken in a concentrated form in the food, whereas in the case of protein and carbohydrate foods a large part of the bulk of the food is composed of water. Fat has another important role in metabolism in that it is the only form of food which can be stored in large amounts as such. This stored fat is valuable in the protection of the body against cold since it is stored partly below the skin where it forms an insulating layer. The food fat has an irreplaceable function in acting as a solvent for the fat-soluble vitamins and also for providing the body with certain indispensable unsaturated fatty acids. It has been seen that fat inhibits the movements of the stomach, and on account of this property, fat taken in the diet prevents the onset of hunger for a longer time. It is rather striking that in spite of these important and definite roles of fat in the body economy, few figures are available to suggest what are the minimum fat requirements. The usual aim is to supply 100 g. daily.

Mineral Salts. The important inorganic substances which are essential in the diet are calcium, sodium, potassium, magnesium, iron, phosphorus, iodine and chloride. In addition, smaller amounts of many other elements are required, copper, bromide, cobalt, zinc, etc. These do not liberate any energy on oxidation, but they are responsible for the maintenance of the normal function of many parts of the body. The concentration of these substances necessary in the body fluids is usually small, but on the other hand there is a constant loss of small amounts in the urine and other body secretions, and this loss must be replaced. The minerals present in highest concentration in the body fluids are sodium and chloride. In the case of most of the mineral requirements, the amounts likely to be in the diet will be more than adequate for the body's needs, and there will be excretion of the excess in the urine. The substances which demand special attention are chloride, iodine, calcium and iron. Sodium chloride is only likely to become deficient when there is a great loss of sweat from the body as in conditions of working in very hot atmospheres. If a subject who is perspiring very freely replaces the fluid loss with water only, there is a danger of the condition called " miner's cramp," which is brought about by chloride deficiency and which can be prevented by replacing the fluid lost with a sodium chloride solution. Iodine deficiency only occurs regionally, and is related to abnormal thyroid metabolism. The two minerals to be considered in ordinary nutritional problems are calcium and iron.

Calcium. The recommended calcium intake can be seen from Table **VI. 5.** Calcium is most abundant in milk and cheese, and is contained only in very small quantities in bread and meat. It is, however, a common practice to fortify bread with increased amounts of calcium. There is a considerable loss of calcium in the intestine as part of the calcium of the food is not absorbed. For this reason the calcium required in the diet is much greater than that actually needed by the tissues. Calcium has a great diversity of functions in the body, and reference to other chapters will show its relation to heart beat, clotting of blood, clotting of milk, permeability of membranes, neuro-muscular excitability and bone formation. Pregnancy and lactation make specially heavy demands, and the dietary calcium should be specially considered in these conditions.

Iron. The chief function of iron is in connection with the hæmoglobin and the cytochrome in the tissues. In women there is a periodic loss of iron with menstruation, but in man the loss of iron from the body is extremely small. It will be recalled that disintegration of the red cells is followed by excretion of the iron-free bile pigment, while the iron is used again for hæmoglobin production. The daily amount recommended, 10–15 mg. certainly does not represent the amount lost from the body. It seəms that most of the iron taken in the food is not absorbed, but a certain surplus is necessary in order that a small fraction should be available. Deficiency of iron is associated with anæmia.

The Vitamins

It is well known that animals cannot be maintained in good health on diets which will supply the necessary calories together with protein, fat and mineral requirements, if certain accessory food factors, the vitamins, are absent from the diet. There are, at present, about 15 different substances which have been recognised as vitamins. The usual conception of a vitamin is an organic substance which is necessary for health, including growth in young animals, and which does not act by supplying energy. The definition is not a rigid one, and it is difficult to separate sharply the vitamins from substances like essential fatty acids or the extrinsic factor. Many of the vitamins have a known composition and chemical formula, and in some cases can be synthesised. Several of the vitamins are known to take a part in the oxidative processes of the body, either as co-enzymes or carriers (aneurin, nicotinic acid, riboflavin, ascorbic acid).

The vitamins can be classified according to their solubility in fats or in water. The following list shows the different members of each of these groups.

Fat soluble :—

> Vitamin A
> Vitamin D_2 (calciferol)
> Vitamin D_3
> Vitamin E (tocopherol)
> Vitamin K

Water soluble. :—

> Vitamin B group
>> B_1 (aneurin, thiamin)
>> B_2 (riboflavin)
>> Pantothenic acid
>> Nicotinic acid amide (P.P. factor)
>> B_6 (pyridoxine)
>> Biotin
>> Choline
>> Folic acid
>
> Vitamin C (ascorbic acid)
> Vitamin P (citrin)

The human dietary requirement of the more important vitamins is given in Table VI. 5.

Vitamin A. Deficiency of vitamin A in the diet leads to cessation of growth, loss of weight and decreased resistance to infection. There is keratinisation of the epithelium in the eye, respiratory tract and genito-urinary tract. In the human subject there is xerophthalmia and night-blindness. The vitamin is related to β-carotene, and represents half the molecule of this with addition of an alcoholic group. β-carotene can be regarded as a forerunner of the vitamin, and can replace it in the diet, if large quantities are given. Neither β-carotene nor vitamin A can be synthesised in the animal body, but they are ingested with green plants and are found in the fatty tissues, especially the liver. There may be also a chemical relation between vitamin A and rhodopsin (visual purple) which may explain the connection between vitamin A and night-blindness.

Sources : Butter, egg yolk, carrots, green vegetables, and particularly fish liver oils.

Vitamin B_1. (Aneurin, thiamin). This is the anti-neuritic part of the B complex, and its absence leads to polyneuritis in the pigeon and rat, and to beri-beri in man. Lesser degrees of deficiency cause fatigue, loss of appetite, dyspnœa on exertion, and neuritis. In the pigeon and rat, bradycardia (slowing of the heart), is characteristic. Experimentally and clinically, symptoms of deficiency occur on a diet composed mainly of polished rice, as the vitamin is present in the outer part of the grain. In a phosphorylated form vitamin B_1 acts as a co-enzyme for the carboxylase enzymes which catalyse removal or addition of carbon dioxide. In the animal body its presence is essential for the oxidation of pyruvate, and in vitamin deficiency there is a raising of the pyruvate level of the blood. Vitamin B_1 is also essential for the conversion of carbohydrate into fat.

Sources : Yeast, wheat germ, meat, fish.

Vitamin B_2. (Riboflavin) Deficiency of riboflavin in the diet causes disturbances in the mouth and tongue, in the cornea and in the skin. In combination with a protein and phosphoric acid it forms flavo-proteins, enzymes concerned with tissue respiration. It is also related to amino-acid-oxidase which takes part in the metabolism of proteins. Its chemical structure is known, and it can be synthesised.

Sources : Milk, meat, green vegetables, eggs.

Nicotinic acid (Niacin, P.P. factor.) This is the pellagra-preventing factor of the B group. Pellagra is a disease characterised by diarrhœa and skin disturbances in the human subject. In dogs deficiency of the vitamin causes blacktongue. Either nicotinic acid or its amide will prevent these disturbances. Chemically nicotinic acid amide forms part of the molecule of both co-enzyme I and co-enzyme II, substances which are known to take a part in the oxidative processes in the body.

Sources : Meat, fish, wheat flour.

Pyridoxine (Vitamin B$_6$). Deficiency of this subtance has been found to produce a disturbance in young rats, which resembles pellagra, but which cannot be cured with nicotinic acid. Pyridoxine, which can be obtained from rice bran, can also be synthesised chemically. It forms part of the enzyme systems necessary for protein metabolism.

Pantothenic acid. When rats are fed on diets deficient in the B complex with added aneurin, nicotinic acid, riboflavin and pyridoxine they develop a greying of the skin, which can be prevented by addition of pantothenic acid to the diet. Deficiency of pantothenic acid also leads to a pellagra-like dermatitis in chickens. The function of pantothenic acid in human nutrition is not known, but it is thought to be essential.

Other vitamins of the B group. Other substances which have been found to be effective in replacing deficiencies in experimental diets are choline, folic acid, biotin, p-aminobenzoic acid and inositol. Little is known about the human requirements of these substances.

Vitamin C (ascorbic acid, antiscorbutic vitamin). It has been known for several hundred years that scurvy could be prevented by including fresh fruits in the diet. Just over 10 years ago it was found that the anti-scorbutic substance in fresh fruits was ascorbic acid. In the animal body ascorbic acid is found in the suprarenal cortex. On oxidation it readily forms dehydro-ascorbic acid, and can be easily reformed from this by reduction. It may act therefore, as a carrier substance in the transport of hydrogen in tissue respiration. It is also known that vitamin C deficiency is associated with disturbance in the formation of the enamel in the teeth, and with the process of calcification of bone.

Sources : Fresh fruits and vegetables, especially the citrus fruits, oranges and lemons.

Vitamin D (antirachitic vitamin). Absence of vitamin D in the diet gives rise to the characteristic appearance of rickets, a disease of children associated with softening of the bones and hence giving rise to abnormal shapes of the parts of the skeleton which have to bear the weight of the body. It is closely related to the metabolism of calcium and phosphorus, the chief bone-forming substances, but the mode of action is not known with certainty. One of the effects is to increase the amount of calcium absorbed from the intestine. The beneficial effect of sunlight on rickets has long been known, and it was found that this is due to the presence in the skin of a precursor of the vitamin, which under the action of ultra-violet light is transformed into the vitamin. An antirachitic substance can be produced by irradiation of ergosterol, and is called vitamin D$_2$ or calciferol. Another antirachitic substance is present in cod liver oil, and can be produced by irradiation of 7-dehydrocholesterol. Irradiated dehydrocholesterol is called vitamin D$_3$, or natural vitamin D. Vitamin D is the vitamin which is most likely to be inadequate in the diet, and hence the widespread habit of giving to children cod liver oil or other vitamin D source.

Sources : Butter, cream, eggs, but especially fish liver oils.

Vitamin E (alpha-tocopherol). Deficiency of vitamin E in rats gives rise to failure of the reproductive organs. In male rats there is deterioration of the testis, and in the female death of the fœtus. In other animals deficiency may be accompanied by muscular disturbances. Little is known definitely about the requirements of the human subject, and the value of treatment with vitamin E for prevention of abortion is still a matter of some dispute.

Sources : Cereals, especially oats and wheat, liver and eggs.

Vitamin K (anti-hæmorrhagic vitamin). Deficiency of vitamin K in the diet of chickens produces a hæmorrhagic disturbance associated with a lowering of the amount of prothrombin in the blood. In the human subject a vitamin K deficiency can be produced when there is an absence of bile in the intestine, *e.g.*, in case of a biliary fistula. The vitamin does not have any effect on such hæmorrhagic diseases as hæmophilia or purpura, and as far as is known is only related to formation of prothrombin.

Sources : It occurs more abundantly in plants than in animals. Cabbage, spinach, cauliflower are good sources, while milk is very poor.

Alcohol

Alcohol is capable of oxidation by the animal body, but it is usually taken not so much for the purpose of providing energy as for the effect it produces on the higher centres of the central nervous system. The relaxation of rigid self-control and discrimination which it produces in suitable doses is found by many people to increase the enjoyment of congenial company, and its widespread use lends interest to a consideration of its metabolism by the tissues of the body.

Alcohol differs from other energy-providing foods in that it can be absorbed from the stomach, although the rate of gastric absorption is much less than that from the intestine. After absorption most of it is metabolised, the remainder being excreted either in the urine or in the expired air. When taken in small doses so that the concentration in the blood does not rise above a certain level, most of the alcohol is oxidised without any accompanying pharmacological action. The first stage in the metabolism is probably oxidation to acetic acid in the liver, and the acetic acid is further oxidised either directly in the tissues or after undergoing further changes in the liver. The final products of oxidation are carbon dioxide and water. Alcohol as such is not oxidised by the extra-hepatic tissues to any appreciable extent.

The oxidation of 1 g. of alcohol in the body yields 7 kilocalories of energy. Alcohol metabolism proceeds at a practically constant rate for any one individual, varying usually from 6–10 g. of absolute alcohol per hour. The food value of alcohol is, however, limited in spite of the fact that it is quickly absorbed and requires no digestion, partly because there is no storage mechanism and partly because of the inconvenient effects of alcohol on the central nervous system.

If alcohol is taken in larger doses it acts on various parts of the body, chiefly on the central nervous system. The effect is mainly dependent on the concentration in the blood although it is also influenced by the rate at which the concentration is attained. Hence the effects of a large dose of alcohol will be reduced if it is taken with food and particularly with fatty foods which delay the emptying time of the stomach. Thus cocktails before a meal are more potent than liqueurs containing a

similar quantity of alcohol after the meal and the practice of starting a
meal with hors d'œuvres with a high content of fat and oils, is conducive
to the retention of a discriminating palate throughout the course of that
meal. The relation between blood concentration and pharmacological
action is of considerable medico-legal interest, as the symptoms of
alcoholism can be roughly related to the concentration of alcohol
in the blood at the particular time (Fig. VI. 5).

Alcohol has a definite diuretic action. If 50 g. ethyl alcohol are
taken in 250 ml. of water it is followed by an output of urine of 600–
1,000 ml. in 2 to 3 hours. The mechanism of the diuresis may be

Alcohol in 1 cc. Urine

| less than 1 mg. | 1-2 mg. | 2-3 mg. | 3-4 mg. | 4-5 mg. |

| Dry & Decent | Delighted & Devilish | Delinquent & Disgusting | Dizzy & Delirious | Dazed & Dejected |

More than 5 mg.

Dead Drunk

Fig. VI. 5. The Relation of the **Degree of Intoxication** to the **Concentration
of Alcohol** in the Urine.

The concentration of alcohol in the urine is approximately the same as
that in the blood and tissues, except during absorption from the alimentary
canal, when the concentrations are changing rapidly. (From Emil Boger
Emerson's " Alcohol and Man," by permission of The Macmillian Co.)

depression of the hypothalamic centre with consequent decrease in the
secretion of the anti-diuretic hormone of the pituitary gland. Alcohol
is neither concentrated nor diluted by the kidney, and the concentration
in the urine may therefore be used as a rough measure of the concentration in the blood plasma.

Water

Water is absolutely essential for the existence of all forms of life,
and it constitutes a large fraction of living tissues, amounting to nearly
70 per cent. in the higher animals. The special properties of water which
are of biological importance are its great solvent power for many kinds
of substances and its high specific heat. Most of the chemical reactions
involved in metabolism take place in aqueous solution, and even the
fatty substances which are not ordinarily water-soluble can be brought
into fine emulsions or even into water soluble combinations by the

actions of certain substances, which are said to be hydrotropic. The high specific heat of water enables it to act as a buffer in minimising oscillations in temperature due to alterations in the processes of heat production and heat loss.

The body water always contains in solution inorganic salts and other substances which give to it a certain osmotic pressure, and the volume of water and amount of salts must be adjusted to maintain the osmotic pressure at a fairly constant value. This does not mean that the salts are evenly distributed throughout the body fluid, and variations of the concentration of individual salts are found in different parts of the body. It is a useful concept to think of the animal body as divided into

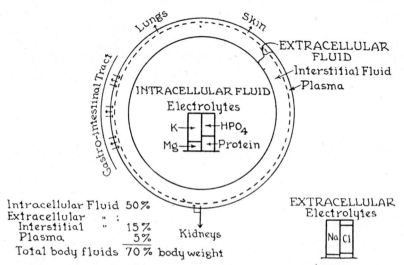

Fig. VI. 6. Schematic diagram of the divisions of the body fluids and their principal ionic contents. (From Howell's " Text-book of Physiology.")

distinct fluid compartments, which are more or less separated by various barriers, but at the same time are in equilibrium with each other. The two major compartments are (1) the intracellular fluid enclosed by the cell walls, and (2) the extracellular fluid which can be again divided into the plasma and the interstitial fluid. The latter, which lies between the cell walls and the walls of the blood vessels, forms the internal environment for the cells, and provides the connection between the intracellular fluid, where the metabolic reactions occur, and the plasma which, by means of the kidneys, lungs and alimentary tract, can have its composition altered in accordance with the body's needs. While there is an equilibrium between the different fluid compartments each has its own characteristic composition and volume. The relative sizes of the compartments and the ionic content of each is indicated diagrammatically in Fig. VI. 6.

Water Intake and Loss. Under ordinary conditions the body loses about 2,500 ml. of water daily, and this must be replaced in the diet.

The loss of water takes place mainly in the urine (about 1,500–2,000 ml.), but in addition, a small quantity is lost in the expired air (about 400 ml.), in the fæces (about 100 ml.), and by evaporation from the body surface of the " insensible perspiration " (about 500 ml.). The supply of water in the diet comes from two sources. There is first the preformed water, which includes not only the amount (about 1,500 ml.), taken as liquid, but also the amount present in the " dry " food substances. On an ordinary diet the latter may amount to two litres. Secondly, water is an oxidation product of the food substances. It has been seen that the ultimate fuel of the cells is the hydrogen present in the food, and the product of oxidation of this will be water. The amount of water produced in this way is small compared with that obtained as preformed water, and on a diet of 3,000 kilocalories is about 360 ml.

When the amount of water in the diet is reduced the amount lost from the body is also reduced, chiefly by a diminution in urine volume. The extent to which water intake can be reduced is limited by the need for water to eliminate excess salt and products of protein metabolism. If we consider only the products of metabolism it is possible to calculate how much water is provided by each food, and how much is necessary to excrete the waste products formed. In addition, a small quantity of water must be used for elimination of the heat produced by the food. Table VI. 7 shows calculations made for various food substances. In making these calculations it has been assumed that each kilocalorie from protein requires 3·0 ml. of water for the excretion of the urea and sulphates formed, and that 65 ml. of water are required for the excretion of 1 g. of ash.

TABLE VI. 7

Grams of Water needed for the Complete Metabolism of 100 Kilocalories from some Food Substances

Food Material.	Preformed Water	Gained by Oxidation	Lost in Dissipating Heat	Lost in Excreting End-products	Deficit of Water.
Protein . .	0	10·3	60	300	350
Starch . .	0	13·9	60	0	46
Fat . .	0	11·9	60	0	48
Beef, sirloin .	25	11·3	60	119	143
Fish, cod .	120	10·4	60	382	312
Eggs, hen . .	47	11·1	60	154	156
Milk, whole .	127	12·5	60	123	43
Bread, white .	14	13·2	60	69	102
Apples, fresh .	150	13·9	60	56	− 48

The figures emphasise the need for fluid water in the diet, as it is seen that of the substances listed only fresh apples provide any extra water over and above that which must be lost from the body as a result of taking the food.

Severe disturbances in the water balance of the body may be present in a number of pathological conditions. The more important of these are (1) disturbances of the kidney, (2) disturbances in the endocrine glands, principally the pituitary and the adrenal cortex, (3) loss of fluid from the alimentary tract either by vomiting or by diarrhœa, (4) metabolic disturbances such as diabetes mellitus, where polyuria accompanies the glycosuria, and where in addition, there is a loss of cations from the body in combination with the ketone bodies excreted in the urine.

The reserves of the body in regard to water metabolism can be appreciated by considering the amount of water present in relation to the total " turnover," *i.e.*, the daily intake and loss. In an adult of 70 kg., the extracellular fluid amounts to about 14 litres and the daily intake and loss to about 2 litres. In contrast to this the child of 7 kg. weight will have an extracellular fluid volume of about 1·4 litres, while the fluid intake and loss amounts to about 700 ml. It is clear that in the infant the margin of reserve is much smaller, and any variation in the water intake and water loss will cause proportionately greater disturbances than in the adult.

Thirst. The need of the body for water is indicated by the sensation of thirst, which is relieved when sufficient water is taken. It would seem likely that thirst must be related to the concentration of water in the tissues, but very careful measurements fail to show any change either in osmotic pressure or in the chemical constitution of the blood at the time when thirst first comes on, although they do so at a later stage, if water deprivation continues. The feeling of thirst is related to a sensation of dryness in the pharynx. The mucous membrane of the pharynx is more exposed to the risk of drying than any other mucous surface of the body on account of its constant exposure to the air currents associated with respiratory movements. This tendency to drying is counteracted by the saliva, and one possibility of the causation of thirst is a diminution of salivary secretion in response to an alteration in the water concentration of the tissues, which is too small to be detected by any other method. This view is supported by the experimental findings that thirst is caused by substances which inhibit salivary secretion such as atropine, while it is relieved by substances which stimulate salivary secretion, such as pilocarpine. Attempts to test this theory by studying the effect of removal of the salivary glands on the water intake of dogs have led to conflicting results,—in some experiments water intake was not affected while in others it was increased.

Hunger and Appetite

The sensations of hunger and appetite are ill-defined feelings of " emptiness " in the one case and pleasant anticipation of food in the other. Although usually related, they are more or less distinct sensations. The hunger feeling is referred to the epigastrium, and is known to be accompanied by contractions of the stomach. Attempts have been made to relate hunger to some measurable change in the blood, *e.g.*, to the blood sugar concentration. That there is no simple relationship is shown by the observations that injection of insulin produces a fall in blood sugar which is accompanied by a sensation of hunger, while on the other hand hunger is a common symptom of diabetes where the blood sugar is raised. Appetite is still more difficult to relate to any physiological or biochemical basis. It is more susceptible than hunger to other influences such as emotion, habit or artificial stimulation by attractively prepared food. Under conditions of modern life other factors besides hunger and appetite take part in the selection of food—in young people training and example, in adults advertising and propaganda. Fashions, fads and the cultivation of a discriminating palate also play a part in the choice of diet.

How far the sense of taste is a reliable nutritional guide is another problem of considerable interest. A good deal of experimental work in this field has been done on rats. Animals suffering from deprivation of some body constituent are given the opportunity to select a diet from a large choice of substances with a view to testing their ability to make good the deficiency. Removal of the adrenal gland causes a fatal loss of sodium from the body, and it was found that adrenal-ectomised rats chose sodium salts out of a number of substances available and by this process outlived a control group of adrenalectomised rats to which sodium was not given. In another set of experiments, rats from which the parathyroid glands had been removed increased their intake of calcium lactate, and thereby prevented the fall in blood calcium which, accompanied by tetany, usually supervenes in parathyroid-ectomised animals.

One of the important principles of animal physiology is the maintenance of the " internal environment " of the body cells, and many reflex processes contribute to this end. It has been suggested that the ability to select diets suitable to physiological need is an example of the behaviour regulators acting towards the common goal of " homeostasis," the term which Cannon used to describe the steady state in the composition of the body fluids so essential for the continued activity of the cells.

TEMPERATURE REGULATION

The ability to maintain a constant body temperature independent of the surroundings gives to man and the other warm blooded animals an independence of activity possessed by them alone. The body temperature varies with the species, being generally higher in those with a more active existence but in each species it is kept within very narrow limits. Normally, in man it varies from just below 98° F. to just below 99° F. Within these limits there is a regular diurnal variation, the highest value being reached in the late afternoon and the lowest in the early morning. In women there may be a rhythmic variation with the menstrual cycle, the temperature being lower during the menstrual period and for some time afterwards. Physiologically, the temperature may rise considerably above the usual range in strenuous exercise when a temperature of 103° F. may be obtained. Exposure to cold may lower body temperature and cases as low as 73° F. have been recorded with subsequent recovery. In many fevers and infections, the temperature rises, commonly to as high as 104° F., and temperatures as high as 112° F. have been recorded.

Heat Balance. The heat of the body is produced by oxidation of the food stuffs. It was the French chemist, Lavoisier (1795) who first pointed out that animal heat and the heat of chemical oxidation were of one and the same nature. The heat produced is lost from the surface of the body and to a lesser extent in the excreta and expired air. It is clear that to maintain a constant body temperature there must be a nicely co-ordinated adjustment between heat production and heat loss, and that either of these processes may independently affect the body temperature.

Heat Production. Heat is produced in all parts of the body where oxidations occur, but especially in the voluntary muscles and in the liver. Moreover, since the voluntary muscles more than any other part of the body are capable of varying their activity, they are of the greatest importance in regulating the production of heat. The importance of the muscles in maintaining heat production can be shown by poisoning an animal with curare. This causes paralysis of voluntary muscle and is accompanied by a fall in body temperature. The significance of muscle movement in relation to temperature is much more commonly seen in the physiological response of the animal to a cold environment ; this is either conscious purposeful movements or involuntary shivering. In the latter there is an inco-ordinated and asynchronous contraction of individual muscle fibres, which result in increased metabolic activity but not in shortening of the whole muscle. On the other hand in the overheated body, *e.g.*, after exercise or in hot weather, the desire is to lie perfectly still thus reducing heat production to a minimum. We have also seen that heat production is stimulated by taking food especially protein, so that heat production can be regulated partly by the type of food eaten. Since the production of heat is associated with the metabolism of the tissues, it is often called the chemical control of heat regulation, in contrast to the processes of heat loss, which for reasons which will be evident are often spoken of as the physical control.

Heat Loss. Heat is lost from the surface of the body by processes of radiation, convection, conduction and by the evaporation of water. The amounts lost by each of these ways depends largely on the conditions of the environment. Radiation occurs when the temperature of the skin is higher than that of the surrounding objects. As far as the animal is concerned, the amount of heat lost by radiation can be controlled by alteration of the skin temperature. This is normally considerably below body temperature, and can be modified by increasing or decreasing the blood flow through the skin vessels. At an air temperature of 15° C. with a person normally clothed, radiation accounts for about 44 per cent. of the total heat loss, so that in temperate climates it is a very important process in thermo-regulation. Under the same conditions, convection and conduction account for about 30 per cent.

of the heat loss. Here the loss is due to the body warming up air in contact with it, which is then replaced by cool air. The efficiency of convection will be increased by draughts, air currents and a wide difference between air temperature and body temperature. Relatively little heat is lost from the body by pure conduction since the air and the clothes in contact with the body are very poor conductors of heat. The part played by conduction is of some significance in the warming of the skin by the deeper tissues, and the poor heat conducting properties of fatty tissue account for the effect of this in preventing heat loss in individuals with an abundant supply of adipose tissue below the skin. It should be noted that all of these processes can only be effective in cooling the body when the temperature of the environment is below body temperature. When this rises above body temperature the effect of radiation, convection and conduction will be in the opposite direction and they will actually warm the body instead of cooling it.

Evaporation of moisture from the skin accounts for a variable amount of heat loss from the body, which in these climates is usually much less than that due to radiation and convection, being not more than 20 per cent. of the total at 15° C. and 50 per cent. humidity. In tropical conditions, however, it may become extremely important and account for the total heat loss from the body. The amount of heat lost by evaporation is controlled as far as the body is concerned by the amount of sweat secreted. Even when the body is not obviously sweating, the skin is kept moist by the so called insensible perspiration, which results in a continuous evaporation from the surface. When active sweating is produced the amount secreted increases enormously, and under tropical conditions has been known to amount to 10 litres daily, although all of this is not removed by evaporation. The heat loss due to evaporation is 0·58 kcal. per gram of water. As regards atmospheric conditions, the heat loss due to evaporation will depend on the humidity and temperature of the air and on the amount of air movement or wind. If the air is completely saturated with water vapour no evaporation can take place, no matter what the temperature, and hence the dryer the air the more efficient is evaporation in cooling the body. Provided the air is not saturated, the degree of evaporation is controlled by the temperature and the amount of wind, but whereas the efficiency of radiation and convection are reduced by a rise in temperature, the efficiency of evaporation is greatly increased. Hence when the environmental temperature exceeds the body temperature, evaporation is the only means by which the body can lose heat, and its effectiveness in eliminating heat is shown by the fact that the human body can maintain its temperature when exposed to an atmosphere as hot as 250° F., *i.e.*, sufficient to cook meat or to boil an egg. This ability to withstand high temperatures depends on a dry atmosphere and hence in places where people have to work at high temperatures, it is of the greatest importance to control the humidity of the atmosphere.

A small amount of heat is also lost from the body in warming the expired air and the excreta. Still smaller amounts of heat are involved in the oxygen going into solution in the blood and carbon dioxide coming out of solution in the lungs.

Physiological Processes involved in Production and Loss of Heat

The processes which are used to alter the production or loss of heat are changes in metabolism, changes in the blood flow to the skin and secretion of sweat. The metabolic changes, while partly under control of the somatic nerves, are at least partly dependent on the sympathetic nervous system and on the secretion of adrenaline. It is found that if the sympathetic nerves be removed in a dog, the capacity to resist lowered external temperatures is greatly reduced. One of the ways in which the sympathetic nerves can affect metabolic activity is in mobilising more glucose from the liver, and Fig. VI. 7 shows how the blood sugar rises or falls in response to temperature changes. The control of the blood flow through the skin is also a function of the sympathetico-adrenal system. The local increased blood flow leads to more general circulatory changes, there is increase in blood volume, increase in red cell count and hæmoglobin concentration, probably due to contraction of the spleen and increase in the cardiac output.

The secretion of sweat is likewise under control of the sympathetic nervous system, but in this case the nerve fibres differ from those controlling the vessels and are exceptional in being cholinergic and not adrenergic. Sweat glands are numerous and unevenly distributed over the surface of the body, being particularly dense on the palms of the hands and the soles of the feet in man. The nerve supply to the glands passes along the main nerve trunks and stimulation of the sciatic nerve in the cat produces perspiration on the toe pad, whereas cutting the nerve prevents sweating in the affected limb, even in circumstances where it occurs in the other limbs. The amount of sweat secreted is very little affected by the degree of hydration of the body.

In many animals another process which plays a part in heat regulation is panting. This occurs in dogs and other animals not provided with sweat glands. When the body is hot the respiration becomes very fast and shallow, so that a large amount of air is passed over the surface of the tongue, and heat is lost by evaporation as well as by convection. These panting movements do not result in an increased ventilation of the lungs, for there is no alteration in the composition of the alveolar air even after several hours of respiration of this type.

Regulation of Body Temperature. While under many conditions of civilised life the physiological processes for controlling heat production and heat loss are largely superseded or at least greatly assisted by other agencies such as clothes, artificial regulation of temperature and humidity of buildings, etc., the physiological processes are still responsible for the fine adjustment of temperature. We have seen that these processes are all under control of the nervous system, and through this their activities are co-ordinated so as to produce the correct balance of heat production and heat loss. The centre for thermo-regulation is in the hypothalamus, which exerts its control through its connections with the vasomotor centre, the nerves to the sweat glands, to the adrenals, the liver and the voluntary muscles. The thermo-regulating centre can be affected either by impulses coming to it from the surface of the body through the afferent nerves or by changes in the temperature of the blood supplying the centre. Fig. VI. 7 shows the results of an experiment illustrating the effect of changes in the temperature of the blood supplying the centre. In this it is seen that if the blood in the carotid artery be warmed, the rectal temperature of the animal falls, and this is accompanied by a fall in blood sugar, while a fall in the carotid temperature leads to a stimulation of the metabolic processes with a rise in rectal temperature. In man it is found that a rise of about 1° F. in the body

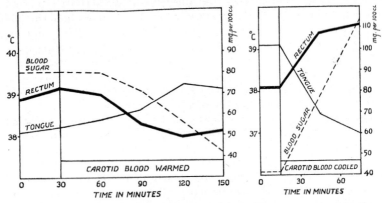

Fig. VI. 7.   The Effect on the **Temperature of a Dog**, as measured in the Rectum, and under the Tongue, and on the **Blood Sugar Concentration**, of **Warming and Cooling** the Blood in the Carotid Arteries, and hence in the **Temperature Regulating Centre.**

Note that the temperature of the rectum moves in the opposite direction to the temperature of the tongue, indicating the efforts of the temperature regulating centre to counteract the warming and cooling of the carotid blood. The changes in the blood sugar concentration do not occur in the absence of the vago-insular system when the blood is warmed, or in the absence of the sympathetico-adrenal system when the blood is cooled. (From data by Geiger.)

temperature gives rise to sweating, which as we have seen is a very effective way of promoting heat loss. The sweating is accompanied by vasodilatation of the skin vessels and increase in the skin temperature so that there is also greater heat loss by radiation and convection.

The regulation of temperature by altering heat production takes place chiefly in response to low temperatures. Its significance can be estimated from Table VI. 8, which shows the metabolism of a dog exposed to various temperatures. It is evident that the largest change in heat production takes place at low temperatures, and that above a certain level this process plays no part in control of body temperature. Indeed if for any reason the other regulating mechanisms break down and the body temperature goes on rising the production of metabolic heat will be stimulated by this rise in temperature on account of the acceleration of the chemical reactions, and a vicious circle is established which will end in heat stroke and in death. This effect of body temperature on heat production is illustrated by the last figure on the table, where it is seen that the production of heat is rising again.

TABLE VI. 8

Showing the metabolism of a dog in response to different external temperatures :—

Temperature. °C	kcal./kg.	
7·6	86·4	⎫ Effective range of
15·0	63·0	⎬ chemical regulation
20·0	55·9	⎭
25·0	54·2	
30·0	56·2	⎫ Stimulation of
35·0	68·5	⎬ metabolism by body temperature.

Nervous impulses arriving at the thermo-regulatory centre can also have an effect on heat regulating processes, although this is much less important than the effect of changes in blood temperature. It can be shown that application of heat or cold to the skin in one part of the body can lead to a reflex change in the skin circulation in other parts, and it is also known that panting in dogs can be produced by application of heat to the skin without causing a rise in temperature of the blood going to the centre.

The reaction of the body in being exposed to different temperatures can be roughly summed up in the following way.

(1) At low temperatures there is increased heat production by voluntary movements and by shivering, and heat loss is minimised by vasoconstriction of the skin vessels.

(2) At moderate temperatures the production of heat varies little, the main factors are now the control of heat loss by alterations of the blood flow through the skin.

(3) At high temperatures, the all-important mechanism is the secretion of sweat. Since the amount of evaporation possible depends on the humidity of the atmosphere, this becomes the determining factor in deciding whether an animal can maintain its temperature constant when the external temperature rises.

Climatic Conditions

The physiological mechanisms for controlling heat regulation are only adequate within a certain range of environmental conditions, and it is of great importance to know what conditions can be tolerated and what can be regarded as suitable for carrying out various activities. The three important climatic conditions whch affect heat loss from the body are the temperature, the humidity and the movement of the air. By temperature must be included not only the temperature of the air in contact with the skin, but also the temperature of surrounding objects, which may be radiating heat to the body or which may be receiving radiant heat from the body. The humidity of the air controls the amount of evaporation of water which is possible, and use is made of this to measure humidity by the difference between the wet and dry bulb thermometer readings. In addition to temperature and humidity, movement of the air, *i.e.*, wind velocity, makes a great difference to

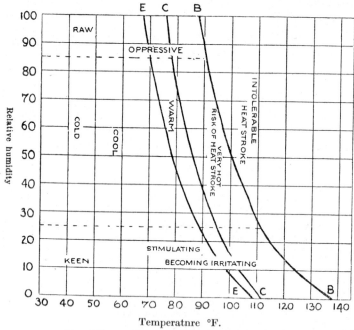

Fɪɢ. VI. 8. Tentative **Classification of Climates.**

Line BB shows limit of tolerance for lightly clad resting subject.
Line CC shows limit of tolerance for same subject walking at 2 miles per hour or resting in sunshine.
Line EE shows limit of tolerance for same person walking at 4 miles per hour in bright sunshine. (After Brunt.)

body comfort. Usually, greater wind velocity will cause increased heat loss by convection and by evaporation.

The Kata-thermometer. Since the conditions for comfort depend on a number of different factors, attempts have been made to combine the influence of these factors in one measurement, and one method of doing this is by use of the kata-thermometer, which measures the cooling power of the air. It consists of a large bulb containing alcohol, and a stem with two graduations, one at 100° F., and the other at 95° F. The bulb is immersed in a waterbath at a temperature higher than 100° F. It is then removed and suspended in the place where cooling power is to be measured. As the temperature of the alcohol falls, an accurate measurement is made of the time required for the level to fall from the 100° to the 95° mark. This time is a measure of the cooling power of the air, and depends on the heat lost by convection, conduction and by radiation. The kata-thermometer can also be used with the bulb covered with a moist silk-net fingerstall. In this case, the cooling power depends on the heat lost by evaporation in addition to that lost by other means. The cooling power is expressed in arbitrary units, and by means of nomograms it is possible to calculate the wind velocity from the kata-thermometer readings and from the temperature. Another method of attempting to express the condition of the environment by one measurement is by the use of effective temperatures. The effective temperature means the temperature of a still, saturated atmosphere which would cause the same subjective sensation as the conditions in question.

In buildings used for industrial processes, certain standards for the atmospheric conditions are laid down by the Factories Act (1937). For each person there must be 400 cubic feet of air space not counting any space above 14 feet from the floor, the temperature for most purposes must not be below 60° F., and there must be a certain minimum difference between the readings of the wet and dry bulb thermometers.

The environmental conditions produce certain sensations which make us speak of them as cold, raw, keen, oppressive, comfortable, heavy, etc. The relations between these terms and the objective measurements is indicated approximately in Fig. VI. 8. The three lines, BB, CC and EE means that the human body under the conditions specified will not suffer from a rise in temperature provided the relative humidity and temperature are represented by a point to the left of the line in each case. If it falls to the right the body temperature rises, showing that the processes of heat loss are no longer effective.

CHAPTER VII

EXCRETION

The Regulatory Function of the Kidney

MANY organs in the body co-operate in preventing any but minute changes in the volume and composition of the blood, but the kidney and lungs have chief control of the chemical exchanges between the external environment and the internal environment which was considered in the chapter on the blood. Thus the variation in the amount and composition of the urine secreted provides the normal means of permanent recovery from a chemical disturbance of body fluids.

The *water content* of the body is delicately controlled by the kidney. The resting human kidneys may secrete about 50 c.c. of urine per hour and this may be increased twenty-fold or more by drinking 2 litres of water in fifteen minutes. This diuresis continues until practically the whole volume of water ingested has been removed from the body. Loss of water from the body, as in sweating, panting, diarrhœa and hæmorrhage, is compensated by a reduction in the rate of urine secretion, down to about 20 c.c. per hour (500 c.c. per day). Any further reduction below this would lead to imperfect elimination of salts and urea, since there is a limit to the concentrating power of the kidney. The water-loss in sweating is, however, controlled by the temperature regulating mechanism unlike the urine flow which is adjusted mainly to maintain the water balance of the body.

The regulation of the *concentration of salts* in the tissue fluids is important in connection with the maintenance of a normal range of (1) osmotic pressure, (2) the relation between sodium, potassium, calcium, and other cation concentration, and (3) the acid-base equilibrium. The complete removal of such soluble substances as are not normal constituents of the blood is a further function of the kidney.

Chlorides are the most abundant salts in the urine, as in the blood. In the plasma they are the chief contributors to the production of osmotic pressure, and the concentration is remarkably constant at 0·12 molar (0·7 per cent. NaCl), whereas in the urine the concentration may vary enormously, from a trace during a salt-free diet to 0·33 molar (2 per cent. NaCl)when large amounts are ingested.

Sulphates are present in the urine mainly as inorganic salts, derived by oxidation from sulphur-containing proteins. A small proportion of sulphates, known as " ethereal sulphates," occurs as esters (of phenol, indol, and skatol) derived from proteins after bacterial decomposition in the intestine.

Variations of the *hydrogen ion concentration* of the plasma produce effects on the respiratory centre which immediately tend to restore it to its normal value. But the change in carbon dioxide output may be associated with a change in the alkali reserve of the blood, as shown in an earlier chapter, and a slower but hardly less sensitive renal mechanism then operates to restore the alkali reserve to its normal value, by eliminating acid or alkali in the urine. The urine is well buffered, mainly as a result of the presence of phosphates in much higher concentration than in the blood. Considerable quantities of acid or alkali may thus be excreted without excessive changes in the pH of the urine. Indeed, the pH has not been observed to fall below about 4·7, or to rise above about 8·2. In man, if the diet is a mixed one, the urine is usually slightly acid.

A reduction of the alkali reserve (acidosis) may be due to (1) taking acid by mouth, (2) the liberation of lactic acid during severe muscular exercise, (3) the secretion of alkali in the pancreatic juice, (4) the formation of keto-acids whenever available carbohydrates are lacking, (5) disease, and (6) drugs, *e.g.*, ammonium chloride or calcium chloride in which the cation is metabolised or not absorbed. In such cases, there is an increased excretion of acid, and the pH of the urine falls ; this is usually accompanied by an increased excretion of buffer substances. If the acid disturbance is large, auxiliary compensation is effected by neutralisation with ammonia, which is formed in the kidney and by the excretion of ammonium salts so formed.

An increase in the alkali reserve (alkalosis) often occurs when vegetables form a large proportion of the diet, owing to the presence in them of salts of organic acids, such as citrates, which are oxidised in the body and eliminated as carbon dioxide. Correspondingly, the administration of the sodium or potassium salts of such acids renders the urine alkaline. Alkalosis also occurs during the secretion of the acid gastric juice, and during the removal of lactic acid, associated with recovery from severe muscular exercise. The normal conditions are then restored gradually by the excretion of an alkaline urine.

Urea is the chief nitrogenous end-product of protein metabolism, and occurs in large quantities in normal urine. The ability of a kidney to concentrate urea is considered a valuable index of the functional activity of the organ in disease. It is estimated by administering 15 g. of urea in 100 c.c. of water by mouth, and collecting bladder urine at hourly intervals ; the first sample may be dilute owing to diuresis, but unless the second sample contains 2 per cent. or more of urea, impairment of renal function is to be inferred.

Other nitrogenous substances in urine occur only in relatively small amounts. Ammonium salts, usually in small concentration, may be increased in acidosis as mentioned above. A large proportion of the ammonia in normal urine is formed in the kidney itself. Uric acid is formed from nucleins, and about one-half persists in starvation, and is therefore regarded as of endogenous origin ; the other half varies in amount with the diet, and is of exogenous origin.

As mentioned in the previous chapter, creatinine in the urine is probably formed mainly from the creatine in muscle. Owing to the constancy of the amount excreted under ordinary conditions and its independence of the diet, it has been regarded as an indicator of endogenous metabolism.

Creatine is a normal constituent of the urine of children up to the age of puberty, and in women during pregnancy, reaching a maximum after parturition. It occurs also in those pathological states in which the excretion of creatinine is increased, that is in which there is excessive breakdown of the body tissues, *e.g.* in starvation, fevers, wasting diseases and atrophy of the muscles.

Normal Urine

The daily output of urine varies widely in amount and composition ; 1,500 c.c. (or 50 oz.) per diem may be taken as representative for a man under average conditions in this country. Its specific gravity is usually between 1·015 and 1·025. The colour varies with the concentration, and is due to urochrome, a pigment of uncertain origin, which is chemically related to hæmoglobin. Urine contains about 4 per cent. solids, the details of which are given in the table below. Proteins are present in negligible quantity, except in some people after they have been standing up (postural albuminuria), and after exercise. A faint cloud of mucus from the walls of the bladder and urinary passages can usually be seen where the urine has been allowed to stand for some time. A concentrated urine often deposits amorphous sodium and potassium urates on cooling ; the precipitate is coloured pink by uro-erythrin, and can be redissolved by warming. Another amorphous deposit may occur in normal urine, namely, phosphates of the alkaline earths ; these have a low solubility in alkaline solution, and are precipitated (*a*) (usually as $Ca_3(PO_4)_2$) when the urine is alkaline when voided, or (*b*) (as NH_4MgPO_4 —" triple phosphate ") when previously acid or neutral urine becomes alkaline on standing owing to bacterial conversion of the urea into

TABLE VII. 1.

Typical Concentrations of the Chief Constituents of Blood and Urine

Constituent.	Per cent. in blood plasma.	Per cent. in urine.	Concentration ratio.
Water	90–93	95	—
Colloids	7–9	—	—
Creatinine . . .	0·001	0·15	150
Urea	0·03	2·0	60
Sulphate	0·003	0·18	60
Phosphate . . .	0·009	0·27	30
Uric acid	0·002	0·05	25
Potassium . . .	0·02	0·15	7
Calcium	0·008	0·015	2
Chloride	0·37	0·6	2
Sodium	0·32	0·35	1
Glucose	0·1	—	—
Ammonia. . . .	0·0001	0·04	400

ammonium carbonate. The phosphate is dissolved by the addition of dilute acetic acid. Crystalline deposits are usually associated with abnormal processes. In acid urine, calcium oxalate, cystine, leucine or tyrosine may be found, whereas in alkaline urine, calcium carbonate and phosphates are the commonest.

Abnormal constituents of urine may be considered according as they are due to abnormal composition of the blood, or to abnormal local conditions in the kidney. Among the former class may be numbered, first, drugs such as iodides, dyes, etc., and other diffusible substances normally foreign to the organism, and secondly, substances normally present, but not normally excreted, which may be eliminated in the urine when their concentration in the plasma is unusually high. Among the latter, *glucose* normally occurs in a concentration of about 0·10 per cent. in blood, but is not excreted unless its concentration exceeds a threshold value of 0·18 per cent. ; if it does exceed it, by even relatively small amounts, the concentration of sugar in the urine may become considerable, and reach values as high as 4 to 6 per cent. *Glycosuria* is defined as a sufficient concentration of glucose in urine to reduce Fehling's solution ; the trace of glucose present in normal urine cannot be detected by this reaction. As mentioned in Chapter VI, transient glycosuria can be induced by swallowing a large quantity of glucose, but the amount must exceed 200 g., and be taken in a short time ; this is known as " alimentary glycosuria " (see Fig. VI. 4, p. 215). Excess adrenaline in the blood produces a rapid conversion of glycogen in the liver into glucose, and consequently an increase of blood sugar, and glycosuria ; such a condition may be brought about directly by stimulation of the splanchnic nerve, or by puncture of the fourth ventricle. Glycosuria is also associated with the hyperglycæmia due to removal or disease of the pancreas, as in diabetes. The mechanism in the kidney, which effects retention of glucose when its concentration in the blood is below the threshold named above, can be damaged by the drug phlorhizin, which produces glycosuria, associated with a normal or even a low concentration of glucose in the blood, and progressive disappearance of glycogen from the liver.

Aceto-acetic acid, β-hydroxybutyric acid, and acetone are often found in the urine during diabetes. They are formed by incomplete oxidation of fats in the body, and are excreted in any condition of carbohydrate starvation, such as absolute starvation, persistent vomiting, or during a diet consisting only of fats and proteins.

Bile pigment (urobilinogen) and bile salts appear in the urine in certain pathological conditions such as jaundice. *Blood pigments,* such as hæmatoporphyrin, are found in cases of poisoning with sulphonal and some other drugs.

Certain individuals are affected by " *inborn errors of metabolism.*" In one group of them, cystine in amounts of about $\frac{1}{2}$ g. per day is always present in the urine. Another small group excrete 3 to 6 g. per day of homogentisic acid (derived from tyrosine), a condition known as alcaptonuria ; and another group suffer from hæmatoporphyrinuria.

The second class of conditions in which an abnormal urine is secreted is associated with disease or injury of the kidney itself. The presence of more than a trace of *protein* in urine is usually an indication of damage to the filtering mechanism whereby the proteins are normally retained, and other constituents allowed to escape from the plasma. It is characteristic of Bright's disease, of failure of adequate blood supply to the kidney, and of the action of certain poisons on it. A transient appearance of protein occasionally occurs in the urine of healthy people, expecially adolescents, after severe exercise and after prolonged standing ; the latter may be due to a rise in pressure in the renal vein.

Albuminous casts of the tubules may appear in the urine secreted by diseased kidneys, and cells derived from the blood or from the excretory organs are present in the urine in certain pathological circumstances.

The Structure of the Kidney

The theory of the secretion of urine is so closely connected with the microscopical appearance of the renal elements, that some outstanding features of the anatomy of the kidney must be considered before the aims of the experimental inquiries to which they have pointed can be appreciated. A text-book of anatomy should, however, be consulted for a more detailed account of the macroscopic and microscopic structures of the kidney and urinary passages.

The *renal element* consists essentially of a long tubule, " the convoluted tubule," one end of which is closed by a structure known as " Bowman's capsule," and the other end of which joins a " collecting tubule," which in turn serves to pass the urine to the " pelvis " of the kidney and so to the ureter. The ureter, therefore, derives urine from many collecting tubules, each of which derives urine from many tributary renal tubules. The complicated course and diversity of histological appearance of the renal tubule need not be considered here, as the physiological analysis of the particular functions associated with the different portions of the tubule is still incomplete in mammals. Bowman's capsule is a sac-like expansion of the upper end of the tubule, into which a tuft of blood capillaries projects ; each capillary carries with it an ensheathing layer of epithelium known as the *glomerular membrane* (Fig. **VII. 1**).

The epithelium of the sac and the glomerular membrane consists of a single layer of flattened cells. The tubules, on the other hand, are lined throughout much of their length by columnar or cubical cells, containing granules, and resembling in appearance cells known to have a secretory function in other organs.

The *blood supply* to these renal elements is arranged in a peculiar manner. A bunch of capillaries occupies the interior of the capsule ; this is known as the " glomerulus " or glomerular tuft. [Bowman's capsule with its enclosed capillaries, regarded as a unit, is termed a Malpighian corpuscle or body.] The glomerulus receives blood from branches of the renal artery by a short, wide, "afferent" vessel. From the glomerular capillaries the blood is collected into a longer and narrower "efferent" vessel, which, in turn, divides into capillaries distributed over the tubules. From the tubular capillaries the blood

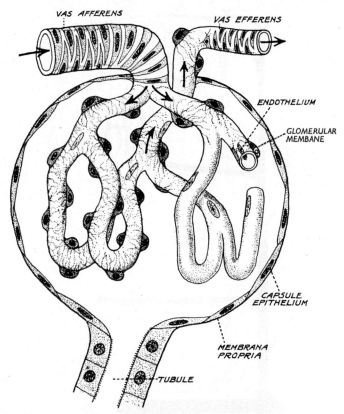

Fig. VII. 1. Diagram of a **Malpighian Body.**

This consists of a tuft of capillaries—the *glomerulus*—within an invaginated membrane—*Bowman's capsule*—which forms the head of a *tubule*. Note that the capsule epithelium is reflected over the outside of the capillaries of the glomerular tuft (in reality, there are many more capillary loops than are shown). Blood enters the glomerulus by the *vas afferens*, and leaves by the *vas efferens* ; the former is considerably larger than the latter. (After v. Mollendorff.)

collects into venous sinuses, whence it reaches the radicles of the renal vein (Fig. **VII. 2**).

In frogs' kidneys, and in amphibian and reptilian kidneys generally, the renal portal system discharges into these venous sinuses. In the normal mammalian kidney, nearly all the blood which reaches the tubules has previously passed through the glomerular capillaries. There are, however, shunts in this circulation which play a trivial part in normal function, but may be of considerable importance in certain

abnormal conditions.   Thus the blood normally approaches the glomeru**l**
through the wide channels of the renal arterioles and vasa afferenti**a**
and emerges through the narrow vasa efferentia to reach the tubula

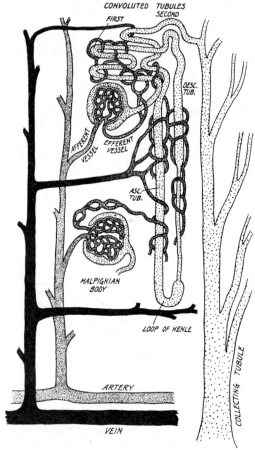

Fig. VII. 2.   Diagram of the **Arrangement of the Blood Vessels** within the
Mammalian Kidney.

The first and second convoluted tubules have been considerably simplified and reduced in length for the sake of clearness ; the ramification of
the capillaries over the tubules has also been somewhat simplified.

Blood flows from the arterioles to the glomeruli, thence to the capillaries surrounding the tubules, and so into the venules. There are thus
two capillary systems in series (compare the capillaries of the intestines
and the liver), and the pressure in the glomeruli is high, while the pressure
in the tubule capillaries is low. (After Mottram.)

capillaries.   Owing to these two anatomical factors—the double capillary
system, and the difference in diameter of the vasa afferentia and
efferentia—the blood pressure in the glomerular capillaries is much
higher than in capillaries in other organs. Its pressure in the tubula**r**
capillaries, on the other hand, may be even lower than the norma**l**

apillary pressure elsewhere in the body. Thus, on histological grounds lone, it appears that blood at high pressure is separated from the umen of the renal tubule only by the thin walls of the glomerular apillaries, and by the single layer of flattened cells composing the inner membrane of Bowman's capsule. This led to the hypothesis that urine s formed, first, by a purely physical process of filtration of the plasma n the glomerulus, whereby the colloid constituents were retained and he crystalloid constituents allowed to escape to the tubule, and secondly by a modification of this plasma filtrate in the course of its passage along he tubule, whereby its composition was changed to that known to occur in urine by a process of active secretion by the cells.

The Secretion of Urine

The essential problem of renal physiology is presented in Table VII. 1. in which the constituents of urine and plasma are compared, and it is shown that some, such as proteins and sugar, are retained in the blood, and others, such as urea and sulphates, are largely concentrated in their passage from blood to urine. A third group of substances, such as chlorides, appear in the urine in lower or higher concentration than in blood, according to the needs of the organism. In order to concentrate substances in solution an expenditure of energy is necessary. This is comparable with the energy necessary to concentrate a gas, as in pumping up a tyre. A source of physical energy, namely, the arterial pressure, is available in the kidney; but the minimum energy required to form urine from plasma can be calculated from the amounts of each substance excreted and the degree to which it is concentrated; and the energy so calculated is greater than that supplied by the arterial pressure; hence a process of active secretory work must contribute, at some stage, to the formation of urine. Active secretion means the performance of chemical work at the expense of energy derived from the metabolism of the cell; in the kidney the metabolism is mainly oxidative, and the kidney consumes oxygen at a high rate.

Theories of renal secretion. In 1842 Bowman, working in London, gave the first description of the main histological features of the kidney. From these he inferred that blood at a high pressure passing through the thin-walled glomerular capillaries would be likely to filter a watery fluid into the nephron. The tubules with cells resembling in appearance those in other glands with a well recognised secretory function, would be likely to add the main solid constituents of the urine to the watery fluid passing down from the glomerulus. In 1844, Ludwig in Germany proposed the *filtration-reabsorption theory* which differed from Bowman's view in supposing that a much larger volume of glomerular filtrate contained all the solid constituents subsequently appearing in the urine, the solids being concentrated during passage along the tubules by transfer of most of the water and some other substances to which the tubules were permeable back into the blood. Cushny emphasised the osmotic work performed by the tubule cells in concentrating the urine by reabsorption of water, and later Richards and his school in America produced the experimental proof that the filtration-reabsorption theory provides an adequate explanation of the formation of urine in so far as most of its normal constituents are concerned. Many foreign substances, such as phenol red or diodone, when injected into the blood stream appear in the urine, however, in much greater amount than can be accounted for by the filtration-reabsorption theory, which confines tubular function to the withdrawal of substances from the lumen of the tubule and their return to the blood. It is now generally agreed that such foreign substances, if present, and a few normal constituents of urine, are transferred to the tubular urine direct from the blood in the peri-tubular capillaries by secretion into the lumen of the tubule. In the hands largely of Homer Smith and his school in America, the filtration-reabsorption theory, so modified, has led to the development of methods of measurement of the glomerular filtration rate and consequently of the exact assessment of both the reabsorptive and secretory functions of the tubules.

Agreement on the main outline of the theory of renal secretion has only recently been reached after nearly a century of ingenious experimentation and often heated polemic which it would be beyond our province to consider here. In the following sections some of the crucial experiments on which the current view is founded will be described, and as far as possible, they will be chosen also to illustrate important physiological properties of the kidney.

The Functions of the Glomerulus. The hypothesis that a protein-free filtrate of the plasma is formed in the Malpighian corpuscle was first suggested on histological grounds. An obvious difficulty involved in this conception is provided by the presence of crystalloids, such as glucose, in the plasma, and their absence in the urine. Nevertheless, there is direct evidence showing that such a filtrate is formed in the capsules of the frog's kidney. Wearn and Richards succeeded in applying Chamber's micro-dissection technique to the frog's kidney by introducing the point of a micro-pipette (7 to 15μ diam.) into the capsular space, and slowly withdrawing fluid from it.

The glomerular fluid so obtained was free from proteins, and could not, therefore, be suspected of contamination with blood ; it contained chlorides and glucose even when these were absent from the bladder urine collected at the same time. Owing to the extremely small amounts available (1 cu. mm. at the most), special methods of chemical analysis had to be devised by Richards and his co-workers ; these have demonstrated the equality of the concentrations in plasma and glomerular fluid not only of all the chief normal constituents of urine such as urea, chlorides, and creatinine, but also of certain diffusible foreign substances, such as inulin, when these had previously been administered to the frog. Here, then, is unequivocal evidence that in the amphibian kidney the glomerular membrane acts as a semi-permeable membrane, allowing crystalloids to pass through it, and preventing the passage of proteins.

The collection of glomerular fluid in mammalian kidneys is techically much more difficult. In special circumstances, protein-free iltrate has been obtained (at the moment from only two glomeruli in the guinea-pig), and it appears to contain glucose and creatinine in about the plasma concentrations. That the glomerulus acts as a filter in the mammal has, however, been confirmed by experiments on the isolated kidney designed, (1) to abolish the secretory activity of the tubules, thus enabling glomerular fluid to be obtained from the ureter, (2) to establish

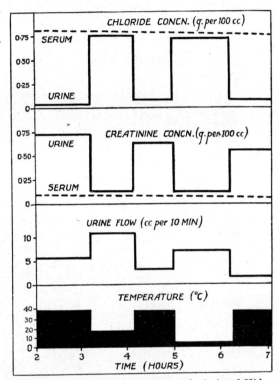

FIG. VII. 3. The influence of **Temperature** on the isolated Kidney of the dog.

Cooling produces an increase of urine flow, and a change in its composition (decrease of creatinine concentration and increase of chloride concentration) such that the composition of the urine, and serum are practically the same. The effects are reversible. (Bickford and Winton.)

the nature of the filter, and the sizes of the particles it does and does not allow to pass, and (3) to demonstrate the appropriate relation between filtration pressure and the rate of filtration.

Starling and Verney developed a method of removing a kidney completely from a dog, and of providing it with blood from a heart-lung circulation, which enabled the kidney to secrete relatively normal urine under experimental conditions which could be varied over a much wider range than in the animal. The heart can be replaced by a pump, but the presence of the lungs in the blood-circuit appears to be essential if the kidney is to continue to function properly. The urine from such an isolated kidney

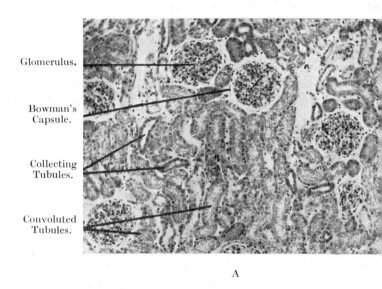

Glomerulus.

Bowman's
Capsule.

Collecting
Tubules.

Convoluted
Tubules.

A

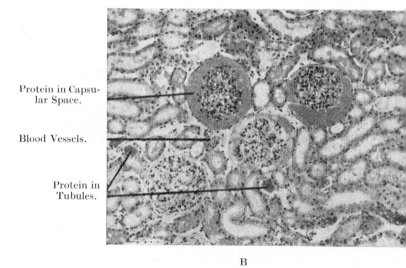

Protein in Capsu-
lar Space.

Blood Vessels.

Protein in
Tubules.

B

FIG. VII. 4.   Sections through Isolated and Perfused Kidneys of Dogs.
    (Magnification × 140.)

A. Perfused with normal defibrinated blood for one and three-quarter
hours.

B. Perfused with normal defibrinated blood for one and a half hours,
and with blood containing egg albumin for half an hour.   Note the presence
of protein in Bowman's capsule, indicating that the glomerular membrane
is permeable to proteins of relatively low molecular weight (less than
70,000).   (Bayliss, Kerridge and Russell.)

:ontains urea and creatinine in about the normal concentrations, but the
:hloride concentration is always less than that in the blood ; the chloride
:oncentration of the urine formed by the kidney *in situ*, on the other hand,
nay be either greater or less than that of the blood, according to the needs
)f the animal.

The important part that filtration plays in the formation of urine
s shown by the effects of cooling the blood with which the isolated kidney
s perfused. As shown in Fig. VII. 3. the urine of the cold kidney is
)ractically of the same composition as an ultra-filtrate of serum (*i.e.*, the
:reatinine concentration is much lower, and the chloride concentration
much higher than that of normal urine) ; the rate of urine flow is even
greater in amount than in the warm kidney. Cold seems to have
abolished the secretory activity of the tubules, leaving the filtration
mechanism relatively unaffected, and the cold kidney therefore provides
a practically uncomplicated glomerular preparation.

It may be argued that this experiment proves the existence of filtration
n the cold kidney, but not in the warm kidney, for even if the glomerular
membrane were secretory in function, cold would presumably abolish that
secretion. But cold does not, as far as is known, increase the permeability
of membranes ; consequently the filtration which takes place when the
kidney is cold, must also take place when it is warm.

Cyanide added to the blood passing through the kidney poisons the
secretory cells and so produces a urine which, like that of the cold kidney,
approaches the composition of a transudate of plasma. This does not
provide quite so convincing a proof of filtration in the unpoisoned kidney,
because cyanide is known not only to abolish secretion, but also to render
membranes (*e.g.*, the renal tubules in the frog) abnormally permeable. Indeed,
prolonged action of cyanide increases the permeability so far that protein
appears in the urine ; cooling, on the other hand, never produces proteinuria
and may even abolish it when already present. The filtration in the cyanided
kidney does not, therefore, so certainly reveal a similar mechanism in the
normal kidney.

The second property of the mammalian kidney proving the existence
of a filtration mechanism in the kidney is concerned with the nature
of the filter. A filter implies a membrane which will allow the passage
of particles below a certain size, but retain larger particles. An ultra-
filter, such as the glomerular membrane, should allow the passage of
molecules below a certain size, but retain larger molecules. The following
table (after Bayliss, Kerridge and Russell) shows that the kidney
differentiates between molecules of different sizes in just such a simple
physical way. Fig. VII. 4. shows that the position of the filter in the
kidney is in fact the glomerulus, since the protein with a sufficiently
small molecule is shown to pass from the blood into the glomerular space.

Proteins Excreted :	Molecular Weight
Gelatin	about 35,000
Bence-Jones	35,000
Egg albumin	35,000
Hæmoglobin	67,000

PROTEINS NOT EXCRETED :

Hæmoglobin		67,000
Serum albumin		72,000
Serum globulin	about	170,000
Casein	,,	200,000
Edestin	,,	200,000
Hæmocyanin (*Helix*)		5,000,000

Note. Hæmoglobin appears twice, since it is not excreted unless its concentration in the serum exceeds a certain threshold (0·2–0·5 g. Hb per 100 c.c. serum). Serum albumin is not normally excreted, although its molecular weight is on the borderline. The pore size of the glomerular membrane has been estimated as 2 mμ.

The third group of properties of the kidney which indicate that filtration occurs, depends on the changes in the nature and flow of urine produced by changes in the arterial pressure. The increase of urine flow obtained when the arterial pressure is raised (Fig. **VII.** 5) itself indicates a physical mechanism rather than a secretory one. The further fact, that the composition of the urine is observed to approach that of the serum at the higher arterial pressure (*i.e.*, the creatinine concentration falls, and the chloride concentration rises, as in Fig. **VII.** 5) is taken to mean that the secretory activity of the tubules in modifying the glomerular filtrate has proportionately less effect when, at high urine flows, the fluid hurries past the tubule cells. Consequently, if the effects of high arterial pressure were exaggerated, the composition of the urine should approach or even reach that of glomerular fluid : hence glomerular fluid, like a serum-transudate, differs from the urine in having a lower concentration of creatinine and a higher concentration of chloride.

Since the glomerular membrane acts as an ultra-filter, retaining plasma proteins, the pressure of the glomerular transudate should run parallel with that of the blood in the capillary tuft, and differ from it mainly by the osmotic pressure exerted by the plasma proteins. This osmotic pressure can be measured in a suitable osmometer ; it amounts normally to about 25 mm. Hg. The glomerular capillary pressure has not been measured directly, but histological reasons are given above for supposing it is much higher than the pressure in other capillaries. The glomerular capillary pressure has been estimated to be about two-thirds of the blood pressure in the renal artery by rather direct calculation from the changes in arterial pressure, ureter pressure, and venous pressure, which produce equal changes in the urine flow. The pressure of the glomerular transudate has, again, not been measured directly, but under special conditions it may bear some relation to the pressure of urine in the ureter. If, for example the ureter be ligatured, the pressure of the urine confined in it (" the maximum ureter pressure ") should approach that in the glomerulus unless there is an appreciable leak or reabsorption of water in the tubules. In the kidney, whether isolated or *in situ*, the maximum ureter pressure is usually about 30 mm. Hg. at an arterial pressure of 130 mm. Hg. But if the loss of water from the tubules be minimised by adding diuretics such as urea or sulphates, or by cooling, the maximum ureter pressure rises to about 70 mm. Hg. The drop of pressure from 130 mm. in the artery to 70 mm. in the ureter is 60 mm. Hg. and is presumably due to a fall of 35 mm. between artery and glomerular capillaries, and a further fall of 25 mm. due to the colloid osmotic pressure of the plasma

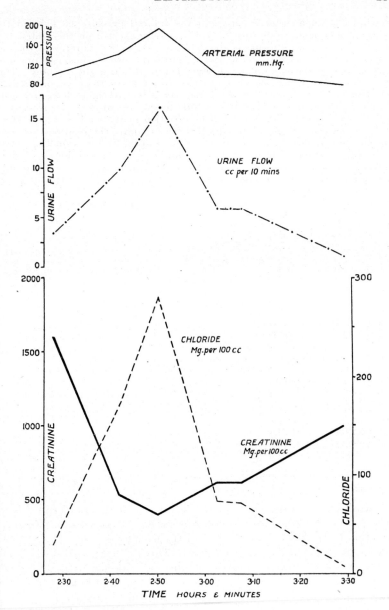

Fɪɢ. VII. 5. The influence of **Arterial Pressure** on the isolated kidney of the dog.

Increase of arterial pressure produces a large increase of urine flow. and a change in its composition (decrease of creatinine concentration and increase of chloride concentration) such that the composition of the urine approaches that of the serum. Serum creatinine 75 mg. per 100 c.c. Serum chloride 760 mg. per 100 c.c. (chloride estimated as NaCl). Temp. 37° C. (Gilson and Winton.)

proteins. If, in another experiment, the arterial pressure be reduced till
the urine flow just ceases with no back pressure exerted on the ureter, the
value of the arterial pressure is about 75 mm. Hg. ; but diuretics or cooling
will re-establish the urine flow at this pressure, and the arterial pressure
must then be reduced to about 40 mm. before the urine flow ceases. The
drop of 40 mm. from the artery to the ureter is, in these circumstances,
presumably due to a fall of 15 mm. from the artery to the glomerular capillaries, and the further fall of 25 mm. due to the colloid osmotic pressure of
the plasma proteins.[1] Although then, variation in the glomerular capillary
pressure and the leak in the tubules rather complicate the relations between
arterial pressure and maximum ureter pressure in the normal kidney (p. 266),
if the leak be sufficiently reduced, as it can be by cooling or adding certain
diuretics, these relations fit in quantitatively with the picture of the glomerulus
as an ultra-filter. We are justified, therefore, in supposing that the filtration

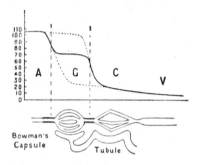

Fig. VII. 6. Diagram (After Morat) to illustrate the effect of Active
Changes in the Vasa Afferentia and Efferentia on the Pressure in the
Glomerular Capillaries.

A. Arteries.   G. Glomerular capillaries.
C. Tubular capillaries.   V. Vein.

If the vas afferens constricts, the pressure will be represented by the
lower dotted line. On the other hand, constriction of the vas efferens
would raise the pressure in the glomerulus till it almost equalled that in
the renal artery, as is shown by the upper dotted line.

pressure is great enough to overcome the colloid osmotic pressure
opposing it.

Two further consequences of the behaviour of the glomerulus as a
filter may be described as important properties of the kidney. First, a
reduction of the back pressure due to the osmotic action of the plasma
protein should increase the urine flow. This is illustrated by the fact
that an increase of urine flow can readily be obtained if the blood be
diluted with physiological saline, either in the isolated kidney or in the
intact animal. It seems also to be concerned in the reduction of urine
flow in man, due to a change from lying down to standing up, for this
change is accompanied by a gradual increase in protein concentration
of the plasma which may amount to 10 per cent. Secondly, a change

---

[1] The glomerular pressure is roughly proportional to the arterial pressure ; hence
the pressure fall between the renal artery and the glomerulus is greater (35 mm.)
at the high arterial pressure than (15 mm.) at the low arterial pressure. The complete
elucidation of these relations involves, additionally, taking into account the increase
of intrarenal pressure (see p. 266) with arterial pressure.

in glomerular capillary pressure should produce a corresponding change in the urine flow, even if the arterial pressure is unchanged. The glomerular capillary pressure may theoretically be raised : (1) by raising the general arterial pressure, when an increased blood flow through the kidney will result ; (2) by dilatation of the afferent glomerular vessels, yielding again an increased blood flow ; or (3) by a constriction of the efferent vessels, yielding a reduced blood flow. In each case the urine flow should be accelerated. (Fig. VII. 6)

In experiments in which the arterial pressure can be directly controlled, as by placing a pump in the course of one renal artery of a rabbit, or in the heart-lung-kidney preparation, the urine flow is found to depend on the arterial pressure, and not on the rate of blood flow through the kidney. The second and third methods of raising the capillary pressure without change of arterial pressure can be brought about in the isolated kidney by caffeine and by small doses of adrenaline, respectively. Larger doses of adrenaline produce sufficient constriction of the vasa afferentia to lower the glomerular pressure, and hence to reduce or abolish the urine flow. This is the usual response to adrenaline in the intact animal. In the isolated kidney the glomerular capillary pressure can, as far as is known, be raised from the normal value of about 60 per cent. of the pressure in the renal artery up to 90 per cent., or it can be lowered to 30 per cent., or perhaps lower, by the appropriate agents.

It has been shown then that the filtration hypothesis of glomerular function accounts for the composition of glomerular fluid in special circumstances such as in the frog's kidney, or in the isolated mammalian kidney where the experimental conditions are favourable. It is known, moreover, that the filtration pressure is positive though there is as yet no evidence that it is sufficiently high to propel the glomerular fluid across the glomerular membrane, bearing in mind the high glomerular filtration rate which the current theory of renal secretion demands.

It was argued by workers who believed that the glomerulus had a secretory function, that its function in the intact animal might be too delicate to withstand the rigorous experimental conditions under which glomerular filtration had been demonstrated. It is necessary, therefore, to indicate the properties of the kidney in the intact animal which justify our belief that the glomerular mechanism is confined to filtration under normal conditions. The elimination or retention by the kidney of proteins with different molecular weights (see Table, **VII. 1**, Fig. **VII. 4**) in intact rabbits and cats, shows that the nature of the filtering membrane in them is the same as in the isolated kidney. The reduction of arterial pressure in almost any way, *e.g.*, hæmorrhage or decapitation, reduces or abolishes urine flow while stimulation of the sympathetic nerves to the kidney produces a similar reduction of glomerular capillary pressure, without, however, necessarily changing the arterial pressure, and, therefore, also reduces the urine flow. An increase of urine flow with rise of arterial pressure is difficult to demonstrate in the intact animal, because most of the agents which increase arterial pressure also produce such vaso-constriction in the kidney that the glomerular capillary pressure falls instead of rising ; the transfusion of blood into an animal will, however, under suitable conditions produce an increase both in arterial pressure and urine flow.

It is clear, therefore, that the properties of the kidney in the animal and its properties when isolated and perfused are sufficiently similar to justify the belief in glomerular filtration in the living animal, although a complete proof of such filtration cannot, for experimental reasons, be derived from observations on the intact animal alone.

The Functions of the Tubules.   Our discussion of glomerular function has advanced us only one step in the solution of the main problem, summarised in Table VII. 1, that of the production of urine from plasma.   The separation of the proteins from the plasma filtrate has indeed been accomplished at the expense of some of the energy provided by the head of pressure of the blood in the glomerulus.   But the main consumption of energy in the kidney is concerned with the concentration of substances such as urea which are much more abundant in the urine than in the plasma filtrate.   Furthermore, the presence under suitable conditions of glucose in the filtrate, and its absence in the urine, must be attributed to tubular activity.   The reabsorptive function of the tubules is unequivocally demonstrated in the frog's kidney by the experiments of A. N. Richards and his colleagues, already mentioned, in which a comparison of the composition of the glomerular fluid and bladder urine showed that, under suitable circumstances, glucose and chlorides might be present in the former, but absent from the latter. Moreover, the quantity of the glomerular fluid which they collected in a given time, multiplied by the number of glomeruli, was much greater than the volume of urine which appeared in the same time.   Water, therefore, is reabsorbed ;   this would account for those substances, which are not reabsorbed, appearing at a higher concentration in the urine than in the plasma.

In the isolated mammalian kidney the reabsorptive function of the tubules is shown by the effects of abolition of secretory activity by cooling or poisons.   Cooling. for example, produces a two- or three-fold increase of water output and an enormous increase of chloride output, as shown in Fig. VII. 3.   Moreover, glucose, which is normally absent in the urine, now appears in about the concentration in which it is present in the plasma.   Cyanide poisoning has much the same effects.   The secretory activity of the tubules, which has been abolished, must, therefore, have the effect of removing all the glucose, and much of the chlorides and water, from the glomerular filtrate and restoring them to the blood.

Richards and his associates have developed their micro-dissection technique to investigate the processes of reabsorption in different parts of the tubules in certain suitable animals, such as the frog and *Necturus*. The procedure involves the insertion of two micro-pipettes into a single tubule, isolating the length of tubule between them by blocking the tubule with droplets of mercury, and then discovering the changes in volume and composition of fluid perfused through the isolated segment. It was found that the reabsorption of glucose proceeded almost entirely in the proximal tubule, whereas the reabsorption of chloride and the changes of acidity were carried out in the distal tubule. Even in the two animals closely examined, the frog and *Necturus*, there were, however, important differences in the functions of the segments of the tubules, and although observations of this kind have shed light of the greatest importance on the functions of the tubules, it is clearly not legitimate to infer from observations on animals at present investigated any exact corresponding functions in the corresponding segments of tubules of mammalian kidneys.

In recent years much complicated and rather indirect evidence has been brought to bear on the problem of assigning specific functions to specific segments of the mammalian tubule. The conclusions cannot yet be regarded as widely enough agreed to justify their description here.

The word " secretion " is commonly used in rather a special sense in connection with the renal tubules ; both the " reabsorption " and the " secretion " which the different theories postulate are really forms of secretion in the general physiological sense ; reabsorption involves an indirect secretory activity of tubule cells whereby substances (*e.g.*, glucose) are removed from the fluid in the tubules, where their concentrations are low, to the blood where their concentrations are higher. Direct " secretion " involves transference of other substances (*e.g.*, creatinine in man) from the blood, where their concentrations are low, to the tubules where their concentrations are higher. Both processes require the performance of chemical work, and the theoretical minimum work necessary to produce a given volume of urine of known composition from plasma can be calculated, as in similar problems in physical chemistry. Measurements of the oxygen consumption of the kidney indicate that this chemical work is only 1–2 per cent. of the energy expended in the metabolism of the organ. This low efficiency may seem surprising ; it is only about one-tenth of that in mechanical work, such as that of muscular contraction, or of a petrol engine. Other examples of the performance of chemical work in which the efficiency has been measured, *e.g.*, nerve metabolism or chemical factories show, however, that the efficiency is about equally low. The arterio-venous oxygen difference is remarkably constant in the kidney, and consequently diuresis due to rise in arterial pressure, and resulting increase in blood flow, is associated with increased oxygen consumption. Diuresis due to osmotic diuretics, such as urea, proceeds without increase in oxygen consumption despite the increase in the osmotic work done, and it is, therefore associated with increased efficiency.

Substances which appear in the urine have been classified into two groups : (1) those that are excreted only if their concentration in the blood exceeds a certain threshold are termed *threshold substances* ; (2) those that are excreted, however low their concentration in the blood may be, are termed *no-threshold substances*. In a general way it might be said that threshold substances are compounds, such as glucose and chlorides, the retention of which may be of value to the animal, whereas no-threshold substances are compounds, such as dyes, which are foreign to the body, or the complete removal of which is of advantage to the animal. According to the filtration reabsorption theory, threshold substances are reabsorbed in the tubules, while no-threshold substances are not reabsorbed ; owing to the reabsorption of water, no-threshold substances must, therefore, appear in the urine at a higher concentration than threshold substances.

Let us now consider the limitations of the filtration-reabsorption theory which allows no addition by the tubular cells of substances direct from the blood stream. Many early workers took objection to the bizarre inefficiency of a process involving in man the filtration of about 130 c.c. per minute in the glomeruli, and the reabsorption of all but the 1 c.c. per minute which appeared as urine. This objection loses much of its force, however, when the details of the process are examined, for the total area of the glomerular membranes in man is estimated at one and a half square metres; moreover, something approaching two million renal units may be concerned, and the filtration of one-twentieth of a cubic millimetre per minute is no incredible feat for each of these. (Richards has collected up to one-twentieth of a cubic millimetre per minute from a single glomerulus in a frog's kidney; the filtration pressure in the mammalian kidney must be at least ten times as great as in the frog's kidney.) Each tubule is several centimetres long (*e.g.*, 5·5 cm.), and can easily be imagined as absorbing most of the small volume of filtrate mentioned. Extensive reabsorption is a familiar concept in other physiological processes, for example, many litres a day are secreted into the alimentary canal, apart from water imbibed, of which only about 100 c.c. a day appear in the fæces. The increase in urine flow when tubular activity is inhibited by cold or by poisoning with cyanide serves as a reassuring indication that glomerular filtration is at a much higher rate than simultaneous urine flow.

Nevertheless, there are compelling reasons for believing that reabsorption of water in the tubules is insufficient to account for the degree of concentration of certain substances in the urine, and for supposing that the tubule cells are able to make additions to the tubular urine by secretion direct from the blood. One of the earliest convincing experiments which demonstrated such secretion was performed by E. K. Marshall. He injected phenol-red into a dog, and analysed its plasma and urine so as to find the concentration-ratio, which was extremely high. Now phenol-red has the peculiarity that a proportion of it forms some indiffusible combination in the plasma—a proportion which is rather variable. Marshall found that only 25 per cent. of the phenol-red in his solution of phenol-red in dog's plasma would pass through a collodion membrane. Consequently the glomerular filtrate, he argued, would only contain the dye in one-quarter the concentration of that in the plasma. He could thus calculate the glomerular filtration rate as four times the product of the urine flow and the concentration ratio of phenol-red. This value was so high that the blood, from which the filtrate would have to be formed, would have to be passing through the kidneys at a rate almost equal to the whole output of the dog's heart. This is clearly impossible. He rejected Ludwig's theory, therefore, and supposed that some of the phenol-red was added to a smaller amount of glomerular filtrate by the tubules, and that the secretory cells had access to the indiffusible 75 per cent. of the phenol-red in the plasma.

An even simpler example of the need for postulating direct tubular secretion is provided by the behaviour of an organic iodine compound known in Britain as diodone and in America as diodrast. If a small dose of diodone is introduced into the blood stream about four-fifths of it disappears from the blood during a single passage through the kidney, *i.e.*, the plasma in the renal vein contains only one-fifth of that in the renal artery. To explain this on the supposition that the secreted diodone was all derived from the glomerular filtrate would require a glomerular filtration rate equal to four-fifths of the plasma flow through the glomerular capillaries. But removal of four-fifths of the plasma water would increase the concentration of plasma proteins and blood corpuscles to a point which would render the blood much too viscid to flow through the blood vessels, and the supposition must, therefore, be false. As will be shown below, only about one-fifth of the excreted diodone is derived from the glomerular filtrate, the rest being added to the tubular urine by the tubule cells supplied by blood in the peritubular capillaries.

While direct secretion by the tubule cells is thus an undoubted feature of the elimination of diffusible foreign substances such as phenolred and diodone, it is noteworthy that this mechanism plays no part in the excretion of the more important constituents of normal urine.

Plasma Clearances

In assessing renal function in connection with the excretion of any given substance, such as urea, it is important to choose a convenient scale. The output per minute in the urine is unsuitable, because the output may be doubled by just doubling the plasma concentration without much change in renal function. The ratio of urine concentration to plasma concentration, known as the *concentration ratio*, is sometimes of value, but it changes with change in urine flow to an extent that with some substances it is doubled when the urine flow is halved. Van Slyke and his colleagues, therefore, introduced the unit : *plasma clearance*, which avoids these drawbacks. If, for example, a substance were present in urine in a concentration of 200 mg. per 100 c.c., and the urine were flowing at 1 c.c. per minute, the amount removed from the plasma would be 2 mg. per minute. Now suppose the plasma were found at the time to contain 1 mg. per 100 c.c. of the same substance, it would follow that the kidneys had cleared from the body as much of the substance as was contained in 200 c.c. of plasma in one minute. The " plasma clearance " is then said to be 200 c.c. per minute.

In general, if the concentration of a substance in plasma and urine are P and U when the urine flow is V, the plasma clearance is defined as $\dfrac{UV}{P}$ for that substance. For reasons indicated later, the polysaccharide inulin is believed to pass unhampered across the glomerular membrane and to appear in the urine in exactly the same amount as in the filtrate, none being added by the tubules or lost by diffusion through them. The whole quantity UV of inulin which is excreted in one minute derives, therefore, from the glomerular filtrate which, like the plasma, contains inulin in the concentration **P**. The rate of glomerular filtration must then equal the plasma clearance for inulin. A substance like glucose which is completely reabsorbed by the tubules has a plasma clearance of zero, because none is cleared from the body, and substances like chlorides and urea which are partially reabsorbed have lower clearances than that of inulin. Diodone, phenol-red and other substances directly secreted in the tubules have plasma clearances higher than that of inulin (Fig. VII. 7).

The first serious *assessment of glomerular filtration rate*, by calculating the plasma clearance, was made by Rehberg in Denmark about twenty years ago before direct secretion by the tubules was generally recognised. Assuming no tubular secretion, he took the substance with the highest known concentration ratio, creatinine (see Table, VII. 1), as the one which would be least or not at all reabsorbed. (The higher concentration ratio of ammonia is irrelevant owing to synthesis in the kidney of this substance.) Quick and reliable methods of estimating the concentrations of exogeneous creatinine in plasma and urine were partly responsible for the wide application of Rehberg's way of measuring glomerular filtration rate to the study of renal function in health and disease. With the subsequent proof of direct tubular secretion invalidating Rehberg's assumption, a search began for a substance which was neither secreted nor reabsorbed by the tubules, and the American schools of Homer Smith and A. N. Richards independently picked out the substance inulin for the purpose.

Inulin solutions, if pure, can be injected intravenously into man and other animals without harm and without apparently affecting the circulation or the activity of the kidney. Inulin is not metabolised in the body. It is freely filterable through the glomerular membrane since its concentration in frog's glomerular fluid is equal to that in the plasma. The belief that inulin is neither reabsorbed nor secreted in the tubules is mainly based on the following observations : (*a*) the molecular weight of inulin is 5,200, and being a long chain polysaccharide, it diffuses at only about double the rate of hæmoglobin. It is, therefore, unlikely to diffuse out of the tubules. (*b*) It is still less likely that inulin (mol wt. 5,200) and creatinine, (mol. wt. 112) should be either reabsorbed or secreted at exactly the same rates under widely varying circumstances of concentration and urine flow. But unless both these substances escaped tubular reabsorption or secretion in the dog, sheep, rabbit, seal and frog, it would not otherwise be possible to explain the exact equality of the plasma clearances for inulin and exogenous creatinine simultaneously measured in these animals. (Creatinine is, in part, secreted in man and some other animals in which its plasma clearance exceeds that of inulin.) (*c*) The inulin clearance is independent of its concentration in the plasma ; whereas the clearances of most other substances which are higher or lower than that of inulin when their concentrations in the plasma are low, approach the inulin clearance progressively as their concentrations in the plasma rise (see Fig. VII. 7). (*d*) In man and animals in which the creatinine clearance exceeds the inulin clearance, there are other

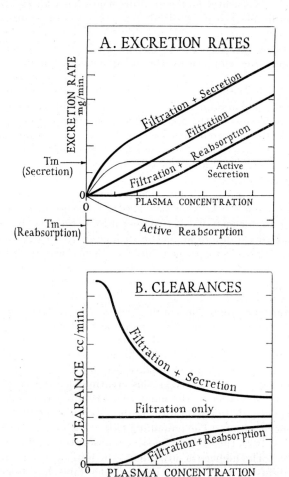

Fig. VII. 7. Diagrammatic representation of the **Effect of Plasma Concentration** on the **Rate of Excretion** and the **Plasma Clearance.**

Three types of substance are considered : (1) exemplified by Inulin, which is neither reabsorbed nor excreted by the tubules ; (2) exemplified by Glucose, which is reabsorbed by the tubules ; and (3) exemplified by Diodone, which is excreted by the tubules. The scales, both of ordinates and of abscissæ are arbitrary and would, in fact, be different for each substance considered. The filtration pressure and rate of urine flow (V) are assumed to be constant and unaffected by the plasma composition.

In A the thick lines show the quantities excreted per minute (urine concentration, U, multiplied by V). These are separated into the quantities filtered per minute (as defined by the inulin excretion rate) and the quantities added or removed per minute by the tubules (thin lines). These latter quantities become constant when the plasma concentrations are such that the Tm values are reached or exceeded.

In B, the Clearances have been calculated as the rate of excretion (U × V) divided by the plasma concentration (P) ; the inulin clearance (filtration only) is independent of P, and the clearances of diodone and of glucose (for example) fall and rise, respectively, towards the inulin clearance as P becomes greater.

substances, *e.g.*, sorbitol and mannitol, whose clearances are identical with the inulin clearance. (*e*) Inulin cannot be excreted by certain fish whose kidneys contain no glomeruli ("aglomerular kidneys"). All constituents of the urine in these species must be secreted by the tubules, and this emphasises the incapacity of tubules to secrete inulin.

On the basis of these considerations there is now widespread agreement that the glomerular filtration rate in the normal kidney may be measured in terms of the plasma clearance for inulin. In kidneys damaged by disease or poison, in which abnormally low inulin clearances are found, the possibility of abnormal permeability of the tubules leading to loss of inulin by passive reabsorption must, however, be borne in mind.

The inulin clearance in man ranges in healthy individuals from 90 to 170 c.c. per minute—the average recently being given by Smith is 131 c.c. per minute for men and 117 c.c. per minute for women—all reduced to the standard size of 1·73 sq. metres surface area. In a given individual the inulin clearance is surprisingly difficult to change. In water diuresis, for example, an increase in urine flow from the resting value of 1 c.c. per minute to nearly 20 c.c. per minute, which is about the maximum, takes place with little or no change in inulin clearance.

Important new light has been shed on the *mechanisms of tubular secretion and reabsorption* as a consequence of measurement of the glomerular filtration rate. Freshly injected creatinine in man yields a clearance 40 per cent. above the inulin clearance if the dose be small, though the percentage falls if the dose be larger or the injection is not recent. Forty per cent. of exogenous creatinine is, therefore, added by direct tubular secretion to the amount in the glomerular filtrate. The urea clearance is about one-half the inulin clearance and little affected by plasma concentration. The remaining half of the urea in the glomerular filtrate is lost from the urine by passive reabsorption in its passage down the tubules. The higher the urine flow, the lower is the proportion lost by such diffusion presumably because the fluid has lingered for a shorter time in the tubules.

Glucose clearance is normally zero. If the glucose concentration in the plasma be increased, a point is reached, known as the threshold plasma concentration, at which glucose begins to appear in the urine. The reabsorption mechanism in the tubules is then working at its maximum rate (known as the glucose-Tm), and it is a remarkable fact that further increases in the glucose concentration in the plasma appears not substantially to affect this rate, of which 350 mg. per minute is a representative value in man. Further increase in plasma concentration, however, continues to increase the amount of glucose in the urine derived from the glomerular filtrate which more and more dwarfs the amount reabsorbed. Consequently, the glucose clearance at very high plasma concentrations approaches the inulin clearance.

Vitamin C is likewise excreted only if its plasma concentration exceeds the threshold, when the tubular reabsorptive process has reached its maximum rate, a representative value for this (Vitamin C-Tm) being 2·0 mg. per minute.

Diodone (diodrast) excretion follows the same plan with a characteristic difference due to its being directly secreted instead of reabsorbed in the tubules. As the blood concentration is increased up to a threshold value, there is little change in diodone clearance, because tubular secretion is removing almost the whole of the diodone from the plasma and dwarfs the increasing amount deriving from the glomerular filtrate. Above the threshold concentration, the clearance begins to fall, because secretion is working at its maximum rate which is unaffected by further increases in diodone concentration. (Diodone-Tm is about 50 mg. (iodine) per minute.) As the plasma concentration rises, the proportion of diodone in the urine derived from the glomerular filtrate becomes larger, and the proportion (though not absolute amount) derived from tubular secretion becomes smaller. The diodone clearance, therefore, falls and approaches the inulin clearance when the diodone concentration becomes very high.

The Renal Blood Flow

If the blood pressure is not very low or high the blood flow through an ordinary long glass tube is doubled if the pressure is doubled. The blood flow through a perfused denervated hind-limb or lung (or most other organs) is more than doubled when the pressure is doubled. By contrast, in the perfused denervated kidney, the blood flow rises only about 50 per cent. when the pressure is doubled (at arterial pressures exceeding 60 mm. Hg). Still smaller changes in renal blood flow are found in lightly anæsthetised animals with active vaso-motor reflexes when the arterial pressure changes as a result, say, of the carotid sinus reflex. In conscious animals it is a matter of some difficulty to discover ways of increasing the renal blood flow, though it may be nearly doubled in fever. It can be reduced by injecting adrenaline and sometimes in conditions such as fright, involving sympathetic stimulation.

The most reliable method of measuring renal blood flow in conscious animals is, at a preliminary operation, to explant a kidney under the skin. After recovery, samples of blood can be withdrawn from the renal vein through a syringe needle without serious disturbance to the animal. If the simultaneous concentrations of a substance, such as urea, in the arterial blood (C_a) and in the renal venous blood (C_v) be measured, and if also the rate of excretion (Q per minute) in the urine be determined then the blood flow through the one kidney must be $\dfrac{Q}{C_a - C_v}$ per minute during steady conditions. This gives the whole blood flow through the renal vein, including such a proportion as may have passed through capsular vessels or anastomotic channels by-passing the circulation through the glomeruli. The method is applicable to damaged kidneys.

A less certain approach to the renal blood flow in man and unoperated animals has been extensively explored by Smith and others, and depends on measurement of the diodone clearance. The argument, in simplified form, runs : Suppose a particular substance were found which was completely removed from the blood in a single passage through the kidney, then the quantity contained in the unknown volume of arterial blood reaching the kidney per minute would be the same as the quantity excreted in the urine per minute. If the concentration in the arterial blood is also known, the blood flow can thus be calculated. One can restate this by saying that if the substance did not pass into or out of the blood corpuscles in passing through the kidney, the plasma flow is equal to the plasma clearance for such a substance. Now the excretion of diodone (diodrast) and the more easily estimated para-amino hippuric acid approach the required conditions. If the plasma concentration of diodone is below the threshold beyond which the clearance begins to fall, the renal venous blood is found to contain only between $\frac{1}{8}$ and $\frac{1}{4}$ of that in the arterial blood. The kidney has extracted, say, four-fifths of the diodone, and so long as this " *extraction ratio* " remains constant, the necessary correction can be made in calculating the renal plasma flow. The extraction ratio fortunately appears to remain fairly constant in normal kidneys. It falls so far, however, in kidneys damaged by disease or poisons that the method becomes inapplicable.

In resting normal men, the diodone (diodrast) clearance at low plasma concentrations averages about 500 c.c. per minute, corresponding to a renal blood flow of about 1,200 c.c. per minute. Taking the resting cardiac output at 5,000 c.c. per minute, it appears that at rest the supply to the kidneys accounts for about one-quarter of the output of blood from the heart. It may be noted, moreover, that the fraction of the plasma removed as filtrate in the glomerulus, known as the " *filtration-fraction*," is about one-fifth.

The Control of Renal Secretion

The effects on the secretion of urine of stimulation and section of various nervous structures may all be interpreted in terms of the changes induced either on the general arterial pressure, or on the calibre of the renal blood vessels, or on both. There is at present no sufficient reason for suspecting a direct nervous influence on the secretory mechanism proper, except for the anatomical fact that nerve fibres do supply the tubule cells.

If one kidney of a dog be carefully but completely denervated, the dog will recover, and the urine can be collected separately from each kidney through exteriorised ureters. The urine coming from the denervated organ is indistinguishable from that coming from its innervated fellow, both as regards rate of flow and composition. The increase of urine due to administration of water (" water diuresis ") and its inhibition by exercise or stimulation of the skin are equal in both kidneys.

The first important factor in the production of urine is, then, the capillary pressure in the glomerulus ; this may follow variations in the systemic arterial pressure, as in the increased pressure and urine secretion in certain kinds of excitement, and the diminished pressure and urine secretion during sleep at night ; or it may vary independently of the arterial pressure and according to the relative degrees of constriction of the afferent and efferent glomerular vessels.

A second factor was disclosed by the direct observations of Richards and Schmidt on the glomeruli situated near the surface of the frog's kidney, which showed that in a given microscopic field the number of active glomeruli, *i.e.*, those through which a flow of blood could be detected, was constantly varying, and that any particular glomerulus showed only intermittent activity. The proportion of active glomeruli was increased by diuretic, and diminished by vaso-constrictor substances. This phenomenon was absent during direct observation of glomeruli in the mammalian kidney. The numerous quantitative studies of clearance, etc., both on conscious man and animals, and on isolated mammalian kidneys have led to the conclusion that variation in the number of active glomeruli plays no part in the variation in renal activity in most normal mammals other than the rabbit.

The third outstanding factor controlling the production of urine is the composition of the blood flowing through the kidney. Allusion has already been made to the diuretic effect of a reduction in concentration of plasma proteins, and reasons given for attributing this result partly to change of the colloid osmotic pressure, diminution of which tends to accelerate glomerular filtration. The actions of special diuretic substances will be considered in the section devoted to them below. Moreover, deficient oxygen supply to the kidney may affect the permeability of the capsular membrane so as to allow some escape of plasma proteins into the urine. There is yet another way by which the composition of blood influences organs it supplies, in virtue of its content of minute amounts of substances known as hormones. Of the actions of these on the kidney, only that of post-pituitary extract has been examined in detail. The classical diuretic effect of pituitary extracts on anæsthetised animals is, in the main, an indirect consequence of the increase of blood pressure induced by their injection. The post-pituitary substances have, on the contrary, more recently been shown to exert an important action directly on the kidney, namely, that of inhibiting the flow of urine, and increasing the concentration of chlorides in it. This action can be demonstrated under three sets of conditions ; (1) water diuresis in man, which is greatly delayed : (2) the heart-lung-kidney preparation of the dog : and (3) the extreme polyuria of diabetes insipidus, a human disease probably due to deficient secretion of the pituitary gland or to disturbance of the nerve structures in the brain just above it. The experiments of Verney and others on the effects of removal of the dog's pituitary gland and subsequent injection of its extracts, on the secretion of urine, indicate that the presence of this hormone in the blood is part of the normal mechanism regulating the activity of the renal tubules.

Damage to the kidney usually leads to the composition of the urine approaching that of the plasma, as, for example, in the polyuria of chronic nephritis. Experimentally, functional removal of a part of the kidney, effected by ligaturing one of the two primary branches of the renal artery in the isolated kidney of the dog, induces a largely increased flow of urine from the part that remains active ; the urine secreted under such conditions shows an increased chloride and diminished urea content, both of which changes are an approach to the composition of the plasma, and may be brought about by an increase of arterial pressure.

The increase of the rate of urine flow from one-half of a kidney when the other half is deprived of blood is so great that the total outflow of urine from the ureter is often actually increased. Now the change in the composition of the urine accompanying diuresis is different according as the diuresis is due to an increase in glomerular filtration rate, or to a decrease in tubular activity. Moreover, the diuresis accompanying an increase in arterial pressure is undoubtedly produced by an increase in glomerular filtration rate. But the change in composition of the urine produced by ligaturing one branch of the renal artery can be matched by raising the arterial pressure in the whole kidney until the same increase in urine flow has been reached. Hence ligaturing one branch of the renal artery results in an increase in glomerular filtration rate in the surviving half kidney. That tubular activity plays no important part in this diuresis is also shown by the fact that about the same increase of urine flow is produced by depriving one-half of the kidney of blood even in the cold kidney, in which the low temperature has in any case abolished secretory activity. The explanation of the diuretic effect is, as far as is known, dependent on a change in the *intrarenal pressure*. The intrarenal pressure is a pressure of the tissue fluids of the kidney, made possible partly by the inextensibility of the capsule round the kidney, and partly by the rigidity of the renal substance. The intrarenal pressure will make the tubules and venules in the kidney collapse unless the pressure of the liquids within them exceeds the intrarenal pressure ; consequently the effect of the intrarenal pressure on the urine flow is much the same as that of an increase of ureter pressure, that is, it provides a back pressure which is transmitted to the glomerular membrane and so retards glomerular filtration. If this be so, one might expect that an increase of ureter pressure, or of venous pressure, would have no effect on the urine flow unless the increase exceeded the intrarenal pressure. In the isolated kidney this is so. Depriving one-half of the kidney of blood reduces the intrarenal pressure in the surviving half, and so increases its rate of glomerular filtration ; it also reduces the pressure which must be exceeded if a rise in ureter pressure is to affect the urine flow.

The intrarenal pressure in the isolated kidney of the dog can thus be estimated in terms of the minimum rise of ureter pressure which affects the urine flow ; it is usually about 10 mm. Hg, but may be considerably greater or less. It is normally enough to reduce the urine flow to about one-half or one-third of what it would be if there were no intrarenal pressure ; but if it is unusually high, it may abolish the urine flow altogether. Most agents (*e.g.*, diuretics, cooling) which increase the urine flow make the kidney swell and increase the intrarenal pressure.

In many diseases of the kidney the urine flow is abnormally low. This has been used as an objection to the filtration-reabsorption theory, since it might be expected that, on this theory, an impairment of the function of the tubules, such as is indicated by histological examination, would result in an abnormally high urine flow. In those diseases in which the kidneys are swollen the reduction in urine flow may be due to the back-pressure associated with an enhanced intrarenal pressure. A second factor tending to reduce the urine flow when the tubules are diseased is the increase in permeability of their walls, resulting in an increased loss of fluid from the tubules by diffusion. Such an increase in permeability can be produced experimentally by poisoning the tubule cells with cyanide or mercuric chloride.

The Action of Diuretics

Oral administration of water or injection of hypotonic saline solution induces diuresis in the *narcotised* animal, which may be attributed to dilution of plasma proteins, with consequent reduction of osmotic resistance to glomerular transudation, and quantitatively more important, a reduction in the reabsorption of water from the tubules. In the *normal* animal the diuresis produced by the same agents is much greater, and the urine more dilute, though there is no greater dilution of the plasma proteins. There would appear to be five significant points in connection with the diuretic reponse of the normal kidney to ingestion of water : (*a*) it occurs without appreciable change in the glomerular filtration rate ; (*b*) the maximum rate of urine flow is only reached some ten to twenty minutes after the whole of the water has been absorbed (or injected) ; (*c*) if the salt concentration of the body fluids is reduced gradually by salt starvation there is no diuresis : conversely if the salt concentration is raised by excessive salt administration, a normal water diuresis can be produced, in spite of the fact that the concentration of the body fluids is not reduced even to the normal value ; (*d*) the response to the administration of water is not affected by complete denervation of the kidneys ; (*e*) the response is reduced, or abolished, by emotional stress, even after all the renal nerves have been divided, and the suprarenal glands inactivated. It would appear that the primary stimulus for the increased urine flow is the dilution, or rate of dilution, of the body fluids ; this does not react directly on the kidneys, however, but requires some intermediary mechanism, probably hormonal, which accounts for the delay in the diuretic response to blood dilution. The inhibition of water diuresis produced by injection of pituitary extracts suggested that there was normally a continuous secretion by the pituitary gland which was reduced or abolished when water was drunk. The pars nervosa of the posterior pituitary lobe which secretes the anti-diuretic hormone is considered, partly for the following reasons but also on histological grounds, to be under the influence of the supra-optic and para-ventricular nuclei transmitted through the supra-optic tracts.

The amount of the anti-diuretic hormone normally present in blood is too small to detect after blood has been withdrawn from the animal, but various lines of indirect evidence point to its presence and to its importance in the control of water output. In hydrated rats, the hormone cannot be detected in the urine, but in rats deprived of water, the hormone is present in the urine : it is absent even in these dehydrated rats if they have previously been hypophysectomised, or if their supra-optic tracts have been severed. By injecting hypertonic solutions direct into the carotid arteries of conscious animals, and evoking the inhibition of urine flow characteristic of pituitary action, Verney has demonstrated that osmotic change is the effective stimulus to the neuro-hypophyseal mechanism. Acetylcholine also inhibits urine flow and produces the changes in com-

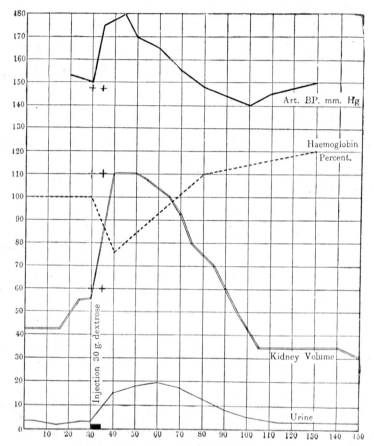

FIG. VII. 8.   Diuresis as a Result of the Intravenous Injection of 30 g. Glucose in 100 per cent. Solution, into a Dog.

The glucose concentration in the blood greatly exceeded the threshold, and glucose was present, therefore, in the tubules in high concentration ; this impeded the reabsorption of water, and diuresis resulted.   As contributory causes of the diuresis, we may note (1) the rise in arterial pressure, and (2) the dilution of the blood, as shown by the fall in hæmoglobin concentration ; these resulted from the withdrawal of fluid from the tissue spaces by the transient osmotic pressure exerted by the hypertonic glucose solution (see pp. 87 and 122).

The kidney volume is expressed in arbitrary units, and the urine flow in cubic centimetres per ten minutes.   (Starling.)

position characteristic of pituitary action, but only if the posterior lobe has not previously been removed.   Acetylcholine is, therefore, presumably involved at some point as a transmitter in the nervous control of the secretion of the anti-diuretic hormone.   Apart from water, alcohol is the only common diuretic which probably increases the urine flow by inhibiting the post-pituitary secretion. Section of the supra-optic tracts regularly leads to atrophy of the pars nervosa of the pituitary gland, and results in a permanent polyuria. Removal of the whole pituitary gland usually fails to produce persistent polyuria, and this fact has been difficult to fit into the picture of the pituitary control of urine flow. The removal of the posterior lobe only, however, together with any pars nervosa tissue that may be in the stalk of the gland and in the tuber cinereum, invariably produces persistent polyuria : whereas the removal of the anterior lobe produces a reduction in urine flow. It is on the lines of the uncertain balance between the anti-diuretic influence of the posterior lobe and the diuretic influence of the anterior lobe that the uncertain effects of total hypophysectomy may be sought.

Low threshold substances such as urea and sulphates are concentrated in the tubules to about one-half the extent that inulin is concentrated, the other half of the substance is reabsorbed. Increase in concentration increases the osmotic pressure of the tubular fluid and so increases the work to be done in reabsorbing water. Consequently, less water is reabsorbed and diuresis ensues. Threshold substances such as glucose have a similar effect when their plasma concentration greatly exceeds the threshold, *e.g.*, in diabetes mellitus (*cf.* Fig. VII. 8).

Xanthine derivatives, such as caffeine, act mainly by increasing the glomerular filtration rate. In frogs, this is brought about by increasing the proportion of active glomeruli, but in mammals this proportion is unaffected and the filtration pressure is increased by dilatation of the vasa afferentia. In the isolated kidney of the dog, and in experimental animals, the blood flow can be directly measured and is markedly increased. In conscious man the diodone clearance is diminished, and if this is not due to the effect of caffeine on diodone secretion, it would indicate reduction in blood flow, presumably due to constriction of the vasa efferentia. All but the smallest effective doses of caffeine affect the secretory activity of the tubule cells, reducing reabsorption of water and further increasing the urine flow.

Summary of Renal Factors Controlling the Urine Flow

A. GLOMERULUS :
  (i.) Filtration Pressure . *Urine flow increased by*
      (*a*) Rise of arterial pressure (*e.g.*, increase in blood volume, or pituitary extract in anæsthetised animals).
      (*b*) Rise of glomerular capillary pressure (*e.g.*, caffeine).
      (*c*) Fall in intrarenal pressure (ligature of branch of renal artery or decapsulation).
    Urine flow decreased by
      (*a*) Fall of arterial pressure (*e.g.*, hæmorrhage).
      (*b*) Fall of glomerular capillary pressure (*e.g.*, adrenaline).

(c) Rise of ureter pressure (*e.g.*, obstruction by stone).

(d) Rise of venous pressure (*e.g.*, postural ; possibly pregnancy).

(e) Rise in intrarenal pressure (*e.g.*, diuresis, and probably acute nephritis).

(ii.) Colloid Osmotic Pressure .

Urine flow increased by
Reduction of concentration of plasma proteins (*e.g.*, plethora and intravenous injection of saline).

Urine flow decreased by
Increase of concentration of plasma proteins (*e.g.*, change from recumbent to erect posture).

(iii.) The proportion of Active Glomeruli .

Urine flow increased by
Caffeine, decreased by adrenaline in the frog. (The proportion is constant in normal mammals.)

(iv.) Permeability of Glomerular Membrane.

Poisons may render membrane permeable to plasma proteins (*e.g.*, prolonged action of $HgCl_2$, HCN, large doses of caffeine).

B. Tubules :

(i.) Changes of composition of contents of tubules.

Reabsorption of water retarded by high osmotic pressure of substances which are relatively less easily reabsorbed (*e.g.*, urea, sulphate, and glucose if exceeding threshold concentration) and by blood dilution.

(ii.) Changes in activity of tubule cells.

(a) General reduction of secretory activity increases the urine flow (*e.g.*, cooling, cyanide, mercurial diuretics, certain diseases).

(b) Specific changes.
Phlorizin reduces reabsorption of glucose.
Post-pituitary extract increases reabsorption of water.

MICTURITION

Urine is secreted by the kidneys continuously, but removed from the body only periodically. Meanwhile it collects and may remain for some hours in the bladder, which acts like a reservoir.

The urine passes from the kidneys to the bladder through tubes, *the ureters*, the walls of which contain plain muscle, and encourage the downward flow by peristaltic contractions. These contractions travel down the tube at about 2 to 3 cm. per second, and are repeated from about one to four times a minute. Consequently the urine enters the bladder in a series of squirts, as can be observed in man by looking through a cystoscope, a tubular instrument inserted through the urethra, which illuminates and renders visible the lining wall of the bladder. If, for any reason, the pressure inside the ureter is raised, its contractions become fiercer and more spasmodic in nature, a change which is readily observed in the isolated kidney of the dog. Such spasmodic contraction of plain muscle produces intense pain, and is illustrated in human disease by renal colic, which is an attack of severe pain and other symptoms due, for example, to passage of small stones from the kidney, blocking and distending the ureter and so evoking spasm of its wall.

Evacuation of the bladder is effected by contraction of the plain muscle in its walls, known as the detrusor muscle. The urethra is guarded by two sphincters—the external being of striated and the internal of unstriated muscle. If the external voluntary sphincter be

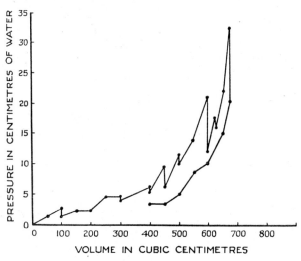

FIG. VII. 9.   Changes in the **Pressure in the Bladder** of a Man during Filling and Emptying.

Upper Curve. Water was slowly run into the bladder, and the pressure was observed after the addition of each 50 c.c. The inflow was stopped at intervals, so as to allow time for the pressure to approximate to its final value, as shown by the short vertical lines.

Lower Curve. After 700 c.c. had been run in, the bladder was allowed to empty, 50 c.c. at a time. The pressures were all lower, indicating that the true equilibrium values had probably not been reached during either filling or emptying.

The pressure is not strictly constant over any range of volumes, but does not vary much between 200 c.c. and 400 c.c. (Denny-Brown and Robertson.)

held open by a catheter, the vesical contents are retained by the internal involuntary sphincter ; even in such circumstances, the subject is able voluntarily to relax the sphincter, and to pass urine normally. As the bladder fills, the intravesical pressure in man rises to about 5 cm. water at a volume of 200 c.c. ; the pressure is maintained at about this value until the volume of urine reaches 400 c.c., after which further filling brings about a steeper rise in pressure, up to 20 to 30 cm. water being reached when the volume is about 500 to 600 c.c. (Fig. VII. 9).

The property of maintaining a constant pressure within the bladder through this range of volume was at one time attributed to an active relaxation of the muscle while the organ was being filled ; and since this is an example of the confusion which often rises in connection with the tone of all the hollow organs of the body, we may set out the relation between tension in the muscle fibres in the walls and hydrostatic pressure of the contents, in a little more detail.

For the sake of simplicity, let us represent the hollow organ as a sphere, and consider the forces acting on an imaginary horizontal plane passing through its centre (Fig. VII. 10). If the radius of the sphere is r, and the hydrostatic pressure of its contents is P, the force exerted by the contents of the upper hemisphere on our imaginary circular plane will be πr^2P. The force exerted by the contents of the lower hemisphere will be equal and opposite. Now the contents of the two hemispheres can only maintain these forces against one another because they are held together by the shell of the sphere, *i.e.*, the muscular wall. Along the circle, where the plane intersects the wall of the sphere, there must, therefore, reside forces just sufficient to hold together the upper and lower halves of the shell. We have seen that the force tending to separate them is πr^2P. If the tension in the wall is T per unit length, the force holding the halves together across the plane will be $2\pi rT$.

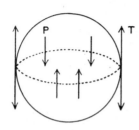

Fig. VII. 10. Diagram illustrating the Relation between the Tension in the Walls of a Hollow Organ, and the Pressure within it.

Consequently $\pi r^2P = 2\pi rT$, *i.e.*, $P = \dfrac{2T}{r}$. Moreover, if the material of which the wall is composed obeys Hooke's law, the tension in the wall is directly proportional to the circumference of the sphere. We can thus write $T = k.2\pi (r - r_0)$, where r_0 is the radius of the sphere when the pressure within it is zero. Hence

$$P = \frac{2k.2\pi(r - r_0)}{r} = 4\pi k \left(1 - \frac{r_0}{r}\right).$$

When r is large compared to r_0, P approximates to $4\pi k$, and is independent of the size of the sphere.

We may infer from this that if the muscle fibres in the walls of the bladder, or other hollow organ, obeyed Hooke's law, the hydrostatic pressure within it should not be proportional to the quantity of fluid it contains. As the filling progresses the pressure will tend to a maximum value, so that except when the organ is nearly empty, the pressure will be sensibly independent of the filling. The *tension* in the walls, however, is directly proportional to the filling, so that sense organs in them may be stimulated when the volume reaches a certain value, even though the hydrostatic pressure remains unchanged.

Muscle and elastic tissue fibres obey Hooke's law approximately, provided the stretch is small. When the extension is large, the resistance to further stretching increases progressively with the extension. The value of the "elasticity" (constant k above) depends upon the "tone" of the muscle fibres ; the volume of a hollow organ, consequently, which corresponds to a given hydrostatic pressure within it, or to a given tension in the walls, may be expected to vary with the state of tone of the muscle fibres included in its walls.

These relations can only be expected to hold when the changes in volume take place relatively slowly ; sudden changes in volume bring into play forces due to the viscous nature of the walls of the organs, which are not considered in the analysis.

In man, the **nerve supply** of the bladder and its sphincters consists of three pairs of nerves :—

(1) *Sympathetic nerves* derived from the aortic plexus and lumbar sympathetic chain. These nerves pass through a " bottle-neck " in front of the fifth lumbar vertebra and the sacrum forming the " pre-sacral nerve " or plexus of nerves. From this plexus arises the hypo-gastric nerves which end in the hypogastric ganglia on either side of the rectum.

(2) The *parasympathetic nerves* (sacral autonomic system) are derived from the second and third sacral nerves ; these also join the hypogastric ganglia, from which thus emerge both sympathetic and parasympathetic nerves to the bladder.

(3) The *pudic nerves* innervate the urethra.

Stimulation of the presacral (sympathetic) nerve causes contraction of the internal sphincter ; and relaxation of the detrusor muscle of the bladder wall has been noticed in man after injecting adrenaline intra-venously. Stimulation of the pelvic (parasympathetic) nerves results in contraction of the bladder and relaxation of the internal sphincter. By far the most important path for reflexes from the bladder is the parasympathetic, and this system of fibres, also, is the chief efferent mechanism in the process of micturition.

The desire for micturition is set up when the volume of urine in the bladder reaches 200 to 300 c.c., and a certain tension in the muscular wall is reached. When the tone of the bladder is increased, *e.g.*, by cold or conditions of emotional strain, this critical tension may be reached with a relatively small volume of urine in the bladder. Up to a certain point, the sensation from a full bladder can be suppressed from a con-scious level in the cerebral cortex, and, on the other hand, it is possible, by introspection, to become aware of small quantities of urine in the bladder.

Voluntary micturition is brought about by impulses passing from the cerebral cortex, by way of the spinal cord and parasympathetic nerves, to the bladder. The detrusor muscle contracts strongly, raising the pressure in the bladder to 100 cm. water, and simultaneously a reciprocal relaxation of the internal sphincter occurs. Voluntary effort to restrain micturition may considerably reduce the pressure within the bladder. Thus we have an example of involuntary muscle under the control of the will. Once micturition has begun, certain reflexes play a part in its completion. (1) Stretching of the bladder wall brings about reflex contraction of the bladder, and this reflex can be abolished by cutting both the pelvic nerves, transecting the spinal cord, or cocainising the interior of the bladder. It is unaffected by division of the pudic or hypogastric nerves. The reflex arc concerned is along the pelvic nerves to a centre in the hind-brain and back again along the pelvic nerves. (2) The flow of water through the posterior part of the urethra also brings about reflex contraction of the bladder, the reflex arc involving the centre in the hind-brain. Transection of the central nervous system only interferes with reflex micturition if the section is below a plane passing from the inferior colliculi, dorsally, to the middle of the pons, ventrally.

Diseases of the spinal cord involving the posterior columns may prevent the sensations from the bladder reaching consciousness, although micturition can still be carried out voluntarily. When the pyramidal tracts are interrupted, voluntary micturition is impossible, although the patient may be quite aware of a full bladder. When the voluntary control of micturition is impaired, retention of urine may result in over-distension of the bladder, and reflex passage of small quantities of urine at irregular intervals ; this condition is known as " retention with overflow."

CHAPTER VIII
REPRODUCTION
Introduction

In all but the lowest mammals the young spend the first part of their life—40 weeks in man—as parasites of the mother, protected by her body from the physical and chemical vicissitudes of the outside world and provided from her blood stream with an unfailing supply of food and oxygen. The *uterus*, the thick-walled hollow organ in which this early development takes place, receives the egg from one of two narrow symmetrical ducts, the *Fallopian tubes*, which open into its upper part. Their free ends are specially adapted to receive eggs from the *ovaries* when these organs discharge them. The lower narrowing part or *cervix* of the uterus projects into and inverts the dome of the *vagina*, and is traversed by a narrow canal through which uterine and vaginal cavities communicate. Upwards through this canal on copulation, pass the *spermatozoa*; these, manufactured in the *testis* of the male, are ejaculated from the *penis* into the upper end of the vagina. Should copulation coincide sufficiently closely with ovulation, one of the highly motile spermatozoa may penetrate the envelope of the ovum which, being now fertilised, begins to subdivide and becomes embedded in the uterine mucosa or *endometrium*.

After a short time, the embryo develops a blood circulatory system which comes into intimate relation, but does not mix, with that of the mother. Food, oxygen and other substances can then diffuse from the mother to the fœtus, which grows, stretching the uterus, for the period of *pregnancy*. The expulsion of the fœtus through the enormously dilated cervical canal into the scarcely less dilated vagina, and so to the exterior, is the process of birth or *parturition*. Afterwards for a time—about 9 months in man—the young receive the whole or part of their nourishment from milk secreted by the mother's *mammary glands*.

After a variable period of growth, in man twelve to fourteen years, the phase of *puberty* or *adolescence* begins, during which the ovaries of the female begin to discharge ova, and the testes of the male to produce functional spermatozoa. Other changes, psychological and structural, occur, and **secondary sexual characters** appear or gain emphasis. In girls, enlargement of the breasts, deposition of subcutaneous fat, and pelvic skeletal changes, determine the typical feminine contour. Pubic hair, with an abrupt horizontal border in the female, and axillary hair, appear in both sexes. The beard begins to grow in boys, and the voice breaks. Procreation is possible at this stage of development, but man is not generally regarded as mature until 5 to 10 years later, when more fully grown.

The **primary reproductive organs** are the testes of the male and the ovaries of the female. The **accessory reproductive organs** of the male are the *epididymes*, the *vasa deferentia*, the *seminal vesicles*, the *prostate* *gland, Cowper's glands* and the *penis* (Fig. **VIII.** 1). Those of the female are the *Fallopian tubes*, the *uterus*, the *vagina, Bartholin's glands*, the *clitoris*, and the *mammary glands* (Figs. **VIII.** 2). While mammals are similar in their primary and accessory organs, they are widely diverse in their secondary sexual characters.

Coitus or Copulation. This is the act of union whereby the male deposits spermatozoa in the genital tract of the female. Most animals

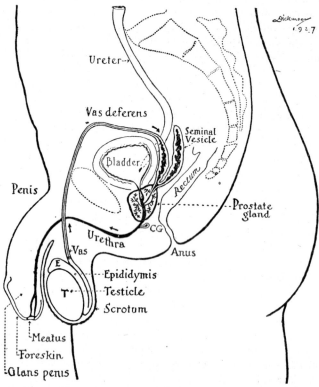

Fig. VIII. 1. The human Male Generative Organs, seen from the side and partly in section. CG. Cowper's glands. The arrows show the path of sperm from testicle to meatus. (From Dickinson and Bryant, " Control of Conception.")

have a strong periodic urge, known as *rut* in males and *heat* in females, to copulate ; but in man periodicity is absent or ill-defined. Coitus is attended in both sexes by excitement, which culminates in the *orgasm* —a paroxysm of sensation—largely contributed by sensory elements in the glans penis and glans clitoridis, and accompanied in the male by the ejaculation of semen.

Coitus has a reflex basis ; it can occur after section of the spinal cord in the dorsal region, and therefore in the complete absence of sensation. The two essential parts of the act are erection, which enables the penis to be inserted into the vagina, and ejaculation.

· *Erection* is due to the distension with blood of the venous sinuses of the corpus spongiosum and of the corpora cavernosa whose resistant fibrous capsules then render the penis hard and rigid. Two principal factors and one subsidiary factor contribute to erection ; dilatation of the pudic arteries and the dorsal artery of the penis, relaxation of the smooth muscle in the trabeculæ of the fibrous tissue, and compression of veins in the corpora cavernosa. Stimulation of the pelvic nerves (2nd, 3rd,

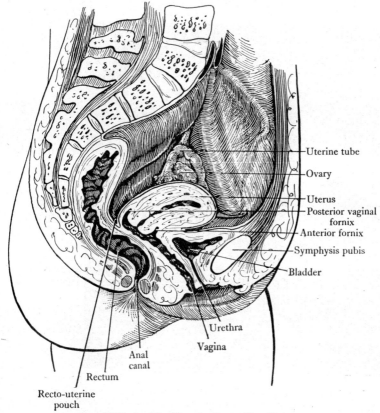

Fig. VIII. 2. The Female Generative Organs.
(From Whillis, " Elementary Anatomy and Physiology.")

and 4th sacral segments) initiates erection, and their section abolishes it. Stimulation of sympathetic fibres from the lumbar region is said to constrict the vessels of the penis and make it flaccid. *Ejaculation* starts with rhythmic propulsive contractions of the vasa deferentia which expel their stored suspension of spermatozoa into the prostatic urethra ; this simultaneously receives the contents of the vesiculæ seminales and of the prostate gland, which share in the motor complement of the orgasm. Waves of contraction pass over the striated muscles of the perineum, and the mixed fluid, or *semen*, leaves the urethra with considerable force. The smooth muscles involved in ejaculation are stimulated by excitation and paralysed by section of their sympathetic supply. Section of the presacral nerve in man, therefore, causes sterility.

The urethral glands of Littre, and Cowper's glands, may serve to cleanse the urethra or lubricate the penis.

Erectile tissue in the vagina and vulva of the female also becomes engorged during coitus, which is further aided by the secretion which the two compound racemose glands of Bartholin discharge into the posterior part of the labia majora.

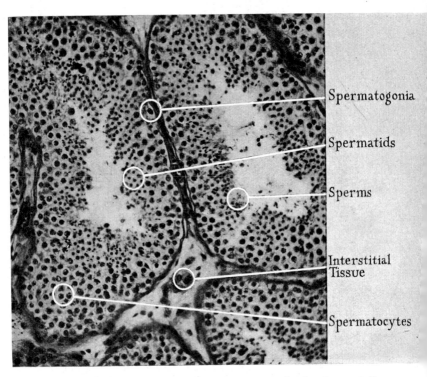

Fig. VIII. 3. Microscopic section of Human Testis, showing seminiferous and interstitial tissue. (From a preparation by Mr. K. Richardson.)

Spermatogenesis and the Spermatozoon

The testis (Fig. VIII. 1) consists largely of seminiferous tubules which in man, have an aggregate length of 1,000 feet. The tubules make spermatozoa, and the ciliated ductuli efferentes pass them on to the epididymis a tube about 15 feet long, where they are stored. They may also accumulate in the vas deferens, but they are not stored in the vesiculæ seminales.

The *primordial germ cells* lining the seminiferous tubules divide repeatedly to form spermatogonia (Fig. VIII. 3). After growing, these divide into *primary spermatocytes*, which undergo *meiosis* or " reduction division " into *secondary spermatocytes* containing only half the parental number of chromosomes. These cells divide into *spermatids* which mature into *spermatozoa*, attaching themselves to giant *cells of Sertoli* from which they receive nourishment. Their tails project into the lumina of the tubules, into which they are ultimately released. Fig. VIII. 4 represents a human spermatozoon, the head comprising little but nuclear material and the rest containing the small remnant of cytoplasm. Failing ejaculation, sperms drift slowly towards the vas deferens where the older disintegrate and are absorbed. Ligature of the vas itself makes no difference to the rate of this movement of sperms, but ligation of the ductuli efferentes halves it. In the guinea-pig, sperm may remain motile for two months, but they are no longer fertile after one month. They have been found functional a year after ligature of the vas deferens in the rabbit.

Repeated ejaculation at short intervals reduces the number of sperms thrown out, but opinion is divided on whether they become " unripe." The normal number is recovered in 18–48 hours.

Spermatogenesis in most lower animals is seasonal. In domesticated and semi-domesticated animals, and in man and some other primates, it is continuous. *Spermatogenesis is entirely dependent on a secretion of the anterior pituitary gland,* the removal of which causes involution of the tubules. Implantations of fresh pituitary or the injection of suitable extracts leads in hypophysectomised animals to recovery or, in young animals, to pre-cocious spermatogenesis. Climatic factors like light and heat, mediated by nervous system and pituitary, play a great part in determining seasonal activity in animals which exhibit it.

The temperature of the scrotum is from 1° to 8° lower than that of the abdomen, and the germinal epithelium of the seminiferous tubules degenerates if the testes are removed to a warmer environment (*e.g.,* inside the abdomen), or if the scrotum is experimentally insulated against heat loss. For a few months, recovery is possible, but the change ultimately becomes irreversible. Heating the scrotum beyond body temperature quickly injures

Fɪɢ. VɪɪI. 4. Spermatozoon, as seen from two sides. Magnified about 2,000 times. (Mottram, after Meeves.)

the germinal epithelium, and prolonged pyrexia may be followed by temporary sterility. Only if they are transplanted into exposed situations, do testicular grafts in animals show spermatogenesis. The dartos muscle, by relaxing with heat and contracting with cold, may act as a thermoregulator.

Of **environmental conditions** influencing spermatozoa, the most important is pH, the optimum for preservation being a little over pH 7·0. Other ions may exert an important and less fully investigated effect. As the pH rises up to 8·5, sperm motility increases enormously, thereby exhausting the small available supply of energy. Sperms in the epididymis (pH between 6 and 7) are quiescent, probably on account of their own production of lactic acid. They live anaerobically and oxygen is said to inhibit motility. Prostatic secretion (pH 7–8) increases, vaginal secretion (acid) diminishes, and cervical secretion (alkaline) increases, motility.

Body temperature is optimal for the motility, a lower temperature for the preservation of sperms. The significance of the natural secretions which they meet is unknown. In spite of their good viability in the epididymis, no protective secretion has been extracted from it, and their activation by prostatic secretion has not been shown to depend on anything except pH. Contrary to the accepted inverse relationship between motility and length of life, the cervix is the place where sperms survive longest. In general, only dead sperms can be recovered after 3 days from any part of the female genital tract, though slight motility has been described exceptionally after a week. Fertility, however, fails before motility.

Transport of sperms is mechanical. Spiral movements of the tail propel them at about 3 mm. per minute, orientation being almost certainly determined by the flow of secretions, in such a way that they move in the opposite direction. Chemiotaxis has not been demonstrated.

The time taken for sperms to reach the upper end of the Fallopian tubes was, at one time, thought to be measured in hours, but practically instantaneous mass-entry into the uterus has been observed in many animals even where the copulatory organs are not specially constructed so as to ensure such a result. It is not known whether this rapid transit occurs in man, but evidence has been advanced suggesting suction by the cervix, and it is not impossible that intravaginal pressure may rise high enough to force semen through a relaxed cervix. The spermatozoa make their way towards the ovary, and generally fertilise the ovum in the Fallopian tube.

The Ovum and Ovulation

In the *germinal epithelium* of the ovary, *primordial follicles* form, consisting of the ovum itself, surrounded by follicular epithelial cells. The latter proliferate, and the follicle, enlarging, becomes surrounded by a capsule in which two layers, *theca externa* and *theca interna*, are recognised. The follicular cells secrete a fluid, *liquor folliculi*, so that the follicle becomes a cyst. The *ovum*, a large cell with a well-defined limiting membrane (the *zona pellucida*) and a nucleus with a distinct nucleolus, does not float free in this fluid. It is supported by a *cumulus* of follicular cells which is continuous with the general mass lining the walls of the follicle (Fig. VIII. 5).

Follicles are continually emerging and enlarging, but until puberty never reach full maturity. After they attain a certain size, the eggs disintegrate, and the interior of the follicle is replaced by fibrous tissue : it is said to become *atretic*. *In the absence of the anterior pituitary gland, follicular growth is limited or absent*, and the ovaries atrophy. They may be restored by injecting anterior pituitary extracts or implanting whole

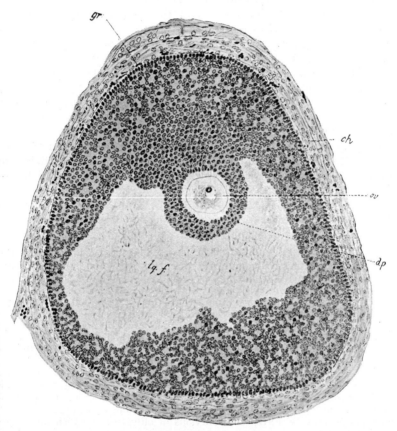

Fig. VIII. 5. Graafian Follicle of mammalian ovary. (Prenant and Bouin.)

Ov. Ovum. *dp*. Cumulus. *ch*. Theca. *gr*. Membrana granulosa. *lq. f*. Liquor folliculi.

anterior pituitary glands. (Successful grafts—transplants—are very difficult to make.)

Gonadotrophic Substances. Two active principles have been obtained from the anterior pituitary which are *gonadotrophic* (a convenient adjective for denoting substances which enable the gonads to grow and maintain themselves). The *follicle-stimulating hormone* (*FSH*), leads, as its name implies, to the ripening of an excessive number of follicles which do not, however, ovulate or form corpora lutea. The *luteinising* or *interstitial cell-stimulating hormone* (*LH* or *ICSH*), causes luteinisation of the follicles, large and small alike, as well as a general increase in the weight of the ovary. In luteinisation, the thecal and follicular cells increase in size so that the follicle becomes solid and the ovum disappears. Vascularisation occurs, and the cells come to contain lipoid (carotenoid) material which is often yellow in colour. The resulting body is a *corpus luteum*. (The formation of natural corpora lutea, as a sequel to ovulation, and the regulation by the anterior pituitary of the internal secretions of the ovary and testis, are described below and on p. 290 respectively.) The anterior pituitary gland of the male secretes FSH and LH (or ICSH), though probably in different proportions from those obtaining in the female, and the maintenance of spermatogenesis is to be attributed to FSH.

A substance with similar properties to the luteinising hormone is found in the urine of pregnant women. Its human physiological significance is probably to maintain for a time the corpus luteum of pregnancy, and if injected into hypophysectomised rats or mice, it luteinises their ovaries. If their pituitaries are intact, these also are stimulated, leading to follicular growth as well as luteinisation and frequently to hæmorrhages into the follicles. The active substance, sometimes called *chorionic gonadotrophin (PU)*, is probably elaborated by the placenta, and the ovarian reaction of small animals to it is the basis of the Zondek-Aschheim test for pregnancy.

Owing to the *apparently* double follicle-stimulating and luteinising action of PU, it was at first postulated to contain two principles, " prolan A " and " prolan B," terms now having no meaning, but often wrongly used as synonyms for the pituitary FSH and LH (ICSH).

Pregnant animals vary greatly in the production, excretion and properties of substances acting on the ovaries, and our description of PU applies only to man. Remarks about FSH and LH are, however, of general application. A further human peculiarity is the excretion after the menopause by women, and also by elderly men, of a follicle-stimulating substance, probably derived from the anterior pituitary.

Yet another follicle-stimulating substance is found in the serum (not the urine) of pregnant mares. It is known as PMS. Clinically, PMS and PU are used instead of FSH and LH because they are easier to obtain. In all, therefore, there are five common gonadotrophic substances (though the post-menopausal may be FSH), the functions of only two of which are known with any certainty.

Ovulation. After puberty, although some follicles still become atretic others reach maturity (Fig. VIII. 6) and *ovulate*. Ovulation begins with a second and more rapid phase of follicular enlargement, during which the ovum becomes detached from the wall of the follicle. Retaining follicular cells around it—the *corona radiata*—it undergoes *reduction division* and extrudes the first polar body. The follicle has now a very thin outer wall, and projects from the ovary. In man it is about the size of a pea. At its thinnest point, the follicular wall bursts or is dissolved and the ovum, leaving the ovary, is picked up by the fimbriated end of the Fallopian tube which it enters. The rupture in the ovary heals and the follicular cells proliferate to form a *corpus luteum*. The granulosa cells begin to hypertrophy, and in a few days they become very large

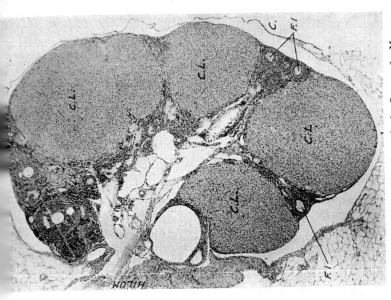

FIG. VIII. 7.   Section through the **Ovary of a Mouse during Di-œstrus.**

F. 1, immature follicles; *C.L.,* corpora lutea; *C.,* capsule of ovary.   (From a photograph supplied by Dr. Parkes.)

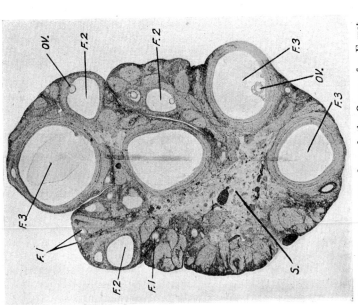

FIG. VIII. 6.   Section through the **Ovary of a Ferret just before Ovulation.**

F. 1, very immature follicles; *F.* 2, developing follicles; *F.* 3, mature follicles; *OV.,* ovum; *S,* stroma tissue.   (From a photograph supplied by Dr. Parkes.)

a yellow material, lutein, is deposited in them. Similar changes occur in the cells of the theca interna. The luteal cells tend to fill up the follicle (Fig. VIII. 7), but a central cavity persists in the human corpus luteum for some time, being filled with liquor folliculi and a small amount of blood. Regression of the corpus luteum, which is much delayed during pregnancy, begins with fatty infiltration of the cells, which are ultimately displaced by a hyaline substance, forming a *corpus albicans* and finally shrinking to a scar. The external cells do not become luteinised in the naturally formed corpus luteum ; otherwise, apart from the details of its formation and initial growth and size, it is similar to those described on p. 282. The principal functions of the corpus luteum, and the timing of ovulation in relation to the other events of the reproductive cycle, are dealt with on pp. 292 *et seq.*

In many animals, including man in whom it occurs monthly, ovulation takes place without any external stimulus. In others, like the rabbit and cat, it is secondary to copulation, which it follows in about 10 hours, the ripe follicles otherwise becoming atretic. If the pituitary is removed within one hour of copulation in these animals, ovulation fails. The remaining 9 hours must be occupied by the final processes of ovulation in the ovary, for hypophysectomy in this interval does not arrest it. In a hypophysectomised animal, injection of neither FSH nor LH alone will cause ovulation, but a carefully balanced dosage of the two will do so. Normal ovulation, whether spontaneous or secondary to coitus,

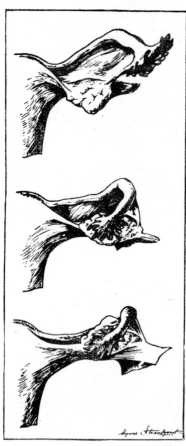

FIG. VIII. 8. Movements of the human tube and ovary about the time of ovulation. At height of contraction (bottom) as the fimbriæ reach the lower ovarian pole, the ovary is rotated so that its opposite side faces the tubal aperture. (Westman, J. Obst. and Gyn. of the British Empire.)

is therefore probably due to the supplementary action of LH when FSH has ripened the follicle. Ovulation in animals can be induced by using PMS and PU, and success has been claimed for trials in women.

By injecting the X-ray-opaque substance lipiodol into the uterine tubes, these have been shown to move so that the ova, though cast into the peritoneal cavity after ovulation, are " collected " (Fig. VIII. 8). The muscle in the round ligament helps by rotating the ovary.

Washings of the tubes in monkeys have shown that the unfertilised ovum rapidly degenerates and is absorbed. In rabbits and guinea-pigs, the ovum has ceased to be fertile 12–18 hours after ovulation.

Fertilisation, Sex Determination and the Differentiation of the Sexes

On being entered by the spermatozoon, the ovum undergoes a second division, and the second polar body is extruded. The male and female pronuclei then unite, and the fertilised egg is ready to undertake mitotic division on a scale sufficient to ensure the production of a new individual.

The division of labour between the gametes, one having the power of movement to make the necessary contact, the other being endowed with the means of nourishing the embryo in its earliest stages, extends from the highest to many of the lowest forms of life. Differences in form and behaviour between the adults which bear the respective gametes are often evident, and in human society become of fundamental importance.

The factors determining the sex of an individual are not difficult to appreciate in a general sense. The nuclei of the ovum and spermatozoon each contain only half the number of chromosomes present in the remaining cells of the body, but by their union they form a cell whose nucleus has the normal sum. Chromosomes in all cells except the gametes are, therefore, paired, and so are the genes which compose them. For every maternal gene which affects, for instance, eye-colour, there is in the complementary chromosome a corresponding paternal gene which influences it in the same or a different way. In the latter event, the final eye-colour will be decided by the " dominant " gene of the pair, and the " recessive " gene will be powerless until the next genera-tion. Apart from this kind of genic inequality, the half-set of chromo-somes in an ovum is similar to that in other ova, and to that in half the spermatozoa of members of the same species. In the other half of the spermatozoa, one chromosome is modified. Half the unions between ova and spermatozoa result, therefore, in cells having nuclei with two exactly paired sets of chromosomes. These cells divide and differen-tiate to form individuals bearing ova, *i.e.*, females. The other half of the unions yield cells in whose nuclei one member of one pair of chromo-somes differs slightly from its fellow. These cells divide and differen-tiate to form individuals producing spermatozoa, *i.e.*, males (Fig. VIII. 9). Females are said to be *monogametic* and males *digametic*. (In moths and birds, the same principle holds good, but the female is the digametic member.)

Voluntary sex-determination in man depends on what means may be found for selectively inactivating one set of spermatozoa. Such factors apparently operate naturally, since 106 boys are born for every 100 girls, and in Germany during the war of 1914–1919, the ratio rose steadily to a peak of 108·5/100 in 1919, declining thereafter to the normal figure. The ratio of male to female stillbirths and aborted fœtuses is yet higher, suggesting that if accidents of pregnancy and parturition were eliminated, the ratio of male to female births would be very high. The presence of conditions favouring such accidents lowers the sex ratio at birth.

Genetic Sex Differentiation.   A survey of the animal kingdom reveals to us that *secondary sexual characters* (variations in parts of the body, other than in the gonads and accessory organs, which characterise

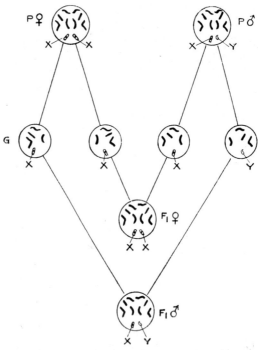

Fig. VIII. 9.   Diagram to illustrate Principle of Sex-determination in an animal with 10 Somatic Chromosomes (5 pairs).   P ♀, Female somatic cell.   P ♂, Male somatic.   G, The two ripe ova and two ripe spermatozoa (one X and one Y).   F₁♀, Fertilised ovum which forms a female.   F₁ ♂, Fertilised ovum which forms a male.

animals as male or female) are governed by two agencies, respectively genetic and chemical.   The first is found in its purest form in the insect world.

We have seen (Fig. VIII. 9), that the combination of two similar sex chromosomes (XX) yields a female, and of dissimilar sex chromosomes (XY) a male.   The accepted explanation is that the X-chromosome carries a factor making for femaleness which, when doubled, is sufficiently strong to balance the tendency of the combined remaining chromosomes to produce maleness.   When single, as in the XY combination, it is not strong enough.   In insects, the form of all sex-variable parts of the body emerge according to the state of this balance.   For example, the shape of a wing is not determined solely by the coincidence of a *single* gene in a paternal chromosome with the corresponding gene in the corresponding maternal chromosome, but by the combined effect of several genes scattered through each complementary half-set of chromosomes. The gene or genes which can influence wing-shape and which reside in the second sex-chromosome have the " casting vote " on sex form.

Sometimes in a genetically female zygote (XX) a fault occurs in the first mitosis of the fertilised egg, and the X-chromosomes of one of the daughter cells are altogether lost. Since each daughter cell gives rise to one half of the body, all the cells in, say, the left half are sexually " XX," and in the right half " OO." The result of this accident is an individual in which the left half of the body in all its sex-variable parts is female, and the right half, male. Such an outcome would be impossible as a result of disturbances of the chemical mechanism of sex differentiation which we shall consider later. Other degrees of genic imbalance which give a range of intersexual forms can be experimentally produced.

Chemical Sex Differentiation. The findings of embryologists, many in lower vertebrates and many depending on experiments difficult to perform and to interpret, suggest the following generalisation :

In vertebrate embryos, the cortical part of the gonad primordium is potentially ovarian, and the medullary part potentially testicular. One of these, as a result of the genetic factors we have described, gains the ascendency, and the other disappears or remains rudimentary. The ascendent gonad is primarily an endocrine organ producing a male or female sex-influencing secretion which determines, among other things, whether the germ cells shall be ova or spermatozoa.

Left to itself, a gonad, genetically predetermined as an ovary, will develop a germinal epithelium and produce ova. The embryo can, however, be " flooded " with male hormone, by direct administration, or by circulatory anastomosis with a male, or by the grafting of testicular tissue. If this occurs *before the potentially testicular rudiment has disappeared*, the medullary part of the gonad develops at the expense of the cortical part, cords later to become tubules are laid down, and the organ becomes a testis. The " genetic " sex of the individual has been reversed, and when adult it may be morphologically and functionally indistinguishable from a normal male.

Most parts of the body are, so far as we know, indifferent to the presence of either chemical sex-differentiator ; but some, while indifferent to one, are sensitive to the other, and become correspodingly modified. The most constant modifications give rise to the *accessory genital organs* : in mammals, to the Fallopian tubes, uterus, vagina, mammary glands and so forth on the one hand, and to the vas deferens, seminal vesicles, prostate, penis, etc. (see p. 275) on the other. Other modifications, such as those in size, skeletal development, distribution of hair, distribution of subcutaneous fat, and pitch of voice, are predictable in any one species, but appear functionally to be of secondary importance. The secondary sex characters of different species vary considerably.

One of nature's best known experiments is on cattle, when the circulations of twins of genetically opposite sex communicate with each other during the early morphologically indifferent stage of development. The male twin develops normally (possibly because its ovarian rudiment disappears before it can be stimulated), but the " female " twin, the so-called " free-martin " is extensively modified. Testes (sterile), and male genital ducts are formed, the ovaries and female ducts being suppressed. The external genitalia are indeterminate, usually of a rudimentary female type, though the clitoris may be enlarged.

Although differentiation of mammalian sex characters is thus vested mainly in the sex hormones, the genetic foundation upon which these work is often subject to modification. This is well seen in the plumage of some birds, but is also apparent in man. Thus, while axillary hair will appear at a certain concentration of either male or

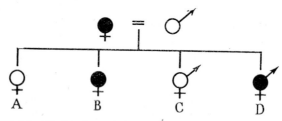

Fig. VIII. 10. The black symbols represent individuals carrying a genetic abnormality. The offspring of A should show no cases. If C were capable of reproduction, offspring would be normal. If D were able to reproduce, males would be normal, females would transmit. Note that if the abnormality did not involve secondary hormonal effects, C would be a normal male, *i.e.*, only half the males would be affected. (After Witschi.)

female hormone, and while the beard will respond to the male but not the female hormone, baldness seems to be associated genetically with the male sex, the " casting vote " resting with a gene or genes in the Y-chromosome. Though not so clear-cut, many traits such as cephalic index, presence or absence of palmaris muscle and height, about which we say " most men are taller than most women," and so forth, are thought to be fundamentally genetic in origin.

Hermaphrodism occurs in man in three forms : male pseudohermaphrodism, female pseudohermaphrodism, and true hermaphrodism. The last is very rare, implying, as it does, the presence of a functional gonad of each sex. In the other forms, the sex of the gonad is indicated by the adjective " male " or " female," while the external genitalia and the secondary sex characters partake so much of the nature of those associated with the opposite sex, that they are indeterminate. For this reason, it is possible for the true sex of a hermaphrodite not to be discovered until after death.

Male pseudohermaphrodism is by far the commonest form of intersexuality, and more than one explanation of its origin has been advanced. The following is one of the most plausible (Fig. VIII. 10). The condition runs in families, and that the individuals are genetically male is shown by their distribution— of 113 offspring of afflicted families, 58 were true females, 42 hermaphrodites, and only 13 classed as true males, possibly in default of proper examination. Since only the females of these families reproduce, the abnormality must be transmitted by a maternal gene or genes. If this transmission were *purely* genetic, about half the males would be normal. It has been postulated, therefore, that the inherited maternal abnormality is something which renders the fœtus, normally immune, susceptible to the quantities of female

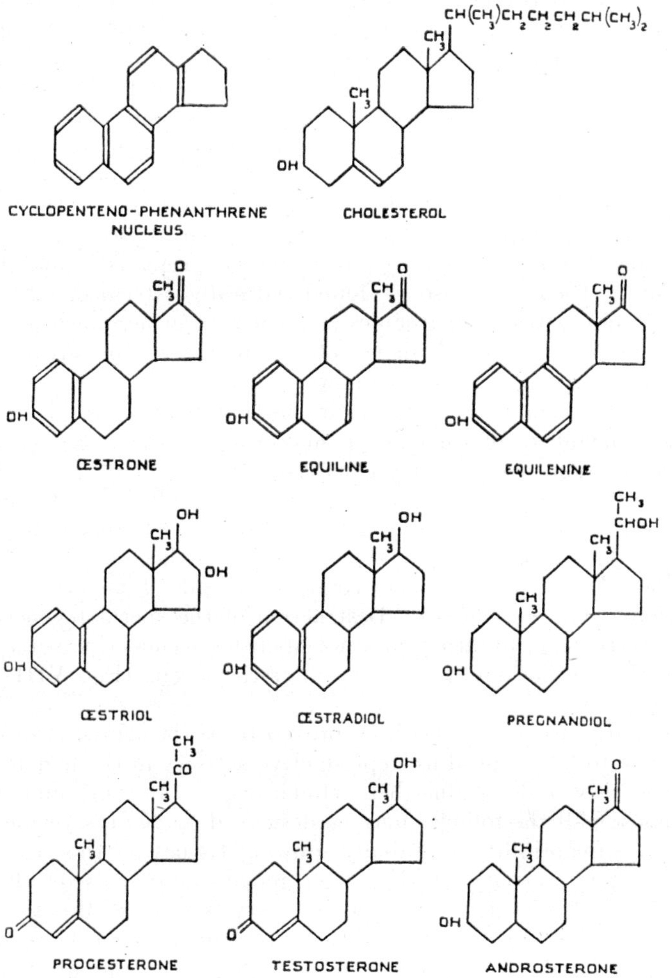

FIG. VIII. 11.   The chemical relationships of the sex hormones.

hormone circulating in the maternal and fœtal blood-streams. It is difficult to imagine what this abnormality can be other than an unusual concentration or a chemical modification of the hormones, for which there is no direct evidence. Some such mixture of genetic and chemical factors seems, however, to be required.

Female pseudohermaphrodism may occur during intrauterine life, or subsequently. It is to be attributed to the masculinising effect of hyperplastic adrenal cortical tissue, which pours male hormone, or substances closely related to it, into the blood-stream (see Chapter **XV**).

The Endocrine Functions of the Testis and Ovary

The substance *testosterone* has been isolated from testicular tissue, and *œstradiol* from the ovaries (Fig. VIII. 11). Discussion whether these substances are the sole chemical inductors of sex differentiation in the embryo is beyond the scope of this chapter, but for our purposes they may be regarded as typifying " male " and " female " hormones respectively. They are members of groups of closely related substances (Fig. VIII. 11), some of which have been isolated from physiological sources, *e.g.*, androsterone from male urine, and œstrone and œstriol from female urine, particularly during pregnancy, and some of which have been obtained synthetically. The " male " group are known collectively as *androgens*, and the " female " group as *œstrogens*. They may be esterified for therapeutic purposes to delay their absorption and therefore prolong their action, *e.g.*, testosterone propionate and œstrone benzoate. They may also be found naturally esterified, *e.g.*, as the œstrone and œstriol glucuronides of pregnancy urine, much less active physiologically and much more soluble in water : an advantage for excretory purposes. It is not known in exactly what form they enter the blood stream to perform their characteristic functions, and the different members of each group may vary in the potency of their actions on some or all of the organs susceptible to them.

The effects of removing the testes can be annulled by administering androgens, which fact, in conjunction with the occurrence of androgens in testicular extracts, proves that the testis is the sole *effective* source of these substances, and that in virtue of this side of its activity it is an important endocrine organ. Destruction of the spermatogenetic cells of the testis (*e.g.*, by heat) does not abolish its endocrine activity, for which there is no doubt that the interstitial cells (Fig. VIII. 3) are responsible.

Similarly, the ovary has been proved to be the source of œstrogens and these to be essential for reproductive activity in the female, but it is not so easy to determine their cellular origin. In some animals (*e.g.*, the mouse), all the follicles may be destroyed by X-rays, owing to the peculiar susceptibility of rapidly growing tissues to this agent, and the secretory activity of the ovary remains unimpaired. In other animals, the internal secretion of the ovary fails under this treatment, and we shall see that there is commonly a high degree of correlation between follicular and œstrogenic activity. It is probable that the follicular cells secrete œstrogen, though interstitial cells may play a large part in producing it.

After removal of the pituitary, the secretion of both androgens and œstrogens ceases. The gonadotrophic hormones of the pituitary have, therefore, a double function—the maintenance of gametogenesis (pp. 279 and 281) in the gonads, and now the maintenance of their internal secretions. We have seen that FSH needs to be supplemented by LH (ICSH) before ovulation can occur. It is now thought that LH is secreted in small quantities throughout the cycle, because a hypophysectomised test-animal does not secrete œstrogens under the influence of FSH alone, though it will do so if a little LH is administered as well. Since some of the œstrogen may come from the interstitial cells of the ovary, this finding is in accordance with the interstitial cell stimulating action of LH. Similarly, in the male, LH maintains the interstitial cells of the testis, and determines their secretion of androgen.

Although LH causes luteinisation, it does not cause the corpus luteum to secrete *progesterone*, through the production of which this organ exerts its characteristic effects. Luteal function seems to be dependent on some other pituitary principle (possibly the so-called lactogenic hormone), and in pregnancy also upon the placenta.

The Endocrine Function of the Testis. Removal of the testes *before puberty* causes absence of changes which usually occur at this time

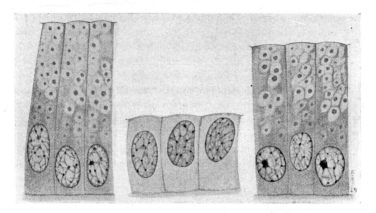

Fig. VIII. 12.   Effect of castration and testis hormone on epithelium of seminal vesicles.   (Moore, Hughes and Gallagher.)

    (1) Cells from normal animal, showing secretion granules.
    (2) Cells from twenty-day castrate.
    (3) Cells from twenty-day castrate treated with male hormone.

in (*a*) the accessory sex organs (*b*) the secondary sexual characters. In man, the penis remains small, and the epithelium of the seminal vesicles, prostate and Cowper's glands remain undeveloped. Secondary sexual characters fail to appear, the individual retaining his soprano voice and lacking a beard.

Castration *after puberty* causes rapid regression of active epithelia in the accessory organs (Fig. VIII. 12), but the more obviously permanent pubertal changes, such as enlargement of the penis and alterations in the larynx, persist. Erection and copulation are known in man to be possible for, at all events, several years, though the desire may be " artificial " from the strictly reproductive point of view. What is called " sex drive " rapidly falls off in animals.

A host of other and vaguer effects are ascribed to castration, some of which are undoubtedly primary. In domestic animals, for example, the modifications of temperament and edibility are sufficiently important to make the practice universal. In man, however, the sphere of the mind is immeasurably larger than in animals, and we learn by common experience that the same bodily defects may render one man useless, and make little difference to another. Also, a person may suffer more pain and anxiety on account of a non-existent disease which he fears than does another suffering from the real thing. The stigmata associated with castration vary so much, and are so deeply rooted in tradition and superstition, that where physiological and psychological effects can interact, it is impossible to disentangle them. A certain degree of " effeminacy," for want of a better word, is frequently discernible in prepubertal castrates.

Injection of androgens into castrates, according to whether they are pre- or post-pubertal, develops or restores the epithelia and the size of the accessory organs (Fig. VIII. 12), and, if previously absent, secondary sexual characters appear. Even in postpubertal castrates the penis may enlarge, erection be facilitated, and the voice become deeper. Changes in personality based on vague feelings of well-being—though these may conceivably have no more mysterious origin than the physical, and therefore, possibly perceptible, response of the accessory organs—undoubtedly occur. The subject of an experiment distinguishes the periods when he is being injected with hormone and when with distilled water, and " feels better " in a variety of ways during the former. It is probable that the chief use of androgens in man will be to cause development of the larynx at the right time in prepubertal castrates, and to assist in the correction of psychological changes which may follow postpubertal castration.

Assay of androgens. In the comb of the castrated cock (*capon*), is found a visible and measurable male sex character, the size of which varies with the concentration of androgen in the blood stream. It is used for comparing the androgen content of injected solutions or extracts of unknown strength with standard solutions.

Some androgens appear to have an action on the seminiferous tubules, so that spermatogenesis may continue after hypophysectomy if injections are begun early enough.

The Endocrine Functions of the Ovary and the Menstrual Cycle. Removal of the ovaries causes failure of development of the accessory sex organs—the uterus, vagina and mammary glands. Axillary and pubic hair fail to grow, the distribution of fat is no longer typically feminine, and skeletal changes in the pelvis do not occur. After puberty, regression of the accessory organs takes place. These deficiencies can all be prevented by the administration of œstrogen, or the transplantation of ovarian tissue. The most striking event after oophorectomy in the mature female is, however, the disappearance of the *sexual cycle*.

In man, this takes the form of **menstruation**, the loss about every 28 days for a period of 3 to 5 days of fluid, containing a high proportion of altered blood, from the uterus.

In animals, the cycle is marked not so much by visible structural changes, as by recurring changes in behaviour indicating increased sexual receptivity, when they are said to be " on heat " or in *œstrus*. (Only at

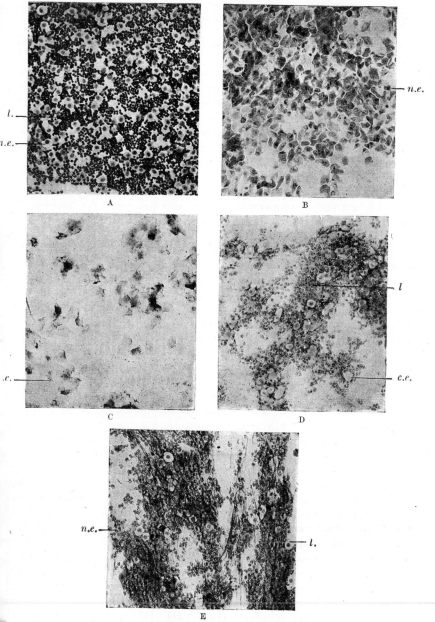

Fig. VIII. 13. **Vaginal Smears** of the Mouse, at Various Stages of the Œstrous Cycle.

A. Di-œstrus : the smear consists largely of leucocytes (*l.*) and nucleated epithelial cells (*n.e.*)

B. Early Œstrus : the leucocytes have disappeared, leaving only the nucleated epithelial cells.

C. Œstrus : the epithelial cells have become cornified and non-nucleated (*c.e.*).

D. Early Di-œstrus : leucocytes have reappeared, and there are fewer cornified epithelial cells.

E. Pregnancy : the smear consists of leucocytes and epithelial cells, mixed with much mucus, and, during the later stages, blood.

In *pseudo-pregnancy* the smear is similar to that in di-œstrus, with the addition of much mucus. (From Parkes' " Internal Secretions of Ovary.")

this time will they receive the male). The cycle in animals is therefore known as the *œstrous cycle.*

In spite of the different nature of the events by which the cycle is marked externally, it has been found in both man and animals to be based on similar events in the ovaries. At œstrus, animals have ripe Graafian follicles and their secretion of œstrogen is at a maximum, as evidenced by hypertrophy of the uterus and vagina and by changes in behaviour, all of which can be reproduced by giving œstrogen to a spayed animal. (Changes in the vaginal epithelium, are useful for following the cycle in rodents (Fig. VIII. 13). Cornification of the vagina of spayed rats, detectable by swabbing, is an important biological test for œstrogen, comparable to the capon's comb for androgen). Ovulation, whether spontaneous or depending on coitus, occurs during œstrus.

Somewhat analogous to the complementary part played by LH in ovulation, after FSH has ripened the follicles, is the probable *rôle* of progesterone in œstrus. This substance is the characteristic secretion of the corpus luteum, but there is considerable evidence that in the intact animal it may be released from the ovaries *before* the corpus luteum is formed. If a little is added to the injections of œstrogen administered to spayed animals with the object of inducing œstrus, it is found that a much smaller dose of œstrogen is effective.

The maximum ripening of follicles in man, though probably marking a peak of œstrogen secretion, passes uneventfully for the individual about 14 days after the beginning of the last menstrual flow. The external event of the human cycle—menstruation—occurs, therefore, when œstrogen secretion is low, and to understand its significance we must examine the changes which œstrogen produces in the uterus. These have been studied experimentally in spayed monkeys, some of which have a menstrual cycle similar to that of man.

The basal layer of the endometrium, lying directly on the muscle, is about 1 mm. thick and contains arterioles and the ends of the uterine glands embedded in fibrous tissue. In the spayed animal, this is covered by a superficial layer only about 0·5 mm. thick, consisting of connective tissue, capillaries and the necks of the glands, and surmounted by low columnar or cubical epithelium. Administration of œstrogen causes hypertrophy of the superficial layer to a depth of 3 or 4 mm., the blood vessels becoming dilated and increased in length, often in the form of spirals, the glands also increasing in length, and the epithelium becoming high and columnar (Fig. VIII. 14). The water content of the uterine tissues is increased. *This is precisely the state of the normal endometrium in mid-cycle, just before ovulation.*

Sudden withdrawal of the œstrogen results in dehydration and shrinkage of the endometrium, and compression and partial occlusion of the spiral blood vessels, leading to very sluggish blood flow and some stasis in the dilated capillaries. The supply of oxygen to the mass of tissue probably becomes insufficient, for the endometrium, instead of involuting gradually as it does when œstrogen is slowly withdrawn shows punctate hæmorrhages and necrosis and is cast off with some blood into the uterus. The débris here undergoes autolysis and is discharged into the vagina. *This process is very similar to that of normal menstruation.*

The interval between œstrogen deprivation and hæmorrhage varies

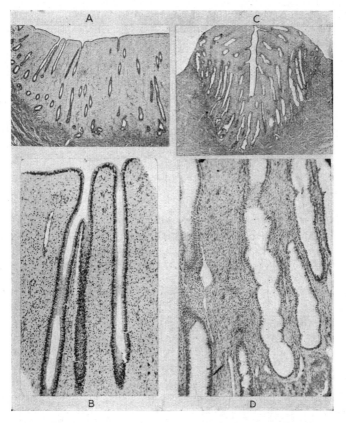

Fɪɢ. VIII. 14. A. and B. : Section of endometrium of spayed rhesus macaque after injection of 27,000 I.U. œstrone, spread over fourteen days. C and D : section of endometrium of spayed rhesus macaque after a similar course of œstrone, followed by a ten-day course of daily injections of 150 I.U. œstrone + 1·5 rabbit units of progestin. The glands are neither as dilated nor as tortuous as they can become. The epithelial cells may attain a great height, but are here flattened by the distension. A and C : × 10. B and D : × 62. (S. Zuckerman.)

considerably, but averages about a week. The slower the rate of deprivation (up to the point where it is too slow to be effective in causing hæmorrhage), the longer is the interval. A period of maximal secretion lasting for a week to a fortnight in the middle of the cycle, with a fairly rapid rate of rise and fall, would give a typical spacing of menstrual flows, and allow the mucosa to have reached its highest by about the 10th or 11th day. Although no one has yet made a reliable direct determination of the rate at which the ovaries secrete œstrogen, fluctuations in the urinary œstrogen output accord with the postulate except for a transient increase in excretion shortly before menstruation. There is evidence, however, that the sensitivity of the endometrium to œstrogen may also vary.

In *anovulatory* menstrual cycles, in which follicle-ripening culminates in atresia instead of ovulation, the mechanism underlying menstruation must correspond very closely to that just described. But such cycles are relatively uncommon : ovulation is the rule, and is followed by the formation of a corpus luteum whose activity must therefore be accounted for. We have previously stated that it secretes a substance *progesterone* (Fig. VIII. 11). This has been isolated from it, will replace it after surgical removal, and can be shown in many ways to reproduce effects normally associated with the presence of the parent body.

Injection of progesterone into the œstrogen-primed spayed monkey causes the epithelium of the uterus to increase in height and become active. Secretion distends the glands, whose enlargement makes them tortuous. Sub-epithelial connective tissue cells become rounded and more closely packed, making a compact superficial zone in the endometrium resembling decidua. These cells respond by proliferation to irritation of the endometrium (*e.g.*, by the presence of a hair), and make a tumour appropriately called a *deciduoma*. Beneath the compact zone is one of œdema and vasodilatation, to the pitch of sinus formation. The basal fibrous layer remains unchanged. *This is exactly the state of the normal endometrium just before menstruation in the human cycle.* Sudden withdrawal of the progesterone injections will precipitate a breakdown of the endometrium similar to that already described, except for the more advanced condition of the mucosa. This may occur in spite of the œstrogen injections being maintained constant.

Samples of endometrium have been transplanted to the anterior chamber of the eye in monkeys, and studied by direct observation. The sum of evidence suggests that œstrogen and progesterone are the two props of the endometrium, progesterone having no influence on it in the absence of preliminary treatment by œstrogen. If either of the two is suddenly withdrawn, the endometrium will break down with hæmorrhage. If they are gradually withdrawn, it will subside without necrosis. Since we have shown each to have an independent effect, it must be presumed that menstruation in normal ovulatory cycles is due to the coincident effects of the withdrawal of both hormones. Possibly the basic cycle is determined by fluctuations in œstrogen concentration (and reactivity of the endometrium), while the exact timing depends on degeneration of the corpus luteum.

There is no doubt that the chief function of the corpus luteum is to prepare the uterus for gestation. The endometrium in the luteal part of the cycle is called *progestational*, and the physiological counterpart of a deciduoma is the formation of decidua in response to implantation of an ovum in it. The decidual cells and glands contain glycogen, there are lipoid granules in epithelium and stroma, and the whole probably nourishes the embryo before its circulatory system is established.

Pregnanediol (Fig. VIII. 11) is excreted as a glucuronide during the luteal part of the human cycle, and is accepted as a metabolic product of progesterone.

The luteal phase in animal cycles is variable. In the rat and mouse it is negligible, the corpora lutea being practically non-functional in the absence of copulation. If this occurs, a long luteal phase follows, which, failing pregnancy, is called *pseudopregnancy*. In dogs and guinea-pigs, the phase is well-marked even in the absence of copulation, but is also often called pseudopregnancy. In rabbits and cats, ovulation is not spontaneous, and a luteal phase is entirely absent unless copulation takes place. Sterile coitus (preceded by ligation of the vas deferens) in the rabbit yields, however, such a well developed progestational endometrium that its aspect at a certain time in pseudopregnancy has been used as a standard whereby to assess the potency of solutions containing progesterone. There is evidence that the secretory power of the corpus luteum depends on the presence in the blood stream of the so-called lactogenic hormone of the anterior pituitary.

Some animals do and some do not bleed during the breakdown of progestational endometrium, and some may bleed at another point, *e.g.*, œstrus, in the cycle. Uterine bleeding in animals is in itself of little help in correlating their cycles with that of man.

The time of ovulation in man has been estimated by several methods, for example (1) by the recovery of ova from washings of the uterus and tubes ; this has not often been done (2) by examining the ovaries during operations over a number of years and (*a*) observing at what point in the cycle fresh corpora lutea appeared, or (*b*) if they were not fresh, assessing whether their apparent age was uniformly related to the progress of the cycle ; (3) by accumulating as many reliable records as possible of cycles during which a single dated copulation had occurred, and correlating the times of these copulations with the incidence of pregnancy.

All these methods have a common defect in that they depend to some extent on information from the patient, which is least serious in the first method and most serious in the third. This disadvantage is partly offset by the very large number of single observations made in the third type of investigation (thousands) compared with that of the first type (perhaps half a dozen recorded cases).

There is no doubt from the results that the most usual time of ovulation is on the 14th day after the beginning of menstruation, or the two or three days preceding or following it. Evidence from the third method of investigation which cannot be disregarded shows, however, that ovulation may not be altogether confined to this part of the cycle, and certain cases of artificial insemination have placed the possibility of ovulation early or late in the cycle on a firm basis. On the other hand, records from 1,000 women of nearly 50,000 dated copulations, in which the middle of the cycle was avoided, are claimed to have shown no instance of pregnancy. There is no good explanation for apparently aberrant ovulations. Investigation of lower primates shows that most ovulations occur from the 10th to the 13th day of the cycle, though the range may extend from the 8th to the 23rd day.

Pregnancy

Fertilisation of the ovum results in its becoming embedded, probably about 10 days later, in the progestational endometrium, which now persists, turning into true decidua. This naturally involves absence of menstruation, or *amenorrhœa*, an important but not conclusive sign of pregnancy. (Menstruation may also be suppressed by emotional disturbances, acting presumably through the anterior pituitary, or by local or general pathological conditions). Chorionic gonadotrophin may be detected in the urine shortly after the first " missed menstruation," though physical examination fails to show the presence of the developing embryo until a month or more after this. The duration of pregnancy is conventionally measured from the first day of the last experienced menstrual period, and is about 40 weeks.

From the 6th to the 16th week, approximately, the mother very often suffers from nausea and vomiting on rising. This *morning sickness* may vary from a trifling inconvenience to a distressing experience, and its cause is unknown. Other symptoms at this time are a feeling of distension of the breasts and irritability of the bladder.

The uterus hypertrophies to accommodate the growing embryo, the fundus rising above the level of the symphysis pubis at about the 12th week, and reaching the xiphisternum at about the 36th week when it drops somewhat, owing to the head of the fœtus sinking into the pelvis. At about the 16th week, movements of the fœtus can be appreciated by the mother (*quickening*), and thereafter become more and more obvious. Symptoms and signs of intra-abdominal pressure may include digestive disturbances, some œdema of the legs, perhaps dilatation of the superficial veins of the leg, dyspnœa and palpitation. Other obvious changes are in the size and vascularity of the mammary glands, which hypertrophy, and from which a clear fluid can be expressed in the latter half of pregnancy. Pigment is deposited in the areola of the nipple which turns from pink to brown in the first pregnancy, and also in the mid-line of the abdomen.

A variable increase in basal metabolic rate takes place in the second half of pregnancy, rising to between 10 and 20 per cent. above the normal. This seems more than can be accounted for by fœtal metabolism, and may be a consequence of increased activity of the enlarged thyroid gland which is also a common occurrence. Nitrogen, however, is retained by the mother in excess of the amount needed by the fœtus, and this is true also of calcium if sufficient is supplied in the diet. The adequacy in the diet of substances like calcium, iron and vitamins needs more careful supervision than its calorific value. There is retention of water by the mother, frequently a decrease in the erythrocyte count of the blood, and an increasing leucocytosis towards term. Other blood changes are lipæmia, cholesterinæmia, and a diminished alkali reserve. The output of the heart progressively increases in the later months, probably to keep pace with the quantity of blood which has to be passed through the placenta to maintain the oxygen supply of the fœtus.

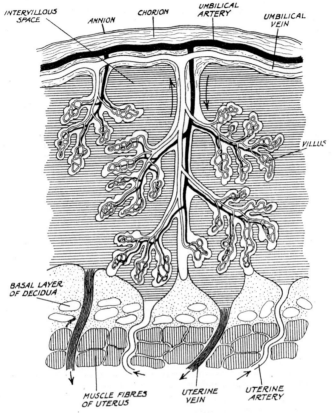

Fig. VIII. 15. Diagram of the Relations between the Fœtal and Maternal Bloods in the **Placenta**.

De-oxygenated blood flows from the fœtus in the umbilical artery, and passes into the villi, which are imbedded in the placental decidua of the uterus ; in these it takes up oxygen and foodstuffs from the maternal blood, and loses carbon dioxide and waste products ; it then returns to the fœtus in the umbilical vein. The intervillous space is well supplied with blood by the uterine arteries, and forms part of the maternal circulation. (After Gray.)

The problem of oxygen supply to the fœtus does not become acute until late in pregnancy, when the fœtus grows very large in comparison to the placenta. It is met not only by fœtal and maternal circulatory adjustments, but also by the affinity of fœtal blood for oxygen being greater than that of the mother in spite of a relative lack of alkali reserve (*cf.* Chap. III, p. 104). Although the bloods do not mix, they are in intimate relation with each other (Fig. VIII. 15), and when diffusion has equalised their oxygen tensions, the fœtal blood will hold a greater quantity of oxygen per unit volume. Carbon dioxide diffuses across the thin capillary endometrium and attenuated syncytium of the placental villi into the maternal blood, and is removed by the mother's lungs. Most of the other metabolic products of the fœtus likewise diffuse freely across the placental barrier to be excreted by the mother. Glucose and amino-acids pass readily in the other direction, and fats probably do so

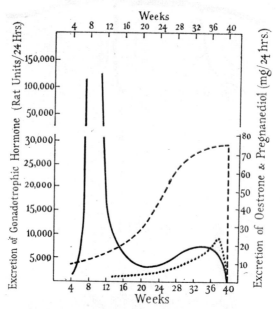

Fig. VIII. 16. Approximate excretion of gonadotrophin, pregnanediol and œstriol per twenty-four hours during pregnancy. The weight of gonadotrophin corresponding to a rat unit is unknown.

——— Gonadotrophin.
- - - - - Pregnanediol.
.... Œstriol.

(Data of Browne, Henry and Venning, and Marrian Cohen and Watson.)

much more slowly. Most proteins and formed elements are stopped at the placental barrier, though some bacteria may penetrate it. The diffusible constituents do not, however, exist in equal concentrations on each side of the membrane, and there is some doubt as to whether this implies secretory activity, or merely special but passive properties leading to the type of inequality exemplified by the Donnan equilibrium. There is little doubt that in the first three months or so of pregnancy, when the syncytium and Langhans layer are fully formed, the tropho-blast contains tryptic and other enzymes which enable it to attack the maternal tissues and stores *e.g.*, of glycogen in the neighbourhood, and plays an active part in nourishing the embryo. Most drugs, some toxins, certain viruses (*e.g.*, smallpox), and probably all non-protein hormones can pass the placenta.

The placenta is now known to be important in other ways, though it is not clear how much this is due to the fœtal and how much to the maternal part. In mice, rats and monkeys when the placenta is fully established, the fœtus (*i.e.*, the future individual) may be removed without disturbing the placenta, and the latter will remain and be delivered at the time for normal parturition. Meanwhile, the extra-uterine signs of pregnancy persist, though if the placenta is also removed prematurely, they disappear. This suggests that pregnancy is by no means a hand-to-mouth adjustment to the demands of the fœtus, but a maternal syndrome with a definite duration, presided over by the placenta.

The urinary excretion of gonadotrophin, œstrogen and pregnanediol

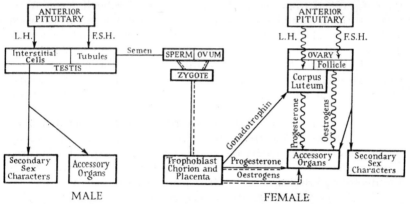

F_{IG}. VIII. 17. Diagrammatic summary of the Inter-relationship of Hormones concerned with reproduction. (L.H. = luteinising hormone ; F.S.H. = follicle stimulating hormone.)

in pregnancy, the two last combined with glucuronic acid, follows the curves in Fig. VIII. 16. The daily amount of œstrogen may reach 150 times, and of pregnanediol 30 times, the maximum found during the menstrual cycle. Gonadotrophin is practically never found except when chorionic tissue (which may occur in certain tumours) is present, but it has been detected in the menstrual cycle at the time of ovulation. In human pregnancy, it may preserve the corpus luteum until the placenta starts to secrete progesterone. The function of œstrogen probably includes the hypertrophy of the uterus, vagina and mammary glands— altogether a considerable mass of tissue—since all of these organs are demonstrably affected by the administration of œstrogen. Progesterone is known to modify the endometrium, the vaginal epithelium, and the mammary glands, after they have been primed with œstrogen. It is regarded as essential for pregnancy, which in many animals (but not after about the 13th week in man), is terminated by removal of the corpora lutea. One reason for its indispensability is its depressing effect on uterine motility and tone, enabling the organ to " give " before the growing fœtus. Progesterone also inhibits menstruation and ovulation. In man it is practically certain that the placenta takes over the manu- facture of the ovarian hormones during pregnancy.

Relaxation or increase in length of the ligaments of the sacroiliac joints makes these more mobile than usual, and a similar mobility of the symphisis pubis may occur. The changes are probably important during parturition, rendering the pelvic canal less rigid, but are not so marked as those which occur in some animals (*e.g.*, guinea-pig and mouse). A second luteal hormone " relaxin " is concerned in these changes in some animals.

A general outline of the somewhat complicated inter-relationships of these hormones—pituitary, ovarian and placental—is given in dia- grammatic form in Fig. VIII. 17.

The Fœtal Circulation. The arrangement of the blood vessels in the fœtus differs from that in the same animal after birth, owing to the fact that the lungs and alimentary canal are functionless, and the whole of the nutrition has to be obtained from the mother through the placenta. The lungs are shunted out of the circulation in two ways. First, oxy- genated blood passes into the child from the placenta in the umbilical vein. This mixes with de-oxygenated blood from the legs, and arrives at the heart in the inferior vena cava, whence it is deflected by the Eustachian valve through the foramen ovale directly into the left side of the heart. From the aorta, this relatively well oxygenated blood passes to the brain and the systemic circulation generally. Secondly, blood from the brain enters the right side of the heart in the superior vena cava, and passes from the pulmonary artery into the aorta, through the ductus arteriosus, entering at a point beyond that at which the vessels supplying the brain leave. The brain, therefore, is not supplied with blood that has, in large part, just left it. It should be noted that none of the blood in the fœtal circulation is truly arterial except that in the umbilical vein ; the blood supplied to the head and upper limbs is more arterial than that supplied to the abdominal organs (most of which, incidentally, are almost functionless) and the lower limbs, since it contains a large proportion of blood derived directly from the placenta, while the rest of the body receives blood that has mainly been through the vessels of the upper regions already.

Parturition. In the later months of pregnancy abdominal palpation reveals a distinct hardening of the uterus at intervals, undoubtedly due to contraction of the muscle. These contractions are not felt by the mother until the onset of labour or parturition, of which the pains which then accompany them may be the first symptom. Simul- taneously there is a small discharge of blood from the vagina. It is difficult to say whether the contractions of labour are painful on account of anoxia of the muscle (a known cause of muscular pain), or if so in what way they differ from the earlier painless contractions of pregnancy. It may be assumed that they are more powerful. A text-book of obstetrics should be consulted for the details of labour, which is traditionally divided into three parts. In the *first stage*, the fœtal head, fitting the brim of the pelvis, compresses the membranes and traps some of the amniotic fluid below it, the bulging " bag of waters " being palpable by a finger passed through the dilating cervix. This fluid medium transmits the pressure exerted by the uterine contractions evenly to the cervix, which eventually dilates sufficiently to pass the head of the fœtus. At some time during this stage, the membranes rupture and amniotic fluid is discharged.

Full dilatation of the cervix marks the beginning of the *second stage*, which ends with the complete delivery of the fœtus. The severing of the umbilical cord should be delayed until the placental blood has drained into the baby, to whom it represents six months supply of iron. During the whole of the first and second stages, the pains, marking rhythmic contractions of the uterus, become progressively more frequent, more severe and more prolonged. They may be separated by 15 to 30 minute intervals in the first stage and by only a few seconds in the the second, which is, however, relatively short in a normal delivery (Fig. VIII. 18).

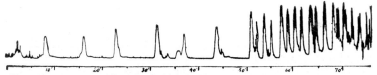

Fig. VIII. 18. Record of the **Intra-Uterine Pressure** of a Woman in **Labour**.

The contractions are relatively infrequent up to the fifty minutes' mark, when the first stage ends and the second begins ; they immediately become more frequent and more violent. The head of the child was born after seventy-five minutes, at the moment indicated by the sudden fall in the pressure below the previous minima, and the body, just after the last rise in pressure. (Bourne and Burn.)

The first stage varies greatly in duration, diminishing with the number of previous pregnancies from, say, sixteen hours to six.

The *third stage* occupies about half an hour, during which the placenta is detached and expelled. The raw bleeding surface thus left is rendered harmless by a firm contraction of the uterus which is said to be enhanced by putting the baby to the breast. If it fails to occur, hæmorrhage is severe. One method of stimulating contraction artificially is to administer the *oxytocic principle* of the posterior pituitary gland subcutaneously.

Many investigators maintain that the posterior pituitary secretion plays a physiological *rôle* in normal labour, and there is evidence that stimulation of the hypothalmic region produces uterine contractions in rabbits when all connection between the two parts, save the blood stream, has been severed. Apart from this, there is little to show that the oxytocic principle which undoubtedly has a powerful stimulating effect on the uterus, is anything more than an active tissue extract. Parturition certainly occurs in animals from which the pituitary gland has been removed, but in view of the uncertainty about the relative importance of the posterior pituitary and hypothalamus, this observation is not conclusive. In view of the equivocal evidence, theories based on the sensitisation of the uterus to the oxytocic principle by œstrogen (which does not have this effect in all animals), or the suppression of oxytocic activity by progesterone, are premature. If the production of progesterone by the placenta were to diminish rapidly at the end of pregnancy, the uterus might well become more active without the aid of the pituitary—but there is too little evidence to justify a discussion of these points.

Distension of the uterus is another obvious stimulus which has been considered to cause the onset of labour upon reaching a certain threshold, but this is ruled out as an essential factor by the delivery at term, in some animals, of placentas of negligible bulk, the fœtuses having been previously removed. Several other stimuli for the onset of labour might be postulated, and the cumulative effect of numerous stimuli is a possibility. Parturition can take place after section of the spinal cord in the dorsal region, and in dogs even after destruction of the lumbo-sacral cord. There is some evidence, however, that in the human being, lumbo-sacral centres are necessary.

Lactation. The mammary glands progressively enlarge during pregnancy, and animal experiments show that this is almost certainly due to the combined effect of œstrogen and progesterone. Although in some animals, *e.g.*, the guinea-pig, œstrogen is capable of bringing about complete development of the mammary gland, in most it serves only to enlarge the duct system while the alveoli proliferate under the influence of progesterone. Even in those animals in which progesterone seems unnecessary for the experimental increase of mammary tissue, it is hard to believe that it plays no part under natural conditions (Fig. VIII. 19). It is now realised that these hormones may act in part indirectly by stimulating the anterior pituitary to secrete appropriate " mammogenic " principles.

There is ample evidence that the pituitary is responsible for causing the mammary glands to *secrete milk*, whether or not it also makes them grow. The lactogenic principle, often called *prolactin*, has been obtained in a very pure state, but it may be only one factor in the endocrine syndrome determining lactation. Circumstances have been described in which it is inactive, probably due to deficiency of another internal secretion. Other things being equal, it will produce milk even from relatively undeveloped glands in animals, and in those which have been brought to full growth, the secretion is profuse.

As mentioned on p. 297, it also has a luteotrophic action and some authorities are inclined to regard this as more important than the lactogenic effect. Several of the anterior pituitary hormones have been found to have properties other than those suggested by their original name and their true physiological functions may be much less certain than these names suggest.

The natural occurrence of lactation does not follow the same pattern in all animals. In the mouse, for instance, secretion into the alveoli seems to run parallel with their development, so that at full-term the gland is in a fully secreting condition and producing milk. This happens, however, under the influence of the placenta, as can be shown by removing the pituitary during pregnancy. But immediately parturition has taken place in these hypophysectomised mice, the mammary glands involute, and no milk is obtained by the litter. The continuation of secretion is therefore dependent on the anterior pituitary. On the

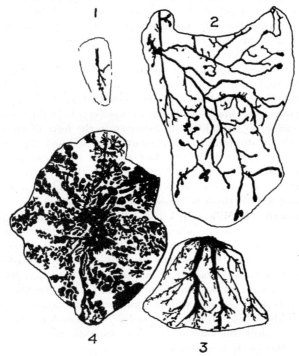

Fig. VIII. 19.   Experimental development of mammary gland.   (After Turner, 1932.)

(1) Mammary gland of male mouse (× 8).
(2) Mammary gland of male mouse after four rat units of œstrin per day for thirty days. This corresponds to the development in a virgin adult female (× 4½).
(3) Mammary gland of spayed rabbit after twenty days' injection of progesterone. This had been preceded by œstrin treatment, but no corpus luteum effect is visible (× 1).
(4) Mammary gland of spayed rabbit after treatment with œstrin and progesterone simultaneously. This corresponds to the stage naturally reached at mid-pregnancy (× 1).

other hand, in the rhesus monkey, from which the fœtus has been taken, and in which the placenta has been left *in utero*, mammary development is less than normal, even though the pituitary has not been molested. No hard and fast rule can therefore be applied to the development of secretory activity in all animals.

In women, a clear fluid called colostrum accumulates in the mammary glands in the latter part of pregnancy, and true milk does not appear until three days after parturition. Secretion is then profuse and dramatic, and is in the nature of a definite event rather than the climax of a slowly developing process. Relief of tension by suckling becomes imperative, but if this is not allowed to take place, lactation will cease in a few days. The act of suckling (or otherwise emptying the breast of milk) is followed by further secretion, and it has been demonstrated that suckling is a specific stimulus to lactation, acting probably indirectly through the anterior pituitary. It is usual to wean children when they are six to nine months old, and although many cases of lactation for a number of years are known, it is unlikely that mere suckling would prolong it indefinitely.

It has now been found that œstrogen will suppress lactation, and it is possible that its dramatic onset in women is due to the sudden drop in the production of œstrogen which occurs at parturition. In non-pregnant goats, mammary development has been brought about by the local application to the udders of œstrogen in the form of an ointment, and on suddenly stopping the treatment, lactation has been induced—again, probably by an indirect effect through the anterior pituitary. When it is necessary to suppress lactation after the birth of a child, the administration of natural or synthetic œstrogen brings about the desired result with little or no discomfort to the mother.

The Properties of Milk. Milk is a white opaque fluid, usually very slightly acid in reaction, containing as its chief constituents a sugar (lactose) and a protein (caseinogen) in solution, and fats in suspension. It also contains two other proteins—lactalbumin and lactoglobulin, in smaller amounts, and salts. It is interesting to note that the ratio of calcium to sodium and potassium in the ash is considerably greater in milk than it is in blood, although it approximates much more closely to the ratio in the whole animal; a similar correspondence between the composition of milk and that of the whole animal is found in the case of the ratio of phosphate to chloride.

If allowed to stand, milk is liable to undergo fermentation by the *bacillus lacticus,* with the formation of lactic acid by hydrolysis of the lactose. The consequent increase in acidity results in the coagulation of the caseinogen on boiling (curdling), or, eventually, in its coagulation at room temperature. On standing, also, the greater part of the fat globules rises to the surface, with the formation of cream; this process can be hastened by the use of a centrifuge, the pattern used in commercial dairying being known as a cream separator. Violent agitation of cream, as occurs in a churn, results in a phase reversal; cream is a suspension of oil and fat globules in a watery medium, while butter is a suspension of watery droplets in an oily medium. The solidity of butter results from its di-phasic nature, just as does that of the grease used for lubricating bearings ; this accounts for the fact that melted butter does not readily become solid again on cooling, since the water droplets have been allowed to coalesce, and the emulsion has been " broken."

Chemically, the constitution of milk is admirably adapted for the needs of the growing animal, and it contains all those substances enumerated in Chapter VI. as necessary for the maintenance of health. The diet of a normal infant has a greater energy value per unit body weight and contains considerably more fat than that of a fully grown person. The chemical composition of the milk is not the same in all animals, however, and the table below (from Starling) shows that cow's milk, for example, contains considerably less lactose and more casein-ogen and salts (except iron) than does human milk. This undoubtedly accounts in large measure for the difficulty that is often found in raising babies on cow's milk, or preparations made from it, when, for any reason, the mother is unable to nurse it.

TABLE VIII. 1

The Percentage Composition of Milk

	Water	Proteins		Fat	Lactose	Salts
		Casein-ogen	Albumin and Globulin			
Human milk .	88·5	1·2	0·5	3·3	6·0	0·2
Cow's milk .	87·1	3·0	0·5	3·7	4·8	0·7

CHAPTER IX

MUSCLE

The Classification of Motile Organs

MOVEMENTS in the human body are conveniently classified according to the kinds of tissue which are concerned in their execution. The distinctions are based on the structures, gross and minute, of the tissues, and description of these must be sought in books devoted to Anatomy and Histology. The success of this classification for physiological purposes depends, of course, on the fact that it also distinguishes between muscles with different functions.

Among the more important motile organs in the mammalian body may be enumerated :—

(1) *Striated muscle,* so called because of the transverse striations visible in its fibres under the microscope. It is also known as striped, skeletal, or voluntary muscle, the latter two names indicating its function in a general way. Such muscles are controlled by nerves connected directly with the central nervous system, and they effect movements such as those of a limb, most of which are under voluntary control. Inactivity in the absence of external stimulation, and the high speed of its movements, are well-marked characteristics of this tissue.

(2) *Unstriated muscle* shows, in contrast with striated muscle, no microscopic transverse striations. It is also known as smooth, plain, visceral, or involuntary muscle, and is controlled by nerves of the autonomic nervous system, one set of which makes it contract, and another set makes it relax. Such muscles effect contractions and relaxations of hollow organs (*e.g.,* the stomach, intestine, bladder and blood-vessels), changes in which usually occur without the individual being aware of them. They also usually exhibit some degree of spontaneous activity in the absence of external stimulation, and this may be expressed as a permanent partial contraction known as " tonus," which may be varied positively or negatively by nervous control ; or it may be expressed by periodic changes of length known as " spontaneous contractions " ; often both these forms of spontaneous activity co-exist. The contraction of unstriated muscle is characteristically slow.

(3) *Cardiac muscle* (heart muscle) is intermediate in many respects between the preceding two varieties. Its fibres are striated, but, unlike voluntary muscle, it cannot *maintain* a contraction. It exhibits spontaneous rhythmic activity, like many visceral muscles, but its speed of movement can be much greater than that characterising visceral muscle. The heart of the humming bird beats ten times a second, and the human heart can reach in exercise a speed of three beats per second.

(4) *Cilia,* lining the walls of the respiratory and certain other passages, are cells with thread-like protoplasmic processes, which

project into the lumen, and by their co-ordinated vibratile motions induce movement of mucus and other substances across their surface.

(5) *Motile cells* of various kinds include the white blood corpuscles, which show " amœboid movements," and spermatozoa. These have been considered in the chapters on Blood, and Reproduction, respectively.

SKELETAL MUSCLE

By " contraction " of a muscle is meant that change in length, or if its length be fixed, that increase in tension, which is the mechanical indication of its activity. It is not intended to imply any change of volume of the muscle substance, for any shortening in length is accompanied by a thickening, as illustrated by the familiar example of the human biceps. Apart from normal activity, muscle can be induced to contract by the application of almost any agent which, if applied in a more intense form, would injure or destroy it. Thus pressure, heat, many chemical substances, and electric currents may excite muscle ; but for experimental purposes, the stimulus usually employed is an electric one, on account of the relative ease with which its intensity and point of application can be chosen and varied. A muscle can be stimulated either directly or through its motor nerve, and a muscle with nerve attached, removed from the body for experimental purposes, is referred to as a *nerve-muscle preparation.*

The *excitatory processes* in muscle and nerve have many features in common, and will be described in the next chapter. The electric stimulus may be derived from an induction coil, from the discharge of a condenser, or directly from an accumulator. The response of the muscle may be made to take a variety of forms. For example, the muscle may be allowed to shorten against the pull of a constant weight. This produces what is known as an *isotonic contraction.* One end of the muscle is fixed, and the other attached to a weight ; the rise of the weight is indicated by a pointer, the free end of which scratches on a revolving smoked drum a magnified record of the movement of the free end of the muscle. This method of recording is useful for the slow contractions of visceral muscle, but the rapid contraction of skeletal muscle produces a jerk rather than a lift of the lever, and the record obtained depends therefore more on the inertia and damping of the apparatus than on the course of contraction of the muscle.

An *isometric contraction* is one in which shortening is almost prevented, and the increase of tension recorded by a strong spring, either through a light straw writing on a revolving smoked drum (Fig. IX. 1), or by a mirror which deflects a beam of light directed on to a rapidly moving photographic plate or paper. Even with such a system, the difficulty of designing apparatus which faithfully follows the rapid changes in muscle is immense. In isometric contraction the muscle performs practically no external work, for work involves movement ; all its energy is converted into heat. In the human body the contractions of muscles are intermediate between the two experimental types described, some like the gastrocnemius being relatively isometric, others like the rectus abdominis being relatively isotonic. Experimental methods have also been used in which intermediate forms of contraction are studied, especially in connection with the performance of mechanical work by the muscles ; the devices allow shortening either at constant velocity or at varying but controlled velocities.

A large proportion of the experiments on muscle to be described have been performed on isolated tissues. This is partly because it is easier to handle muscles after removal from the body—for example, to suspend their ends from two really rigid supports—and partly because an isolated muscle is not subject to the influence of fortuitous changes occurring elsewhere in the body. On the other hand, removal from the body involves an arrest of circulation through the muscle, and since

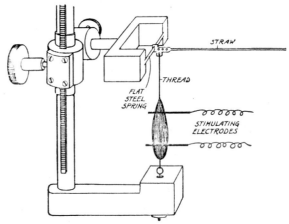

FIG. IX. 1.   **Isometric Lever** for recording the tension developed when stimulating an isolated muscle which is, as nearly as possible, prevented from shortening.

surviving tissue requires a supply of oxygen for its maintenance in a state in which it can continue to function, isolation raises certain difficulties in technique and problems in interpretation which might be avoided in experiments on the whole animal. Chemical reactions are retarded by a fall in temperature, and the rate of oxygen consumption of the muscles of cold-blooded animals, at room temperature, is much less than that of warm-blooded animals, at body temperature. It happens that a thin muscle, such as the frog's sartorius, can maintain its excitability for several hours when isolated and placed in air or oxygen, and kept moist by bathing with suitable fluids (Ringer's solution), whereas under similarly convenient conditions insufficient oxygen diffuses from the surface into the body of a mammalian muscle to keep it functionally active. For this reason, and on account of the relative difficulty of keeping the temperature of surviving mammalian muscle constant, most of the crucial experiments on isolated muscle and nerve have been performed on tissues taken from the frog.

The Isometric Twitch

The mechanical response of a muscle to a single induction shock (the effect in the secondary coil of a make or break of the current in the primary of an induction coil), or single discharge of a condenser, is termed a " twitch." The essential features of an isometric twitch are (1) the latent period, lasting for $\frac{1}{500}$ of a second or less after the stimulus, during which no mechanical response can be detected ; and (2) following this, an abrupt increase of tension, which, after reaching a maximum value, declines gradually to its initial value. The time relations vary with many factors, the process being more rapid at higher temperatures

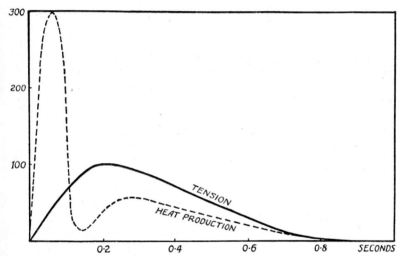

Fig. IX. 2. An isometric twitch of a frog's sartorius muscle, cooled to 0° C. in order to slow up the mechanism. The dotted curve represents the rate of heat evolution during the twitch. Ordinates may be taken approximately to represent grams of tension developed and gram-centimetres of heat evolved per second. The shape of the heat curve during the first 0·1 second is less certain than the remainder. (After Hartree.)

and in fresher preparations. But the whole affair is over in about $\frac{1}{10}$ second in a frog's muscle, and in about $\frac{1}{30}$ second in a mammalian muscle.

The time-course of the twitch is shown in Fig. IX. 2, and is important, because the discontinuities (*e.g.*, the abrupt ascent) are characteristic of synchronous contraction of the individual fibres and are absent in the asynchronous contractions which are produced by nervous reflexes. A word may be said about the *latent period* which has suffered an apparent decrease in value with progressive improvement of the recording apparatus, so that it has now become almost negligible. If a muscle be stimulated through its motor nerve an interval occurs during which the impulse is travelling down the nerve (0·001 second for 3 cm. of frog's sciatic nerve), a considerable delay occurs probably during the passage along the terminal ramifications of the motor nerve (0·003 second), and finally there is the " true latent period " of the muscle (0·002 second). The corresponding values are all much less in mammalian tissues.

The tension developed in an isometric twitch depends on the length of the muscle when stimulated. Obviously, if the muscle is allowed to shorten freely to its fully contracted state before being called upon to exert tension, then no tension can be set up. It is found, also, that if stretched excessively before being stimulated, then again little or no tension is set up. A maximum value of the tension produced is obtained when the length of the muscle is about that which it has in the relaxed state *in situ*, with its normal attachments.

The isometric twitch has been described in some detail in the hope that the reader will compare the records obtained with the best apparatus and those obtained with class apparatus. The striking difference between the two may induce him to beware of making an inference from observations without having very careful regard to the properties of the apparatus used. It is wise to try to estimate the kind of error or distortion that the apparatus is likely to introduce into a record.

Electrical Variations in Muscle

If two electrodes are placed in contact with resting muscle and the external circuit is completed by a sensitive galvanometer, no current passes. This shows that all points along the length of the surface of an uninjured resting muscle are at the same electrical potential.

If, now, the muscle be injured locally at a point where one of the electrodes is applied and the other electrode rests on uninjured muscle a constant current flows through the galvanometer from the uninjured to the injured end. This current is the result of a potential difference between the injured and uninjured surfaces (the " injury potential "). The current which passes through the galvanometer has no physiological significance—it stops when the galvanometer is removed—but the potential difference is present all the time. When such a muscle is stimulated there is a momentary decrease of the injury potential, referred to as a " negative variation " or *monophasic response*. This is due to a transient change of potential at the surface of the muscle beneath the second electrode, the first still resting on the injured tissue. A galvanometer connected to two electrodes placed on an uninjured muscle records the results of stimulation by showing a *diphasic response*, for when the change of potential, associated with excitation, occurs under the first electrode the current flows from second to first, and when later the excitatory process has passed along the muscle as far as the second electrode, the current passes from first to second. These effects are illustrated in the diagram, Fig. IX. 3, and are referred to as the *action* potential.

Certain precautions have to be taken to obtain these simple results ; for example, a parallel-fibred muscle should be chosen, non-polarisable electrodes should be used, and the muscle should be isolated. Detailed treatment of action potentials and their theoretical significance will, however, be deferred until the chapter on peripheral nerve.

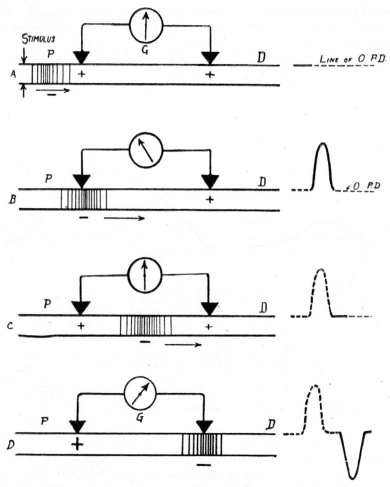

Fig. IX. 3. Scheme showing how the transmission, along a fibre, of an electrically negative zone is recorded in a galvanometer as a diphasic change of potential. (After Fulton, " Muscular Contraction.")

A. Before the zone reaches either electrode—zero potential difference.
B. Zone reaches the first electrode—negative potential difference.
C. Zone between the electrodes—zero potential difference.
D. Zone reaches and passes second electrode—positive potential difference and subsequent return to zero.

Note.—If the left electrode were placed on a permanently negative zone (injured region), the steady potential difference between the electrodes would only be affected when the zone of excitation passed the right electrode, and then it would be reduced. This is termed the " monophasic " (negative) variation.

Comparison of the time relations of the action potential with the mechanical response in a twitch shows that the electrical phenomena are almost over before the mechanical change begins. The action potential is therefore connected with the excitatory process, since it cannot be a consequence of the contractile process which it precedes. In sustained contractions produced by rapidly repeated stimulation of a motor nerve, action potentials correspond in frequency to that of the stimulus. These relations between mechanical and electrical responses are illustrated in Fig. IX. 4.

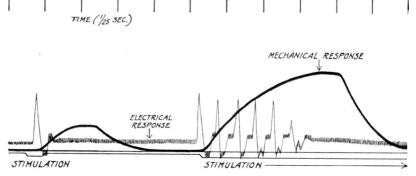

Fɪɢ. IX. 4.   The relation between the **Mechanical and Electrical Responses** of a gastrocnemius muscle of a frog with normal circulation, to (1) a single induction shock, and (2) a rapid succession of six shocks. (These six shocks occurred at times indicated by the corresponding action potentials ; stimulation did not continue as indicated by the arrow.) In the twitch the electric response is almost over before the mechanical response begins. In the short tetanus there is a discrete electric response to each shock, whereas the mechanical responses are fused. Note the secondary electrical changes complicating the diphasic action potential, which are characteristic of records obtained from muscles *in situ* or immersed in Ringer's solution. The simple monophasic and diphasic forms of action potential are only obtained from muscles when isolated and suspended in air. (After Fulton.)

The All-or-None Property of Muscle Fibres

Fig. IX. 5 illustrates the increased mechanical response of a muscle to an increase in intensity of electrical stimulus, brought about by reducing the distance separating the primary and secondary of an induction coil. This gradation of response might be due either to a gradation of the tension developed by each individual muscle fibre, or to a variation of the number of fibres contributing to the successive responses, or to both. The matter has been put to the test by stimulating single muscle fibres with minute electrodes, and observing the result, both microscopically and photographically, by illuminating fine globules of mercury placed on the surface of the muscle. In such experiments it is usually observed that the weakest shock which produces any result at all produces a maximal contraction of a single fibre.

With very small electrodes placed very close to the fibre it is possible to elicit responses only from the part of the fibre adjacent to the electrodes. These responses can be " graded " in that as the stimulus is increased a greater length of the fibre is involved ; but before the stimulus has been increased to an intensity sufficient to excite more than a fraction of the fibre the response changes suddenly to a maximal response of the whole fibre. This confusing result suggests the possibility that normally fibres respond to nervous stimuli by maximal contractions (all-or-none principle) in virtue of some conducting membrane covering the whole fibre, but that it is also possible to stimulate electrically any small section of the proto-plasm of the fibre with a stimulus which is too feeble to excite the outer " conductive " layer or membrane

As the stimulus is increased above the value which excites a con-traction of the whole fibre, no change in its effect is observed until it reaches an intensity which makes the current spreading to an adjacent fibre just strong enough to excite it also. Further addition to the

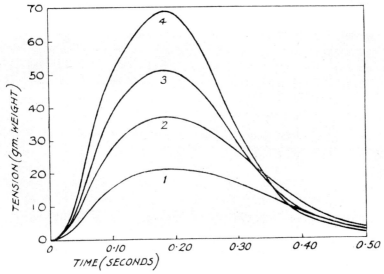

Fig. IX. 5. The influence of increasing the **intensity of the stimulus on the tension developed** in the isometric twitch of a sartorius muscle isolated from a frog. Curves 1 to 4 represent the responses to pro-gressively greater stimuli. (From data given by Hartree and Hill.)

strength of stimulus adds, one by one, to the number of active fibres, but no fibre can be observed to contract less fully with a weaker stimulus than it does with a stronger stimulus. Such an experiment is illustrated in Fig. IX. 6, in which the discontinuous increase of contraction—one more step for an additional fibre—can be seen. The fact that each step corresponds with one fibre depends on microscopic observation. It is evident then that a single fibre can contract without exciting its neighbours ; this insulation provides for a finely graded response of a whole muscle which contains many fibres by graduating the proportion of active fibres, although each fibre contracts either fully or not at all.

A possible misapprehension must here be mentioned. The all-or-none theory does not assert that a muscle fibre contracts to the same extent under all conditions, for it is known that many circumstances, such as the amount of initial stretch in the fibre, or fatigue, will affect the magnitude of the response. It is only claimed that the single fibre contracts as fully as it can under the particular conditions, or not at all, with continuous variation of the intensity of the stimulus, and that consequently the graded mechanical response of a whole muscle to such variation is due to a variation in the number of contributing fibres and not to a gradation in the response of individual fibres.

It will be shown later that the all-or-none principle applies also to the response of the single nerve fibre, and consequently to the muscle-nerve preparation. The all-or-none type of response was first noticed in heart muscle, in which the whole muscle responds in this way. This is due to the fact that the fibres of the heart muscles are structurally and functionally continuous, and a contraction of one thus spreads

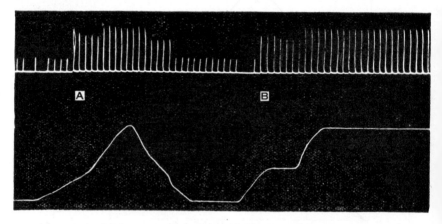

Fig. IX. 6. The **All-or-None Response** of a single muscle fibre stimulated with pore electrodes. (Pratt and Eisenberger.)

The upper record shows the deflections of a mercury droplet on the surface of a frog's sartorius muscle, stimulated with successive break shocks by an electrode 7μ in diameter. Upward movement of the lower line indicates the approximation of the secondary to the primary of an induction coil. Note that graded increase of intensity of the stimulus produces either no effect on the response, or an abrupt increase corresponding with the excitation of an additional fibre.

necessarily to all the rest. The absence of a graded response in cardiac muscle, and its presence in skeletal muscle, emphasises the importance of the insulation of the individual fibres in the latter.

In experiments with skeletal muscle, different intensities of stimulus are employed according to the result desired. If the stimulus is just strong enough to excite all the fibres, it is called a *maximal stimulus;* this can be arranged by increasing the stimulus to a point at which further increase produces no addition to the mechanical response. A rather more intense stimulus, called a *supra-maximal stimulus,* may be employed, though it produces no greater a response, if it be feared that in a series of observations on the same muscle, the excitability of some fibres may be declining, and it is wished to ensure a response from even the least excitable in the later observations. Maximal or slightly supra-maximal stimuli are used in all the experiments in which the chemical changes or heat production of a muscle are in question, for the activity of a muscle will only bear a consistent relation to its weight if all its fibres are contributing. A stimulus short of the maximal intensity cannot be counted on to evoke a response in the same number of fibres on different occasions. Likewise, if the influence of a first contraction on a second contraction, immediately following it, is being investigated, maximal or supra-maximal stimuli must be employed; otherwise it would be possible for different fibres to take part in the two successive responses of the muscle, and the interpretation of the results would become confused. On the other hand, experiments on the excitability of muscles are often conducted so that only just perceptible contractions are counted as the desired response. This involves activity of only those most excitable fibres which are most accessibly situated with reference to the stimulating electrodes. It is found that reproducible results are more easily obtained with these, than if reliance be placed on less excitable and less accessible fibres.

The Effects of Repeated Stimulation

If two maximal stimuli are applied to a muscle, the result depends on the interval of time between them. If the interval is short enough, say, $\frac{1}{200}$ second or less, the second stimulus has no effect whatever; the response of the muscle exactly resembles its response to a single stimulus. This is interpreted to mean that the muscle is inexcitable for a brief period following the first stimulus. This period is called the *absolute refractory period*. If the interval between the two stimuli is a little longer, the muscle responds to the double stimulus by a single response, slightly greater and more prolonged than the response to a single shock. Its contraction is, however, not by any means twice as great; the response to the second stimulus is considerably modified by the first.

As the interval between the two stimuli is increased, there comes a stage at which the tension record shows two distinct maxima, and with still greater separation of the stimuli, say by $\frac{1}{5}$ of a second, the muscle responds with two distinct twitches. Responses which are partially or completely super-imposed are said to *summate*.

A sustained contraction can be produced by stimuli applied in such rapid succession that the responses are fused, as shown in Fig. IX. 7; such a prolonged mechanical response is called a *tetanus*, and the stimulus which evokes it, tetanic stimulation. The most economical frequency of stimulus which will produce a tetanus will evidently have an interval between successive stimuli, such that each response begins just before the relaxation phase of the preceding contraction is due. In such a tetanus, the individual responses will appear as slight humps punctuating the main curve of contraction; the frequency is about 20 per second for a frog's muscle. If the frequency of stimulation be increased, the individual humps disappear and the responses become completely fused into a continuous contraction; the increase of tension is, however, relatively small—for example, only a 10 per cent. increase of tension might be produced by increasing the frequency of stimulation from 20 to 100 per second.

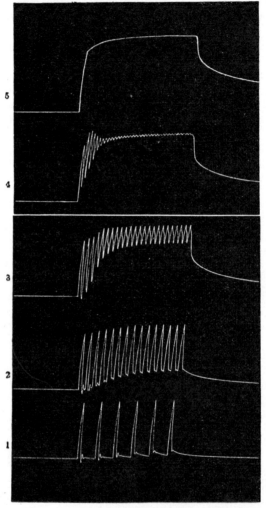

Fig. IX. 7.   Records showing progressive **Fusion of Individual Mechanical Responses** of a muscle, as the frequency of stimulation is increased from curves 1 to 5.   Note that the individual responses last longer after a preceding period of activity, so that a sustained contraction (as in curve 4) may ultimately be maintained at an economical frequency of stimulation, which is low enough to allow intermittent relaxation when first applied.   (From Howell, "Textbook of Physiology.")

The foregoing considerations lead to the result that time is required for the establishment of a maximal tetanic contraction, a fact demonstrated in Figs. IX. 4 and IX. 8.   The time depends on the muscle considered. For example, the internal rectus muscle from the eye of a cat (a very rapidly acting muscle) requires to be stimulated as fast as 250 times per second before the responses fuse completely, and in these conditions the stimulus must consist of at least 20–30 shocks (about $\frac{1}{10}$ second) before the tension is fully developed. For the gastrocnemius of the cat the minimal rate of stimulation is about 50 per second, and the minimum number of shocks at this rate is about 10.

Enormous tensions may be developed by muscles in good condition when submitted to maximal tetanic stimulation and prevented from shortening. A frog's gastrocnemius muscle, weighing only 0·5 g., may occasionally develop a pull of 1,000 g. But for the losses incurred when the muscle is allowed to shorten, this pull in each leg would enable the frog to jump several feet vertically into the air. Both the gastrocnemius and the quadriceps muscles of a well-grown cat may develop tensions in the neighbourhood of 50 kg. in isometric contraction. Such stresses are often sufficient to break the tendons, and there is some doubt as to whether such maximal contractions ever normally occur in the living animal. Later on we shall indeed see that even a small amount of shortening very greatly reduces the tension developed by a muscle, and consequently in the living animal such dangerously large tensions would not ordinarily be produced even by maximal stimulation.

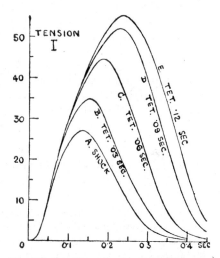

Fig. IX. 8. The primary effect of increasing the **Duration** of a tetanic stimulus is to increase the duration of the tetanus. But since **Time** is taken for a maximal tetanic contraction to be set up, stimuli of shorter duration than this affect the **Height** of the tetanus as well as its duration. Compare with this Fig. IX. 4. (Hartree and Hill.)

Voluntary contractions of muscles in a living animal are always tetanic contractions. This belief rests on no simple direct proof, but rather on the fact that tetanic stimulation is the only means known of inducing a muscle to repond with a sustained contraction under experimental conditions. Muscles in an intact animal never contract with anything like the speed observed in a single twitch. If they did, movements would be hopelessly violent, and the structures to which the muscles were attached might be unable to sustain the stresses set up without injury.

If then, voluntary contraction is regarded as a tetanus, the question arises : what is the order of frequency of the individual stimuli ? No satisfactory answer can be given, for the following reason. In an ordinary movement, the effort does not produce anything like a maximum contraction of a muscle ; consequently only a fraction of the total number of its fibres are contributing at any one time. There are two ways in which a smooth submaximal contraction might be achieved. First, some fibres might be thrown into tetanic contraction with a frequency of stimulus great enough to produce complete fusion of responses, and other fibres might remain inactive ; and secondly, all the fibres might contract intermittently, with irregular or different frequencies, and the statistical resultant might become the sustained contraction of the whole muscle. Experiment favours the second alternative, for the electrical variations occurring in muscles undergoing voluntary contraction are irregular and small, whereas those in tetanus produced by stimulating all the fibres synchronously, are regular and large. The voluntary or tonic contraction therefore probably differs from the experimental tetanus, in that individual fibres contract intermittently and each at different moments from its neighbours, instead of continuously and all at the same time. It is evident that such a " natural " tetanus will not result in fatigue as quickly as the " experimental " tetanus.

The Chemical Composition of Muscle

Muscles prove on analysis to contain 80 per cent. of water, and nearly all the rest is protein. These facts are neither surprising nor helpful, for much the same could be said of any tissue other than bone. There is a small quantity of carbohydrate which acts as a food store. The carbohydrate is mainly in the form of glycogen, a substance which, like starch, gives rise to the sugar, glucose, on hydrolysis. It is quite soluble and its solutions have very little osmotic pressure. There is also present in the muscle a quantity of fatty substances, usually not enough to be a serious store of food. These fatty substances are probably part of the structure of the cells.

In addition to those constituents common to most tissues, the muscle contains a few substances which seem to be peculiar to it. One of these is creatinephosphoric acid ; creatine is an amino acid, the chemical name of which is methylguanidine-acetic acid, and its anhydride—creatinine—is a constant constituent of normal urine. Creatinephosphoric acid is also known as phospho-creatine. It very readily hydrolyses in acid solution, giving creatine and phosphoric acid. It is present in muscle mainly as the potassium salt, for the muscle is neutral in reaction and the chief metal present is potassium. The muscles of invertebrates contain no creatinephosphoric acid, but in its place, apparently serving the same purposes, argininephosphoric acid.

Two other constituents characteristic of vertebrate muscles are carnosine and anserine (β-alanyl histidine and β-alanyl-methyl-histidine). The proportions of the two in a muscle depend on the animal species ; the muscles of the ox, horse, man and dog contain carnosine but little anserine : the opposite is true of the cat and rabbit. Finally, muscle tissue contains adenosinetriphosphoric acid, a compound of a substance adenine, related to uric acid, with the sugar ribose and three molecules of phosphoric acid. This substance is sometimes called adenyl-pyro-phosphoric acid.

It is reasonable to suppose that these compounds have some part to play in the special function of muscle tissue, since they are not found in other tissues (or are found only in traces); and, indeed, there is good evidence supporting this view in the case of creatinephosphoric acid and adenosinetriphosphoric acid, but nothing definite is yet known about the possible use of carnosine and anserine.

The variety of the chemical operations carried out by any living cell, and the remarkably accurate balance maintained between them all, put it beyond doubt that the cell possesses an intricate and complex architecture, but of the details of this structure we know almost nothing; they are on too small a scale for observation by microscope, but too large a scale for study by the methods of physical chemistry. The existence of this sub-microscopic structure should, however, never be forgotten despite our present ignorance of its nature, for it is largely in virtue of this structure that a cell is able to convert the potential chemical energy of its food directly into the mechanical, electrical or other energy which it is its function to produce. When we say that a muscle contains 1 per cent. of a compound X, we mean that 1 g. of X could be isolated from 100 g. of muscle. It is not implied that the muscle is a 1 per cent. solution of X. X may be contained in only certain parts of the muscle cells, and its actual concentration in these regions may be very high. Or X may be insoluble and deposited on cell walls. Or it may not be in the cells at all, but merely a constituent of the serum and lymph between the cells. If, for example, a frog muscle is immersed in Ringer's solution some of its constituents diffuse out; CO_2 and urea are constituents of this kind, whilst glycogen, proteins, carnosine and potassium ions are examples of substances which do not escape. Measurement of the diffusion of substances in and out of living and dead muscles has produced evidence of the existence of definite chemical

TABLE IX. 1.

The approximate amounts of certain substances in frog muscles, living and dead (expressed as a percentage of the weight of the tissue).

	Resting.	Fatigued to Exhaustion.	Dead.
Protein (including myosin) . .	19	19	19
Glycogen	0·7	0·5	trace
Lactic acid	trace	0·2	0·8
Creatinephosphoric acid * . .	0·5	0·1	0
Adenosinetriphosphoric acid * .	0·5	0·5	0
Carnosine	0·3	0·3	0·3

* Present mainly as potassium salt.

structure in the living tissue ; indeed, urea is the only constituent so far examined which appears to be distributed evenly through the water of the tissue as though it were a simple jelly. This subject is taken up again in a later section (action of electrolytes).

The table on p. 321 gives the amounts in frog muscle of certain constituents known or believed to be concerned in the contractile function of the tissue. Many more substances are present but they are not peculiar to muscle tissue and probably serve purposes common to all tissues.

The Chemical Basis of Contraction

The characteristic protein of muscle, myosin, which probably forms the contractile elements, is found to be of the " open-chain " type like the protein (keratin), which forms the structure of a hair. Now owing to the spatial distribution of their valency bonds, atoms of carbon cannot link together to form really straight chains. The nearest approximation to a straight chain in a protein molecule is probably this :

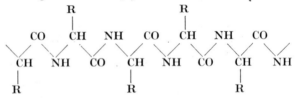

for the natural angle between any two valencies in a carbon or nitrogen atom is about 120°. On this scale, the whole molecule is about 40 feet long. A swivelling action at certain points in the chain could lead, without any serious alteration in these angles, to a shortening of the chain, thus :

On the same scale the molecule would now be about 25 feet long, and still shorter and more involuted forms are clearly possible.

There is good evidence (derived from X-ray analysis of hair structure, similar to the X-ray analysis of crystals) that the shrinkage of woollen fibres in careless laundering is due to a change of this kind in the keratin molecule, and the shortening of a muscle in rigor mortis seems, from similar evidence, to be due to the same kind of behaviour of the protein myosin. It is therefore a plausible guess that the contractile function of living muscle also has the same kind of physical basis, but even if this guess is correct, we have yet to inquire what causes these changes in the myosin to occur, and so permits the muscle to do work.

It has been known for sixty years that isolated muscles, like intact animals, absorb oxygen and give off carbon dioxide, and that these processes are accelerated by activity. The isolated muscle thus depends in the last resort on oxidations for its energy, but the reader will have seen from an earlier chapter that it is a mechanism working on a principle not unlike that of a submarine, which, when under the sea, propels itself from a source of energy (lead accumulators), requiring no atmospheric oxygen ("anaerobic"), and which takes the opportunity, when it again has access to air, of recharging its accumulators by means of energy derived from an "aerobic" source, namely, an internal combustion engine fuelled with oil. The muscle uses as its fuel for this recharging purpose, not oil, but a mixture of fat, protein and carbo-

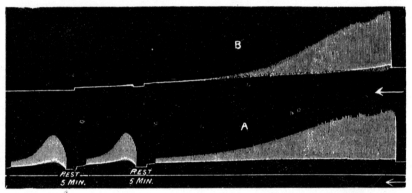

FIG. IX. 9. Showing that oxygen is required for recovery, not for contraction.

Sartorius muscles A and B were both stimulated once per second and allowed to contract isotonically under a load of 6 g. (temp. 19° C.). Muscle A was exposed throughout to oxygen ; muscle B was in nitrogen. Notice that the time scale runs from right to left. (Fletcher.)

hydrate in which, generally speaking, carbohydrate predominates. Fig. IX. 9 illustrates well this mechanism. The isolated muscle in oxygen "tires" nearly as fast as that in nitrogen, for oxygen cannot diffuse into it fast enough to bring about complete recovery between successive twitches ; but when both exhausted muscles are given a rest, the one in oxygen clearly carries out a "recharging" process.

To obtain information as to the nature of the mechanism in the muscle corresponding to the accumulators of the submarine, it is necessary to compare the chemical composition of a "discharged" muscle (one fatigued in nitrogen), with that of a similar muscle resting in oxygen. Two reactions are found to have occurred to a considerable extent in the fatigued muscle, namely

Creatinephosphate + water   ⟶   Creatine + phosphate
Glycogen + water   ⟶   Lactic acid

11—2

Now both these reactions are exothermic, that is, energy is liberated when they occur, energy which *in vitro* would appear as heat, though in the muscle it might be manifested in some other way on account of the structure of the tissue. If the fatigued muscle is allowed access to oxygen, both these reactions are found to be reversed, leading to the restoration of both glycogen and creatinephosphate, whilst food (including some of the lactic acid), is burnt. Clearly, creatinephosphate and glycogen are the biological equivalent of the submarine's accumulators, for they provide energy when oxygen is lacking and are restored subsequently by means of energy derived from oxidations. Heat measurements, to which we shall refer presently, confirm this conclusion that oxidation of food is not the direct source of energy for muscular contraction. It is a " recovery process." But are these two anaerobic reactions direct sources of energy ? They are not. The lactic acid production was ruled out by the discovery, made several years ago, that the production of lactic acid in an anaerobic muscle is inhibited by poisoning the muscle in a very dilute solution of sodium iodoacetate. The reason for this we shall discuss presently, but meanwhile the discovery itself made possible the demonstration that such a muscle, lacking oxygen and unable to produce lactic acid, can still do mechanical work, and the only chemical reaction occurring progressively in it as it becomes fatigued is the breakdown of creatinephosphate. The " lactacid " mechanism, if one may use this abbreviation, is therefore not essential to muscle contraction, but this does not mean that it has no function, for a quantitative examination of the behaviour of such poisoned muscles shows that they can only perform 60 to 70 twitches in anaerobic conditions instead of the 200 or so of a normal muscle similarly deprived of oxygen. The poisoned muscle, fatigued to exhaustion, proves on analysis to have no creatinephosphate left. It must have used up its creatinephosphate therefore more extravagantly than the normal.

If the breakdown of creatinephosphate is the only reaction available to provide energy for a muscle deprived of oxygen and poisoned with iodoacetate, we should expect to find a strict proportionality between the quantity of creatine phosphate disappeared and the amount of mechanical and heat energy liberated by the muscle in its activity. This was found to be the case by Lundsgaard, who took the gastrocnemius muscles of a number of frogs and soaked them all in a Ringer's solution containing iodoacetate until, as he knew from previous experience, their lactic acid producing mechanism was out of action. Some of these muscles were killed and analysed at once to provide information as to the creatinephosphate contents of all the muscles in the resting state. Different individual muscles were then mounted on isometric levers and given a succession of single shocks, some receiving only a few stimulations, some more, and some being stimulated to exhaustion. Each was killed and analysed at the end of its period of activity.

To obtain a measure of the amount of activity evoked from each muscle was not so simple. Since the levers were isometric, that is, did not allow any shortening of the muscle, but merely registered the tension developed, no energy was liberated as work. The energy in such cases always appears as heat and might have been measured, but for the considerable technical difficulties, by the rise in temperature of the muscles resulting from the activity. Lundsgaard, however, made use of a simple relationship pointed out by A. V. Hill several years ago, that the heat produced in each centimetre length of the muscle in an isometric twitch is proportional to the tension developed. In the case of the gastrocnemius muscle of the frog, every 100 g. of tension developed means the production of 8 g. cm. of heat in each centimetre length of the muscle (42,600 g.cm make 1 calorie). Lundsgaard therefore measured in each case the length of the muscle, the number of twitches recorded and the magnitude of the tension developed in each twitch. By adding together all the tensions and multiplying the result by the length of the

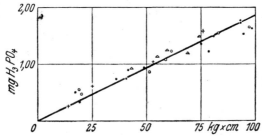

Fig. IX. 10. The effect of a series of **isometric contractions** on the **creatine phosphate content** of muscles poisoned with iodoacetate and deprived of oxygen.

Ordinates : creatinephosphate broken down, expressed in terms of its phosphoric acid content.

Abscissæ : activity, measured by the sum of the tensions developed in all the twitches multiplied by the length of the muscle.

Two different species of frogs were used and some of the muscles were in addition poisoned with curare, but all the muscles appear to have behaved similarly. (Lundsgaard.)

muscle, he obtained a product (known as the " total tension-length," or briefly, ΣTl) which was an indirect measure of the total heat liberated during the activity. When this figure was plotted on a graph against the amount of creatinephosphate that disappeared from the muscle, the points representing the different muscles fell on a straight line (Fig. IX. 10). The results of the whole group of experiments could therefore be stated in the very simple form that for every g.cm. of " tension-length " developed, so many mg. of creatinephosphate disappeared from the muscle ; in other words, when lactic acid production is prevented by iodoacetate, the muscle contracting in nitrogen produces energy strictly in proportion to the amount of creatinephosphate it breaks down.

It may be said in passing that although evidence derived from mammalian muscles is much less complete, it is in harmony with this conclusion. Indeed, the action of iodoacetate was first discovered by the fact that a dog poisoned with this drug died and passed into rigor without any lactic acid appearing in its body. It developed an " alkaline rigor."

The " lactacid mechanism " (lactic acid production) is therefore not directly a source of energy for contraction. But neither is creatine-phosphoric acid. Experiments similar to those of Lundsgaard quoted above have shown that in the muscle poisoned with iodoacetate and deprived of oxygen, the creatinephosphate breakdown associated with a short tetanus or group of twitches occurs, at least in part, *after* the activity is over. Only a few seconds after, but that is enough to rule out this reaction as a *direct* source of energy.

There remains one chemical reaction about which we have said nothing yet, for it does not occur progressively as the muscle fatigues. It is the breakdown of the substance adenosinetriphosphoric acid into adenosine-monophosphoric acid (adenylic acid) and inorganic phosphate. Although this reaction has never been demonstrated in intact muscles, it occurs readily in extracts of muscle tissue, and it is known to be exothermic. It has been shown that the enzyme promoting the breakdown is probably the protein myosin, and independently of this it has been found by optical studies of myosin solutions that the length of the myosin molecule is markedly affected by the addition to the solution of adenosinetriphosphoric acid. Three other facts give us some guidance at this point, first, that the myosin molecules are known (from X-ray studies), to be arranged lengthwise in the muscle fibrils, not just distributed haphazard ; second, the absorption spectrum for ultra-violet light [1] indicates (but does not prove) that adenosine derivatives are concentrated in the " isotropic " bands of striated muscle ; lastly, it is observed that when a striated muscle contracts it is the anisotropic bands that shorten. These suggestive, but far from conclusive, facts enable us to form a working hypothesis as to the mechanism of muscular contraction as follows :

(1) The myosin molecules forming the fibrils of the muscle are normally in their elongated form, but on the arrival of an electrical or nervous impulse they shorten (or develop tension if shortening is made impossible). This shortening is itself an exothermic process, so no energy is needed from any other source.

(2) " Relaxation " consists in the elongation of the myosin molecules, the necessary energy coming from the breakdown of adenosinetri-phosphoric acid, of which reaction the myosin is the controlling enzyme.

(3) The adenylic acid thus released is quickly and completely re-phosphorylated, the necessary energy and the necessary phosphate both being supplied by the breakdown of creatinephosphate. (This process can certainly be brought about in saline extracts of muscles.)

(4) As quickly as possible, the creatine thus liberated is re-phosphorylated, the necessary energy and the phosphate coming from the " lactacid " reaction, and resulting in the appearance of lactic acid. But this step is apt to lag behind, especially in fresh muscles, and may be prevented altogether by poisoning with iodoacetate.

(5) As time permits, oxidation of foodstuffs (of which lactic acid is itself one), provides the energy needed to resynthesise glycogen from

[1] Adenosine derivatives absorb strongly ultra-violet light of wavelength 2,600 A.

the accumulated lactic acid (except for the small fraction which is oxidised). This process is altogether slower than (4), taking minutes. as against seconds for the " lactacid " step.

It is to be emphasised that this description of the succession of events in muscular action is a " working hypothesis," that is, an attempt to weave together the known facts with the least possible use of guesswork. It is not the only possible hypothesis, and the reader would do well to see for himself to what extent it succeeds in incorporating the facts in this and other textbooks.

Heat Production of Isolated Muscles

To measure the small quantity of heat liberated by a contracting muscle is not a simple matter. The amount of heat is such as to raise the temperature of the muscle by a thousandth of a degree, and to measure such minute and very rapid changes of temperature an electrical thermometer must be used ; mercury thermometers are far too sluggish and insensitive. Use is made of the fact that if two wires of different metals are joined at both ends, and one junction is heated, a current flows round the loop of wire. It is on this simple principle that the seemingly elaborate " thermopiles " used in this work are built (Fig. IX. 11).

The heat which is evolved when a muscle performs a twitch is not liberated in one batch. There is first a small quantity evolved as the muscle is developing tension, then another as it relaxes. These two together are called the " initial heat," and this quantity is the same and its distribution in time the same, whether oxygen is present or not ; it is still the same when the muscle is poisoned with iodoacetate. It seems reasonable to associate this heat with processes (1) and (2) of our working hypothesis.

In the events which follow relaxation we have to distinguish between two cases. In the absence of oxygen little or no more heat appears, but it is during the first few seconds of this post-relaxation period that the biochemist observes two reactions occurring : the partial restoration of the creatinephosphate and the production of lactic acid. The first of these requires energy, and the second produces energy. It seems that the muscle succeeds in coupling the two processes together almost completely, so that the " delayed anaerobic heat " observed is very small and sometimes non-existent.

If oxygen is present during the experiment, a " delayed oxidative heat " is observed, which is about equal in amount to the " initial heat," but takes several minutes to be evolved. It begins to appear immediately after relaxation if oxygen has been present all the time, or immediately after the admission of oxygen if the gas is withheld until later. This heat is wasted energy. The rest of the energy derived from oxidation during this period is appearing in the form of re-synthesised glycogen and creatinephosphate.

Turning to the " isometric tetanus," we find its heat accompaniment to consist of a " contraction heat " and a " relaxation heat," marking its beginning and end, as in the case of the single twitch, but there is also a steady evolution of heat during the maintenance of the contraction. This steady "maintenance heat," which clearly represents the cost of maintaining the effort, is markedly affected by the temperature of the muscle, and a tetanus at 20° is in fact more than twice as

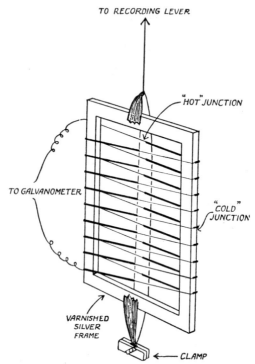

FIG. IX. 11. Diagram of **Hill's thermopile** used for measuring the heat production in a pair of sartorius muscles taken from a frog. A long wire composed of alternate equal lengths of copper and constantan soldered together is wrapped spirally round a varnished silver frame, of such a size that each segment of copper or constantan wire forms a quarter turn. There are therefore four junctions to each turn ; two of these are arranged to lie on the silver frame (" cold " junctions), the others are so situated that the muscles lie on them (" hot " junctions). In this way " hot " and " cold " junctions alternate in the series. The instrument is therefore in effect a series of thermo-couples, each having one junction heated by the muscle and one junction cooled by the silver frame. The " thermoelectric " voltages generated therefore add together and increase the sensitivity. Silver is used for the frame because it conducts away heat very rapidly, but the frame and the wires must be varnished to prevent electrical short circuits.

costly, as judged by the maintenance heat, as a tetanus at 10°. This effect of temperature is not surprising when we remember that a tetanus is a succession of fused twitches (p. 318), and that a single twitch lasts longer at lower temperatures. At a lower temperature, it will take fewer twitches to fuse into a tetanus of a given duration. What is more surprising is the size of the temperature effect, which is reminiscent of the effect of temperature on the speed of a chemical reaction (doubled for a rise of 10°) and not of a physical process, of which the speed is usually increased only about 3 per cent. by a rise of 10°.

A greater economy in maintaining tetani is also noticed in fatigued muscles, as against fresh, and in the muscles of slowly moving animals (toad, tortoise) as against fast (frog).

What happens chemically during and after the tetanus seems to depend on the state of fatigue of the muscle, as is the case also with a rapid series of twitches. A muscle with its full store of creatine-phosphate does not make much use of the " lactacid " mechanism for resynthesising creatinephosphate, until something more than half the latter is used up ; but when only a fraction of its store is left, resyn-thesis seems to keep pace with breakdown ; at any rate no further disappearance of creatinephosphate can be observed, but lactic acid is produced, and at a rate proportional to the rate of energy development.

Finally, when oxygen is admitted there occurs an " oxidative recovery heat " similar in magnitude to the " initial heat " (including the maintenance heat), accompanied by the same chemical changes as we discussed in the case of the twitch.

The Performance of External Work by Isolated Muscles

If a tetanised muscle is allowed to shorten, and thus do work, an extra amount of heat is produced, as was shown by Fenn in 1924. A. V. Hill, in 1938, using a very thin thermopile (55μ thick), which responded within a few milliseconds to changes in temperature of the muscle, showed that the amount of this extra heat produced is propor-tional to the *speed* of shortening. In mechanical records of isotonic contractions, moreover, it is found that the speed of shortening at any particular length of the muscle, and hence, therefore, the rate of total energy production, is proportional to the amount by which the isotonic tension applied to the muscle falls short of the isometric tension at that length. Since the isometric tension varies with the length, so also does the speed of shortening. This whole phenomenon is, in effect, the same as that discussed in Chapter I, but in inverse form, *i.e.*, the speed of shortening of a muscle increases as the tension set up decreases. We shall return to this point again later, in the section on the speed of muscular movement.

Expressed in symbols, we have, if x is the distance shortened, v the rate of shortening, P the applied tension, P_o the isometric tension, and a and b are constants of proportionality :—

$$\text{Extra heat produced} = a.x$$
$$\text{External work done} = P.x$$
$$\text{Total energy output} = x(a + P)$$
$$\text{Rate of energy production} = v(a + P).$$

Hill's observations showed that :

$$v(a + P) = b(P_o - P)$$

or, on re-arrangement :

$$(P + a)(v + b) = b(P_o + a) = \text{constant.}$$

This equation can be regarded as defining the relation between the velocity of contraction and the applied tension, and it is significant that the same values of the constants *a* and *b* are found whether measurements of heat production are made, or whether mechanical records are made of the rate of shortening under different loads.

The relation between the total amount of heat produced by an isolated muscle, and the amount of shortening permitted, are shown

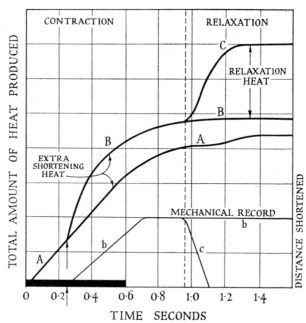

TIME   SECONDS

FIG. IX. 12.   Diagram showing the relation between **Heat Production** and · **Mechanical Work** in an isolated muscle.

Heavy lines—amount of heat produced (note that Fig. IX. 2 shows *rate* of heat production).
Thin lines—changes in length of the muscle.
AA.—isometric contraction.   No mechanical work done.
ABB.—isometric up to the arrow, then isotonic.   Weight held up during relaxation; no relaxation heat.
bb.—corresponding mechanical record.
ABC.—exactly as ABB but the muscle is lengthened by the load on relaxation.   The work done by the load on the muscle is converted into heat.
bc.—corresponding mechanical record.
The small relaxation heat under isometric conditions is due to the impossibility of preventing some parts of the muscle shortening, while other parts lengthen; conditions cannot be made perfectly isometric.

diagrammatically in Fig. **IX. 12.**   The chemical changes associated with muscular contraction are not thought to be altered in any way by the performance of work.

A few remarks may be made as to how much external work can be obtained from an isolated muscle, and under what conditions it will reach a maximum value.   An isometric contraction allows the maximum development of tension, but since the pull is exerted through an infinitesimal distance of shortening, hardly any work is realised. ˙ Isotonic   contraction   with   a negligible load allows the maximum degree of shortening, but, since the weight lifted is small, very little work is performed. Somewhere between these two extremes there is an " optimum " load on which the muscle can do most work, but this is not the greatest amount the muscle can do, for the problem is complicated by the fact that as the muscle shortens its weight-lifting ability falls off, until when it has reached its shortest natural length it obviously could not lift a weight, however small, any further. To get the most out of a single contraction, therefore, we should change the load as the shortening proceeds, using at each stage the " optimum " load for that degree of shortening. This can be done by finding the isometric tension produced by the muscle at a number of different initial lengths, and plotting the " tension-length " diagram. The area beneath this diagram gives the theoretical maximum work that could be obtained from the muscle.

This maximum work is termed " theoretical," since it can never in fact be realised ; for even if we overcame the technical difficulty of changing the load as the contraction proceeded, the contraction will be infinitely slow (in the equation given above, $P_0 - P$ would be zero, and so, therefore, would be v). Natural exhaustion would terminate the experiment prematurely. An alternative method of deducing the theoretical maximum work is to plot the work done under conditions of optimal loading against the speed of contraction, and to extrapolate to zero speed. We discussed this in Chapter I (p. 13). In real life the work realised falls short of the theoretical maximum, because the load must always be small enough to permit reasonably fast movement. Under the best conditions that can be obtained in practice, the actual work done rarely exceeds 30 per cent. of the " theoretical maximum."

THE " OXYGEN DEBT " MECHANISM IN MAN

Let us see how this somewhat elaborate chemical mechanism justifies itself in real life. If the muscles of a runner could perform work only as fast as oxygen is supplied to them, sprinting would be impossible, though a long-distance runner's speed would be unaffected, because his muscles are working only as fast as current oxygen supply will permit. Any chemical " accumulator " device such as we have discussed must find its justification in allowing us to work even faster for a short time, as the sprinter does for the whole of his race, and as even the long-distance runner must until his heart has had time to respond to the demands of exercise.

The amount of work possible in excess of the current oxygen supplies will clearly be limited on the one hand by the amount of creatine-phosphate held in reserve in the muscles and, on the other hand, by the amount of lactic acid accumulation which the body as a whole can tolerate (the amount of glycogen held in reserve is never found in practice to be a limiting factor). Now the amount of creatinephosphate in a resting skeletal muscle amounts to slightly more than 5 g. per kg., and the average man has about 30 kg of muscles. He has, therefore, energy stored in his muscles to the extent of 150 g. of creatinephosphate, each gram of which can liberate on hydrolysis, 0·05 kilocalories. This gives a total of $7\frac{1}{2}$ kilocalories of energy available without the need of oxygen. The energy liberated by the formation of 1 g. of lactic acid from glycogen is 0·35 kilocalories, and the amount which can be allowed to accumulate in the body without ill effects is about 80 g. This amounts therefore to a much larger reserve of about 30 kilocalories.

It should be emphasised that the object of converting glycogen to lactic acid is to get energy, not lactic acid. It appears that the only way of getting energy from glycogen anaerobically is to turn it into lactic acid, and it seems further that there is no way at all of getting energy anaerobically from proteins or fats.

The " lactacid " mechanism and, to a smaller extent, the creatine-phosphate reserve therefore amount to a store of energy which can be released without the use of oxygen. This represents a certain oxygen debt (p. 9), for a certain amount of oxygen will subsequently be needed

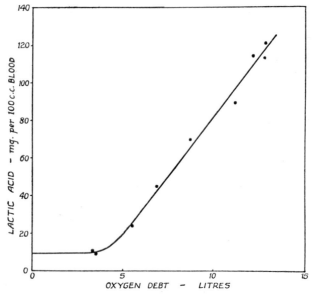

Fig. IX. 13. Showing that no **lactic acid** accumulates in the blood as a result of relatively mild exercise, although an **oxygen debt** is incurred.

The subject, a young athlete, took ten minutes' steady exercise of different degrees of severity, and the extra oxygen absorbed by him during recovery (that is, used to pay back the oxygen debt incurred) was compared with the lactic acid concentration in his blood immediately after the exercise. (After Margaria, Edwards and Dill.)

for the combustion processes, the energy from which will serve to reverse the breakdown reactions. How far will this account for the known ability of the average man to contract an oxygen debt of 15 to 20 litres ?

Let us suppose that in very severe exercise, such as sprinting " all-out " to exhaustion, the body uses up practically all its reserve of creatinephosphate and accumulates lactic acid up to the limit that can be tolerated. About 30 or 40 kilocalories of energy will have been derived from these anaerobic sources, and this amount of energy must be stored again during the oxidative recovery, as resynthesised glycogen and creatinephosphate. But this process we saw is only about 50 per cent. efficient, so the oxygen needed will be that equivalent to 60 to 80 kilocalories. Now 1 litre of oxygen liberates about 5 kilocalories of energy, whatever the foodstuff burnt; 70 kilocalories will require 14 litres of oxygen. We arrive therefore at the conclusion that at least a substantial fraction of a man's ability to contract oxygen debts (and therefore to undertake short periods of very energetic work) can be accounted for by the reserves of creatinephosphate and of glycogen in his muscles. We have identified at least the greater part of the mechanism corresponding to the submarine's accumulators.

In man, short spells of vigorous exercise, leading to oxygen debts of 3 to 5 litres, often are not accompanied by any appearance of lactic acid in the circulation; the acid only appears when larger debts (say 5 to 15 litres) are incurred (Fig. IX. 13). This suggests that the "lactacid" mechanism is only called upon in man when the creatinephosphate reserves are seriously depleted.

Intermediate Stages

We have referred hitherto to the formation of lactic acid from glycogen as though it were a simple reaction. Glycogen is, however, a complicated polyglucoside and lactic acid a simple three-carbon molecule, and it is hardly to be expected that this conversion could be effected in one step. Experiments with intact muscles give little information about the intermediate stages of the process. Most of our knowledge has been obtained by making cell-free extracts of muscles and observing what substances can be converted into lactic acid by the enzymes contained in the extract. The results are very complicated and have to be interpreted with care. If a motor car were minced up, many reactions would occur between its component parts, such as the solution of the tyres in the petrol, which never occur in the intact motor car. It may be said, however, that there is good evidence for the formation, at an early stage, of hexosediphosphoric ester, which, in turn, breaks up into two molecules of triosemonophosphoric ester (the triose being glyceraldehyde or dihydroxyacetone, or both), and this gives rise, after some internal rearrangement of the molecule, to lactate, phosphate, and heat. In the healthy intact muscle, the energy need not be, and apparently is not, released as heat, but is passed, in the form of " energised " phosphate radicles, to a " phosphate acceptor " ; both creatine and adenylic acid can " accept " and " donate " phosphate in appropriate circumstances and their importance to the muscle seems to lie chiefly in this. Just as primitive warriors may laboriously push a boulder stage by stage up a mountain side in order to drop it over a cliff edge on to the heads of their enemies, so the muscle takes inorganic phosphate and passes it from compound to compound, up a chemical energy gradient till it reaches the highly energised and comparatively explosive state of adenosinetriphosphate.

The Removal of Lactic Acid

We have examined the conversion of glycogen into lactic acid, and we must next consider the reverse process. It is to be expected that this too occurs in many stages, but very little is known about it, for the process is one which can apparently only be carried out by intact tissues with a supply of oxygen, whereas we have seen that the only way of getting information about intermediate products is to use minced-up tissues or tissue extracts. There is evidence that although the frog muscle can effect this re-formation of glycogen itself, there has occurred in the more highly evolved animals a greater degree of specialised function, whereby the muscles work in association with the liver. The lactic acid diffuses out of the muscles and is carried by the blood stream to the liver, which converts it into glycogen. The muscles take glucose from the blood to replenish their glycogen stores and the blood sugar is kept up to the mark automatically by the formation of more glucose from glycogen in the liver. Thus there is a cycle of events which we can depict diagrammatically,

| Events in liver | Lactic acid ↓ Glycogen ↓ Glucose | ← ————————— | Lactic acid ↑ Glycogen ↑ Glucose | Events in muscle |

The occurrence of part of the recovery process in non-muscular tissue in such animals modifies, of course, our description of the events in the muscle, though from the point of view of experiments on man himself and on intact animals, it does not affect the consideration of the total energy exchanges. The mammalian heart also can take up lactic acid from the blood in significant amounts, probably burning it (see later).

HEART MUSCLE

The functions of the heart, as an organ, have been considered in the chapter on Circulation, but for the sake of comparison between the different kinds of contractile tissues, some of the simpler properties of cardiac muscle will be analysed here.

Fig. IX. 14. Diagram showing the arrangements of the chambers of the **frog's heart.** (A, auricle; V, ventricle; B, bulbus arteriosus.) (W. M. Bayliss, " Introduction to General Physiology.")

A frog's heart, removed from the animal, will continue to beat for many hours if kept moist and cool. A mammalian heart, removed from the body, continues to beat for a short time. It is evident that the rhythmic activity of heart muscle is not due to rhythmic stimulation through the nerves leading to it. The tenacity of the isolated heart of the frog is due to its relatively low oxygen requirements, whereas the mammalian organ needs for continued activity more oxygen than it can obtain by diffusion from the surface. As in the case, therefore, of experiments on skeletal muscles, the experimental methods are simpler for isolated heart muscle taken from the cold-blooded frog than that from the warm-blooded mammal.

The anatomical features of the frog's heart are diagrammatised in Fig. IX. 14, and should be compared with those of a mammalian heart. Histologically the muscle cells are striated, but differ from skeletal muscle fibres in being shorter, and in being connected together so that the cells of the whole heart are in protoplasmic continuity.

The beat of the isolated heart of the frog can be simply recorded in the manner shown in Fig. IX. 15 on a smoked drum. For special purposes, a strip of auricle or ventricle can be cut, one end fixed, and the other attached to a lever. In any experiment in which the heart muscle is deprived of its normal circulation, it is kept moist with a solution of salts, corresponding in concentration to those in the blood, and known as Ringer's solution.

The spontaneous rhythmic contraction of cardiac muscle is, as we have shown, an intrinsic property of the muscle, and not due to external stimulation. The property is shown in different degree by different

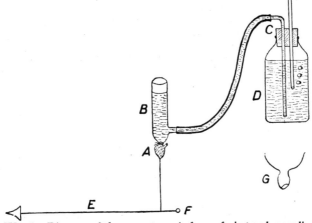

Fig. IX. 15. Diagram of the **arrangements for perfusing and recording the beats of a frog's heart.** A, frog's heart tied on the end of the glass cannula B, which has a side tube connected to a siphon C. This dips into Ringer's solution in the Mariotte's bottle D. A light straw lever E is pivoted at F. G, enlarged view of tip of the cannula. (W. M. Bayliss, " Introduction to General Physiology.")

portions of the heart. If the sinus venosus, at the junction of the great veins, be separated from the rest of the heart by tying a ligature round the sino-auricular junction (First Stannius' ligature), the sinus continues to beat at its natural frequency (about 30 per minute at 15° C.) ; the auricle and ventricle are however quiescent. After a short time the auricle begins to beat, and with it the ventricle, first slowly, then more frequently, but the natural auricular rhythm is always slower than that of the sinus. When the new rhythm has become established, the auricle can be functionally disassociated from the ventricle by tying a second ligature round the auriculoventricular junction. The ventricle then stops beating, and only begins to contract again, if at all, after a long interval, and even then only infrequently.

Clearly, when the whole heart is contracting, the rhythm of ventricle and auricle is dominated by that of the sinus, and we must next inquire how the excitation is transmitted from the latter to the other chambers of the heart.

There are two outstanding features of the *conduction* of a contraction through the heart. First, if a contraction is initiated at any one point in heart muscle, every other portion of the muscle is involved in subsequent contraction. The excitation can be conducted in any direction. This functional continuity of cardiac muscle has its parallel in the protoplasmic continuity of the cells of which it is composed, and is in sharp contrast to the insulation of the individual fibres of skeletal muscle. If any part of the heart contracts, it all contracts ; whereas the contraction of only a proportion of the fibres in skeletal muscle is the means by which a graded response to a submaximal stimulus is produced. The second feature is the delay in conduction during the passage from one chamber of the heart to the next. The speed of transmission in the frog's auricle or ventricle is about 10 cm. per second, but there is a delay of about one-third of a second at the junction between any two of the chambers. This delay is obviously essential for the proper functioning of the heart, since it allows time for the blood to pass from one chamber to the next one before the latter begins to contract. The excitation is conducted by muscle fibres, which are somewhat specialised in certain regions of the heart (as already discussed in Chapter II).

The *all-or-none* response is characteristic of cardiac as of skeletal muscle, but it can be much more easily observed in the heart owing to the absence of insulation between the fibres. If a stimulus is strong enough to excite the heart at all, variation of its intensity produces no change in the force of contraction of the organ. It must be emphasised that many other factors, such as stretching and drugs, can produce changes in the degree of contraction of cardiac muscle, and that variation in intensity of stimulus, with which the all-or-none type of response is alone concerned, may never occur except under experimental conditions.

The isolated apical half of the frog's ventricle, left to itself, does not beat, but responds to an electrical stimulus in much the same way as does a resting skeletal muscle. There are, however, certain important points of difference between the responses of the two tissues. Immediately following the stimulus there is an *electric response* which falls within the interval known as the *latent period* of the *mechanical response*. Qualitatively these effects are the same for both tissues, but in cardiac muscle they take five to ten times as long as in skeletal muscle. A second stimulus applied soon after the first discloses, however, more striking differences. It will be recalled that in skeletal muscle there is a short period, after application of a first stimulus, during which a second stimulus produces no effect, and this was called the *absolute refractory period*. This period was over long before the maximum tension had been developed, and consequently if a second stimulus fell soon after this period, the muscle responded to the double stimulus by a single fused contraction of increased height. Now, in cardiac muscle the refractory period lasts very much longer, and indeed continues for just about the same time as is occupied in the phase of contraction. Consequently a second stimulus produces no effect at all unless it is applied so long after the first that the responses of the two are independent contractions occurring one after the other. *No summation* of contractions and *no tetanus* can therefore be produced under normal conditions in heart muscle.

In cardiac, as in skeletal muscle, there is a short space of time following the absolute refractory period, during which an abnormally intense stimulus can produce a contraction ; this interval is termed the *relative refractory period*, and falls during the relaxation of heart muscle.

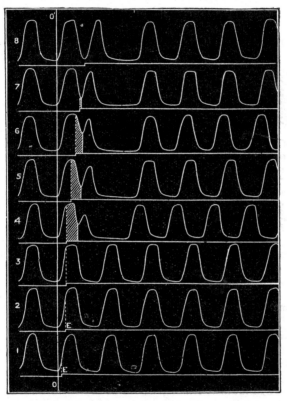

Fig. IX. 16. Tracings of **spontaneous contractions of frog's ventricle,** to show **refractory period** and **compensatory** pause. (Marey.)

In each series the surface of the ventricle was stimulated by an induction shock at E, as indicated by the tracing of the signal.

The contraction produced in this way and starting during the previous relaxation is usually less effective than a normal one, owing to imperfect recovery of the contractile process.

Let us consider the spontaneously beating heart, and interrupt its rhythm by interpolating an electric shock applied to the ventricle. Fig. IX. 16 shows the ventricular contraction during such an experiment, in which a series of shocks was applied, each at a slightly later phase of the normal contraction. In the lower three records, the stimulus fell in the absolute refractory period and produced no effect. In the upper

oncs it fell later, and produced a smaller or greater contraction according
as it occurred sooner or later. This contraction took place, abnormally,
before its time, and was accompanied by its own refractory period. It
was followed by a pause known as the *compensatory pause*, before the
next (normal) contraction, because one of the regular stimuli transmitted
from the sinus found the ventricle in a refractory state, and so produced
no effect. Comparable effects are sometimes produced in the human
heart by abnormal contractions (premature contraction or extra-systole)
originating at some irritable focus independently of the normal rhythm.

If the resting isolated ventricle be stimulated artificially, and the frequency of the stimulus increased (see Fig. **IX. 17**), the muscle responds
with more frequent individual contractions up to a point. When,
however, the interval between successive stimuli becomes so short that it
is less than the refractory period, the muscle will suddenly respond only

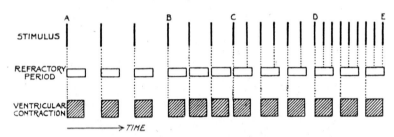

FIG. IX. 17. Scheme illustrating the influence of increases of **frequency of
stimulation** on the **frequency of contraction** of heart muscle. The
uppermost row of lines represents the stimuli. The intermediate
row of rectangles represents the refractory period accompanying
each contraction. The lowest row of squares represents the duration
of the contractions. With increasing frequency of stimulus a ratio of
stimulus to contraction frequencies of 1 · 1 (A to B and B to C), 2 · 1
(C to D), 3 · 1 (D to E), respectively, is produced.

to alternate stimuli. If the frequency be further increased so that of
three stimuli, the second and third fall within the refractory period
accompanying the response to the first, the muscle will respond only
to every third stimulus. Analogous events are observed in certain cases
of " heart-block " in human disease, in which the ventricle responds to
only a fraction of an abnormally rapid sequence of stimuli coming from
the auricle. If the frequency of stimulation be constant, and the
duration of the refractory period be sufficiently increased, a similar
omission of the response to alternate stimuli may be observed. It may
be emphasised again, that the foregoing phenomena are dependent on
the refractory period lasting for about as long as the phase of contraction, and that this is a property peculiar to cardiac muscle.

If the rate of stimulation be increased gradually, the refractory period
will itself become gradually shorter and so enable the heart to beat faster
than it could have done had the rate of stimulation been suddenly increased.
This may explain the fact that in certain conditions the human heart can
attain a rate of 200 beats per minute ; such a rate would be impossible
without an actual shortening of the normal refractory period.

Close resemblance between skeletal and cardiac muscle may be seen in the variation of response with initial length of the fibre. In heart muscle this property can be shown, as in skeletal muscle, by applying a series of stimuli to an isolated strip of ventricle, the ends of which are fixed at a series of different distances ; at increased lengths of the muscle there is an increased development of tension. More satisfactorily, however, it is found that distension of a complete ventricle by increasing the pressure of liquid within it, produces greater amplitude of contraction, and thereby a greater output of the liquid (see Chapter II—" *the law of the heart* ")—Fig. II. 13.

Metabolism of the Heart Muscle

The heart of the frog appears to work on the same chemical basis as the skeletal muscles of that animal. It differs from a skeletal muscle in certain ways, which might have been anticipated from a knowledge of its different function. As we have seen, the heart cannot be tetanised, and there is a strict limit even to the rapidity with which it can beat. A single beat of a heart corresponds to a single twitch, not to a short tetanus, of a skeletal muscle, and not more than one beat a second can usually be attained. As compared with a heart which is hardly beating at all, this is found to represent not more than a fivefold increase in its metabolic rate, whereas the skeletal muscle is designed to accelerate its metabolic rate up to a hundredfold, or, by drawing on its anaerobic accumulator mechanism, it can develop energy at thousands of times its resting rate.

We are not surprised, therefore, to find that the anaerobic accumulator mechanism of the heart is of comparatively trivial dimensions. The normal organ contains about one-tenth as much creatinephosphate as a skeletal muscle, and if the experiment be performed of shutting off the oxygen supply to an isolated heart and at the same time inhibiting lactic acid formation with sodium iodoacetate the heart fails after twenty or thirty twitches, and is then found to have used up all its creatinephosphate. If the oxygen supply is shut off, but the lactic acid mechanism left working, the heart lasts longer, apparently because the energy released by the conversion of glycogen to lactic acid is used to resynthesise creatinephosphate between the beats. But in these circumstances lactic acid is accumulating and producing an acid reaction in the heart, and unless measures are taken to combat this, the heart soon fails. The obvious and simple way of combating the acidity is to add sodium bicarbonate to the fluid perfusing the heart. This neutralisation of the lactic acid permits the heart to go on beating in the absence of oxygen for two or three hours, when it stops, not because of the accumulation of end products, but apparently from lack of carbohydrate which can be turned into lactic acid. For if at this stage glucose is added to the perfusing fluid an immediate and quite dramatic recovery ensues.

Certain other carbohydrates and their derivatives can take the place of glucose in this connection, and indeed the heart which has been

" run out " in this way is a very useful indicator of the availabliity of any substance to provide energy in the absence of oxygen. It is found, for example, that amino acids are useless to the heart lacking oxygen, although certain of them can be utilised by the heart when there is oxygen available to burn them with. Again, it is found that the substance pyruvic aldehyde (or methylglyoxal, CH_3COCHO), long suspected on indirect evidence to be formed intermediately when glycogen is converted to lactic acid, has the same beneficial action as glucose, though not to the same extent, and this lends support to the idea that glucose is converted into lactic acid *viâ* pyruvic aldehyde. The salts of fatty acids are useless, like the amino acids, as sources of energy to the anaerobic heart.

The isolated heart supplied with oxygen appears to be able to burn protein as well as carbohydrate. Its respiratory quotient has been measured and found to be about 0·85, indicating that either fat or protein is being burnt as well as carbohydrate, but chemical analysis does not show any progressive loss of fat from the isolated beating heart. On the other hand, there is a steady excretion into the perfusing fluid of urea and ammonia, which is to be expected if protein is being burnt. To sum up, the isolated frog heart supplied with oxygen is able to get its energy by the combustion of carbohydrate or protein, though it must be left undecided whether it can burn fat. With its oxygen supply shut off, the heart falls back upon a glycolysis mechanism, which, provided that the resulting acidity is neutralised, will tide the heart over an hour or two of oxygen lack. In either event (that is, whether oxygen is present or not) this energy appears to be used, not to provide directly the energy of contraction, but to resynthesise creatinephosphate between the beats, for if oxygen is shut off and the glycolysis mechanism thrown out of action (by the use of iodoacetic acid), the heart stops when its small reserve of creatinephosphate is used up.

The heart of the frog, surviving in artificial conditions, is no direct concern of the student of human physiology. Since the behaviour of this organ, and its response to drugs, are similar in many respects in the frog and in man, it may be supposed to be a similar piece of machinery ; but it would obviously be of greater value to study the metabolism of a mammalian heart, nourished with blood and performing work.

The isolated heart of the dog, weighing about 100 g., has been found to utilise oxygen at the rate of about 350 c.c. per hour. This corresponds to the burning of 200 to 500 mg. of food every hour, the amount depending on the nature of the foodstuff. The determination of the nature of the foodstuffs burnt has proved very difficult. Reliable measurements of the respiratory quotient are not yet available ; some observers believe its value to be unity, whereas others using probably better methods find the lower values (0·85 to 0·95) which would bring the dog's heart into conformity with that of the frog and with other mammalian tissues.

A more direct attack on the problem is no easier. If the food burnt were food previously stored in the heart, no evidence could be obtained by analysis of the blood. A comparison of the glycogen and fat contents of hearts which have survived several hours with hearts killed after only half an hour or so would give only very approximate information as to the disappearance of these substances, for the hearts differ considerably in the amounts of these substances contained. Any foodstuff taken up by the heart from the circulating blood may be detected by analyses of the blood at intervals, provided it is shown that the observed change in the composition of the blood would not have occurred in the absence of the heart. It was found, for example, by Lovatt Evans and co-workers that blood removed from contact with any tissue converts its glucose into lactic acid at a steady rate of 15 to 20 mg. glucose per 100 c.c. per hour. The fact that glucose disappears steadily from the blood circulating through a heart is therefore no proof that the heart is absorbing this glucose. In fact, the disappearance of glucose is no faster when the heart is in the circulation than when it is removed. On the other hand, lactic acid does not accumulate so fast when the heart is included in the circulation; frequently it actually diminishes in amount; from which it seems likely that the heart absorbs lactic acid. Such absorption has been clearly demonstrated by the same workers, who found that on the average, for hearts weighing about 100 g., the lactate content of blood leaving the coronary sinus was 60 mg. per 100 c.c. when the content in the arterial blood entering the coronary circulation averaged 68 mg. per 100 c.c. Thus from every 100 c.c. of blood passing through the coronary circulation 8 mg. of lactate was taken up. Since it takes about two minutes for this quantity of blood to pass through the coronary circulation, it can be calculated that the amount of lactic acid thus absorbed by the heart would, if it is oxidised, account for about half the measured oxygen consumption of the heart. If the supply of lactic acid in the coronary blood is insufficient, the heart has to make use of its glycogen reserves, converting them first to lactic acid. Pyruvic acid can also be used, and probably also fat. Nothing is known about the metabolism under anaerobic conditions, for the mammalian heart is very sensitive to oxygen lack, and does not survive long enough for metabolic experiments to be performed.

Heart muscle contains considerable quantities of myoglobin. As discussed in Chapter III, this substance acts as a reservoir of oxygen, supplying the sudden demands by the muscle fibres after each contraction. It has been calculated that the amount present in the heart is just about sufficient to provide the oxygen required by a single maximal contraction—*i.e.*, for about 0·5 seconds; at moderate activity, the supply would last about 7 seconds.

UNSTRIATED MUSCLE

The muscles of which the viscera, other than the heart, are largely composed have certain features in common, which distinguish them from skeletal and cardiac muscle, and which make it convenient to consider them as one group. The organs which have been most carefully studied are the stomach, intestine, bladder, ureter, uterus, and the arteries. Their musculature is composed of relatively short fibres which show no cross-striation, and ramifying among these is an abundant network of small nerve cells and fibres. They are controlled by a double set of autonomic nerves, stimulation of which produces results which are opposite in effect. Isolated strips of muscle can be examined in much the same way as can skeletal muscles.

One of the most striking differences between skeletal and visceral muscles is the difficulty of assigning a particular value to the resting length of the latter. The pressure in the bladder may be very little different according to whether it is distended or empty. Similarly, isolated unstriated muscle, stretched by the small constant tension of an isotonic lever, may adopt various lengths at different times, and it may be impossible to name the external influences which presumably have brought about the change ; this phenomenon—a slow change of length without a corresponding change of tension—is termed *tonus*, and the muscle is said to have more tone when shorter than when longer.

Most unstriated muscles, under suitable conditions, show *spontaneous rhythmic contractions* which vary in frequency from one (spleen) to twelve (small intestine) per minute. It is fair, in the present state of knowledge, to assert that nobody knows how these tonic and rhythmic activities in plain muscle are brought about, and if we attribute them mainly to a mechanism corresponding to the tetanus in skeletal muscle, it is because no likely alternative hypothesis is available and because the known properties of plain muscle, described below, make this view tenable.

Stretching produces an immediate contraction of both skeletal and visceral muscle in the living animal, but a profound difference in the mechanism of this response is disclosed by comparing the effects on isolated muscles. Many isolated smooth muscles are readily excited by stretching, or, if in the form of a hollow organ, by distension. Isolated striated muscle, on the contrary, is almost unaffected ; and its large response in the intact animal is due to a nervous mechanism involving nerves passing to and from the central nervous system. One is led, therefore, to suspect that unstriated muscle incorporates both the muscular and nervous elements which can be so readily distinguished in the " reflex " responses of striated muscle.

In support of this view is the fact that the muscles which respond to stretch and show spontaneous contractions generally include within them the histological constituents, nerve plexuses, which such a mechanism requires, whereas unstriated muscles which are devoid of nerve cells show, when denervated, neither a response to stretch nor spontaneous contractions. Exceptions to this rule are held by some to prove the myogenic origin of spontaneous contractions ; but although a plain muscle devoid of nerve cells can, in exceptional circumstances, initiate contractions, this is not necessarily an indication of the normal origin of a " spontaneous " contraction. Similarly, the twitches which an isolated sartorius undergoes in abnormal saline solutions are not to be taken as proof of the myogenic origin of skeletal movements.

A distinctive feature of unstriated muscle is the extreme *sluggishness* with which it responds to any change in environment. One example of this is observed when such a muscle is stretched by a constant weight ; its length increases quickly at first, but it may not reach its new equilibrium length for anything up to an hour or more, showing that it is much more "viscid" than skeletal muscle. Muscle "viscosity" is considered in a special section below. Another aspect of the slowness of plain muscle is seen in its mechanical response to excitation, which may occupy a minute (frog's stomach), whereas the corresponding twitch of skeletal muscle is over in one-tenth of a second.

The *excitability* of smooth muscle varies very much according to the nature of the stimulus. Most agents which excite skeletal muscle are also effective with smooth muscle, but the latter is less sensitive to electrical stimulation. On the other hand, unstriated muscle is more sensitive to *chemical stimulation*, and many drugs, *e.g.*, adrenaline, will produce well-marked effects at dilutions, such as one in one hundred million, which have no detectable influence on striated muscle even in very much larger concentrations. This property contributes admirably to the performance of the normal slow functions of visceral muscle, which can be controlled in part by substances circulating in minute amounts in the blood.

Another qualitative difference between skeletal and visceral muscles which may be mentioned is the relatively great capacity of the latter to change their length—they may shorten to a quarter or less of their extended length—while, on the other hand, their capacity for developing tension is relatively small. In an organism, skeletal muscle may be said to function relatively isometrically, and visceral muscle relatively isotonically. If, in fact, smooth muscle is induced by an abnormal stimulus, such as stretching, to develop any considerable tension, this is accompanied by the intense pain of " spasm " (*e.g.*, colic in the intestine).

A property which smooth muscle shares with cardiac and skeletal muscle is the effect of increase of initial length in producing more forcible contraction. This is well shown by the retractor penis of the dog, a small strip of muscle, which is exceptionally suitable for the analysis of the properties of plain muscle, since its fibres are parallel and devoid of nerve cells ; it exhibits no spontaneous contractions or response to stretch, and its size is a convenient compromise between the large muscle which yields a robust contraction and the small muscle thin enough for its interior fibres to have access by diffusion to oxygen and other substances in a fluid bathing it. Its mechanical responses at various lengths are shown in Fig. IX. 18.

The chemical changes which accompany the contraction of unstriated muscle have been investigated much less completely than the corresponding changes in striated muscle.

The difficulty in discovering the chemical mechanisms in plain muscle is partly due to the small quantities present of the substances supposed to react in such changes, and hence to the technical difficulties involved in detecting small changes in these amounts ; it is due also to the confusion arising from the incomplete understanding of the phenomena of tonus and muscle " viscosity," which has prevented experimental conditions being so chosen that the muscle would contract with the greatest expenditure of energy, and so incur chemical changes large enough to detect.

Plain muscle can continue active for a considerable period in the absence of oxygen, but it fatigues more rapidly and recovers less com-

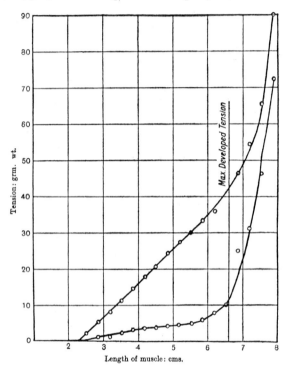

F ɪ ɢ. IX. 18.   **Tension-length Curve of Unstriated Muscle** (dog's retractor penis).   The upper curve shows the tension of the electrically stimulated muscle, the lower curve that of the unstimulated muscle. Note the increase of tension development (difference between the two curves) with increase of length, up to an optimum length, as in the case of striated muscle.

pletely in its absence than its presence.   Cyanide abolishes spontaneous contractions and tonus, and eventually renders the muscle inexcitable.

It has been shown in an invertebrate smooth muscle (retractor of the byssus of *Mytilus edulis*—the common sea-water mussel) that argininephosphate breakdown accompanies activity due to electrical stimulation till the muscle is fatigued, and that argininephosphate resynthesis accompanies the complete recovery which results if the muscle is allowed to rest in oxygenated sea-water.   Older observations on mammalian plain muscles indicate the formation of lactic acid from glycogen accompanying activity, at least under partially or completely anaerobic conditions.   We may infer provisionally, therefore, that the chemical mechanism underlying the contraction in plain muscle has much in common with that in skeletal muscle.

The Speed of Muscular Movement

If an isolated plain muscle is not stretched, it gradually contracts to its shortest length. If, now, it is stretched by a sufficient weight, it gradually lengthens. The greater the weight, the more quickly it lengthens. Such properties of muscle recall the phenomena due to viscous resistance to the flow of liquids.

The necessity for including " viscosity " as a property of muscles, arises from three classes of experiment. (1) The tension developed in a stimulated muscle while it is being stretched is greater than that developed while it is being released, so that there is a loss of energy in a complete cycle of stretch and release. (2) The external work done by a muscle decreases as the rate of doing the work increases. (3) A muscle whose length is suddenly changed, alters its tension slowly ; and one whose tension is suddenly changed alters its length slowly. These phenomena were, until recently, adequately explained by the conception of a force within the muscle which is formally analogous to that associated with the flow of a viscous fluid. The work of A. V. Hill, referred to above, on p. 329, has now shown that in the stimulated skeletal muscle of the frog, the phenomena are not such as could be explained by a true viscous force. The experimental evidence summarised at the beginning of this paragraph, however, is still valid, and it is convenient to speak of a muscle possessing a " viscosity," in addition to the " elasticity," which results in its shortening once more, after a stretching weight has been removed. But we can make no statements as to the way in which this " viscosity " varies with the rate of change of length of the muscle, nor have we any knowledge as to the nature of the forces concerned.

The statement that the viscosity of a muscle is greater or less under one set of conditions than another implies two sets of observations : first, that the ratio of a stretching force to the speed of lengthening is greater or less ; and secondly, that the removal of a stretching force results in slower or quicker shortening. One only of these may be affected by a change in the elastic components of the muscle system, but a change in the time relations which is symmetrical, that is, which appears both in lengthening and shortening of the muscle, is taken to mean a change in viscosity.

There are two consequences of muscle viscosity which are of obvious physiological importance, the extravagance of quick contraction, and the relatively low frequency of stimulation needed to maintain a sustained contraction. An example of the first has been considered in the first chapter (Figs. I. 8 and I. 9), when it was shown that the external work performed in a maximal contraction of the human arm muscles becomes less the quicker the contraction. Likewise in isolated muscles, striated or unstriated, the tension developed on stimulation is smaller the greater the velocity of shortening allowed. The high viscosity of unstriated muscle would render its contraction too slow for the proper functioning of the viscera were it not that certain stimuli which induce powerful contractions also produce large reductions of the viscosity. For example, adrenaline, in a concentration which produces maximal contraction, reduces the viscosity of the retractor penis tenfold or more, as shown in Fig. IX. 19.

The second important aspect of muscle viscosity is its effect in retarding relaxation after a contraction, and so reducing the frequency of stimulation, and therewith the energy, required to maintain a sustained contraction. Since contractions in the body are nearly always of

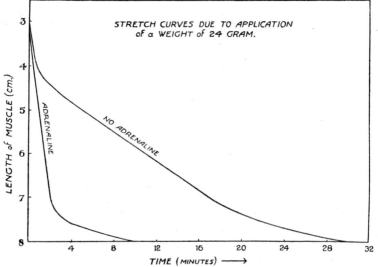

FIG. IX. 19.　The effect of **adrenaline** on the **viscosity** of the retractor penis
(dog).

　　The initial length of the muscle is represented by the upper boundary of the chart. The muscle was stretched by a sudden application of a load of 24 g. The weight was removed, the muscle given time to shorten to its original length. Adrenaline was added, and the muscle, stretched again by the same weight, lengthened much more quickly. The corresponding curves obtained when the weight was removed show that the muscle shortens much more quickly in the presence than in the absence of adrenaline. (Winton.)

the nature of sustained contractions due to repeated stimulation, this aspect of viscosity is of greater physiological significance than its interference with the development of tension in a short contraction, as considered above. These points are well shown by the invertebrate plain muscle described above, the retractor of the foot of *Mytilus*. In this muscle an interrupted or alternating current stimulus lasting ten seconds induces a quick contraction which is over in about a minute ; an uninterrupted direct current stimulus of the same duration, on the other hand, induces a somewhat smaller contraction, after which relaxation takes an hour or two (Fig. IX. 20, A). The viscosity of the muscle after a few seconds' stimulation with direct current can be shown to be over a hundred times the value found after a similar short stimulation with alternating current ; this large increase of viscosity persists for an hour or two unless interrupted by an alternating current stimulus, which immediately reduces the viscosity to its low value. The viscosity of the unstimulated muscle is intermediate between the low and high values found after appropriate stimulation.

The quick response evoked by alternating current enables the muscle to execute rapid movements, but, as shown in Fig. IX. 20, B, a

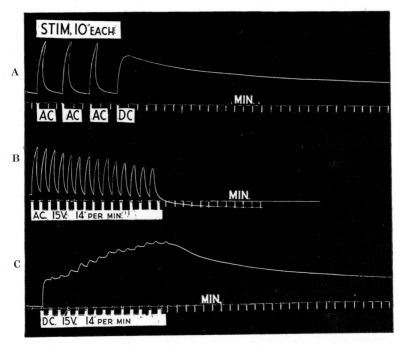

Fig. IX. 20. **Changes in viscosity** due to **electrical stimulation** of the foot retractor of *Mytilus*, and their significance in enabling the muscle to sustain a tetanic contraction without fatigue. (Winton.)

A. Three contractions due to stimulation for 10 sec. with alternating current (50 cycles) (AC) involve much quicker relaxation than that due to stimulation with direct current (DC) of the same duration.

B. A series of contractions due to alternating current applied for 14 sec. once a minute, showing little fusion but the gradual progress of fatigue.

C. A series of contractions due to direct current applied for 14 sec. once a minute, showing summation and almost complete fusion.

series of such stimuli is incapable of maintaining a sustained contraction for long ; for if applied once a minute, relaxation is quick enough to prevent fusion, although even at this frequency fatigue slowly develops ; if applied at a frequency high enough to yield a fused response, fatigue rapidly supervenes and abolishes the response after a few minutes. The viscid state induced by direct current stimuli, on the other hand, favours economical maintenance of contraction ; for, if applied once a minute, as in Fig. IX. 20, C, relaxation is so slow that the contraction builds up by summation (*cf.* Fig. IX. 7), and can be sustained for several hours.

It is clear, then, that large changes of viscosity can occur in isolated muscles, both mammalian and invertebrate ; that they do so in life is suggested by the comparable changes of viscosity which follow denervation of Holothurian (plain) muscle. The changes in viscosity in mammalian viscera in the body have not yet been studied. The mechanism of the change of viscosity in muscle is as completely unknown as is the mechanism of the development of tension.

Muscular Tone

We have defined " tonus " in its simplest form as that disproportion between tension and length which is a relatively permanent characteristic of unstriated muscle. It might perhaps be regarded as a sustained submaximal contraction without too obvious a stimulus, and so the meaning of " muscular tone " is extended to include that small permanent state of tension which enables skeletal muscles, when connected with the central nervous system, to maintain the postural relations of the body of terrestrial animals. The longer the muscle, in proportion to its sustained tension, the lower is its tone.

An altogether different meaning has come to be attached to the word tone (and tonus), in connection with the activities of various organs, and particularly of the heart. As we have seen, a contracting heart produces greater tension the greater the initial length of its fibres. Conversely, in order to develop a given pressure (aortic blood pressure), the beating heart requires a shorter initial length of fibre when fresh than when fatigued. Its physiological condition, for a given output of work, is thus better when the heart is small than when it is dilated. This physiological condition is what is meant by the " tone of the heart." A similar meaning is implied by the familiar pharmaceutical use of the word " tonic." As long as " tone " is applied to the heart, it retains some connection with " muscular tone," owing to its dependence on the size of the heart ; but when " tone " is applied to organs such as the kidney, or to the intact animal, it implies physiological fitness, as measured by the reserves available under conditions of excessive activity or disease.

Muscular tone appears to be a form of sustained contraction. In skeletal muscle, the only form of sustained contraction which has been thoroughly experimentally analysed is the tetanus. Nevertheless, till recently, the hypothesis that tonus is a form of tetanus was considered untenable for the following reasons : (1) the oxygen consumption of muscles developing " tonic " tension appears to be less than that corresponding to the same tension induced by tetanic stimulation ; (2) tonic contraction may continue for an indefinite period without the development of fatigue ; (3) the electrical variations, which occur regularly in a muscle undergoing tetanic contraction, are small and irregular in tonic contraction.

Without going fully into the evidence, it may be stated that tonic contraction in skeletal muscle has nevertheless been shown to be due to repetitive stimulation, as in tetanic contraction ; the two differ, however, in that tonic contraction affects the individual fibres of the muscle in turn, intermittently and asynchronously, whereas tetanic contraction affects a particular set of fibres, with regular volleys of stimuli, so that they contract continuously and synchronously. Hence in tonic contraction, fatigue of any particular fibre is avoided by giving it a rest while its neighbouring fibres are contracting. Moreover, the action potential of a particular fibre is short-circuited by neighbouring fibres which are not contracting at the same time, and so it cannot so easily be detected by the electrodes and galvanometer. The experiments which claimed to show that the oxygen consumption of muscles undergoing tonic contraction was too low have been criticised on technical grounds, and the chief objections to a tetanic theory of tonus in skeletal muscle have therefore been met.

The occurrence of tonus in visceral muscle cannot be so confidently explained on the basis of a tetanus-like contraction. The chief difficulty in the way of such an hypothesis is that little or no increase in oxygen consumption appears to be associated with the maintenance of large tensions for long periods, as compared with the relaxed condition. The difficulty is perhaps not as insuperable as it seems, for owing to the high viscosity of plain muscle, the duration of the unstriated muscle twitch is very long, and a tetanic contraction can be maintained with a frequency of stimulus only about one-thousandth of that necessary with skeletal muscle ; and since the rate of oxygen consumption required to maintain a tetanus varies with the frequency of the stimulus, it would in any case be very much less for visceral than for skeletal muscle. So little, indeed, is the oxygen consumption calculated as necessary for a tetanus, that it might fall within the range of error of the experiments on the tonus of unstriated muscle mentioned above.

A second difficulty encountered by the tetanus theory of tonus in plain muscle is that, if electrical stimuli be applied at a frequency great enough to produce a fused response, the response is short-lived owing to fatigue. This, as shown in the section on muscle viscosity, can be overcome if a suitable form of stimulus is chosen.

A third, but less formidable, difficulty in accepting the tetanus-like character of tonus is the question as to where the repetitive stimuli should come from. In skeletal muscle they come from the central nervous system, and no tone is observed in denervated muscle. In unstriated muscle, on the other hand, tonus is a prominent feature of the behaviour of isolated muscles. A possible solution is indicated by the sensitivity of these muscles to stretching. Stretching a strip of suitable plain muscle, or distending a suitable hollow organ, may produce contraction. Most plain muscles incorporate a local nerve plexus, which is probably excited by stretching. The maintenance of a constant tension may therefore be regarded as adequate to produce the succession of stimuli which might elicit a tetanic contraction. It will be shown later that there is good reason for supposing that the small constant stretch of skeletal muscle is also the factor exciting the tissue to tonic activity, though in this case the excitation passes by way of nerves to and from the central nervous system.

Although this response to stretch plays a part in the manifestation of tonus in some plain muscles, it cannot be regarded as a complete explanation, since certain other muscles show no response to stretch, and are nevertheless capable of developing tonus, even in the absence of nerve cells. This essential muscular tonus seems to depend on the existence in plain muscle of a constant tension, which is small, and which appears not to vary with the length of the muscle. Associated with this small contractile force is an extremely high viscosity, which enables the muscle to resist a stretch, or, at least, to yield to it so slowly that it may be an hour or so before any considerable lengthening has occurred. The fact that the small restoring force is independent of changes in the

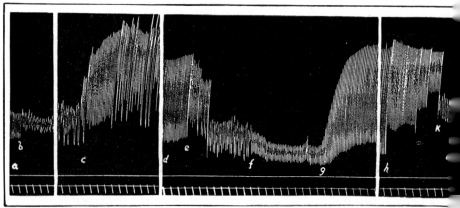

Fig. IX. 21.   **The Action of Electrolytes on the Heart of the Tortoise.**
(*a*) Excised heart before perfusion.
(*b*) Perfusion with sodium chloride, 0·75 per cent., and bicarbonate, 0·01 per cent.
(*c*) Addition of 3 c.c. of 0·1 molar calcium chloride to 100 c.c.
(*d*) Further addition of 0·1 molar potassium chloride—6 c.c. to 100 c.c.
(*e*) Solution changed to 0·75 per cent. sodium chloride again.
(*f*) Potassium chloride added, 6 c.c. to 100 c.c.
(*g*) Calcium chloride added, 3 c.c. to 100 c.c.
(*h*) 3 c.c. calcium chloride added before each step in the tracing.
(*k*) Enough potassium chloride added to correspond with the calcium chloride prese
(*l*) Normal Ringer's solution.
    The smallness of the beat initially is due to the action of acid metabolites, which are f
during the anoxæmia accompanying dissection ; they are rapidly removed by the perfusion
Recording : systole is upstroke.
        (From Bayliss's "Principles of General Physiology.")

length of the muscle suggests that the essential muscular tonus is not a tetanus-like affair. The powerful contractions which some plain muscles (*e.g.*, the adductor muscle of Pecten) sustain for long periods are clearly not of this class, and may well be due to a tetanus-like mechanism like that responsible for tone in skeletal muscles. The great sensitivity of vertebrate plain muscles to substances like adrenaline normally present in the blood, and the dependence of the powerful contractions such substances can evoke on the length of the muscle, suggest that tonus of these muscles may in some cases be due to a simpler mechanism—a direct continuous chemical action on the muscle —than the indirect discontinuous excitation by nerve impulses concerned in the tonus of skeletal muscle.

The Action of Electrolytes on Isolated Tissues

When contractile tissues are removed from the body for experimental purposes, their nervous connections are severed, and their normal chemical environment is changed. This latter change must, however, not be too drastic if functional activity is to continue, and, consequently, it is necessary to study the substances which must be present in a solution bathing an isolated muscle.

Owing to its automatic rhythmic activity, the heart is the most convenient indicator of responses to changes in its perfusion fluid, and the classical experiments of Ringer on this organ form the basis of our knowledge of the subject. If a frog's heart is isolated and left to itself, it continues to beat as long as it is moist, and then stops. If it be placed in a solution, of whatever composition, of which the *osmotic pressure* is substantially different from that of the blood, it soon ceases to beat. Let us confine our attention, therefore, to solutions which are isosmotic (isotonic) with blood. Solutions of non-electrolytes, such as glucose, are incapable of maintaining the heart-beat. Isotonic solutions of sodium chloride (0·65 per cent.), on the other hand, will maintain the beat for some little time. Soon, however, the heart ceases to beat and remains relaxed. If, now, a small amount of calcium chloride is added to the solution, the beats begin again ; but after a short while, the relaxation after each beat becomes progressively less complete, until, at last, the heart remains fully contracted, and ceases to beat. If at this stage a suitable small amount of potassium chloride is added to the solution, contractions begin again, and the heart may continue to beat fairly normally for many hours. It is clear, therefore, that at least three salts must be present in an adequate physiological solution— sodium, potassium, and calcium chlorides—and the heart survives longer still if the solution is made slightly alkaline by adding sodium bicarbonate. Ringer found, by trial and error, the concentration of each of these salts which favoured longest survival of the heart-beat of the frog and tortoise. Locke, working with isolated mammalian hearts, found the addition of glucose an advantage, and the compositions of these " physiological fluids " are given below :—

	Ringer's Solution. (Frog's heart.) gram.	*Frog's blood.* gram.	*Locke's Solution.* (Mammalian heart.) gram.	*Mammalian blood.* gram.
NaCl	0·65	0·55	0·9	0·7
KCl	0·014	0·023	0·042	0·038
CaCl$_2$*	0·012	0·025	0·024	0·028
NaHCO$_3$	0·02	0·1	0·02	0·23
NaH$_2$PO$_4$*	0·001	0·14	—	0·036
Glucose	—	0·04	0·1–0·25	0·13
Water	to 100	(100)	to 100	(100)

* The weights given refer to the anhydrous salts. Appropriately greater weights of the hydrated forms, which are in common use, should be employed in making up Ringer's solutions.

The addition of a small quantity of magnesium chloride is beneficial in experiments with isolated mammalian intestine (as in Tyrode's solution), but has little effect on the heart.

The subject of the action of individual ions on contractile tissues is at the moment in an exceedingly confused state, owing to the fact that different tissues respond in different fashion to excess or deficiency of any particular ion. Certain general rules appear, however, to obtain : (1) the unique position of sodium salts, which must be present in much larger amounts than any others. Not more than one-half the amount present in Ringer's solution can be replaced by any other non-toxic substance, such as glucose, which can bring the osmotic pressure up to the required value ; (2) the interdependence of the concentrations of calcium and potassium salts, which must be present in about the right ratio, though their absolute amounts may vary considerably. Excess of potassium salts induces contraction of most muscles other than the heart ; (3) the relative unimportance of anions, so long as they are not toxic ; chlorides are usually employed, as these salts are all soluble, but the presence of sulphates, bromides, nitrates, carbonates, etc., has little influence on the survival of activity of an isolated tissue ; (4) the hydrogen ion concentration must be not far removed from that of a neutral solution. Most tissues are favoured by a hydrogen ion concentration slightly on the alkaline side of neutrality. Slight acidity produces slowing or arrest of the heart-beat, relaxation of the tone of most unstriated muscles, and phenomena analogous to fatigue in striated muscles.

If living frog muscles are immersed in a modified Ringer's solution in which a proportion of the sodium chloride has been replaced by an equimolecular amount of sodium nitrate (leaving therefore the sodium concentration unchanged), they come into equilibrium in the course of an hour or two by exchange of chloride and nitrate ions, and when equilibrium is reached it is found that the concentration of chloride in the muscle is one-quarter that in the Ringer's solution, no matter what be the actual chloride concentration chosen. If the same experiment is performed with dead muscles, the concentration ratio is four-fifths, and is similarly independent of the actual concentration chosen. A simple explanation is as follows. It is known that only four-fifths of the muscle (dead or alive) consists of water, and if simple osmotic equilibrium were established the apparent concentration of chloride in the muscle should be four-fifths that in the Ringer's solution, for then the chloride concentration in the water of the muscle would equal that in the water of the Ringer's fluid. Therefore, in dead muscles all the water of the tissue dissolves chloride. But in living muscles, if the equilibrium is also osmotic, only one-quarter of the muscle consists of water capable of dissolving chloride ions ; *i.e.*, only $1/4 \times 5/4$, or $5/16$ of the water of the tissue ; $11/16$ of the water is for some reason unavailable to chloride ions in the living muscle. It is probable that the muscle cells themselves, containing $11/16$ of the water of the muscle, are enclosed within membranes impermeable to chloride ions. The remainder of the water is contained in the intercellular " spaces " and is accessible to chloride ions. This view would, at any rate, explain the ease with which sodium chloride can be washed away from the muscle by perfusion with sugar solutions.

A particular relation of the potassium ion to the excitability of skeletal muscle may be noted, for it has been shown to account for the practical necessity of washing frogs' muscles with Ringer's solution when isolated ; this has the effect of removing the excess of potassium salts which diffuses out of those few fibres which are injured by the manipulative procedure. (The potassium concentration is much higher in muscle cells than in the tissue fluids.) If the muscle is not bathed with fluid, it becomes inexcitable. Placing the muscle in a Ringer's solution modified to contain about threefold the normal amount of potassium chloride likewise induces inexcitability ; both in this case and in the muscle which is unwashed after isolation, excitability can be restored by washing it with Ringer's solution.

The effects of these and other ions on innumerable tissues and species have not yet been incorporated into a comprehensive theory of their action. It is a striking fact that for proper functioning of the cells, the electrolyte composition of the fluid bathing them must be quite different from that of the fluid within them. Thus, it is so common as to be almost a general rule that cells contain potassium ions and practically no sodium ions, while the fluid outside must contain sodium ions and very little potassium ions. Many cells, also, contain practically no chloride, but much phosphate ; the outside solution, in life, contains mainly chloride, but this can be replaced by other univalent ions. These differences in electrolyte composition are maintained in spite of the fact that it is now known that the cell membrane is not entirely impermeable to any kind of ion. The permeability, both to water and to all substances in solution, is affected by the electrolyte composition of the external fluid. In the absence of calcium, the permeability is increased, and in the absence of all electrolytes it is increased still further. In some cases, at least, the presence of polyvalent anions can counteract the reduction of permeability produced by calcium, or other polyvalent cations. Normal functioning of the cell is only possible in the presence of a normal permeability of the cell membrane, but it would be unwise to conclude that the actions of electrolytes, which have been discussed above, are the result only of effects on the cell membrane ; such effects, however, are undoubtedly important.

CHAPTER X

NERVE

The Structure of Nerve

WHEN unicellular organisms are exposed to a sudden change in their environment, they usually respond by removing themselves or the source of irritation. When the response of the cell involves the liberation of an amount of energy out of proportion to that of the stimulus, the cell is said to be excitable or irritable. Its response may be local or may spread over the whole of the cell surface. When, for example, the unicellular alga *Nitella* is injured at one end, a wave of excitation travels along the whole length of the cell. In the multicellular organisms, muscle fibres have retained these powers. They can be excited at any point on their surface, and can conduct an impulse from one end of the fibre to the other. As the wave of excitation passes along the surface, the underlying protein molecules shorten.

Even in the lowest metazoa, one cell receives the stimulus, and others give rise to the movement. The link between them is a nerve fibre, a cell process whose sole function is to transmit excitation from one cell to another. As the centralisation of nerve cells and fibres progresses and the central nervous system becomes increasingly complex, it requires more and more rapid and efficient conducting pathways to all parts of the body. These are grouped together to form nerve trunks, in which a connective tissue sheath surrounds afferent fibres, which transmit excitation to the central nervous system, and efferent fibres which excite the effector organs of the body.

The nerve fibres are specialised protoplasmic processes of nerve cells and are called *axons* or axis cylinders. A nerve cell consists of a cell body or *perikaryon* which contains the nucleus, and a number of branching processes called *dendrites*. One of these is elongated to form the axon. When a living axon is cut across in some nerves, the contents are sufficiently fluid to flow out. In other nerves, tough neurofibrils have been described. Surrounding the axon there is a layer of protein and lipoid material. The smallest fibres have only a thin layer which is made up chiefly of protein and therefore does not stain with the lipoid stains. These fibres, of about 1μ in diameter, are said to be unmyelinated. With a greater fibre diameter, the thickness and lipoid content of this myelin sheath increases. In vertebrates fibres more than 2μ in diameter stain deeply with fat stains, *e.g.*, osmic acid, and are known as myelinated fibres. The presence or absence of a myelin sheath depends more on the fibre diameter than on the nature of the fibre, and before they terminate, myelinated fibres may branch repeatedly and give rise to fibres so small that they lose their myelin sheath.

As fibres leave the central nervous system, they acquire a sheath called the *neurilemma*, or the sheath of Schwann. This is a tough, homogeneous membrane which survives when the rest of the fibre is destroyed, as, for example, by pinching. This sheath dips in to form a series of intersections a few millimetres apart, the *nodes of Ranvier*. In the middle of each segment so formed there is the nucleus of a Schwann cell. Branching of the fibre occurs at the nodes, which appear to be points at which the nerve is most easily excited electrically.

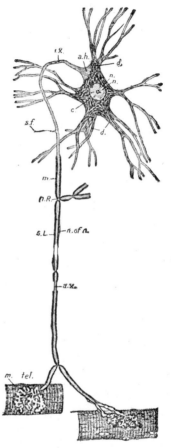

It is known that the presence of the cell body is essential for the continued life of the nerve cell, perhaps in the synthesis of the constituents of the axoplasm. If a nerve trunk is cut across, the portions of the nerve fibres that have been separated from the cell body slowly degenerate, and in 3–4 days have ceased to conduct. This process is called Wallerian degeneration, after Waller, who described it in 1852. The axon disappears, and after 10–14 days, the myelin sheath breaks up into deeply staining fat globules. However, all peripheral nerves have remarkable powers of repair, and in this, the Schwann cells play an essential part. Nerve fibres within the central nervous system have no neurilemmal sheath and do not regenerate. When a peripheral nerve has been cut, the Schwann cells of the lower fragment proliferate and grow centrally towards the stump. If they succeed in bridging the gap, neurofibrils grow out from the stump and enter the surviving neurilemma tubes and grow down them. The gap may be bridged in as little as 8 days, and after that the axons grow at a rate of about 4 mm. per day. The outgrowing fibres are at first very small, difficult to excite, and only able to conduct very slowly.

Fig. X. 1. Diagram of a **Motor Nerve** cell with its nerve fibre. (After Barker.)

a.h, axon hillock ; *d*, dendrites ; *a.x*, axis cylinder ; *m*, medullary sheath ; *n.R*, node of Ranvier.

The axis cylinder may end in a " motor end-plate " on a muscle fibre, or in any one of a large variety of sensory endings, or on another nerve cell. The point of junction between two nerve cells is called a **synapse.** The synapse and the motor end-plate show a number of properties in which they resemble each other and differ from nerve fibres. When Wallerian degeneration takes place, it stops short at the

end of the axis cylinder.   The cell body and axis cylinder are therefore
believed to form a discrete functional unit, the **neurone.**

Nerve fibres signal events by transmitting " impulses " from one
end to the other.   Each impulse consists of an area of activity whose
intensity, duration and speed of conduction are remarkably constant in
any one fibre.   In a particular fibre, therefore, only the frequency of the
impulses can vary.   The most obvious indicator of the passage of
impulses along a frog's nerve is the
contraction of an attached muscle, and
most of the properties of nerve fibres were
worked out by this means.   There are,
however, a number of physical changes
which can be detected in the nerve itself
during the passage of an impulse.   These
include a small change in the electrical
potential of the surface of the fibre, a
change in the transverse electrical resistance, a very small increase in heat
production, and increases in oxygen
consumption and carbon dioxide production, with concomitant chemical changes.

Of all these physico-chemical changes,
the electrical potential change is the
easiest to record faithfully.   The resistance changes require elaborate apparatus
for their detection, the increase in heat
production can only be measured with
great difficulty and considerable time lag,
and the chemical changes can only be
detected after the passage of a large
number of impulses.

In recording the potential changes at
points on the surface of the nerve, set
up by the passage of an impulse, and,
indeed, in recording all other potential
changes in the body, it is difficult to
decide on the best position for the
indifferent electrode, or reference point.

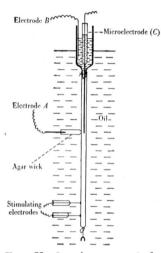

FIG. X. 2.   Arrangement for
recording resting and action
potentials from a giant nerve
fibre of a squid.

A cannula is inserted into the
cut end of the axon, which hangs
freely in oil.   The micro-electrode
(C) is inserted through the
cannula as far into the interior
of the axon as is desired ; contact
with the outer surface of the axon
is made by means of the wick
soaked in sea-water (electrode A).
The cannula is filled with sea-
water, and a third electrode (B)
inserted in it acts as if in contact
with the cut end of the axon.
(Hodgkin and Huxley.)

The most clear cut records have been
obtained by putting a micro-electrode into the axoplasm inside the
nerve fibre, with the other electrode on its outer surface, as indicated
in Fig. X. 2.   A steady " resting " potential difference of 50–90 mV. was
found between the electrodes, with the outer electrode positive to the
inner one.   Each time an impulse passed down the nerve, the resting
potential was abolished for 1–2 msecs., and was even momentarily
reversed in sign (compare Fig. X. 10).   This sudden disappearance of
the resting potential is called the *action potential,* and is the sign of
nervous activity which is most easily studied.   The nerve impulse is

always accompanied by an action potential, and in fact, the electrical potential changes play an essential part in the excitation and transmission of the impulse. As the action potential consists essentially of the reduction of the resting potential, it is first necessary to describe the origin of the resting potential, and the way in which it can be removed.

The Resting Potential of Nerve

When a nerve fibre is at rest, it is by no means inert. It is normally " fully charged," and can liberate energy rapidly when it is excited. It is this sudden liberation of energy which constitutes the nerve impulse. After a short period of activity, the resting state is rebuilt by processes of which almost nothing is as yet known. We know at least something of the way in which the resting potential is produced, as a result of electrical studies and the analysis of the composition of axoplasm. Leads from the inside and outside of a fibre can only be obtained in the giant unmyelinated fibre of the squid, which may reach 0·1 mm. in diameter. If the outside electrode is placed near the cut end, it is clear that there is then no potential difference between the electrodes. If the outside electrode is moved along the fibre away from the cut end, the potential difference grows rapidly over the first few mm., and then remains steady over the rest of the fibre. The process of local " killing " of a nerve fibre consists of abolishing the charge on the membrane by local crushing or burning, so that an electrode on the outside of the fibre leads directly from the axoplasm. This method can, therefore, be used for studying the resting potential in nerves whose diameter is too small to admit a micro-electrode. In these conditions, very much smaller potentials are recorded from the nerve, owing to inevitable short circuiting of the electrodes by connective tissue and tissue fluid. The resting potential was formerly called the " injury potential," but it is, in fact, revealed rather than produced by an injury. It slowly diminishes when the oxygen supply is cut off, and disappears when the cell dies. If the electrodes are both inside the cell, or both on its uninjured surface, there is no potential difference between them. The resting potential must, therefore, be due to an accumulation of negative ions inside and positive ions outside the cell. If these ions could cross the cell membrane freely, there would be no potential difference between the cell and the exterior. We should, therefore, expect to find the cell membrane impermeable to anions or cations or both. In fact, the nerve cell membrane behaves as though it were permeable to small cations, including hydrogen ions and potassium ions, and almost impermeable to larger cations and to anions.

The simple view that the cell membrane can act as a molecular sieve, permitting the passage of potassium ions, but not of larger particles, leads to difficulties. For example, it is established that if nerves are bathed in salt solutions containing a small excess of sodium and chlorine ions, both ions pass into the axoplasm in the course of a few hours. It is therefore better to think of a selective activity of the cell, maintained by the expenditure of energy, by which the concentration of sodium in the cell is kept low, and the concentration of potassium is kept some 20–30 times greater than that in the extracellular fluid.

Two solutions of the same substance in different concentrations can be made to set up a potential difference between them, if they are separated by a membrane which is permeable to only one of their ions. These " diffusion potentials " can be calculated for the observed difference in concentration of potassium ions, and it has been shown that they are large enough to account for the observed resting potentials. There is now a little evidence as to the structure of the cell membrane. It seems likely that it contains a layer of long chain fatty acid or lecithin molecules, orientated at right angles to the surface. As long as the potential difference across the membrane is maintained, the molecules remain closely packed together, forming a palisade which only permits small cations to pass. At rest the electrical resistance of this membrane is quite high, being about equal to that of a similar thickness of olive oil and 10 million times greater than that of a similar thickness of isotonic KCl solution.

The measurement of the resting potential, or its modification by applying potentials to it from outside sources, is made difficult by effects which occur under the electrodes when current is flowing. These " polarisation " effects can be seen clearly if two metallic conductors or electrodes are immersed in water and a small potential is applied to them. The initial current flowing will fall off rapidly until it reaches a steady value. If a switch is arranged so as to disconnect the electrodes from the potential source and to connect them immediately to a galvanometer, it is apparent that there is a " back E.M.F.," which has opposed the flow of current, and which persists for a short time after the applied current has been interrupted. This is a " polarisation potential " due to the accumulation of products of electrolysis at the electrodes. In this case, there will be an accumulation of oxygen molecules from OH^- ions at the anode, and hydrogen molecules from H^+ ions at the cathode. A salt solution in the same conditions will have, in addition, hydrochloric acid at the anode and sodium hydroxide at the cathode, owing to the interaction of the Na^+ and Cl^- ions with water. These substances will tend to diffuse away from the neighbourhood of the electrodes. The rate at which polarisation occurs can be decreased by limiting the current flowing, or by increasing the area of the electrodes. These polarisation effects are very obvious in electrical burns. If a direct current is passed through the body, the burnt area at the cathode can be shown to be alkaline, that at the anode to be acid.

This confusing effect can be avoided by using non-polarisable electrodes (Fig. X. 3). The electrode is a metal in contact with a solution of one of its own salts, for example, silver coated with silver chloride, or mercury in contact with calomel. When a current passes between these electrodes in a common salt solution, chloride ions combine with the metal at the anode and form more silver chloride. As this is very insoluble, the surrounding fluid is already saturated with it, and its concentration is unchanged. At the cathode, sodium ions react with the silver chloride giving metallic silver and sodium chloride. As long as the film of silver chloride persists, no polarisation occurs. The passage of a small constant current between two such non-polarisable electrodes in a saline solution is not opposed by any back E.M.F. If, however, a nerve or muscle is substituted for the saline solution, the current falls off rapidly, and it is found that a polarisation potential has developed. The tissue therefore contains one or more membranes, at present unidentified histologically, which prevent the free flow of ions and permit their

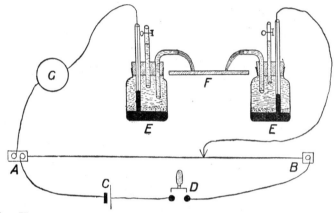

Fɪɢ. X, 3. Measurement of the Potential Difference between Two Points on a Tissue by means of **Non-Polarisable Electrodes.**

A, B, potential divider. C, battery. D, switch. E, E, non-polarisable electrodes. F, tissue. G, galvanometer.

The non-polarisable electrodes are of the calomel pattern ; they consist of bottles filled with Ringer's solution, with a layer of mercury, into which the connecting wires dip, at the bottom ; above the mercury is a layer of calomel (HgCl), which serves to saturate the Ringer's solution. The cell is really made up of a mercury electrode in contact with a solution of calomel ; the Ringer's solution serves only to increase the conductivity, and to make it more suitable for application to living tissues. (From W. M. Bayliss, " Introduction to General Physiology.")

accumulation in such a way as to set up a back E.M.F. The larger part of this polarisation potential is due to modification of the resting potential which the nerve itself maintains across the surface membrane. This ean be clearly demonstrated in isolated nerve fibres.

In a nerve trunk, the connective tissue sheath or *epineurium,* can also obstruct the passage of ions, and can give rise to a back E.M.F. Such intermediate membranes account for a small part of the polarisation potential.

The electrical behaviour of the cell membrane can be represented by the network in **Fig. X. 4.** The cell membrane is regarded as made up of a series of condensers, with fairly high resistance leaks across them. The internal and external " plates " of the condensers are connected laterally by relatively low resistance paths, and there is a source of E.M.F. in series with the transverse resistances. If a condenser is charged up, the charge spreads out to those on either side, and also tends to decay through the leaks across the membrane. These changes in the distribution of charges on the cell membrane are called *electrotonic potentials*. The time course of the decay of these electrotonic potentials has been measured, and has been found to be exponential, like the decay of the charge on a condenser.

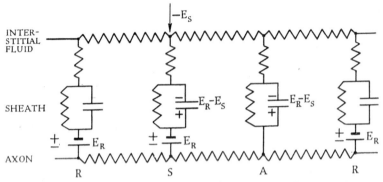

FIG. X. 4. Schematic **Circuit Diagram** of a Nerve.

The longitudinal resistances at the top and bottom of the diagram represent the resistance of the fluid surrounding the nerve fibre, and of the contents of the axon, respectively. The sheath contains capacitances, resistances and sources of electric potential (shown as batteries), whose exact arrangement is still in doubt. At R.R, the nerve is shown at rest, with a resting potential E_R. At S, a stimulating potential E_s is applied ; the resting potential is reduced, and this leads to the disappearance of the source of potential, E_R, and the nerve becomes active (A). The transverse resistances become reduced at the same time. The currents flowing between the active part and the neighbouring resting parts give rise to the electrotonic potentials, whose rate of spread, and rate of rise and fall at any point, depend on the values of the resistances and capacitances. These electrotonic potentials result in the reduction of the resting potential, exactly as at S, and thus in stimulation of successive points along the nerve.

In the circuit shown, the sheath capacitances become charged to a potential E_R–E_s, opposite in sign to E_R, on stimulation. On disappearance of E_R, this charge remains for a short time, so that the action potential may consist not merely in a disappearance of the resting potential, but in the appearance of a potential of the opposite sign (compare Fig. X. 10).

If each section of the diagram represents 1 square centimetre of nerve sheath, the value of the capacitance is about 1 μF, and of the total transverse resistance is about 1,000 ohms. (After Rushton, and Hodgkin and Huxley.)

This electrical representation is incomplete, since recent evidence has suggested that the cell membrane can also act as a rectifier, that is to say, its resistance is much greater to currents passing in one direction than in the other. With an applied current, the transverse resistance of the membrane decreases at the cathode, and increases at the anode, so that the current density at the cathode becomes much greater than at the anode.

The Excitation of Nerve

In the intact animal, nerve cells are excited either by more or less specialised endings, such as tactile or Pacinian corpuscles, or by other nerve cells. The mechanism of natural excitation is still obscure, but much has been learnt about the process of excitation by using artificial stimuli, which must now be considered. A nerve fibre can be excited anywhere in its course by chemical, thermal, mechanical, or electrical stimuli. The application of crystals of salt, warming or pinching, all excite the nerve fibres, but at the same time often produce irreversible damage. Very light mechanical stimulation, as, for example, by falling droplets of mercury, can be used without causing much injury. Elec-

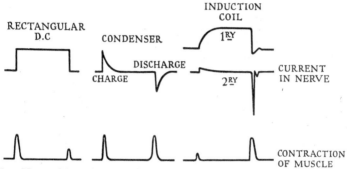

Fig. X. 5. Diagram showing the types of current change produced by various types of stimulating circuit, and the responses produced in a muscle. The rectangular direct current results in a contraction at the make of the current, and another, smaller, contraction at the break ; so long as a steady current is flowing, the muscle remains at rest. The duration of the current produced by the charge and discharge of a condenser depends upon the capacity of the condenser and the resistance through which it is charged and discharged ; no current flows after the condenser has become fully charged or discharged. In the secondary of the induction coil, there is a small current of relatively long duration at the make of the primary current, and a very much larger and very much shorter current at the break of the primary current ; the latter is more effective in stimulating nerves and muscles than the former.

trical stimulation is, however, the method of choice, since it can be continued for hours without causing any deterioration of the nerve, and can be easily controlled in strength and duration. The nerve responds to all these stimuli in the same way, by setting up an impulse of constant size, shape and duration. Most stimuli evoke a single nervous impulse, while some, especially chemical stimuli, give rise to a series of impulses in each excited fibre. In every case, however, the unitary response, the nerve impulse, is the same in all respects (p. 372).

The effectiveness of an electrical stimulus depends on strength, duration and rate of rise. In order to excite, the current must rise at more than a certain critical rate. If a current rises more slowly than at this critical rate, it will fail to excite even if it reaches eventually a strength well above that necessary with steeply rising currents. A nerve accommodates itself to the passage of a current, and with slowly rising currents, the nerve is accommodating itself to the current so fast that excitation never occurs.

For this reason, all the kinds of electrical stimuli in common use rise sharply to their maximal values. These are the induction coil shock (faradic stimulus), constant current (galvanic stimulus), and condenser discharge. The classical way of obtaining a short-lasting pulse with simple apparatus is by means of the induction coil. In it, a large current is made to flow through a primary coil of few turns. This can be surrounded by a secondary coil with about twenty times as many turns. Current only flows through the secondary coil when the current in the primary coil is changing, namely at " make " and " break " of the primary current. Owing to the self-inductance of the primary coil, the current in it grows slowly at " make," and drops sharply and is

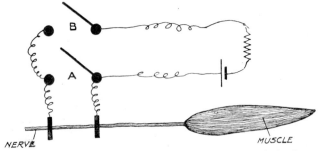

NERVE   MUSCLE

FIG. X. 6.   Diagram of the **Circuit** for producing **Rectangular Current Pulses.**

A and B are two knock-down keys, which are opened successively by a rapidly moving arm (or bullet). When both A and B are closed, current passes round the circuit, but is prevented from reaching the nerve by the short-circuit key, A. As soon as A is opened, current passes through the nerve ; it ceases when the battery circuit is broken by opening the in-circuit key, B.

momentarily reversed at " break." As the current in the secondary coil varies with the rate of change of current in the primary coil, there is a pulse at " make " followed by a pulse at " break," which is shorter, in the opposite direction, and the peak voltage of which is 2–5 times larger (Fig. X. 5). Usually the " make " shock is unwanted, and is eliminated by suitable switches. The shock can be varied in strength by changing the current in the primary circuit, or by altering the distance, and, therefore, the magnetic coupling, between the coils. With a nerve in the secondary circuit, the duration of the break shock is about 1 milli-second in a coreless coil, and 3 milli-seconds in a coil with an iron core. The maximum E.M.F. at the peak of the " break " shock is about 50 volts. If repetitive stimuli are wanted, a magnetic break and make like that of the electric bell can be included in the primary circuit.

With a stimulus of constant duration it is possible to show that tissues have a *threshold* for stimulation. With stimuli of insufficient

strength to reach threshold, no response occurs at all. When the
threshold strength is reached, a single response occurs. In excitable
systems which behave as a single unit, for example, the heart, a single
nerve fibre or muscle fibre, the response of the tissue cannot be
increased by increasing the strength of the stimulus above threshold.
The response of the tissue is, in fact, " all or none." Any change in
excitability of a nerve will, however, result in a change in its threshold.
Changes in the threshold of a nerve can be measured by finding the
strength of a stimulus needed to excite, and expressing it as a percentage
of the strength of the normal threshold stimulus.

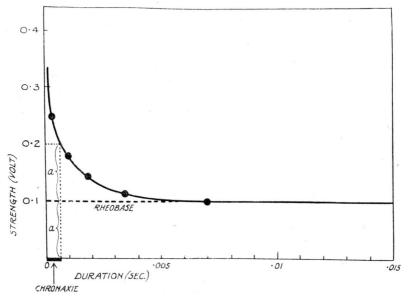

Fig. X, 7. **Strength-Duration Curve** of the Sciatic Nerve of the Toad at a
temperature of 10°.

Note that the **chronaxie** is derived by drawing a horizontal line at a
height representing twice the **rheobase** voltage (a), and determining the
distance (time) between its intersection with the strength-duration curve
and the vertical axis. (From data by Keith Lucas.)

In a nerve trunk, which is, of course, made up of many nerve fibres,
the size of the response increases as the strength of the stimulus is
increased, up to a point when all the fibres are excited. The strength
of the stimulus is then said to be maximal. This is due to the fact that
the thresholds, and to some extent the accessibility, of the different
fibres in the nerve trunk vary, and as the strength of the stimulus is
increased, more and more fibres respond.

Much detailed information about excitation and the steps which
lead up to it has been obtained by using short lasting, unidirectional
square topped currents. Such currents can be generated in the circuit
of Fig. X. 6 by opening two break keys in quick succession. Keith Lucas

designed convenient devices in which the keys were set at varying distances apart and were opened by a heavy pendulum or spring arm moving at high speed. The duration of these pulses greatly affects the strength needed to excite. With very short pulses, a high voltage is required, and as the voltage applied is reduced, it is only possible to excite by allowing it to act for a longer period. Below a certain strength, called the *rheobase*, no shock will excite, however long it is allowed to continue. A shock which is just rheobasic always excites after a finite interval, which is called the *utilisation time*.

When the least intensity of a stimulus able to excite is plotted against its duration, the resulting **strength-duration curve** has the same general shape for all excitable tissues (Fig. **X. 7**), although the scales of time and intensity values vary enormously. It is found by experiment that a constant value for the time relations of excitation of any tissue can be obtained by measuring the least duration needed for excitation by a current which is twice rheobasic strength. This value was called the *excitation time* by Keith Lucas, and if measured under certain defined conditions was named *Chronaxie* by Lapicque. The accurate measurement of rheobase is difficult, as it varies spontaneously and changes slightly even while the testing current is flowing. Changes in the interelectrode resistance, for example, have much less effect on measurements of the excitation time, which seems to be a fundamental property of excitable tissues.

Nerves can be stimulated by means of condenser discharges. The strength of the shock depends on the voltage to which the condenser has been charged, and this is very easy to measure. Its duration depends on the capacity of the condenser and the resistance through which it discharges. If the resistance is kept constant, the duration of discharge varies only with the capacity of the condenser. The time constant, t, of the discharge of a condenser is the time taken for the P.D. across it to fall to $1/e$ $(1/2.9)$ of its initial value. In any condenser stimulating circuit the time constant can easily be calculated since

$$t = RC,$$

where t is in seconds, R resistance in ohms and C capacity in farads. A time constant of 0·1 msecs., suitable for the stimulation of large nerve fibres can be obtained by discharging a 1·0μ F. condenser through a resistance of 100 ohms. Voltage-capacity curves for excitation with condensers are similar in shape to the strength-duration curves for direct current pulse.

Most of the experimental data can be accounted for if one makes the assumption that excitation occurs when the charge on the condenser elements of Fig. X. 4 has been reduced to a critical value. If one ignores the actual sign of this potential, it may be referred to as the " local potential," and excitation may be said to occur when it *rises* to a critical value. The changes which occur during excitation by direct current pulses fall into three ranges according to the length of the pulse. In the first, the duration of the pulse is exceedingly short, being less than 5 microseconds. For these pulses the quantity of electricity needed to excite, is constant, and is independent of the shape of the pulse. This would mean that the local potential rises so rapidly that it reaches its critical value before there is time for any appreciable fraction of the current to leak away through the parallel leak resistances. For stimuli which last from 5 microsecs. to about 1 milli-sec., the building up of the local potential is being opposed by its tendency to leak through the membrane. On the classical theory, the fact that a pulse of certain duration is just strong enough to excite means that at the moment of excitation, the rate of increase of the local potential is just greater than its rate of decay. Over this range of duration of the current pulse, therefore, the empirical constant, excitation-time, should provide a measurement of the spontaneous rate of decay of the local potential. In the third range of current durations, greater than one milli-second, the critical level of local potential needed for excitation, *i.e.*, the threshold changes as the current continues to flow. The physical basis of this

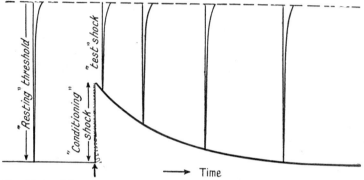

Fig. X, 8. Diagram illustrating the transient state of increased excitability in the neighbourhood of the cathode, left by a brief " conditioning " shock, itself just below the threshold for excitation. The required size of the " test " shock is shown at four different time intervals. The dotted curve shows the time relations of the action (spike) potential. (From Katz " Electric Excitation of Nerve.")

change is not understood. It occurs to a slight extent with rheobasic currents, and is of great importance with long lasting sub-threshold currents, and with slowly rising currents.

These changes in the local potential are accompanied by changes in excitability. If, in order to avoid the disturbing effects of setting up a nerve impulse, a short shock of 95 per cent. of threshold strength is applied to a nerve, the excitability of the nerve is raised for about 1 msec. This can be detected by applying a second shock of the same strength through the same electrodes. This was discovered by Keith Lucas, and called the *local excitatory state* of nerve. Its maximal duration was called the *summation interval*. If they are applied within this interval, two shocks, neither of which is capable of setting up an impulse alone, will succeed in exciting the nerve. By varying the strength of the testing shock, it is possible to plot the curve of the rate of decay of excitability after the first shock.

This technique, coupled with the recording of the local potential changes under the stimulating electrodes has recently demonstrated that the local excitatory state consists of two processes. The first, a physical charging or discharging of the condenser units of Fig. X. 4 should be

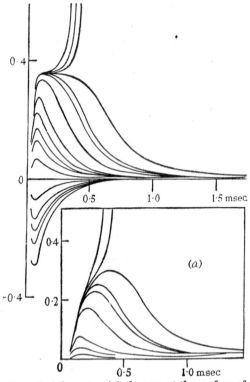

Fig. X, 9.   Record of the potential changes at the surface of an isolated nerve fibre of the crab *Carcinus mœnas*, under the stimulating electrode. Positive potentials indicate that the stimulating electrode was cathodal to the indifferent electrode.   The ordinate scale gives the value of the potential recorded as a fraction of that of the propagated spike.   The successive curves were obtained by using different strengths of stimulating shock, as follows : Uppermost 6 curves—1·0 times threshold (cathodal), only the top 3 giving rise to propagated spikes, owing to slight variations in the actual threshold of the fibre ; then, in order, 0·96, 0·85, 0·71, 0·57, 0·43, 0·21, times threshold, all cathodal.   The stimulating electrode was then made anodal, and the curves below the axis of abscissæ were obtained with the following strengths of stimulus : − 0·21, − 0·43, − 0·57, − 0·71, − 1·00, times threshold.
   In the inset (*a*), the above anodal local potentials have been subtracted from the cathodal local potentials obtained with the corresponding strength of stimulating shock.   The physical response is the same for cathodal and anodal shocks, and the difference between the recorded curves thus gives the physiological, or **local response.** The strengths of shock for the curves shown are : 1·0 (upper 5 curves, 2 giving propagated spikes), 0·96, 0·85, 0·71, 0·57, times threshold. (Hodgkin.)

symmetrical but of opposite sign at the cathode and the anode.   This was found to be true for shocks of less than 50 per cent. threshold strength, but for stronger shocks, the potential changes at the cathode are unduly prolonged. At first, this *local response* dies out a few milli-metres from the stimulating electrode, but as the shocks reach thres-hold it passes through an inflection and suddenly grows up into a full sized action potential (see **Fig. X. 9**). Exactly comparable changes in excitability occur. This local response, sometimes called the *physio-logical response* to distinguish it from the earlier *physical response*, is simply a new born impulse which has yet to grow up to a size which is capable of propagation. This local response leaves behind a local refractory period and is believed to resemble a full grown impulse in every way except in occupying a very much smaller length of nerve. It has been found that there is a critical length of nerve which must be excited for propagation of the impulse to occur. If the shock applied is only strong enough to excite less than this critical length, a local response is set up which spreads out for a few millimetres, and then dies out.

In a series of excitable tissues, the excitation time and the summation interval vary together, since they both depend on the rate of decay of excitation. The refractory period and the duration of the active phase also vary with the excitation time. There is, however, no relation between excitation time and conduction rate, and other time constants of a tissue, including that of the process called accommodation may vary independently of it.

The process of accommodation is the slow change in threshold which occurs during the passage of current. It may be measured by stimulating the nerve with slowly rising currents, or by determining the strength-duration curve for break excitation. At the rate of rise of current which is just able to stimulate, accommodation in the nerve is just unable to keep pace with the increasing current. With sub-threshold currents, the electrotonic potential changes (p. 360), are, at first, accom-panied by an increase in excitability at the cathode and a decrease at the anode. These excitability changes were called " physiological electrotonus " by Pflüger. They do not run parallel to the electrotonic potentials, since although the electrotonic potential changes remain constant, as the current continues to flow, the nerve begins to accommo-date itself to the presence of the current and the excitability slowly returns toward normal. When the current is broken, the electrotonic potentials decay in a few milliseconds, but the accommodative changes in excitability which took longer to appear, take longer to disappear. Consequently, for an appreciable interval, the nerve is less excitable than usual at the cathode, and more excitable at the anode. These states are called post-cathodal depression and post-anodal enhancement respectively.

With stronger currents, the increase in excitability at the cathode during the flow of current may reach the threshold at which an impulse is set up. At the anode, after the current has ceased to flow, the post-anodal enhancement may also be great enough to excite the nerve. In this way, excitation occurs at the cathode at make and at the anode at break (**Pflüger's Law**). With very strong currents, the decrease in excitability which occurs at the anode while the current is flowing, may be able to block the passage of a nerve impulse completely. After the current has been broken, the post-cathodal depression may again prevent the conduction of an impulse. In this way, with an " ascending" current, the excitation which occurs at the make is blocked at the anode, and with a " descending" current, the excitation which occurs at the anode at break, fails to pass the cathode. The stronger the current used, the more rapidly the nerve accommodates itself, and the shorter the time during which it need flow for the accommodative rise in excitability to reach threshold. The strength-duration curve for break excitation will, therefore, measure the rate at which the nerve accommodates itself to a constant current.

This time constant of accommodation, is usually about 50 times as long as the excitation time, and can vary independently of it. When a nerve is treated with solutions containing high calcium ion concentrations, the time constant of accommodation decreases, and the nerve becomes less excitable. In corresponding clinical conditions in man, muscle tone is low, and there is general lethargy. When the concentration of ionised calcium is diminished, the time constant of accommodation is raised, and the make of a constant current may give rise to a number of impulses instead of only one. With the further decrease in the ionised calcium concentration, the nerve becomes spontaneously excitable. This is the basis of the hyperexcitability of nerve and muscle seen in the tetany of overbreathing and in parathyroid deficiency.

The Nerve Impulse

The contraction of the frog's muscle is sufficient indicator of the arrival of a nerve impulse to provide a great deal of information about the behaviour of the impulses in motor nerve fibres. Their velocity can be measured by stimulating a frog's sciatic nerve, first near its muscle, and then as far away as possible. In the second case, the increased latent period before the beginning of the muscle twitch is due to the time required for conduction between the two points of stimulation. In the frog, these fibres conduct at 29 metres per second, and the corresponding mammalian fibres at body temperature conduct at about 100 metres per second. This conduction rate, though possibly " as quick as thought," is far below that of electricity, light, and sound in air, but is much greater than the rate of diffusion of particles under any conditions possible in the body. Possible analogies are the chemical wave transmission that occurs in detonator fuses, or the surface wave of Lillie's " Iron Wire " model.

This is a model which shows many of the phenomena found in nerve. When an iron wire is placed in 70 per cent. nitric acid, it rapidly becomes *passive*, *i.e.*, a coherent film is formed of an iron oxide which is resistant to acid. The film is electro-positive to the metal. If the film is removed at any point, the local currents between film and bare metal destroy the edge of the film. As this process continues the area of activation spreads down the wire. After a short period during which the metal is exposed to attack by the acid, the film is rebuilt by anodal oxidation. In this way, a wave of activity arises, which travels along the wire at rates varying from a few centimetres to a few metres per second.

The Electrical Changes during the Passage of the Nerve Impulse. As we have seen, when an impulse travels along a nerve fibre there is always an accompanying change in electrical potential, which is of very short duration (Fig. X. 10).

The measurement of small but steady potentials, such as the resting potential, can be made with a potentiometer and a sensitive galvanometer,

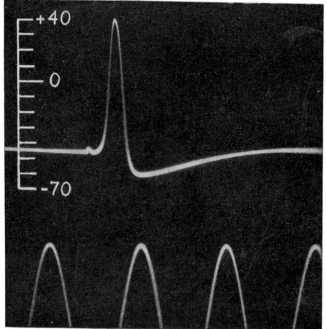

Fig. X. 10.   **Resting and Action Potentials** from single fibre of the squid *Loligo forbesi*, recorded between inside and outside of the axon. The vertical scale indicates the potential of the internal electrode in millivolts, the sea water outside being taken as zero potential.   The time marker indicates 500 cyc./sec.   (Hodgkin and Huxley.)

as indicated in Fig. X. 3.   The measurement of small potentials of very short duration is rather more difficult.   For this work, even the string galvanometer moves too slowly and has too little sensitivity.   Magnetic or cathode ray oscillographs have very little inertia, but are quite insensitive, and the potential change picked up must therefore be greatly amplified.   Owing to the shunting effect of inactive fibres, the potential actually picked up may be only 1/1000th of that at the surface of a single active fibre.   A potential of 10–20 microvolts may have to be amplified to as many volts.

This **action potential** is seen in its simplest form when two electrodes, one on intact nerve and the other on its crushed end, are connected to a recording system.   There will be a resting potential of about 5–10 mV. between such electrodes as long as the nerve is at rest (p. 357).   When an impulse passes under the electrode on living nerve, the resting potential is momentarily reduced. Most amplifiers cannot deal with a steady input potential, so that the resting potential is not recorded, and the action potential of the impulse appears as a short lasting negative *spike*, followed by negative and by positive after-potentials. These after-potentials are usually less than 5 per cent. of the spike in height, but last 50–100 times as long. (*cf.* Table **X. 1**).

Little is known as to the significance of these after-potentials. Their appearance is variable in different types of fibre and in different conditions. The negative after-potential is increased after a short period of tetanisation of the nerve, and both after-potentials appear to be associated with the metabolic processes of recovery.

If both electrodes are on intact nerve, action potentials of opposite sign are set up as the impulse passes under first one electrode and then the other. Since an impulse occupies about 4 cm. of nerve at a time, there will be some interference between the two halves of the resulting double (diphasic) action potential, unless the electrodes are further apart than this.

Isolated single nerve fibres can be prepared from invertebrate and frog nerves, and with difficulty from mammalian nerves. In such preparations, the duration and amplitude of the spike are constant over a wide range of conditions. In particular, the shape of the spike does not change as it is conducted away from its point of origin. If a whole nerve trunk is used, the action potential recorded near the stimulating electrodes looks simple, but as one leads from points on the nerve further and further away, the duration of the spike increases and a number of crests begin to appear (Fig. **X. 11**). The intervals between these crests depend on the distance the impulse has travelled. Each crest is, in fact, due to the presence of a group of nerve fibres which all have approximately the same conduction rate; but different groups of fibres have different rates of conduction. The three main elevations

TABLE **X. 1.**

Some Properties of Three Groups of Mammalian Nerve Fibres after Grundfest

Group	A	B	C
Diameters of fibres, microns .	20 to 1	3	unmyelinated
Conduction velocity, metres per second	100 to 5	14 to 3	2
Spike duration, milli-seconds .	0·4 to 0·5	1·2	2·0
Negative after-potential—			
Size, per cent., of spike .	3 to 5	None	3 to 5
Duration, milli-seconds .	12 to 20	—	50 to 80
Positive after-potential—			
Size, per cent. of spike .	0·2	1·5 to 4	1·5
Duration, milli-seconds .	40 to 60	100 to 300	300 to 1000
Absolute refractory period, milli-seconds	$\begin{cases} \alpha\ 0\cdot4 \text{ to } 1\cdot0 \\ \delta\ 0\cdot6 \text{ to } 1\cdot0 \end{cases}$	1·2	2·0

have been labelled **A**, **B**, and **C**. The correlation of these spikes with groups of fibres of different diameter has been achieved by comparing the elevations with maps of the number of fibres of different diameter at the same point on the nerve. By the examination of different nerves, it is possible to associate particular elevations with the presence of particular groups of fibres. The **A** group consists of large myelinated fibres which conduct at rates varying from 120–10 metres per second; the **B** group, found only in the autonomic system consists of small myelinated fibres which conduct at 15–7 metres per second, and the **C** group,

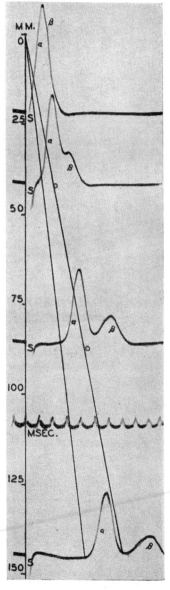

Fig. X, 11. Action potentials recorded from the sciatic nerve of the frog, showing the existence of fibres with different rates of conduction.

The records have been mounted, in each case, at a distance from the zero ordinate (at the top) proportional to the distance between the stimulating electrodes and the leading-off electrodes, and with the stimulus escape (S) on the axis of ordinates. It will be seen that the impulses in the β-fibres progressively lag behind those in the α-fibres (both of the A group). The inclined straight lines drawn from the zero ordinate through the start of the lowermost action potential record, show that the velocity of conduction is constant. (From Erlanger and Gasser, "Electrical Signs of Nervous Activity.")

made up of unmyelinated fibres, of 1–2 μ diameter, conducts at 2–0·5 metres per second. The conduction rate in nerve fibres of the same type is, in fact, proportional to their diameter. The autonomic post-ganglionic trunks are almost entirely composed of C fibres. Large numbers of C fibres are also found in the dorsal spinal roots. Some at least of these afferent fibres convey impulses concerned with pain. The B fibres form the bulk of pre-ganglionic trunks, and a few exist in post-ganglionic nerves. The A fibres include all afferent and efferent connections with striated muscle, and the fibres responsible for the sensations of heat, cold, touch and "first pain." In some species, they can be divided into α, β, γ, and δ subgroups in order of decreasing fibre diameter.

The All-or-None Law

When an impulse is conducted along a nerve, it might either start with a certain amount of energy which is progressively lost *en route,* or it may depend on the energy contributed by each segment in turn.   The first case would correspond to a rifle bullet, the second to the burning of a fuse or a train of gunpowder.   It is easy to decide between these possibilities if conduction in a short tract of nerve be impaired by its immersion in some drug, such as alcohol vapour, and an impulse made to pass through this region.   The impulse will be smaller than usual when it emerges into normal nerve if it has lost part of its initial energy

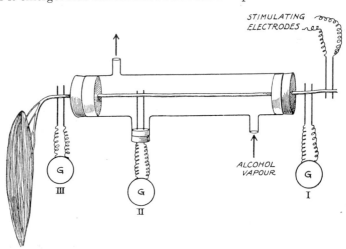

FIG. X. 12. **Apparatus for Demonstrating the All-or-None Relation** between the Stimulus and the Response in a Nerve.

Alcohol is passed through the chamber, and narcotises the nerve. Stimuli are applied to the proximal end outside the chamber, and the action potentials are recorded by the galvanometers G, G, G (I) before the impulse has reached the narcotised part, (II) in the narcotised part, and (III) beyond the narcotised part. However much reduced the action potential may be in the narcotised portion, so long as it gets through at all, it is of the full normal size beyond.

in the depressed region, but it will regain its normal size if it depends on the energy contributed by each segment.   This can be demonstrated by arranging a long nerve trunk so that the middle portion only passes through the chamber containing alcohol vapour.   The action potentials corresponding to an impulse in the nerve are recorded (1) before it reaches the chamber (2) while traversing the narcotised region, and (3) after emerging from the chamber into normal nerve (Fig. X. 12).

The degree of narcotisation of the middle zone depends on the concentration of the vapour and the duration of its action, and can, therefore, be controlled.   In these conditions, the action potentials in the narcotised region progressively diminish with the increasing depth of narcosis, while in the first and third portions where the nerve is unaffected, they remain unchanged. If the narcosis is pushed to the point at which the action potential in the affected regions just disappears, conduction fails, and no action potential is detected in the final region of normal nerve, nor will a muscle attached beyond this region show any response. But, however much reduced it may be in the narcotised zone, short of extinction, the impulse recovers its full size on reaching normal nerve. It may therefore, be likened to the burning of a fuse which has a damp patch in the middle. If the flame passes the damp patch, it will return to its normal temperature and rate of spread when it reaches the dry fuse beyond. Thus, the magnitude of the nervous impulse, like the magnitude of contraction of skeletal and cardiac muscle, bears an all or none relation to the intensity of stimulation. If the condition of the tissue at the particular moment changes, the size of the response can change, although it is still independent of the size of the stimulus. Only the propagated nerve impulses show All or None behaviour. Non-propagated local responses vary in size with the strength of the stimulus, and their conduction rate varies with their size.

The Changes in Excitability after a Nerve Impulse

For a short time after an impulse has been set up, it is impossible to excite the nerve again, however strong the impulse be made. This, the *absolute refractory period*, corresponds roughly to the duration of the spike, *i.e.*, 0·4–0·5 m.sec. in A fibres. After this, a second impulse can be set up, but at this stage of recovery the stimulus must be stronger than usual. When the excitability of the nerve has risen to normal, the *relative refractory period* is over. It is 7–10 times as long as the absolute refractory period, and during it, the conduction rate is greatly reduced. Immediately after the spike potential, *i.e.*, during the negative after-potential, the excitability of the nerve rapidly increases, and in some circumstances may become supernormal; the conduction rate is then also slightly increased. The period of reduced excitability and conduction rate coincides in time with the positive after-potential. The rapid recovery of excitability only occurs in a rested nerve well supplied with oxygen. If a nerve is stimulated at increasing rates, the recovery of excitability is considerably delayed (Fig. X. 13).

If a nerve is stimulated at a rate of 300 per second or more, each impulse will be set up during the relative refractory phase of its predecessor, since in mammalian A fibres the relative refractory period lasts about 3 m.secs. The impulses are then smaller than usual, and as they are conducted along the nerve, they lag behind one another. At higher rates of stimulation, the rate of response may suddenly drop to half, as each fibre suddenly ceases to respond to each alternate stimulus. A similar phenomenon occurs in heart muscle. The absolute refractory period in the largest mammalian fibres sets an upper limit of 2,000 impulses per second, but no fibre can conduct more than a few impulses at such a frequency.

At rates of 50–100 per second, and in the presence of an adequate

supply of oxygen, an isolated nerve can conduct impulses for many
hours. This is the basis of classical experiments on the so-called
" unfatiguability of nerve." The only detectable sign of fatigue under
such conditions is that the excitability of the fibre is slightly diminished
for some minutes after the end of excitation. When, however, a nerve
is deprived of oxygen, it ultimately fails to conduct. At an early
stage, the rate of recovery of excitability after the passage of an impulse
is decreased, and the nerve can no longer conduct a train of impulses,
though it can still respond after a rest to a single stimulus. A fibres
cease to conduct after 30–40 minutes, B fibres show changes after
2–3 minutes, but C fibres can tolerate about 2 hours of complete asphyxia
before they fail. Cocaine, on the other hand, blocks C fibres first, and

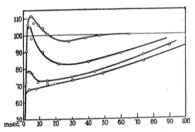

FIG. X. 13.   **Recovery of Excitability** in Saphenous Nerve of a Cat, *in situ.*
The abscissæ give the time interval between conditioning and testing
shocks ; the ordinates give the threshold strength of the testing shock,
as per cent. of the threshold of the resting nerve. The conditioning
stimulus was as follows : Uppermost curve—single shock ; next lower
curve—3 shocks at 90 per sec. ; third curve—7 shocks at 250 per sec. ;
lowermost curve—23 shocks at 250 per sec.   (Gasser and Grundfest.—
From Erlanger and Gasser "Electrical Signs of Nervous Activity.")

the largest myelinated fibres last.   Compression of the nerve blocks
conduction earlier in the larger myelinated nerves than in the smaller
myelinated nerves, and last of all in the unmyelinated fibres.

The Membrane Theory

It has been suggested earlier (p. 358) that the cell membrane may
consist of radially arranged long chain fatty acids or lecithin molecules
which act as a sieve of molecular dimensions. The observed potentia
and the estimated thickness of the membrane suggest that there is a
potential gradient of 50,000 volts per cm. across the membranes. I
this potential is diminished, the packing of the radial molecules migh
well change, so altering the membrane permeability.

When an impulse passes, there is certainly a drop in electrica
resistance across the membrane. This resistance has been measure
directly and has been found to fall to $\frac{1}{40}$th of its resting value. Th
structure of the membrane is not greatly affected, but apparentl
" pores " appear in it.

Excitation probably occurs whenever the charge on the cell mem
brane has been reduced to a critical level. At this instant, the mem

brane becomes "permeable," and the remaining charge is abolished through the neutralisation of positive and negative ions which pass through the membrane. Currents now flow towards this permeable region from the edges of the active area outside the membrane, and away from it inside the cell. This reduces the charge on adjacent parts of the cell membrane, and if the area excited is large enough, the charge at adjacent edges will fall below the critical level and the cell membrane there, too, will become permeable. This process continues, and the wave of excitation spreads out in both directions from the excited point. After a certain period of activity, the cell rebuilds the charge on its surface, and restores its impermeability by methods of which we know little.

New and strong support for this theory has been forthcoming recently. If the nerve impulse is blocked at a point on a fibre, it is possible to make it "jump the block" by making a direct electrical connection between points on each side of the block. A local current set up by the impulse passes round the external connection and activates the normal fibre beyond. The resistance of the path outside the nerve through which the local currents must run, can be increased by lifting the nerve out of a saline bath into the air, when it will be covered only by a thin film of saline. The rate at which an active point can depolarise an adjacent point is reduced, as the external longitudinal resistance has increased, and the conduction rate of the impulse is found to be approximately halved. If, on the other hand, the nerve be laid on a set of silver plates connected together externally, the external resistance is decreased, and the conduction rate rises.

Direct evidence of the existence of local currents which travel ahead of the impulse and begin the process of excitation, was found by stopping the impulse at a narrow cold block on the nerve. Although the impulse itself was unable to pass, the local currents spread out beyond the block and appeared as a small potential only $\frac{1}{5}$ of the size of a normal action potential, and died out after conduction over a few millimetres. This small potential was able to increase the excitability of the nerve to 95 per cent. of threshold, and was, in fact, due to a local response set up below the block.

It is possible to regard the excitation and conduction of the nervous impulse as a purely electrical phenomenon. Recently, however, it has been suggested that the liberation of active chemical substances by the impulse plays an important part in transmission. Nerve fibres have been found to possess preformed acetyl choline, and high concentrations of the enzyme cholinesterase, limited to the sheath. The action potential can be reversibly abolished by soaking the nerve in eserine, which has been shown to penetrate the nerve sheath and to inactivate the cholinesterase. It is alleged that this results in the persistence of acetyl choline, which would otherwise be hydrolysed, and that this leads to the persistent depolarisation of the cell membrane. It has, therefore, been suggested that the liberation of acetyl choline plays an essential part in the production of the nerve action potential. There are, however, a number of nerve fibres in which no acetyl choline has yet been discovered, and there is, as yet, no direct evidence for the suggested persistent depolarisation by locally formed acetyl choline. It is clear from the previous arguments that the electrical excitation of nerve depends on the depolarisation of a system which behaves essentially like a leaky condenser, and that the excitation of adjacent points on the nerve is also a purely electrical process. It is however, possible, after the surface membrane has reached its point of critical depolarisation, that acetyl choline may be liberated, that it may then contribute to the amplitude of the action potential produced, and may even be concerned in the production of an action potential which exceeds the resting potential in height, and therefore, reverses the charge on the cell membrane.

Although there is sufficient evidence to provide a fairly coherent account of the behaviour of unmyelinated nerve fibres, there are still gaps in our knowledge of conduction in myelinated fibres. The myelin sheath consists of radially arranged lecithin molecules, separated by concentric flat layers of protein, and has a very high resistance to currents flowing radially. The nodes of Ranvier are devoid of myelin, and provide points at which the nerve can be most easily excited by applied currents. They may also play an important part in the conduction of the impulse, since there is some evidence that the local circuits can sometimes flow outside the myelin sheath so that excitation jumps from one node to the next. It is not yet established that this is the normal mode of spread of the impulse. It is remarkable that myelinated fibres in the dorsal spino-cerebellar tracts, which do not possess nodes, have conduction rates of about 150 metres per second, which is about 50 per cent. faster than fibres of corresponding diameter in the peripheral nervous system.

Energy Requirements.

It is at once evident from the experiment described in support of the "all-or-none" intensity relations of the impulse, that the energy associated with the impulse is in no way derived from the energy of the stimulus, but rather that as each element of the fibre is traversed, it contributes its full quota of energy. A definite production of heat is associated with the passage of an impulse along a nerve. The heat production can be divided into (1) an "initial" evolution of heat, corresponding in time with the duration of the impulse, *i.e.*, a few thousandths of a second in frog's nerve; and (2) a "delayed" evolution of heat which may last over thirty minutes at room temperature.

In muscle the total heat produced as a result of stimulation is about double the initial heat; in nerve the ratio of total to initial heat is much greater and more variable. Thus, for a single stimulus, the ratio is about 30; if stimulation is continued, however, the ratio falls, reaching eventually a value of about 10.

The resting nerve, like other tissues, requires the presence of oxygen for continued vitality, and a steady consumption of oxygen and output of carbon dioxide can be observed in isolated nerves, the respiratory quotient being about 0·8. The resting metabolic rate of a gram of nerve is about the same as that of a gram of muscle, but is more difficult to measure owing to the small size of the nerves. The energy derived from this source is, no doubt, largely used in maintaining the state of polarisation. Oxygen must be present if a nerve is to continue conducting impulses for long. Stimulation at the greatest frequency to which the nerve will respond results in an increase in the metabolic rate to about twice the resting value (stimulation of a muscle may increase the metabolic rate 1,000 fold) ; the metabolic rate does not fall to the resting value for some thirty minutes after the stimulation has ceased. Measurements of the oxygen consumption and carbon dioxide production agree in their time relations, therefore, with those of the heat production, and the chemical and thermal measurements agree also as to the amount of energy required for the propagation of a single impulse (10^{-6} calories per gram of nerve). There is no evidence that oxidation of carbohydrates plays any part in the increased metabolic rate, but there is an increased formation of ammonia, and a diminution in the amount of combined phosphate. The conduction of a nerve impulse is probably associated with the breakdown of adenyl pyrophosphate, and of creatine-phosphate. During recovery, the creatinephosphate is resynthesised.

Even in the absence of oxygen, nerve fibres retain their excitability and capacity for conducting impulses for a considerable time, and the heat production is unchanged so long as impulses can be propagated. Lactic acid is produced by the resting nerve, but is not rebuilt into glycogen, or even oxidised, when oxygen is readmitted ; the duration of functional survival is not diminished, moreover, by the inhibition of glycolysis by iodoacetate. Nerves, therefore, do not behave like muscles in the absence of oxygen ; and the energy necessary for functional survival is obtained, not from the breakdown of glycogen into lactic acid, but from the oxidation of the substances concerned in the recovery process by hydrogen acceptors whose nature is not yet known. When all these are completely reduced, conduction fails.

In an isolated nerve in an oxygen-free gaseous medium, conduction fails before the energy supplies are exhausted ; recovery occurs if the nerve is bathed in oxygen-free Ringer or isotonic sodium chloride solution. It is not clear exactly what mal-distribution of ions takes place, but the evidence suggests that the failure of conduction is not due to the accumulation of potassium ions in the inter-fibrillary spaces, as is the case in the reversible inexcitability of muscles.

The Excitation of Nerve Fibres in the Body

An analysis of the mechanism of nervous action has been made with artificial stimuli applied to the nerve trunk. Natural stimuli excite afferent nerves at their distal ends, which may be naked nerve endings, or may be connected to complex end organs, which respond to a specific stimulus (see Müllers Law, p. 471). The nerve fibre we have seen is sensitive to stimulation by pressure, stretch, heat and chemical substances. The end organ has a very much lower threshold for stimulation by one or other of these agents, and it in turn excites the nerve fibre.

The muscle stretch receptor shows the simplest relation between the stimulus and the discharge in the nerve. If the muscle of a nerve muscle preparation is suddenly pulled, action potentials can be detected in the nerve ; by leading off from electrodes placed at several points along the nerve, it can be shown that these electric variations are travelling away from the muscle. The actual magnitude of the response is smaller than that measured in motor nerves, because the sciatic nerve contains about 3,000 fibres, of which only a few are sensory fibres, and the rest are short-circuiting the currents due to them.

These sensory impulses in the sciatic nerve are irregular, and of

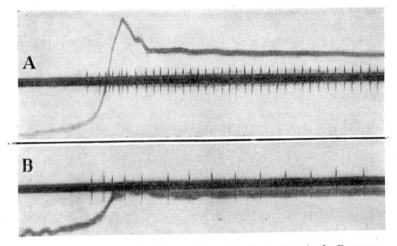

Fig. X. 14.   Action Potentials set up by a Stretch Receptor in the Peroneus longus muscle of a Cat, stretched by Different Tensions.

The nerve supplying the muscle was divided, bundle by bundle, until the impulses from only one stretch receptor were transmitted to the lead-off electrodes.

A. Muscle stretched to a final tension of 140 g.   Final frequency of impulses 66 per second.

B. Muscle stretched to a final tension of 10 g.   Final frequency of impulses 23 per second.

Action potentials shown by vertical lines on thick horizontal line. Muscle tension shown by continuous curve.

The frequency of the action potentials set up by a steady pull depends on the tension in the muscle.   (Matthews.)

different sizes.   If, however, the mixed nerve trunk in which the impulses are detected is gradually divided at a point between the muscle and the leading-off electrodes, it is possible to leave intact a bundle of fibres in which there is only one fibre connected to a muscle stretch receptor.   The impulses are now regular, and all of the same size (Fig. X. 14).   Moreover, variation of the strength of the stimulus, by varying the tension in the muscle, makes no difference to the size of the impulses—thus demonstrating the all-or-none law—but only alters their frequency (Fig X. 14).   In an intact nerve, there are many fibres connected with many different stretch receptors.   These have different sensitivities, and hence respond to a given stretch by initiating impulses at different frequencies the summed response led off from the whole nerve, therefore, is irregular, both in respect of frequency and size of impulses.

The frequency of the discharge of a muscle stretch receptor depends not only on the magnitude of the stretch, but also on the rate at which the stretch is applied. As is shown in Fig. X. 15, a sudden stretch sets up initially a rapid discharge which subsequently slows down. The same stretch applied gradually sets up a discharge which builds up gradually to the same frequency as that finally attained after the sudden stretch.

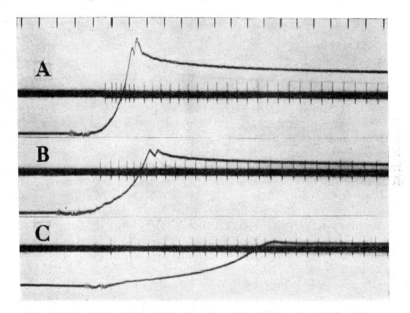

Fig. X. 15. **Action Potentials** set up by a **Stretch Receptor** in the Soleus muscle of a Cat, **stretched at Different Rates.**

The nerve supplying the muscle was divided so that impulses from only one sense organ were recorded. The muscle was then stretched at three different rates (A, B and C), until it was under a tension of 260 g., as indicated by the thinner line in each record. The initial frequency of the action potentials depends upon the rate at which the muscle is stretched, but the final value is the same in each case (31, 29 and 30 per second respectively). Time marker, 1/20 second, at the top. (Matthews.)

The rate of change of the applied stimulus, therefore, is a factor in setting up the discharge of the stretch receptors, just as it is in setting up the impulse in a nerve. The discharge from the stretch receptor, however, continues so long as the stimulus is continued, unlike that in the nerve, which only takes place at the beginning and end of the stimulus.

These experiments, therefore, reveal the response of a single muscle spindle ; it is not fair, however, to suppose that all sensory fibres necessarily transmit regular series of impulses, because several end organs are often connected with a single fibre, which therefore receives what Adrian describes as " an irregular jumble of impulses with occasional regular patches."

The importance of these sensory impulses evoked by stretching muscles can hardly be over-estimated, for, as will be shown in the next chapter, their arrival at the central nervous system is part of the " stretch reflex " upon which the tonus and co-ordination of the skeletal musculature largely depend.

The end organ must be able to deliver a very strong stimulus to the nerve fibre, since some endings, for example, the pressure receptors in teeth, can excite their fibres during their relative refractory period, when the thresholds are above normal. Usually the maximal rate of discharge in nerve fibres is considerably lower. The smooth relation between the frequency of response and the intensity of stimulation between 5 and 300 impulses per sec., is probably due to the special properties of the ending, in which excitation is built up more slowly with weaker stimuli. With higher rates of response, a stronger stimulus produces a higher rate of discharge, because each stimulus is able to excite earlier in the relative refractory period.

With a steady stimulus, the discharge from the muscle stretch receptors and lung stretch receptors is maintained at the same frequency for long periods. The majority of endings give rise to a discharge whose rate falls more or less rapidly with a constant stimulus. The receptors round hair follicles discharge only while the hair is first moved, and are unaffected by steady deformation. This property of endings has been called *adaptation*, and probably corresponds to accommodation in nerve. Such endings, therefore, respond to the rate of movement of the hair, not to the amount of its displacement. This process of adaption can be speeded up by increasing the calcium ion concentration of the fluid bathing the ending ; while if the calcium concentration is reduced, a rapidly adapting ending first becomes slowly adapting, and then begins to discharge spontaneously. This is closely parallel to the behaviour of accommodation in nerve fibres, when the calcium concentration ion is varied.

CHAPTER XI

THE SPINAL REFLEX SYSTEM

The Spinal Cord

LYING in the vertebral canal, the spinal cord looks rather like a large nerve trunk, with exceptionally numerous and regular branches. The resemblance, indeed, extends to functional activity, for both, normally, conduct nervous impulses, and both may, under experimental conditions, be excited by electrical or other stimulation. The cord includes, however, another and more complex group of activities which differentiates it from the nerve trunk, and which we shall refer to as reflex activity. This co-ordinating power of the cord is associated with the presence of the " grey matter " which occupies a roughly H-shaped area of a transverse section, and which consists largely of nerve cells, in contrast with the " white matter " which consists of nerve fibres.

Nerves, corresponding with the vertebral segments, branch off each side of the cord. Each of these mixed nerves has two roots, the one arising from the anterior (ventral) surface of the cord, and the other arising from the posterior (dorsal) surface. If the anterior roots are divided, the corresponding muscles are paralysed, whereas section of the posterior roots leads to complete loss of sensation in the affected region. Consequently it is inferred that the anterior roots contain the efferent (motor) fibres, and the posterior roots contain the afferent (sensory) fibres. The motor nerve fibres arise from cells in the anterior horns of the grey matter of the spinal cord. The afferent fibres are connected with cells in the posterior (dorsal) root ganglia which lie outside the spinal cord. The same posterior root cells send in to the spinal cord fibres which deliver the sensory messages.

The anterior horn cell and its motor fibre are referred to as the *motoneurone*. Such a nerve fibre appears generally to innervate a considerable group of muscle fibres, about one hundred on an average. The motoneurone, together with the group of muscle fibres which it supplies, is termed a *motor unit*.

Conduction Across a Synapse

If we cut the posterior roots between the posterior root ganglia and the spinal cord, we find that, following the usual rule, the parts of the fibres which have been separated from the ganglion cells degenerate. We can follow the degenerating fibres into the posterior columns and as far as the base of the anterior horns, but no degenerating fibres are found in the anterior roots. If we stimulate the posterior roots in a spinal animal, there is an outburst of impulses in the anterior roots. As we know that degeneration stops at cell boundaries, it is clear that these impulses must have crossed at least one cell boundary at a *synapse* in their passage across the cord. The features of conduction which are peculiar to the cord can be attributed partly to the properties of the synapse, and partly to the anatomical arrangement of the fibres and cells of the cord.

The Artificial Synapse. It has been said by Keith Lucas that one should aim at describing the behaviour of the central nervous system in terms of processes which are known to occur in peripheral nerve. It is, therefore, of some significance that it is possible so to arrange two nerve fibres that transmission of a nerve impulse from one to the other can be made to take place. The properties of these artificial junctions are sufficiently similar to those of synapses to justify the name *artificial synapse* (Fig. XI. 1). If two giant unmyelinated nerve fibres are placed side by side in close contact, and an impulse is set up in each of them,

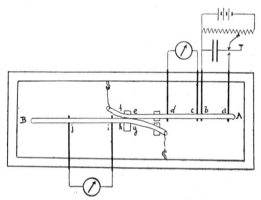

Fig. XI. 1.   Diagram of the experimental arrangement for studying the transmission of impulses from one axon to another (**Artificial Synapse**). (Arvanitaki, *J. of Neurophysiology.*)

the local circuits set up will flow through the surrounding tissue fluid and the adjacent nerve fibre, and the impulses will interfere with each other. If the nerve fibres have nearly the same conduction rate, this will result in the synchronisation of the impulses so that one remains a little ahead of the other. Each impulse produces a triphasic change in the excitability of the adjacent fibre, so that its excitability is first decreased, then increased and finally decreased again (Fig. XI. 2). These changes go parallel with the reversals of the transverse current across the cell membrane. If one fibre is made very excitable, by lowering the concentratiion of calcium ions in the solution round it, an impulse in the other fibre may excite it.

Similar effects can be obtained in myelinated fibres at the cut ends, where there is a low resistance path between axons. No appreciable interaction occurs between myelinated fibres in the intact nerve trunk. A similar spread of excitation has also been seen in nerve fibres in the central nervous system in the posterior columns of the spinal cord, where transmission from one fibre to another can occur at the point of transection of the cord.

These experiments on artificial synapses suggest two important points. First, transmission of an impulse from one fibre to another appears to be due to the effects of the local electrical circuits set up, and may occur in the absence of a specialised transmitting mechanism. Secondly, for a fibre to be excited in this way, it must be made abnormally excitable. In the central nervous system, cells which can be excited by a single afferent fibre do exist (*e.g.*, in the lateral geniculate body), but are rare. As a rule a large number of afferent impulses must reach a cell for it to be excited.

The Nerve Muscle Junction. A striated muscle fibre can, however, be excited by a single nerve impulse in its motor nerve, and the nerve–

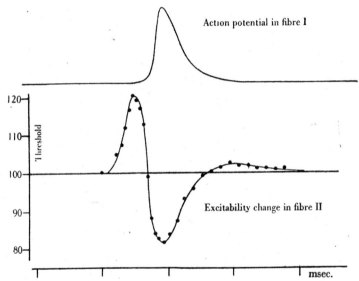

Fig. XI. 2. Excitability Changes in a Nerve Fibre (fibre II) when an impulse passes along another fibre (fibre I) in contact with it. (Katz and Schmitt.

muscle junction provides an example of the simplest transmission process in the body. The motor nerve fibre divides into several branches near its end, each branch loses its myelin sheath, pierces the sarcolemma, and ramifies in a specialised area of the muscle fibre, the end-plate or " sole." This structure has a number of peculiar properties. There is a delay of about 2 msecs. in the conduction of an impulse across it, and it is very sensitive to asphyxia, fatigue and a number of poisons. The arrival of an impulse at the nerve-muscle junction is followed by the liberation of a transmitter agent which may well be acetylcholine. It has been shown by Dale and his colleagues that acetylcholine is liberated as a result of the arrival of impulses at the nerve-muscle junction and that the close intra-arterial injection of acetylcholine leads to twitch-like contractions of a normal mammalian muscle. As a whole, the evidence that acetylcholine is the transmitter agent at the nerve-muscle junction is strong. This agent is rapidly formed, and is removed by two processes, a fast and a slow. The fast process may possibly be diffusion. The slow process is the hydrolysis of acetyl-choline by an enzyme, cholinesterase, which is present at the nerve–muscle junction in high concentration. The adjacent active membrane of the nerve-muscle junction is depolarised when the transmitter agent reaches it, and gives rise to a local potential change, called the end-plate potential. This depolarisation of the nerve-muscle junction can also be produced by very small doses of acetylcholine. When the end-plate potential reaches a height of about 30 per cent. of its maximum, a local

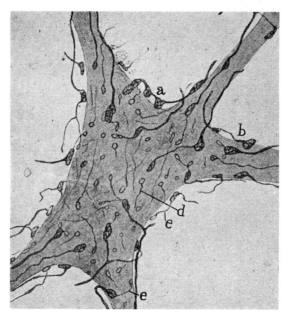

FIG. XI. 3. Bulbs and Terminal Masses round a Motor Cell of the Spinal Cord.

a, b : Strong bulbs. d, e : Fine bulbs which simulate rings. (Cajal, " Histology.")

response is set up in the muscle fibre. This rapidly grows up to its full height, in just the same way as an impulse in a nerve fibre, and is pro-pagated along the muscle fibre at 3–5 metres per sec. The process of chemical transmission will be considered more fully in Chapter XIII.

Synaptic Transmission. Unlike the nerve-muscle junction, the nerve cell receives impulses which reach it from a number of different directions. The cell body or perikaryon has a number of short processes or dendrites which increase the total available area on which afferent nerve fibres may end. The perikaryon and dendrites together may be referred to as the soma of the neurone. Most afferent nerve endings possess one or more swellings called " boutons de passage " or " boutons terminaux." These structures lie in very close relation to the perikaryon or dendrites of the cell which they excite. When a nerve fibre branches to give several boutons terminaux which all end on the one neurone, they are usually spaced well apart, separated by boutons from other fibres. A motoneurone in the spinal cord has several hundred boutons on the surface of the soma. In the cells of the autonomic ganglia it is difficult to find boutons, and many fibres end by encircling the cell body.

Autonomic Ganglia. It is difficult to study synaptic transmission in the spinal cord, as the arrangement and interconnection of its cells is exceedingly complex. The autonomic ganglia have a much simpler arrangement. In the superior cervical ganglion all the fibres of the afferent or preganglionic trunk end on ganglion cells, all of which send their axons into the postganglionic trunk. There are no *interneurones*, which in the cord connect one cell with another. As a result, the fundamental properties of synaptic transmission are easy to demonstrate.

(1) As in the nerve muscle junction, conduction through the ganglion occurs in one direction only. An impulse set up in postganglionic fibres reaches the cell body, but does not excite the preganglionic fibres.

(2) There is an interval between the arrival of an impulse at the synapse and the setting up of an impulse in the ganglion cell. This, the *synaptic delay* is about 4–5 msecs., in the case of the fibres of highest conduction rate.

(3) Conduction across the synapse is much more susceptible to poisons than is conduction along a nerve trunk. Nicotine blocks conduction in the autonomic ganglia, but the general anæsthetics, *e.g.*, the barbiturates, have little effect on the ganglia, although they interfere with conduction at some synapses in the central nervous system. Anoxia depresses the synapses of the central nervous system profoundly but has comparatively little effect on the synapses of the superior cervical ganglion.

(4) The arrival of an impulse at a ganglion cell produces a prolonged increase in the excitability of the cell. In the superior cervical ganglion, this period lasts for 100–200 msecs., and is followed by a period of reduced excitability for the next 200–300 msecs. These periods of increased and reduced excitability are accompanied by negative and positive after-potentials respectively. Analogous states to the super- and subnormal states seen in nerve fibres and described in the previous chapter, contribute towards the observed negative and positive after-potentials.

Eccles has shown that there is a junctional potential which he calls a *synaptic potential*, which behaves in much the same way as the end-plate potential. It precedes and outlasts the spike, and its later stages contribute to the negative after-potential. It seems to be due to a depolarisation of the cell bodies. When it reaches a critical size, the cells are excited and an all-or-none impulse is set up and propagated along the post-ganglionic axons. It is not yet clear whether the transmitter agent responsible for setting up this synaptic potential is a chemical substance released by the pre-ganglionic impulse, or simply the local electrical circuits to which the impulses give rise, or some combination of the two. Acetylcholine is probably ionised in solution and if it were released at the synapse, its movement would depend on the potential gradients set up by the nerve impulse.

The evidence that acetylcholine plays an important part in synaptic transmission is discussed in detail in Chapter XIII. The essential points are : that acetylcholine can be obtained by stimulating preganglionic fibres when the ganglion is perfused with Ringer's solution containing eserine : that injection of acetylcholine into the arterial blood supply to the ganglion is followed by the discharge of the ganglion cells : and that stimulation of the postganglionic trunk and stimulation of the degenerated preganglionic trunk do not cause the liberation of acetylcholine. This amounts to strong evidence that acetylcholine is liberated in close relation to preganglionic nerve endings.

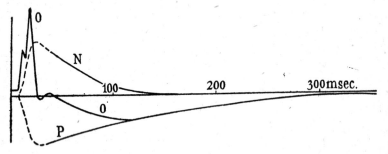

FIG. XI. 4.   **Synaptic Potentials** in the Superior Cervical Ganglion of a cat.
   The slow negative (N) and slow positive (P) waves have been drawn so as to give, when summed and combined with the action potentials of impulses along the postganglionic fibres, (initial spikes), the observed potential waves (O). (Eccles).

The excitatory effect of a preganglionic volley on a ganglion cell is sudden and short lasting. It reaches its maximum in 2 to 3 msecs., and has disappeared after 6 msecs. There is no known method by which this primary " detonator " effect can be prolonged. If the discharge of an impulse can be delayed for 4–6 msecs., by making the ganglion cell refractory, then no impulse is set up. The preganglionic volley can, however, give rise to states of facilitation which last up to 100 msecs. Unlike the " detonator " action, these delayed states of increased excitability can be increased and prolonged by eserine, and may be related to the liberation of acetylcholine. The detonator action must either be due to a different mechanism, or if it is due to the sudden release of high concentrations of acetylcholine, the rapidly acting mechanism for the removal of acetylcholine cannot be its hydrolysis by cholinesterase. It is possible that diffusion away of acetylcholine from its site of liberation could occur sufficiently rapidly to account for the fast and constant rate of disappearance of the detonator action.

In the **central nervous system,** transmission across a synapse has been studied by Lorente de No. By sinking electrodes into the posterior longitudinal bundle in the cat, and leading from the oculomotor or trochlear nerve, he obtained a preparation in which only one synapse separated the stimulated neurone from the nerve cell whose activity was observed. He found that the synaptic delay varied from 0·5– 0·9 msec., that all processes occurred about 5–10 times as fast as those of the superior cervical ganglion. The only important difference was that there was no phase of supernormality in the recovery of the excita-bility of the oculomotor cell to synaptic stimulation after the discharge of an impulse. After a single impulse, the relative refractory period was followed immediately by a short period of subnormality, but if the cell responded twice or more in 2 msecs., the period of subnormality was prolonged for 30 msecs. or more. If the effects of two afferent impulses on the motoneurone were to be summed, they had to arrive within about 0·5 msecs. of each other. Recent work on the motoneurones of the spinal cord has shown that they also have a synaptic delay of 0·5– 0·9 msecs.

We are now in a position to understand that a number of the pro-perties of the spinal cord as a whole are due to the presence of synapses in its grey matter. Thus, stimulation of the posterior roots gives rise to nerve impulses in the anterior roots, but stimulation of the central end of cut anterior roots produces no activity in the posterior roots (Law of Forward Direction). This, the phenomenon of *irreciprocal conduction* also occurs at the nerve muscle junction and at the synapses of the autonomic ganglia. There is a delay in the conduction of impulses across the cord. This is partly due to the fact that the nerve fibres in the cord are small and their conduction rate is low, and partly to synaptic delays. The spinal cord is also very sensitive to oxygen deficiency and to poisons. For example, anæmia of the lumbar cord of rabbits produced by compression of the aorta for only one minute, may result in a reversible loss of reflex activity in the hind limbs. If the anæmia is prolonged for more than about half an hour, this paralysis of the hind limbs becomes irreversible. The general anæsthetics such as ether, abolish the conduction of impulses across the spinal cord in con-centrations which leave the conduction of impulses in peripheral nerve trunks quite unaffected.

Reflex Action

When some simple action of an animal, such as a movement, or a secretion of a gland, can be traced to a particular change in its environ-ment, it may be called a "response," and the external agent which initiated it may be called the "stimulus." In physiology these terms are usually confined to events in which the energy imparted by the stimulus is small compared with the output of energy in the response, and such events belong, therefore, to the class of "trigger-reactions." If, for example, a cook unwittingly touches too hot a stove, she imme-diately withdraws from the contact. The energy involved in her move-ment is disproportionately greater than the corresponding heat trans-ferred to her skin. Moreover, the response could be confidently pre-

dicted by an observer, and he would readily interpret it as " purposeful."
The movement may involve many muscles, some of which may be
widely removed from the point of incidence of the stimulus, and yet
the distribution of muscular activity is such as to produce a co-ordinated
movement, quite unlike the result of direct stimulation of a motor nerve
or of a muscle.   Such are some of the characteristics of reflex responses.
They differ from the more local result of direct stimulation of a motor
nerve in which co-ordination is absent and the effects are more circumscribed.   They can be distinguished from other forms of behaviour by
the confidence with which a stimulus can be predicted to evoke a particular response under a narrow range of conditions, and by the fact that a

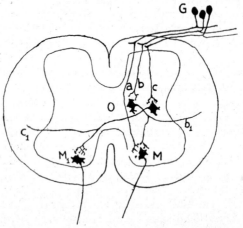

Fig. XI. 5.   The Elementary **Spinal Reflex Arcs.**

G represents the cells of the spinal ganglia : *a*, *b*, and *c* are collaterals from
the posterior columns ; *a* ends on motor cells, *M*, of the same side ;   *b* ends
on an internuncial neurone which originates a fibre, b_1 which passes into the
white matter after giving off a collateral which ends on the motor neurone
M ; *c* ends on an internuncial neurone which originates a fibre, c_1, of the
white matter on the opposite side, and a collateral which ends on the
motor neurone M_1. (Lorente de No, after Cajal, *Arch. Neurol. Psychiat.
Chicago.*)

similar response is evoked in different members of the same species.
Reflex activity in man may or may not be accompanied by conscious
sensation.
     Now it is evident that a reflex action, such as the withdrawal from a
painful stimulus, involves at least (1) a sensory receptor, (2) a sensory
nerve, (3) one or more motor nerves, and (4) one or more effector
organs such as muscles.   Reduced to its simplest anatomical terms,
a reflex requires, therefore, two nerves, each complete with its cell and
fibre, and an effector. In such a " simple reflex," the path traversed
between the site of the stimulus and that of the responding organ is
called the " reflex arc."   Most reflex arcs are, however, more complicated, and include neurones intercalated between the sensory and motor
units (Fig. XI. 5).

The interval occurring between the application of the stimulus and the beginning of the response is called the **reaction time.** As will be shown, most reflexes in vertebrates involve paths which pass through the central nervous system, the afferent nerve impinging on the cell of an intercalated neurone in the cord, and that in turn upon a motor nerve cell situated in the grey matter of, say, the spinal cord, and so influencing the motor nerve. Consequently, the time taken for the nervous impulse to pass along the lengths of the afferent and efferent nerve trunks can be measured, and by deducting these, and the latent periods of the receptor and effector from the total reflex time, the delay in the central nervous system can be deduced. This central delay is called the **reduced reflex time.**

One of the difficulties encountered in the study of reflex mechanisms is that of ensuring that a particular stimulus, only, shall be effective at any given moment. This difficulty can be minimised, and the results greatly simplified if experiments are performed on animals which have been decapitated, and which have thus been deprived of many of the higher centres of sensory reception. If the central nervous system be severed in the region of the mid-brain, the result is referred to as a *decerebrate animal,* whereas section of the cord in the cervical region produces what is termed a *spinal animal,* and complete destruction of the central nervous system is called " *pithing* " an animal.

A frog is usually decapitated by cutting with scissors between the back of the mouth and the neck. This leaves the lower jaw, by which the " *spinal frog* " may be suspended from a pin. After a short while taken in recovery from the shock and local irritation of the operation, the animal hangs limply with extended hind limbs, and remains so indefinitely unless disturbed. An injurious stimulus, such as acid applied to the skin, however, produces movements which have the characteristics of reflex responses mentioned above, *i.e.,* they are co-ordinated movements of the limbs rather than independent contractions of individual muscles ; they may be widespread and involve muscles remote from the stimulus, and the character of the responses to the same stimulus is the same every time. If the acid is applied to the foot, the hind limb is flexed ; if applied to the back, wiping movements are induced. It is evident that such reactions are in some sense " purposeful " and enable even the spinal animal to show a measure of that adaptation to the environment which is familiar in the living animal. These reflexes in the spinal frog are abolished by destroying the spinal cord, and it may be inferred, therefore, that the reflex arcs concerned pass through the cord.

We shall consider more fully below the reflexes of mammalian preparations, but it may be well to give examples of some of the reflexes which have been studied in intact animals. A frog placed on its back regularly turns itself over ; irritation of the cornea results in closing the eye ; in the breeding season stroking the chest of a male frog evokes the " clasp reflex " normally elicited by the female. In man, coughing and sneezing, the reaction of the pupil to illumination of the eye, and the

secretion of saliva when food is placed in the mouth, are familiar
instances of reflex actions. The integrity of a reflex is an indication of
the condition of functional activity of the appropriate reflex arc, and
tendon " jerks " and pupil reactions are of particular value in the clinical
examination of the nervous system, and will be considered later in this
connection.

Spinal Reflexes in Mammals

Fundamental contributions to the analysis of reflex mechanisms
have been made by Sherrington and his colleagues, and most of what
we shall have to say about it has been derived from the experimental
work of this school. The reflexes which have received particular atten-

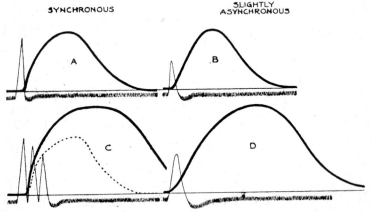

FIG. XI. 6.   Scheme of the **Mechanical** (heavy line), and the **Electrical** (light
      line) **responses of a muscle** to (1) a single volley of impulses arriving
      (A) synchronously, and (B) asynchronously and (2) a short series of
      impulses, (C) each member of the series being synchronous, and (D)
      each member of the series being asynchronous. For the application of
      these distinctions to the analysis of a reflex, see text. B and D should
      have been drawn to show longer durations than A and C. (After
      Fulton.)

tion involve movements of the hind limbs of dogs and cats ; among
them, the *flexor reflex* represents the withdrawal of a limb from an
injurious stimulus applied to the foot, and may also be evoked by stimulating any sensory nerve in the limb ; the *crossed extensor reflex* is an
extension of one hind limb produced by stimulation of the skin or a
sensory nerve of the opposite hind limb, and may be regarded as a
tendency to push away the irritant, or remove the animal from the
disturbance ; the *knee-jerk* produced by tapping the patella tendon is
typical of the reflex contraction which results from sudden stretching of
certain muscles ; and the *scratch reflex* illustrates a rhythmic discharge
from the central nervous system, and is induced by a continuous
stimulus applied to the side of the back. Each of these reflexes involves
a considerable group of muscles, and in experimental analysis it is
usual to select a convenient muscle and attach it to a recording lever,
while all other muscles likely to be affected are immobilised. Electrical

stimulation is employed, usually as a single or a series of induction shocks, and it is often advantageous to apply it directly to an afferent nerve trunk.

The Experimental Analysis of a Reflex. We have examined, in an earlier chapter, accurate records of the differences between the isometric responses of isolated muscles to single and repeated shocks; and we have discussed what modifications of the contraction curve are associated with the asynchronous excitation of the muscle fibres which occurs in movement, as contrasted with the synchronous excitation which results from the application of an experimental stimulus direct to the muscle or its motor nerve. The action potentials recorded by a galvanometer connected to the muscle under these various conditions have likewise been described. We can now, therefore, proceed to utilise the mechanical and electrical responses of a muscle which has been reflexly excited, as indicators of the character of the stimulus which reaches it from the central nervous system, and thus determine in just what way the simple stimulus to the afferent nerve becomes elaborated by the co-ordinating mechanism in the spinal cord.

The salient points in the muscular response which are useful in distinguishing different kinds of stimulation may first be recapitulated. A single volley of impulses reaching the muscle synchronously as in a nerve-muscle preparation excited by a single shock, produces first a short electric response, and then an increase of tension which begins abruptly, rises gradually to a maximum, and then declines. The duration of the mechanical response is notably constant for any one muscle under the same conditions. Consequently a double volley of impulses separated by a short period, which must, of course, exceed the refractory period, can be distinguished from a single volley, by the greater duration of the resulting contraction, the former being at least half as long again as the latter. Similarly, a succession of three or four volleys can be recognised by the characteristic duration of the contractions. With larger series of volleys, the increment of duration of contraction with each further volley becomes too small to be detected with confidence, so that in a prolonged contraction the number of impulses cannot be counted. Only if the tetanus is quite short can the number of volleys involved thus be estimated.

A single asynchronous volley can be detected (1) by the shape of the mechanical response curve, by the rounding-off of the abrupt initial rise of tension, for example, and by the lower maximum tension and greater duration than is produced by synchronous excitation; (2) by the shape of the electrical response curve obtained from an electrode in contact with a large number of muscle fibres, which consists of an irregular succession of deflections, small in proportion to the tension developed. A prolonged tetanus is indicated by the long duration of the response, but if the volleys constituting the tetanus are asynchronous and slightly out of phase, the electric response may be smothered, that of one muscular element counteracting that of another, so that often no electric variations can be detected after an initial kick.

The knee-jerk is the best-known representative of the class of reflex contraction evoked by sudden stretching of a muscle. The contraction follows so quickly upon the tap upon the patella tendon, and lasts so short a time, that it was first believed to be due to some direct response of the affected muscle. Clinical experience, however, favoured the view that the central nervous system played a part in the reflex, for the response was absent in tabes (a form of syphilis of the nervous system), whereas it was abnormally great in nervous diseases which resulted in increased tonus of the legs. Analysis of the mechanism in decerebrate animals showed that the latent period was indeed very short, but not so short as would be expected if the reflex arc did not include paths to and from the spinal cord; moreover, the reflex is abolished by cutting either the posterior roots or the anterior roots

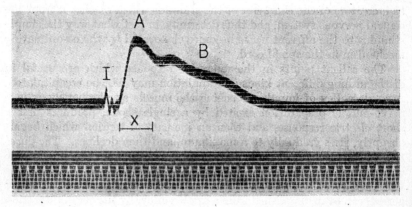

Fig. XI. 7.   Optical Record of the **Knee-jerk** in Man.

I, impact due to the blow; A, primary contraction; B, secondary contraction; Time beneath in 0·02 sec. (Wiggers "Physiology in Health and Disease.")

of the nerves to the hind limb. Deducting from the latent period the times taken for the nervous impulse to travel up the afferent and down the motor nerve, we arrive at the reduced reflex time, which has been estimated at about $1\frac{1}{2}$ msecs. This, then, is the interval during which the excitatory influence is delayed in the central nervous system, and the interval is so short that it cannot include the time which would be occupied in travelling up to and down from the brain. The knee-jerk is therefore a purely spinal reflex; this is confirmed by its persistence in decapitated animals. Isometric records of the contractions obtained in this way show that the knee-jerk is due to a single volley of nearly synchronous impulses.

Variation of the knee-jerk has long been regarded as an important and easily detected sign in the diagnosis of nervous diseases. Its absence is quite rare unless there is some pathological process to account for it. The significance attached to its absence in a patient depends on whether other tendon jerks (*e.g.*, the Achilles jerk) are also absent, as in general weakness, inflammation of the brain, asphyxia or narcosis, or whether the loss of the knee-jerk is unique and other tendon reflexes are preserved, in which case a local lesion affecting some part of the reflex arc is to be suspected. Impairment of the knee-jerk may be associated with muscular diseases affecting the extensors of the knee, or with neuritis affecting the corresponding nerve (anterior crural) or with tumours, etc., affecting either the sensory or motor elements in the arc. Exaggeration of the reflex is produced by a lesion of the pyramidal tracts in any part of their course between the cortex and the lumbar region of the cord ; and it is also common in neurotic and excitable patients ; the reflex may also often be enhanced in normal people by inducing them to concentrate on some other activity, such as forced clenching of the fists, a process known as " reinforcement " of the knee-jerk. There is some evidence that there is a continuous slow stream of excitatory impulses in the pyramidal tract. Presumaby a " fringe effect " from the excitation of the arm motor area in the forced clenching

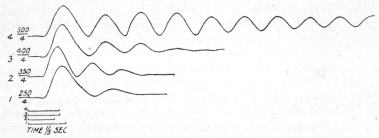

Fig. XI. 8. The Development of **Clonus,** with Increasing Initial Tension, from a Knee-Jerk, in a patient suffering from spasticity in the legs, due to a spinal tumour.

The fraction in small figures at the beginning of each record indicates by its denominator the force of the blow, and by its numerator the initial tension in the muscle in g. wt. (Pritchard.)

of the fists results in an increase in the activity of the pyramidal cells of the leg area. This would raise the excitability of the quadriceps motoneurones to a higher level.

Owing to the clinical importance of this reflex, therefore, its mechanism in man has received considerable attention. The responses of the human quadriceps femoris can be isolated and accurately recorded by attaching a blunt-hooked arrangement to the upper border of the patella, so that this can be drawn away from the hip with a known initial tension, maintained by a spring. The leg meanwhile is fixed in a splint. Sudden stretch is applied to the quadriceps muscle by a hammer which hits a prong attached to the hook, and the contraction of the muscle is recorded by photographing the subsequent movement of the prong.

A condition which is essential to eliciting a response is that some initial stretch of the muscle shall be present, and in normal people the least stretch which will suffice is about 300 g. weight. Moreover, the greater this initial stretch—up to about 600 g. weight—the smaller is the intensity of the least effective stimulus, and so the greater the excitability of the reflex.

Under conditions which give rise to an abnormally high tonic contraction of the extensors of the hind limbs (decerebrate rigidity, or spasticity due to disease in man), the response to stretching, instead of being a momentary contraction, is a rhythmic succession of contractions, known as a *clonus*. The dependence of this clonic response on a high initial tension is shown in Fig. XI. 8.

We come, therefore, to the following conception of the mechanism of the knee-jerk. A stream of irregular impulses, originating in sense organs in the muscle, can be detected in the sensory nerve so long as some degree of tension on the muscle is maintained, as described in the previous chapter. The sense organs thus supply a steady stimulus to the central nervous system, which is greater, the greater the tension on the muscle. The effect of a sudden stretch of the muscle, superimposed on this tonic background, is to induce all the sense organs to fire off synchronously, resulting in an immense outburst of simultaneous sensory impulses which pass to the spinal cord, and induce the discharge of a volley of motor impulses to the muscle.

The *flexor reflex* in the hind limb is evoked by any harmful or *nocuous* stimulation, of the kind which, if applied to ourselves, we should expect to be painful. It can also be evoked by a single electrical stimulus applied to a nerve trunk. The timing and intensity of such stimuli are much easier to control than those of mechanical stimuli applied to the skin. The disadvantage in work on reflexes of stimulating nerve trunks is that one is stimulating simultaneously some hundreds of nerve fibres, which are connected to different kinds of sensory endings, and which, if stimulated separately would have different and even perhaps, opposed reflex effects. This difficulty is of least importance in studies on the flexor reflex, since the effects of nocuous stimuli are *prepotent*, that is, their effect over-rides that of any other stimuli set up at the same time.

When a weak stimulus is applied to the foot, the ankle is dorsiflexed, and as the strength of the stimulus is increased, the response spreads to include flexion of the knee and then of the hip. It is usual to study the response of one muscle by denervation of all the other muscles in the leg. Tibialis anterior and semi-tendinosus have been most intensively studied, as they are convenient muscles for myographic recording.

The response of tibialis anterior to a weak shock applied to the posterior tibial nerve is due to a slightly asynchronous volley of impulses, similar to that shown in Fig. XI 6. A stronger shock gives rise to a similar initial volley, which is followed by irregular repetitive firing. This activity in motoneurones which outlasts the stimulus is called *after-discharge*.

Repetitive stimulation of an afferent nerve gives rise to a reflex tetanus, in which primary waves, corresponding to the frequency of stimulation, can be clearly seen in the electrical record. With stronger stimulation, after-discharge corresponding to each primary wave, gives rise to secondary waves which confuse the record.

As the strength of the stimulus is increased, the tension which can be set up in a muscle reaches a maximum. This is always less than the maximal tension of which the muscle is capable. If several afferent nerves are stimulated in turn, it is found that each nerve can only stimulate a fraction of the motoneurones of the muscle, a phenomenon called *fractionation*. The sum of the tensions produced by successive stimulation of a number of afferent nerves is many times greater than that set up by a maximal stimulus applied to the motor nerve. Obviously

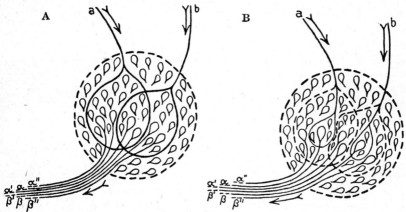

Fig. XI. 9. Diagram showing two Excitatory Afferent Fibres, *a* and *b*, with their respective fields of threshold excitation in the motoneurone pool of a muscle. Axons are drawn for only 4 of the motoneurones activated by *a* alone (α, α', α'' and β') and 4 of those activated by *b* alone (β, β', β'' and α').

In A, both afferents concurrently activate not 8 but 6 of these motoneurones, *i.e.*, there is a contraction deficit by occlusion in α' and β'.

In B, with weaker stimulation of the afferents, *a* by itself activates 1 unit, α, and *b* activates 1 unit, β. Concurrently, they activate 4 units (α', α, β', and β) owing to summation of the subliminal effects in the overlap of the subliminal fields enclosed in broken lines. (Creed and others " Reflex Activity of the Spinal Cord.")

the paths activated by these afferent nerves must converge on to the motoneurones which form the *final common path* in the reflex.

This *principle of convergence* has several important consequences. If, while one afferent nerve is being maximally excited, a second afferent nerve which alone produces a strong reflex effect, is also excited, there is very little further increase in tension. Here the muscle is already producing the maximum tension of which it is capable, in response to the impulses set up in its motoneurones by the first nerve. Stimulation of the second nerve will make some of the motoneurones discharge faster, but there will be no increase in the tension in the muscle, although the contraction may be smoother and show less fatigue. The impulses in the second nerve are " shut out " from any obvious effect on the muscle, and the phenomenon is, therefore, called *occlusion*. A further consequence of convergence is seen in the effect of applying weak stimuli instead of maximal stimuli to a pair of afferent nerves. If these stimuli are applied simultaneously, or within a few milliseconds, the tension produced is often greater than the sum of the tensions produced by stimulating the two nerves separately. This is explained by assuming that surrounding the group of motoneurones which are stimulated by one nerve alone, there is a *subliminal fringe* in which the excitation produced on the motoneurones does not reach threshold. When the sublimal fringes of the afferent volleys overlap, their motoneurones are excited from two sources, and may be made to discharge, in addition to those cells which are excited by each stimulus alone (Fig. XI. 9).

If the stimuli are further weakened, there is a point at which neither stimulus has any reflex effect by itself, but when they are applied together, a reflex contraction appears. This *summation* of stimuli establishes the view that a stimulus can produce sublimal excitation of the cells of the spinal cord.

The reduced reflex time of the flexor reflex is about 5·5 msecs., while the corresponding figure for the neurones which are responsible for the knee-jerk is 0·9–1·6 msecs. The flexor reflex appears, therefore, to represent one stage further than the knee-jerk in integrative complexity, for it involves a larger group of muscles, and the multiplication of impulses by, and greater delay in, the central nervous system.

The crossed extensor reflex, on the other hand, represents a considerable advance in the degree of integration. It is measured by recording the contraction of the quadriceps femoris of one limb, and it is elicited by stimulating an afferent nerve in the opposite hind limb. The latent period of the response is much longer than that of the reflexes hitherto described, and amounts to about five times that of the flexor reflex and nearly ten times that of the knee-jerk. The analysis of the response to a single shock applied to the afferent nerve shows that a succession of asynchronous volleys of impulses reaches the muscle. If a succession of shocks is similarly applied, the frequency of stimulation may be reduced even to 5–10 per second without the tetanus breaking up into incompletely fused individual responses, whereas the corresponding lowest frequency for fusion of a motor nerve tetanus, or flexor reflex tetanus, is about 40 per second. In this class of more highly developed reflex activity, the magnitude of the mechanical response becomes greater as the duration of the rhythmic stimulus is increased ; this implies the activity of a progressively larger proportion of the muscle fibres, and consequently a more extensive radiation of the influence of the afferent impulses upon the motoneurones in the cord. The phenomenon of **after-discharge** is prominent in this group of reflexes.

Reflex Inhibition. If, while the crossed extensor reflex is being evoked by stimulation of a sensory nerve in the opposite (contralateral) hind limb, a sensory nerve of the hind limb on the same side (ipsilateral) is stimulated, the flexor reflex immediately develops, and the crossed extensor reflex is inhibited. Flexion has taken the place of extension. A weak shock applied to a nerve in the ipsilateral limb can easily inhibit the crossed extensor reflex which has been evoked by strong stimulation of a nerve in the contralateral limb.

Here both stimuli applied are of the same kind, as in each case, pain fibres are being excited in the bared nerve trunks. The result depends on the relative strength of the stimuli used. There is an algebraical summation of the excitatory and inhibitory stimuli set up, so that a weak excitatory stimulus may be completely inhibited by a strong stimulus applied to the same leg, while, if the inhibitory stimulus is weakened, the crossed excitatory stimulus may have almost its full effect.

When one stimulus is potentially harmful or *nociceptive,* and the other is not, the harmful one is always prepotent. For example, even a weak single shock applied to the sciatic nerve can inhibit the knee jerk. If a regular succession of knee-jerks be evoked in a spinal animal, at a rate of about three per second, these extensor responses can be inhibited

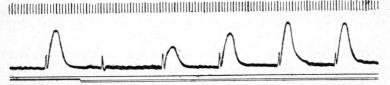

FIG. XI. 10. **Reflex Inhibition of the Knee-Jerk** of a Spinal Cat on Stimulation of the Sciatic Nerve with a Single Induction Shock.

The inhibitory stimulus (a single shock) occurred at the moment indicated by the descent of the signal ; the kick at the beginning of each response is due to the regularly repeated tap on the tendon. Recovery after inhibition is gradual. Time marker, above, indicates 0·02 sec. (After Ballif, Fulton and Liddell.)

by a single shock applied to an afferent nerve in the same limb. The inhibitory stimulus, so applied, results in the abolition of some three to six responses, after which the knee-jerks gradually build up again to their normal value (Fig. XI. 10). Clearly, the effect of the inhibitory stimulus outlasts the actual time of application of the stimulus by some one to two seconds, and this phenomenon is referred to as " inhibitory after discharge."

Now, when considering the nature of reflex inhibition, it may be well to recall other kinds of inhibition which result from excitation of a nerve. Among the best-known examples are the action of vagal stimulation in reducing the heart frequency, and that of splanchnic stimulation in producing relaxation of the musculature of the alimentary canal. There is a second system of nerves (sympathetic and vagus respectively) supplying these organs, the stimulation of which, on the contrary, results in excitatory effects. Excitatory and inhibitory actions on the contraction of skeletal muscle cannot, however, be attributed to any such dual nerve supply, for no inhibitory nerves to striated muscle have been found. The reflex inhibition considered above must, therefore, depend on a central nervous mechanism which is in communication with the muscle only by means of its motor nerve and stops the passage of all impulses down it.

The Theory of Reflex Mechanism

The co-ordination of movement introduced by the central nervous element in the reflex arc may be considered from two aspects. First, it is evident that some kind of permanent anatomical pattern must underlie the orderly distribution of the excitatory process to appropriate groups of muscles, and this is generally conceded. It is also clear that there must be some mechanism in the spinal cord by which the effects of similar stimuli may be summed while others annul one another. Such processes are esssential if the response to a number of stimuli with conflicting effects is to be the single completed movement which is best adapted to the preservation of the individual. This, the " integrative activity " of the central nervous system, is clearly present even in the spinal cord isolated from the brain. Whatever the interaction between different reflexes which compete for, or co-operate in, the control of a particular muscle, the final effect is exerted through the same motor nerve, which is, therefore, referred to as the " final common path."

The essential facts which a theory of reflex activity has to cover are the existence of *persistent* states of increased and decreased excitability in the spinal cord after the arrival of a stimulus, and their mutual inactivation. Sherrington's view, which others have called the **Humoral Theory,** has held the field for the last twenty years. According to this theory, the arrival of an excitatory stimulus is followed by the setting up of a *central excitatory state* in the spinal cord. This central excitatory state, or c.e.s., outlasts the impulse which set it up. In the same way, an inhibitory stimulus is said to give rise to a *central inhibitory state,* or c.i.s., which opposes the effect of c.e.s. It was thought most likely that c.e.s. and c.i.s. neutralised each other in the same way as do acids and alkalies, or cations and anions. Both these states must be produced at the final common path, on the motoneurone in fact, and may also exist at interneurones, but when the theory was formulated, there was no evidence on this point. The actual nature of c.e.s. and c.i.s. was left open. By analogy with the chemical substances liberated at the endings of autonomic nerve fibres, some people thought that c.e.s. and c.i.s. might be due to the liberation of specific chemical substances. The Oxford school favoured the view that c.e.s. was a physico-chemical state, corresponding perhaps to the depolarisation of a cell membrane. Sherrington suggested that c.e.s. might be similar in nature to the local excitatory state seen in peripheral nerve, but of longer duration.

Central Excitatory State. When a volley of impulses reaches a nerve cell, it is supposed that c.e.s. is built up, and that when it reaches a critical level, the cell discharges. This reduces the amount of c.e.s. present, which has to be built up before the cell can discharge again. Hence the frequency of efferent impulses depends on the rate of building up of the c.e.s. ; this in turn depends on the number of afferent impulses which reach the centre in a given time. Consequently, there is a graded relation between the motor reflex response and the strength of stimulus applied to sensory endings, for the stronger the stimulus, the greater the number of endings stimulated, and the higher the frequency of impulses set up by each of them.

The c.e.s. is supposed to develop slowly in comparison with the

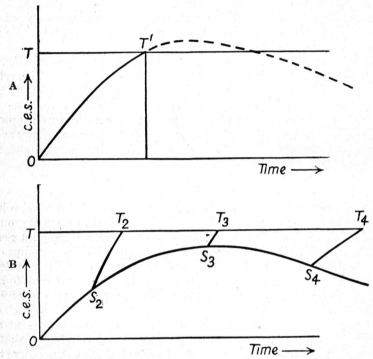

FIG. XI. 11. Diagrammatic Representation of the **c.e.s. of a motoneurone** (ordinates) plotted against time (abscissæ). In A, the level of c.e.s. reaches threshold after the first stimulus. In B, the first stimulus is just subliminal.

OT is the threshold value of c.e.s. TT' is the synaptic delay. $OS_2S_3S_4$ shows the rise and fall of c.e.s. following a subliminal incoming stimulus. S_2T_2, S_3T_3 and S_4T_4 show the rise in c.e.s. following a second stimulus at varying intervals after the first, and demonstrate the shortening of the synaptic delay after the second stimulus, and its variation with the interval between the stimuli. (Creed and others, "Reflex Activity of the Spinal Cord.")

duration of a nerve impulse. If two weak afferent volleys are set up at an interval of 6–8 msecs., the latent period of the response to the second volley is greatly reduced, and may not exceed 0·5 msecs. (Fig. XI. 11). This is attributed to the addition of the c.e.s. produced by the second volley to that already present due to the first, so that there is a rapid rise to threshold level. In the flexor reflex, c.e.s. is detectable for 15–16 msecs. after a single volley. During this time a further stimulus will excite more motor units than usual, after a shorter latent period. In the crossed extensor reflex, c.e.s. is detectable for as long as 50 msecs. after a single afferent volley. As no fibres in the posterior root end on the anterior horn cells of the opposite side, there must be at least one interneurone, and there may be many more, in this pathway. The greater complexity of the pathway across the cord is probably related to the longer duration of the c.e.s.

If there is no discharge of an efferent impulse, the c.e.s. disappears spontaneously. It can also be removed by neutralisation by c.i.s. This is a graded process, and is the only manifestation of c.i.s. C.i.s. takes longer to appear and longer to disappear than c.e.s., and is sometimes detectable 200 msecs. after the arrival of an impulse. C.e.s. may also be removed by stimulating the motor nerve trunk. This sets up impulses which travel centrally as well as peripherally. The impulses which run backward to the spinal cord are called *antidromic*. They decrease the amount of c.e.s. present on a motoneurone, probably by depolarising the perikaryon and dendrites in the same way as a normal nerve impulse. There is some evidence that antidromic impulses may sometimes fail to pass the axon hillock, and therefore fail to reach the soma. The interpretation of many experiments in which antidromic impulses have been used is, therefore, somewhat insecure.

When the intensity of a stimulus is only just great enough to evoke a reflex, the response is quite localised and confined to a small group of muscles ; if, however, the stimulus becomes more and more intense, the response becomes more and more widespread, involving groups of muscles more and more remote ; the excitatory process is then regarded as spreading more widely in the spinal cord. This is referred to as *irradiation* and might be attributed to the development to a larger extent, and consequently to a more widespread diffusion, of the excitatory state, involving a larger number of irritable structures in the central nervous system. When two stimuli, each of which is too weak to stimulate when applied separately, are applied simultaneously to adjacent parts of an afferent field, they may evoke a reflex response. This process has been called " spatial summation " or " simultaneous spinal induction," and is, of course, an aspect of convergence. When the two sublimal volleys are applied within a few milliseconds to the same or to adjacent points, the process is known as " temporal summation," or as " successive spinal induction." The term " facilitation " is limited by some to the similar effect that a just liminal stimulus has on a subsequent volley. In every case the effect can be attributed to the summation of persistent c.e.s.

Since this theory was first put forward, further work has been done on the site and mechanism of the production of c.e.s. Its main outcome has been to stress the importance of the interneurones. Earlier work by Sherrington and his pupils had shown that the persistence of c.e.s. on the motoneurones depended partly on a continuous bombardment of impulses which continued to arrive for some time after the initial volley. In 1922, Forbes had suggested that this maintained bombardment might be due to the presence of " delay paths " in the spinal cord. Impulses which travelled over these delay paths would have to cross a number of synapses, each with its synaptic delay, and would arrive at the moto-neurones after various intervals. This possibility has been taken a stage further by Lorente de No, who has histological and functional evidence of the existence of closed chains of neurones. If such a chain is excited by a single impulse, it will continue to " reverberate," giving off impulses by the collaterals of its cells, until it is stopped by " fatigue," or blocked by refractory period. The participation of such reverber-ating chains in the grey matter may account for the differences in the time relations of the flexor and the crossed extensor reflexes. Lorente de No believes that c.e.s. may be accounted for by the interactions between the so-called " detonator actions " of impulses, which last only

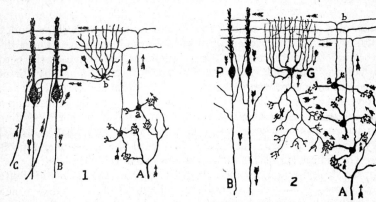

Fig. XI. 12.   Diagrams illustrating the existence of **Reverberatory Chains** in the central nervous system (in this case, the cerebellar cortex).

A, mossy fibre ; P, Purkinje cells ; B, axons of Purkinje cells ; a, granule cells ; b, basket cells ; G, Golgi cells ; C, climbing fibres. The arrows show the direction of transmission of the impulses.

1 shows a non-reverberatory arc, from mossy fibres, through basket cells, to Purkinje cells.

2 shows a reverberatory arc, introduced by the Golgi cells. (Lorente de No, after Cajal, *Arch. Neurol. Psychiat., Chicago*).

about 0·5 msecs., and that all facilitatory effects of greater duration are due to the activity of reverberating chains of interneurones.

On this view, the larger part of the reduced reflex time is taken up in starting reverberatory activity in the interneurone pools. If two sub-liminal stimuli are set up at an interval of 6–8 msecs., the second volley reaches the cord after this activation of the interneurone pool has already occurred, and those impulses which pass direct to the anterior horn cells find them already subjected to internuncial bombardment. The anterior horn cells may, therefore, be excited by the second volley with a delay of no more than 0·5 msecs. It has been suggested that the reduced reflex time should be divided into *nuclear delay*, the time needed to start reverberatory activity in internuncial cell pools, and *synaptic* delay, the minimal time for excitation of the cell which forms the final common path.

It is however possible that in addition to the detonator action, there is a period of increased excitability lasting for rather less than 10 milliseconds, after motoneurones have discharged an impulse. This has been called " residual facilitation," and corresponds in time to the synaptic potential which exists in the central nervous system, as well as in the autonomic ganglia (p. 385). C.e.s., therefore, is a term which describes the increased excitability of the spinal cord as a whole, and is built up by detonator facilitation, residual facilitation, the reverberatory activity of neurone circuits, and possibly also by autorhythmic activity of some specialised nerve cells.

The importance of interneurones has led us to distinguish between reflexes which can employ two neurone arcs, and those which must employ multineurone arcs. The tendon jerks provide an example of the former class, the flexor reflex of the latter. In the tendon jerks, the stimulus consists of a sharp tap, which produces an almost synchronous volley of impulses in the proprioceptive fibres. These fibres have almost the same conduction rate, and their impulses therefore arrive at the cord as a volley. Sufficient impulses reach the motoneurones by direct connections to excite them with latent period characteristic of delay at a single synapse. In the flexor reflex, the nocuous stimuli seldom set up a synchronous afferent discharge, conduction rate in the corresponding fibres varies over a wide range, and when these somewhat dispersed volleys reach the cord, they have to excite the internuncial pools before the excitation of the motoneurones can reach threshold.

In the stretch reflex, the afferent discharge reaching the cord is quite asynchronous, and there are probably seldom enough impulses which arrive simultaneously by two-neurone arcs at motoneurones for excitation to occur. Reinforcement of their effects by internuncial activity is probably essential. In adverse conditions such as anæsthesia, anoxia or spinal shock, we find that the stretch reflex is abolished much more readily than the knee-jerk, and in all these conditions internuncial activity is depressed.

Central Inhibitory State. The nature of the central inhibitory state is, at present, obscure. There is no evidence of the existence of a specific chemical substance which might occur in the central nervous system and make cells less excitable. When c.e.s. is thought of as a state of local depolarisation of a cell membrane, c.i.s. may be thought of as a state of stabilisation or anodal polarisation of the cell membrane, by which the excitability is reduced, and the spread of local responses abolished. Such an effect is exerted on adjacent nerve fibres ahead of an advancing impulse (Chap. X), and it is possible that the arrival of an impulse at certain boutons might cause only the stage of decreased excitability of the cell body. Such a process would have a very short latent period, and a process called " direct inhibition," which is probably of this type, is known to exist.

An alternative view that inhibition is due to the break up of activity in reverberatory circuits has been put forward by Lorente de No. He found that if a nerve cell were made to discharge twice within 2 msecs. by afferent impulses, the double response was followed by a profound subnormality which lasts up to 30 msecs., long enough to block activity in long chains of reverberatory neurones. Though this mechanism may well exist, it requires accessory hypotheses before it can account for inhibition which can prevent the discharge of even a single impulse by the motoneurones. It can, however, account for inhibitory processes at the internuncial neurones.

Since there has been much support for the theory of chemical transmission at the nerve muscle junction and in the autonomic ganglia, repeated attempts have been made to revive the view that c.e.s. is due to the liberation of unitary quantities of a chemical substance. So far, the evidence is unsatisfactory. Attempts have been made to identify acetylcholine in the perfusate from the brain and from the spinal cord after stimulation of afferent nerves, but as it is very difficult to perfuse the central nervous system independently of other tissues, the results are not impressive. Bremer has shown that the injection of very small doses of acetylcholine into the carotid artery increases the excitability of the cortex, and increases the after-discharge following afferent stimulation. Acetylcholine also increases the after-discharge in the flexor reflex in the frog. In the mammal, acetylcholine increases the amplitude of the flexor reflex, but diminishes the knee-jerk (Bülbring and Burn). Acetylcholine is present in efferent tracts, but is almost absent from afferent tracts. Its distribution in different parts of the central nervous system is very patchy, and does not run parallel to the richness of the tissue in cell-bodies or synapses. It seems that acetylcholine may play an important rôle in the transmission of impulses at some synapses, but no part whatever at others.

The Reflex Response to Stretch

We have already considered an example of a reflex induced by sudden stretching of a muscle, namely, the knee-jerk ; and we have remarked that such tendon reflexes can be demonstrated in spinal animals as well as more highly integrated preparations. The stretch which evokes a " jerk " is sudden and momentary, and the magnitude of the response depends on the rate and the amount of stretching. If, however, instead of releasing the muscle directly after stretching it, the muscle is kept at its new and longer length and prevented from shortening, its tension remains increased. This relatively permanent increase of tension with constant stretching is much greater if the muscle is innervated than if it is denervated ; it can also be largely reduced by cutting the appropriate posterior nerve roots, or by reflex inhibition brought about by exciting an antagonistic reflex. This postural response to constant stretch is therefore reflex in nature ; it is well marked in decerebrate or more complex preparations. The reaction is most prominent in the extensor muscles of the limbs, and since these muscles are so firmly contracted in a decerebrate cat or dog that the animal can be made to support itself on its limbs, they have been picturesquely termed the antigravity muscles. This stretch reflex varies in magnitude with the amount of stretch, and may be evoked by as little as a 1 per cent. stretch. The response continues for one half-hour or more without being reduced by fatigue. A remarkable feature of this postural reflex is the sharply localised nature of the response. If, for example, the quadriceps femoris be divided into four, and one part only be stretched, only that part will show the reflex contraction. The reflex arc evidently starts with proprioceptive receptors in the muscle itself, sensitive to stretch, and impulses pass to and from the spinal cord to terminate in

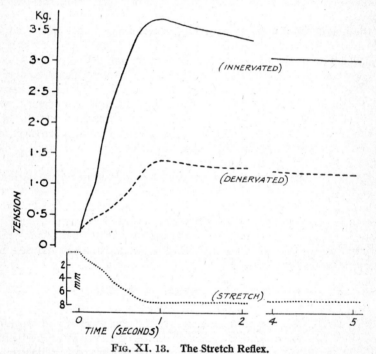

Fig. XI. 13.   The Stretch Reflex.

A stretch of 8 mm. produces a much larger development of tension in the " innervated " quadriceps muscle than in the same muscle (" denervated ") after division of the posterior nerve roots.   (After Liddell and Sherrington.)

muscle fibres situated in the immediate vicinity of the receptors. Thus the reflex may be regarded as a device which ensures that each group of muscle fibres shall contribute its quota toward resisting a pull applied to the whole muscle.

Reflex Tonus

The stretch reflex has been aptly described as " tonus in the making," for some degree of stretch is essential if tonic contraction of a muscle is to be maintained. This can be shown in an animal with high extensor tone, as in " decerebrate rigidity " ; detaching the patella tendon results in flaccidity of the quadriceps muscle, whereas application of a pull on the tendon results in redevelopment of the tonic contraction. As in the stretch reflex, so in decerebrate rigidity, the postural reaction is unaffected by cutting all the cutaneous nerves, but is abolished by cutting the posterior nerve roots, and can be completely inhibited by stimulating an afferent nerve in the same limb, which would tend to produce the antagonistic flexor reflex. The way would seem clear, therefore, to regarding tonus as a reflex contraction maintained in response to the permanent stretch associated with attachment of both ends of the muscles to a rigid skeleton. Certain difficulties have, however, been put in the way of this interpretation, which regards tonus as of the same general nature as a tetanus. Among them, the absence of fatigue, and the relatively small increase of metabolism in tonic as compared with tetanic contraction, have been prominent. These difficulties have led to the exploration of alternative hypotheses, such as that which attributes tonus to an action of the sympathetic nervous system directly on the skeletal muscles. The cogency of the objections to the reflex theory of tonus is, however, largely removed by a consideration of the consequences of asynchronous contraction at a slow rate of the different fibres in a muscle, as contrasted with the synchronous contraction of all the fibres produced by electrical stimulation. It should be noted that the greatest tonic tension never exceeds one-tenth of the maximum tetanic tension, and it is not necessary to suppose that more than one-tenth of the total number of fibres are contracting at any one moment. The local nature of the stretch reflex would then suggest that each small group of fibres would contract so as to relieve the tension on its own receptors, and such small groups would be active in irregular rotation, so as to produce a completely asynchronous contraction of the muscle. Such rotation of activity has been seen to occur in muscles under slight stretch, but it seems to be exceptional. Often the same single unit continues to discharge for minutes at a time without rest. So far, all attempts to demonstrate action potentials in muscles which are resting, but which still show " tone," have been unsuccessful.

We have so far considered the factors which operate in keeping the muscles under a constant small tension in the motionless limb and must now examine what changes occur in the distribution and amount of this " tonic " tension when the limb is moved. These changes are best studied in animals that have had time to recover from the shock of an operation for decerebration, and may therefore be termed " chronic decerebrate " preparations. Chronic (as contrasted with " acute ") spinal preparations show much the same features in this respect, both exhibiting well-marked extensor tonus in anti-gravity muscles. Now, when an attempt is made to flex the extended hind limb by bending the knee, a resistance is encountered which opposes the movement. If, however, the experimenter perseveres in the attempt to bend it, and applies considerable force for a considerable time, the limb suddenly " gives," and flexes easily without needing much force. This is the " clasp knife " reaction. The movement involves lengthening of the extensor muscles (*i.e.*, loss of extensor tone), and is referred to as the " *lengthening reaction*." The limb will now retain its position, if undis-

turbed, for quite a long time.   If the limb is extended, so that the
extensor muscles are allowed to shorten, the tension in the tendon is at
first abolished.   But soon, the tension in the muscles increases until they
are exerting the same tension at the new shorter length.   This is called
the " *shortening reaction.*"   A similar resistance to movement and sudden
yielding to force can be obtained with the limb midway between flexion
and extension, and results in the limb having plastic properties, so
that it " stays put " in any given position, as in Fig. XI. 14.

The experimental analysis of the mechanism of these reactions is
carried out on the quadriceps femoris, attached at its peripheral end
to an isotonic lever, while all other structures in the limb are completely

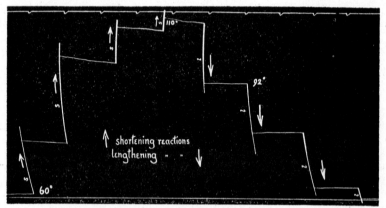

FIG. XI. 14.   **Shortening and Lengthening Reactions** in the Vastus-
Intermedius Muscle of a Decerebrate Cat.

Initially the knee was bent, so that the leg was at an angle of 60° to the
thigh ; at s, s, s, the knee was passively extended, with the result that the
vastus-intermedius muscle shortened in such a way as to cause the limb to
" stay put " more or less in the position in which it was placed ; in this way,
the knee was straightened as far as an angle of 110°.   Subsequent passive
flexion resulted in a lengthening of the vastus-intermedius muscle (1, 1, 1,)
in just the same way that passive extension resulted in shortening.   Time
marker, above, indicates seconds.   (Sherrington.)

immobolised by denervation or mechanical fixation.   Under such conditions, the reactions appear, much as shown in Fig. XI. 14, a fine gradation
of the effect enabling the muscle to adopt any length to which it may
have been shortened.   The reactions disappear, however, if either the
nerves to the muscle or the corresponding sensory spinal roots are
severed ; it is evident, therefore, that they depend on an intact afferent
supply from the muscle.   It will be noted that these are the same
conditions as those necessary for obtaining the stretch reflex, and it is
to the operation of this stretch reflex that the shortening reaction is
attributed.   When the muscle is being shortened, the tension due to the
isotonic stretch is temporarily removed ; directly, however, the movement of shortening is over, this tension is reimposed, and evokes the
stretch reflex.   This interpretation of the shortening reaction is con-

firmed by the way in which it becomes grafted on to changes in muscle
length produced reflexly, so that it comes to resemble a very prolonged
after-discharge. A short-lasting after-discharge, is however, not dependent on the integrity of the sensory nerves coming from the responding
muscle, and is present after these are cut, whereas the longer lasting
shortening reaction disappears under such conditions. The shortening
reaction produced as a result of the crossed extensor reflex is shown in
Fig. XI. 15, which also illustrates that cutting the afferent nerves from
the responding muscle abolishes the reaction.

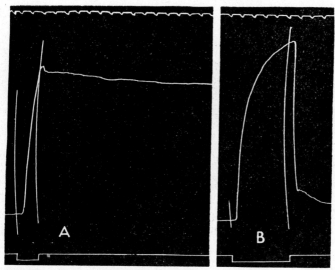

FIG. XI. 15. **Shortening Reaction,** following a Contraction of the Vastus-
Intermedius Muscle of the Cat, produced by the Crossed Extensor
Reflex.

The afferent nerve supply from the muscle was intact in A, and had
been divided two hours previously in B. The popliteal nerve of the opposite
limb was stimulated in each case during the time indicated by the signal;
in A the muscle remained contracted after the end of the stimulus (" stayed
put "), while in B it relaxed after a short after-discharge. The arcs
drawn across the muscle tracing indicate the exact moments of starting and
stopping of reflex stimulation. Time marker, above, indicates seconds.
(Sherrington.)

Whereas the stretch reflex accounts for the occurrence of the shortening reaction, the lengthening reaction reveals a mechanism which we
have not hitherto considered. The application of a small pull to an
innervated muscle excites it to resist the pull. The application of a
considerable pull, especially if continued for some time, stimulates
another set of receptors in the muscle, which results in reflex inhibition
in the tonus in the muscle, *i.e.,* in the lengthening reaction. There
appears to be a dual proprioceptive mechanism in muscles—one
excitatory and one inhibitory—which enables the muscle to resist a
relatively small pull, but to yield to a pull so great that one might
regard it as likely to be injurious to its consequences.

Reciprocal Innervation

We have seen how the small degree of contraction of the whole
skeletal musculature, which persists throughout life, may be traced to
the stretch derived from the attachment of the relatively shorter muscles
to the relatively larger skeleton.   It is the variation in the state of tonus

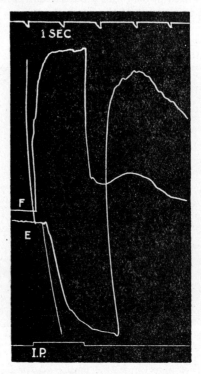

FIG. XI. 16.   **The Reciprocal [Innervation** of Antagonistic Muscles in a
Decerebrate Cat.

F shows the reponse of the semi-tendinosus muscle, a knee flexor ; E
shows the response of the vastus-intermedius muscle, a knee extensor.
During the period shown by the signal (I.P.), the popliteal nerve of the
same limb (ipsilateral) was stimulated, bringing about a flexion reflex.
The flexor, accordingly, contracted, while the extensor relaxed.   Note
the **rebound** contraction of the extensor muscles following the reflex
response.   The arcs drawn across the muscle tracings indicate the moment
of stimulation and show that the responses of the two muscles were practically simultaneous.   (Sherrington.)

which is responsible for the maintenance of the postural relations of the
limbs and body.   Movements must be regarded as superimposed on a
background of this continued tonic activity, and it is one of the most
remarkable examples of co-ordination that when one group of muscles
say the extensors, contract, the antagonistic group, namely the flexors
not only lengthen passively, but actually relax from their state of tonic
contraction (Fig. X1. 16).   A complete reflex movement of a limb, there

fore, involves augmentation of tonic contraction in one group of synergic muscles, and concomitant diminution of the tonic contraction in the antagonistic group. The occurrence of this simultaneous excitation of one group and inhibition of an opposed group of muscles is called the law of *Reciprocal Innervation*. It is well marked in the flexor and crossed extensor reflexes, and in the alternate movements of scratching and stepping ; and it occurs in spinal and decerebrate animals, but in intact animals voluntary movements need not involve reciprocal innervation. It has already been mentioned in connection with the vaso-motor reflexes.

It does not occur in the " positive supporting reaction," in which both flexors and extensors contract simultaneously in order to fix all the joints in the leg. The stimulus is the pressure of the foot on the ground, which stimulates the skin of the sole, and also by separating the toes, stretches the interossei. Subsequent contraction of the extensors and flexors converts the limb into a rigid pillar.

Locomotion

The stepping reflex is rather more complex than any hitherto considered ; nevertheless, the essential co-ordinating mechanism is present in the spinal animal, as is shown by the well-known examples of decapitated fish and ducks swimming, of decapitated chickens running, and even of decapitated pigeons flying. A spinal cat or dog will perform stepping movements if its weight is supported. The analysis of the stepping-reflex may be considered under three headings : (1) the stimuli which evoke flexion and extension of a limb ; (2) the conditions under which flexion and extension alternate in any one limb ; and (3) the effects of the movements of one limb upon the movements of the other.

Electrical stimulation of one foot of a spinal dog (or frog) induces flexion of the same limb, and extension of the opposite limb. Subsequent stimulation of the other foot reverses the responses of the limbs. These are the flexor and crossed-extensor reflexes, respectively, described above. Now, if the sole of the foot of a spinal dog is lightly touched instead of being vigorously stimulated, the limb responds by a brief extensor thrust instead of by flexion, and the opposite limb now becomes flexed. These are the " direct-extensor " and " crossed-flexor " reflexes respectively. It is evident that different sorts of stimuli applied to the same spot may elicit widely different responses ; in both cases, however, the opposite limbs are related by the fact that when one flexes the other extends, and *vice versa*. Under certain circumstances the mere passive bending of the joints of one limb will induce extension of the other.

The stretch-reflex, already considered, contributes an important element of co-ordination to the rhythmic movements of a single limb. During the phase of flexion, bending of the knee stretches the extensors, which thereupon proceed to contract. The consequent extension of the knee results in stretching of the flexors, and this inhibits the extensor contraction, allowing them to relax and the limb to flex. A characteristic of reflexes which contributes to the same end is known as the **rebound phenomenon** (Fig. XI. 16); by this is meant the tendency for antagonistic muscles to contract spontaneously, directly reflex stimulation of a group of muscles ceases. If, for example, a powerful electrical stimulus has evoked a flexor reflex, a well-marked extension of the limb will follow interruption of the stimulus.

Thus a variety of stimuli, such as irritation of the pads of the feet or stretching of the limb muscles, have to do with the initiation and maintenance of the alternate movements of stepping. The rhythmicity of the movement of one limb, as well as the opposed phases of the movements of two opposite limbs, appear to depend on the influence of one reflex movement in evoking another reflex as an immediate consequence, and this in turn evoking a further one, and so on. Such a successive relation between simple reflexes results in what is known as a *chain-reflex*, of which reflex stepping is a good example.

Fig. XI. 17. The Scratch Reflex interrupted by a brief Flexion Reflex. S, signal indicating application of a stimulus evoking the scratch reflex. F, signal indicating application of a stimulus evoking the flexion reflex.

The increase in the amplitude of the scratch reflex after the end of the flexion reflex is not always observed. (Sherrington, "The Integrative Action of the Nervous System.")

In addition to these rhythmic reflexes which are due to rhythmic changes in the stream of afferent impulses which reach the centre, the spinal cord can give rise to rhythmic reflexes in response to steady stimulation. If the skin of the flank of a spinal dog is stimulated, the hind limb of the same side carries out scratching movements repeated 3–4 times a second (Fig. XI. 17). This reflex response is still rhythmic even after removal of the afferent nerves from the muscles of the leg, and can also be provoked by steady faradisation of a point on the cut surface of the spinal cord. It shows a very high degree of spatial and temporal summation, and the fact that the foot is brought to scratch the point stimulated provides evidence of the accuracy of the co-ordination which can be carried out by the isolated spinal cord.

The Influence of Chemical and Physical Agents on Reflex Excitability

We have already referred to the relative instability of excitability in reflexes as compared with that of nerve trunks. The sensitivity to lack of oxygen is well illustrated by exposing frogs at different temperatures to an atmosphere containing no oxygen. At 2° C., the reflex excitability is maintained for days, at 10° to 20° C. it persists only for about two hours, at 25° C. for half an hour. This is interpreted as due to the more rapid utilisation of the small store of oxygen at the higher temperature. At 38° C., a frog in a normal atmosphere passes into a condition known as heat paralysis, which again is attributed to lack of oxygen in the central nervous system owing to the rate of oxygen utilisation at this temperature exceeding the rate at which oxygen can be absorbed from the atmosphere.

The action of convulsants like strychnine in causing tetanic contraction of all the skeletal muscles is well known. The action is located in the spinal cord, for (1) it does not affect a muscle whose motor nerve is cut, and is therefore not peripheral in its action ; (2) it acts in spinal frogs and mammals, and does not act, therefore, by affecting the brain. The action of strychnine is to increase the reflex excitability, as is shown by the absence of convulsions if all afferent stimulation is prevented by cutting the posterior nerve roots, or even by rendering the skin of the frog insensitive with cocaine. Somewhat similar effects are produced by tetanus toxin. Narcotics affect all living tissues if in sufficient concentration, but reduce reflex excitability in doses which are far smaller than any needed to affect non-nervous tissues.

CHAPTER XII

LOCALISATION OF FUNCTION IN THE CENTRAL NERVOUS SYSTEM

It has been the custom to include in text-books of physiology a somewhat detailed account of the anatomy and histology of the central nervous system, and indeed no one would question the importance to physiology and neurology of such anatomical description. The study of human physiology is, however, almost invariably accompanied by that of anatomy ; and since the structure of the nervous system is now very adequately expounded in the standard works on this subject, it no longer seems necessary to duplicate anatomical description by including it in so short an account of the physiology of the nervous system as the following.

THE frequent occurrence of localised injuries of small parts of the nervous system in chronic nervous diseases has focussed the attention of neurologists especially upon the conducting functions of the great tracts, and this is so because a lesion damaging a conducting bundle will often produce much more extensive dislocation of function than one of similar size affecting the grey matter. The knowledge of the position, direction and limits of the nervous tracts which has resulted from histological research involving the method of section, degeneration and staining, now forms an anatomical setting which enables the consequences of pathological lesions or of experimental injury to be interpreted in terms of the interruption of function.

Now, the results of dividing the nervous system by a complete transverse cut indicate that different stages of automatic activity are exhibited according to the amount and kind of nervous tissue that remains active. We have considered, for example, the properties of the " spinal " and " decerebrate " preparations. Within the region of the spinal cord itself integrity of certain segments can be detected by the persistence of reflexes whose arcs pass through those segments. For instance, stroking the skin of the sides of the belly produces contraction of the sub-adjacent muscles (abdominal reflexes) so long as the eighth to the twelfth thoracic segments of the cord and the pyramidal system are functioning normally. The knee-jerk similarly represents a function of the second, third and fourth lumbar segments, the ankle-jerk (extension of the ankle obtained by tapping the tendo Achillis), that of the first and second sacral segments, and the plantar reflex (stroking the sole of the foot) that of the first and second sacral segments. These, and corresponding reflexes in the upper extremities, are of great diagnostic importance, for " the percussion hammer provides the clinician with a form of interrogation which forces from the nervous system a succinct answer . . . in the form of a clearly visible somatic change—a piece of objective evidence which, if properly interpreted, can throw light upon the integrity or impairment of definite and distinct parts of the nervous system." (Pritchard.)

412

When a group of nerve cells forms a " focal point " for a number of reflex pathways concerned in a particular function, it is said to be a " centre " for that function. For example, the lowest segments of the spinal cord receive afferent impulses from the bladder and rectum, and control their activity through the nerves and ganglia of the sacral autonomic system. These spinal centres for micturition and defæcation are excited chiefly by impulses which signal the degree of distension of the bladder and rectum. It is, however, possible to postpone the emptying of the bladder in conformity with the demands of the environment. This is carried out by " higher centres " in the cerebral cortex, which are capable of inhibiting the " lower centres " in the spinal cord. The distinction between higher and lower centres depends simply on the variety of sensory impulses which reach the centre. The lower centres are connected to a few types of receptors which all lie in or near the organ controlled. The higher centres can be modified by a wide range of afferent stimuli, including those from the distance receptors.

In general, higher centres can have either a restraining or an exciting influence on lower centres. If the connections between higher and lower centres are cut, the removal of a pre-existing restraining influence will be followed by a sudden increase in the activity of the lower centres. The best example of this " release " is the sudden appearance of decerebrate rigidity after transection of the mid-brain. On the other hand, when a predominantly excitatory influence is cut off, the lower centre will become temporarily inexcitable. In the absence of the c.e.s., which is normally produced by impulses from the higher centre, other afferent impulses cannot set up enough c.e.s. on the cells of the lower centre to reach threshold. The sudden profound inexcitability of the spinal cord below a transection, which constitutes spinal shock, is an example of the removal of a predominantly excitatory influence from higher centres. Although phenomena of release are of great importance in the central nervous system, as one ascends the vertebrate and particularly the primate series, the excitatory influences of the higher centres become of greater importance, and as Sherrington has said, " In the higher types more than in the lower, the great cerebral senses activate the motor organs and impel the motions of the individual."

With these principles of interpretation in mind, we may now consider a summary of the effects of transecting the nervous system at certain levels, though the detailed explanation of the consequences is dependent on knowledge of the anatomical paths and connections of the main conducting tracts.

Peripheral Nerves

We have seen that the great peripheral nerve trunks contain both sensory and motor fibres, and cutting them will therefore produce loss of all sensation, and paralysis of the muscles throughout their distribution. If, however, we cut the individual spinal roots which combine to form the nerve, the result differs from that of cutting the nerve trunks in two ways. First, the loss of function will depend on whether the anterior roots or the posterior roots are cut—paralysis of the muscles resulting from the former, and loss of sensation resulting from the latter. Secondly, the anatomical distribution of the disability is quite different;

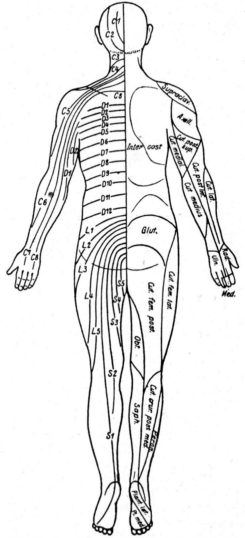

FIG. XII. 1. Distribution of the Nerve Supply to the Skin : left, segmental ; right, cutaneous nerves. (After Bing.)

when the roots are cut it is arranged segmentally as shown in Fig. XII. 1.

The Spinal Animal

In all vertebrates, transection of the spinal cord in the lower cerebral region is followed by an immediate loss of reflex activity below the section, called spinal shock. This begins to pass off in the frog in a few minutes, and in the dog and cat in about a quarter of an hour, and in the monkey in about an hour. In man, the first signs of recovery appear after some days. In the cat and dog, the flexor reflex and the tendon jerks are active within an hour, but the crossed extensor reflexes are not readily obtainable for several days. In the monkey, spinal shock is still more profound. At first, the limbs are entirely inert, peripheral stimulation is completely ineffective, and direct stimulation of the posterior roots elicits only feeble and tremulous responses. The cutaneous and tendon reflexes reappear during the next two or three weeks. Tone in the limbs remains permanently low, and all the reflexes obtainable are weak, poorly sustained and easily fatigued. The bladder is atonic at first, with retention of urine and dribbling overflow. After a time the bladder begins to empty itself reflexly.

Spinal transection in man is not unknown, but the cases which survive are usually those with lesions at or below the mid-thoracic region, rather lower than the experimental transections so far considered. The immediate effect is the loss of all movement and all sensation below the level of the lesion. Sensation is lost permanently, since nerve fibres in the central nervous system do not regenerate, but recovery of reflex movement and bladder function occurs. The main feature of the activity of the isolated spinal cord is that maintained contractions of the extensor muscles do not reappear, although tendon jerks may be present. The activity of the flexor muscles is greatly exaggerated, and increasing the strength of a painful stimulus to the foot will give rise to flexion of the ankle, knee and hip of the same side, followed by flexion of the opposite leg, an increase in the excitability of the bladder, and profuse sweating. This extreme overaction has been called the "mass reflex," and is probably the result of irradiation of excitation to all the neurones of the cord, except those of the extensor systems. These extensor moto-neurones and their associated internuncial neurones probably receive a great volume of excitatory influences normally from higher centres, and their depression after transection is correspondingly profound.

Unilateral section of the spinal cord, so that the left side is completely severed while the right remains intact, produces a characteristic pattern of sensory and motor defects. The muscles of the left side of the body below the lesion will be completely paralysed, owing to the interruption of the pyramidal tract, whose fibres originate in the cerebral cortex. The muscles can, therefore, no longer be moved voluntarily, though they can take part in reflex activities. When spinal shock has passed off, their tone may be enhanced. There is also vaso-dilatation on the same side. Loss of sensation occurs to some extent on both sides, some sensations being more affected on one side, and some on the other. Deep sensation such as the sense of position of the limbs will be lost on the side of the lesion, cutaneous pain and temperature sensation will be lost on the opposite side, while sensitivity to touch will be impaired on both sides. The distribution of the loss of sensation depends on the facts that the different senses are segregated in different tracts in the spinal cord, and that these tracts cross from one side of the cord to the other at different levels, on their way up to the brain.

Such, in a general way, are the effects of dividing the spinal cord. Simple reflexes are present, there is some vaso-motor control, since the arterial pressure is higher than that in a pithed animal, but the animal does not breathe. If, however, the section (Fig. XII. 2, Section III) through the brain-stem passes anterior to the medulla, a decerebrate preparation is made, and the animal breathes spontaneously, and exhibits a more complex organisation.

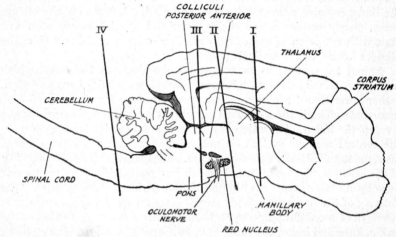

FIG. XII. 2.   Sagittal Section through the Brain of a Cat.

The lines I to IV represent the positions of the transverse sections referred to in the text in connection with the preparation of : I, the thalamic animal ; II, the mid-brain animal ; III, the decerebrate animal ; and IV, the spinal animal.   (After Magnus.)

The Decerebrate Animal

In the absence of external stimulation the preparation remains motionless except for respiratory movements : its temperature falls progressively unless warmth is applied from without.

We may enumerate some of the relatively simple but important reflexes whose " centres " are located in the medulla, and can therefore be detected in the decerebrate, but not in the spinal preparation :—

(1) The swallowing reflex, which has been considered in the chapter on digestion.

(2) The masticating reflex, for which branches of the trigeminal and glosso-pharyngeal nerves are the afferent elements, and the facial, hypo-glossal and trigeminal nerves the motor elements.

(3) The salivary reflex, which is initiated by stimulation of the taste buds, and impulses conveyed by the corresponding branches of the trigeminal, glosso-pharyngeal and olfactory nerves, and the secretory paths of which run in the facial, glosso-pharyngeal and sympathetic nerves.

(4) The vomiting reflex, in which the vagus and glosso-pharyngeal are the chief afferent nerves, and a variety of nerves carry the motor excitation to produce activity of the stomach, the œsophagus, the glottis, the muscles of the abdominal wall and thorax, and the diaphragm, etc.

(5) The reflexes of coughing and sneezing, the first arising as an irritation of the superior laryngeal, and the second of the endings of the trigeminal nerve in the nasal mucosa.

(6) Tear secretion, which may be induced by chemical irritation of the trigeminal endings, as, for example, by ammonia or acetic acid.

(7) The blink reflex, in which mechanical stimulation of the endings of the trigeminal nerves in the conjunctiva and cornea produce impulses which result in a motor discharge through the branches of the facial nerve to the orbicularis oculi.

FIG. XII. 3.   A Suspended **Decerebrate** and **Decerebellate Cat,** showing
exaggerated extensor tone (decerebrate rigidity).
The labyrinths are intact, and the head is in a relatively normal position
(*cf.* Fig. XII. 4).   (From Pollock and Davis.)

(8) A number of reflexes from the pinna of the ear, mostly concerned with the prevention of entry or the removal of foreign bodies.

There is thus rather a concentration of reflex activity, similar in kind to that of the spinal cord, in the relatively small region known as the medulla. In addition to its function as a reflex centre, it includes the great conducting pathways which form the tracts we have mentioned as passing along the cord. Over and above this, however, some of the most important automatic regulator mechanisms can be located in the medulla, and chief among them are the respiratory centres, the cardio-inhibitor (vagus) centre, and the vasomotor centres, each of which has been considered in previous chapters in an appropriate context. The mechanisms of which these centres are part function in a fairly normal manner in the decerebrate animal, and such abnormality as there is, is due to the absence of the restraining influence of the higher centres. The over-activity of the respiratory centre in the decerebrate animal may be quoted as an example, for it brings about undue lowering of the carbon dioxide concentration in the blood, resembling that produced by over-ventilation or forced breathing in man ; the survival of this experimental preparation is favoured by increasing the " dead space " of the respiratory passages (*e.g.*, connecting a few inches of rubber tubing to a cannula fixed in the trachea).

The distribution of tone of the skeletal muscles in the decerebrate cat or dog is abnormal, as has already been described. It must not be supposed, however, that the " exaggerated standing," illustrated in Fig.

Fig. XII. 4. Tonic **Neck Reflexes** in a Suspended Decerebrate Cat.
The labyrinths have been destroyed, and consequently the head has dropped (*cf.* Fig. XII. 3). This depression of the head induces reflex flexion of the fore limbs and extension of the hind limbs. (From Pollock and Davis.)

XII. 3, means more than that a preparation with extensor rigidity will stand when placed on its feet. If laid on its side, it remains lying, and shows no signs of righting itself—that is, the " righting reflexes " are absent. The characteristic postural tone, moreover, is by no means invariable, for Magnus and his colleagues have shown that it is determined by the position of the head. Varying the position of the head on the trunk changes the degree of extension of the various neck muscles ; this gives rise to a corresponding reflex change in the position of the limbs, as in Fig. XII. 4 ; this relation can be abolished by severing the posterior roots in the cervical region. Even when these " neck reflexes " are abolished in this way, the position of the head still affects the distribution of tone, but this time it is not the position relative to that of the trunk, but the position of the head in space, which is the effective stimulus, and gives rise to " labyrinthine reflexes."

The uncomplicated neck reflexes can therefore only be studied after extirpation of both labyrinthine organs.

Some effects of these neck reflexes can be seen in operation in the ordinary behaviour of domestic animals. Bending the head downwards results in flexion of the fore-limbs and extension of the hind-limbs as in taking food off the ground (Fig. XII. 4). Bending the head upwards produces extension of the fore-limbs and flexion of the hind-limbs, as in

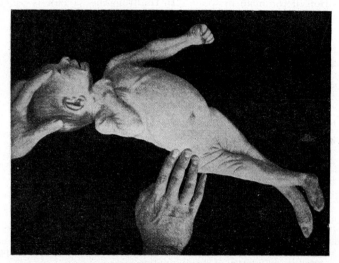

Fig. XII. 5. Tonic **Neck Reflexes** in a New-born Infant, whose brain had been disorganised by a cerebral hæmorrhage.

Rotation of the head so as to bring the chin over the left shoulder induces extension of the fore and hind limbs on the left (face) side, and flexion of the limbs on the right (occipital) side. (After Magnus and de Kleijn.)

looking up at a shelf. Rotational or sideways bending movements of the head are in general associated with extension of the limbs on the side to which the head " faces," and flexion of those on the occipital side, as in Fig. XII. 5.

The labyrinthine reflexes contribute a strong influence in keeping the head up, as may be seen by comparison of Figs. XII. 3 and 4, showing the decerebrate cat, before and after extirpation of the labyrinth, in which the head of the latter animal has drooped, producing the associated changes in limb posture mentioned above as characteristic of this neck reflex. The labyrinthine reflexes due to rotational and other movements of the head are combined with the neck reflexes in the decerebrate preparation to produce a somewhat complicated pattern of attitudinal response.

14—2

The Labyrinth

The labyrinth lies in the petrous bone in close anatomical relation with the inner ear, with which it has, however, no physiological connections (Fig. XIV. 28). It consists essentially of (1) the semicircular canals, lying in three planes at right angles to each other, and concerned with the initiation of transient reflex responses to rotational movements of the head ; (2) the utricle which encloses a solid otolith lying against the projecting filaments of the hair cells of the macula, and concerned with the initiation of steady reflex responses according to the orientation of the head in the gravitational field ; and (3) the saccule, which also contains an otolith and is perhaps also concerned with signalling the position of the head in space. In the frog, the saccule is concerned

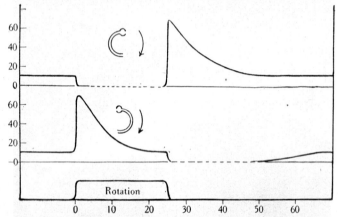

Fig. XII. 6. Frequency of **Action Potentials** from the horizontal **Semicircular Canal** of a cat, when acceleration and deceleration are separated by an interval of steady rotation.

There is a steady discharge during rest which is suppressed by rotation in one direction, and augmented by rotation in the opposite direction. Cessation of the rotation leads to an after discharge, or a silent period according to the direction of the rotation. (Adrian.)

only with the detection of low frequency vibration. In the cat, there are apparently two separate systems which signal tilts from side to side, and fore and aft respectively, but they have not yet been identified anatomically.

When the head is rotated, the endolymph in the semicircular canals, owing to its inertia, lags behind. This flow of endolymph relative to the walls of the canal will displace the cupola, which consists of hair cells whose bases are embedded in a gelatinous matrix in which they are in contact with a number of nerve endings. Electrical studies have shown that the nerve endings discharge spontaneously while the head is at rest. When the cupola is displaced in one direction, the frequency of discharge is increased and with displacement in the opposite direction it is decreased (Fig. XII. 6). As a result, short lasting rotations are accurately signalled. In steady rotations, the discharge of impulses behaves as though the cupola were displaced during the period of acceleration, and then drifted slowly back to its resting position during the period of steady rotation. Suddenly stopping the rotation of the head will displace the cupola in the opposite direction, and although movements of the endolymph die down in about 3 seconds, the cupola seems to take about 25–30 seconds to return to its resting position. During this time, the subject will experience a sensation of rotation in the opposite direction, and will show oscillatory movements of the eyes.

Removal of the labyrinth on one side is followed by turning the head and eyes toward that side, and in consequence of this abnormal position of the neck and of the existence of the neck reflexes, the tone of the limb muscles is high on the affected side and low on the normal side, while the trunk is curved with its concavity on the affected side. Any maintained deviation of the eyes which is brought about by the labyrinth will normally be counteracted by the cortex, which induces a quick movement back towards the fixation point. This results in an oscillatory movement of the eyes, consisting of a slow movement towards the side of less labyrinthine activity and quick jerk back. This phenomenon is called *nystagmus*.

The functions of the labyrinth are most prominent in the rabbit, and become less and less important in comparison with the visual and other cortical mechanisms, as animals higher in the scale of the mammalian series are examined. If, for example, the labyrinth is removed on both sides in a cat or ape, and time is allowed for the immediate effects of the operation to pass off, the lesion can only be detected in special circumstances : (1) if the animal be immersed in water its orientation is so disordered as to make swimming impossible, and (2) if the animal be dropped to the ground from a height, it looses the power of so righting itself that it falls on its feet whatever its original position. In other circumstances, in which labyrinthine reflexes normally play a part, compensatory cortical mechanisms are completely effective in concealing the defect.

The Mid-Brain Animal

Section II in Fig. XII. 2 results in the formation of the mid-brain animal. It differs essentially from the decerebrate animal in the absence of decerebrate rigidity and in the possession of " righting reflexes." These are initiated by the skin of the trunk, the labyrinth, the proprioceptors of the muscles of the neck and enable the animal to turn over when it is laid on its back or its side. Rademaker thought that the essential nervous structure for the existence of righting reflexes was the red nucleus, but animals can retain their righting reflexes after its complete destruction.

The mid-brain animal is liable to show occasional outbursts of activity, running and jumping movements and hyperpnœa. In spite of the absence of extensor rigidity, and the relatively normal relation of tone between flexors and extensors, the animal can now stand, but the standing reflexes are more complex than those which we have shown as

responsible for the "exaggerated standing" of the decerebrate preparation. The normal control of posture, which allows standing,
involves more co-ordination and flexibility, and depends on labyrinthine, neck, proprioceptive, and in the intact animal even ocular
reflexes.

The postural reactions of the body at rest, or *static reflexes* were
divided by Magnus into *stance reflexes*, which maintain an attitude, and
righting reflexes, which restore it after a disturbance. The maintenance
of the standing position in a mid-brain animal requires (1) local static
reflexes, *e.g.*, the stretch reflex; (2) segmental static reflexes, for example,
involving both hind limbs; (3) general static reactions which may involve
the whole body. These include tonic neck and labyrinthine reflexes
which maintain the position of the head, and a further set of reflexes
which maintain the compensatory pose of the eyes. In addition,
there are a number of reactions to movement, the *statokinetic reflexes*.

It may here be remarked that the experimental investigation of postural
reflexes has been largely carried out on cats and rabbits, and that it must
not be supposed that exactly the same distribution of importance of function
can be attributed to the various corresponding parts of the brain in man.
Evidence obtained from disease, trauma and malformations of the human
nervous system suggests that whereas the mechanisms described are present,
the part played in maintaining postural tone by the higher centres is relatively
greater. The reference of posture to the eye and its movements, including a
reflex path through the cerebral cortex and the pyramidal system, is one
aspect of this more extensive control by the higher centres in man than in
the lower mammalia.

The Thalamus Animal

Section I. (Fig. XII. 2) passes through the thalamus, and gives rise to
the "thalamus animal," sometimes referred to as the "Magnus animal."
This preparation shows the postural neck and labyrinthine reflexes,
and also the righting reflexes, while the distribution of tone between
extensors and flexors is normal. It differs from the simpler preparations,
previously described, particularly in its power of performing highly
co-ordinated movements, such as walking and jumping, in the appearance
of occasional outbursts of extreme activity, and in the stability of its
internal environment. The differences are chiefly attributable to the
retention of the hypothalamic region and the thalamic nuclei which form
part of the main afferent system.

The main manifestation of hypothalamic activity is known as
"sham rage." Trifling stimuli will make the animal lash its tail, growl,
spit and claw wildly, its pupils to dilate, and its hair to rise. Most of
these activities, which are carried out by the sympathetic nervous
system, can also be elicited by direct electrical stimulation of the
hypothalamus. The posterior part of hypothalamus consists of the
lateral and posterior nuclei, and is connected with the sympathetic
system. The anterior part includes the paraventricular, the supra-
optic and the tuber nuclei, and is connected to the parasympathetic
system and the pituitary. Electrical stimulation of the posterior part

is followed by acceleration of the heart, a rise in blood pressure, inhibition of the stomach and intestine, dilatation of the pupil, and hyperglycæmia. Stimulation of the anterior part produces the opposite effects, with the addition of profuse sweating. Direct warming of this region produces widespread vaso-dilatation of the skin, and sweating. Shivering has also been produced by stimulation of the hypothalamus, which is probably the principal centre for temperature regulation.

All the nervous mechanisms which are concerned in keeping the internal environment of the body constant are related in some way to the hypothalamus. Water metabolism, carbohydrate metabolism, temperature regulation, and fat deposition are all disturbed when there are lesions of the hypothalamus. Disturbances of sleep are also common in man and animals after destruction of posterior and lateral nuclei. The mode of action of this hypothetical "sleep," or better, "waking centre," is as yet obscure. It is possible that it may modify the excitability of the cortex by widely distributed impulses from the thalamus.

The nuclei of the thalamus can be grouped into three sets according to their connections. One group has only sub-cortical connections. A second group receives fibres from sub-cortical nuclei and sends projection fibres to the cortex. Very little is known of the function of either of these groups. The third group receives fibres from the great ascending afferent tracts and its nuclei send their projection fibres to the sensory cortex. There is a sharp localisation of different parts of the body in these nuclei. Impulses from receptors for deep pressure and muscle sense pass only to the thalamus of the opposite side, while impulses concerned with cutaneous sensations are relayed to both sides. It has been found that a single volley of afferent impulses reaching the thalamus sets up in the thalamo-cortical fibres in the internal capsule, a burst of a few impulses at a very high frequency followed by a variable amount of after-discharge. The thalamus is not merely a relay station, but probably has some integrative activity and is especially concerned with the appreciation of pain. Impulses from the spino-thalamic tracts and the medial lemniscus converge upon it and are relayed together to the cortex. Lesions of the thalamus in man sometimes produce a peculiar syndrome in which stimulation of the opposite half of the body gives rise to intense paroxysms of pain. This was at one time ascribed to the release of the thalamus from a hypothetical inhibitory control exerted by the sensory cortex, and there are certainly extensive cortico-thalamic connections by which the cortex could affect the excitability of the thalamus. Destruction of the sensory cortex alone does not, however, give rise to this overaction of painful sensations. The sensory functions of the thalamus will be further discussed in connection with the sensory cortex.

The Cerebellum

Until recently, our ideas of the function of the cerebellum have been derived almost entirely from the study of cerebellar lesions in man.

Attempts to lay bare the underlying mechanism by the usual methods of experimental physiology were not, at first, very successful. This was due in part to the fact that there are no reflexes which can be abolished by removal of the cerebellum, so that the effects observed are always changes in excitability of other parts of the nervous system, which may be difficult to define. There was also a failure to realise that the cere-

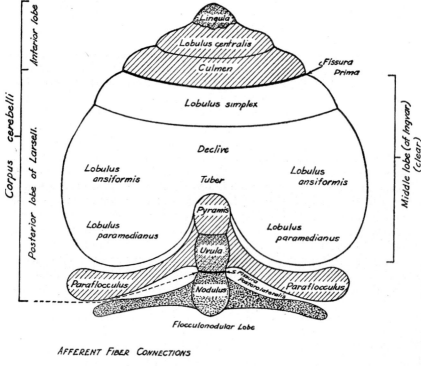

AFFERENT FIBER CONNECTIONS

Vestibular ⎤
            ⎬ *Paleocerebellum*
Spinal   ⎦

Corticopontocerebellar - Neocerebellum

FIG. XII. 7. Diagram of the primate **Cerebellar Cortex**, showing the principal divisions and afferent fibre connections. (Fulton, after Larsell, "Physiology of the Nervous System").

bellum consists of two phylogenetically distinct parts, the palæocerebellum and the neocerebellum (Fig. XII. 7). The palæocerebellum is associated with spinal and vestibular mechanisms. The neocerebellum, which has evolved comparatively recently, is related to the cerebral cortex. The neocerebellum forms almost the whole of the organ in man, and experimentally, its activity can only be studied in monkeys or apes.

The neocerebellum (Fig. XII. 7) comprises the lateral lobes and part of the vermis. Its main afferent connections are with the pontine nuclei *viâ* the middle cerebellar peduncles. These nuclei receive their fibres almost entirely from the cerebral cortex. The efferent fibres of the lateral lobes run to the dentate nucleus, whose fibres pass by the superior cerebellar peduncle to the thalamus and cerebral cortex of the opposite side. Each lateral lobe is concerned with the movements of the limbs of the same side of the body.

Stimulation of the neocerebellum results in an increase in the excitability of the motor cortex of the opposite hemisphere. There is also an increase in its resting electrical activity. Both these effects are abolished if the superior cerebellar peduncle is cut. Removal of the lateral lobe in the chimpanzee is followed by a severe loss of tone in the

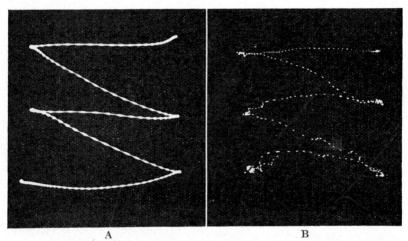

A   B

Fig. XII. 8. Records obtained by photographing points of light attached to the tips of the forefingers, as a patient with a lesion of the right side of the cerebellum attempted to move each finger slowly and accurately between series of luminous red points (not visible in the photographs) in a dark room. Each flash of light corresponds to 0.04 sec. The range of each movement was about 75 cm.

A is the record obtained from the left hand (normal).

B is the record obtained from the right hand (affected), and the irregularity in the rate, and in the directions of movements, and the failure to arrest the finger accurately at the points, are well shown. (Gordon Holmes, " Brain ".)

limbs of the same side. This recovers slowly, and is then associated with clumsiness of voluntary movements. Damaging the dentate nucleus or cutting the superior cerebellar peduncle produces the same symptoms together with tremor. There is, therefore, strong evidence that the neocerebellum has normally a tonic excitatory influence on the cerebral motor cortex, and through it, maintains the tone of the muscles.

Destruction of the neocerebellum in man is always accompanied by a loss of tone in the limbs of the same side (atonia). There is also considerable weakness of voluntary movement (asthenia). The most conspicuous feature in man which is not easy to demonstrate even in apes, is the disorderly performance of voluntary movements (astasia). The arm is moved rapidly and jerkily, and tends to overshoot and oscillate before reaching the mark. (Fig. XII. 8). Reversing a movement is difficult, and a series of alternating movements, *e.g.*, pronation and supination of the wrist, are performed slowly and awkwardly. There is no interference with the synergistic action of muscles, but there is often " decomposition of movement," so that the movements of one joint, *e.g.*, the elbow, is finished before movement at the wrist begins. It seems, therefore, that the cerebellum is responsible for the distribution of excitation to muscles in time and space.

The palæocerebellum (Fig. XII. 7). has two functional divisions : the flocculo-nodular lobe, which is concerned with equilibration, and a section concerned chiefly with spinal mechanisms. This latter consists of the anterior lobe, and posteriorly, of the pyramis and uvula, separated by the neocerebellum. Extirpation of the flocculo-nodular lobe of one side has precisely opposite effects to the removal of the labyrinth of the same side. Bilateral removal of this lobe in monkeys produces a staggering gait without any interference with the voluntary movements of the extremities. This is prevented if both labyrinths are previously destroyed. The flocculo-nodular lobe then inhibits the activity of the labyrinths.

The anterior lobe normally inhibits the extensor mechanisms of the spinal cord. Its stimulation abolishes decerebrate rigidity on both sides, and its removal is followed by a maintained increase in tone of the extensor muscles. If it is removed in an animal already decerebrate, the extensor rigidity becomes extreme, as in the cats of Figs. XII. 3 and 4. The results of the removal of the whole of the cerebellum in different animals are conflicting, as they depend on the relative development of the palæo- and neocerebellum. In the dog, in which the neocerebellum is not greatly developed, there follows a hypertonia owing to the removal of the anterior lobe. In the chimpanzee, there is hypotonia, owing to the removal of the excitatory effect of the neocerebellum on the motor cortex.

Lesions confined to the palæocerebellum are rare in man, since it only forms a small part of the organ. Destruction of the flocculo-nodular lobe occasionally occurs in children, who show unsteadiness in walking, with a tendency to walk on a wide base, but there is no hypotonia, no tremor, and no interference with voluntary movements of the hands or legs.

THE CEREBRAL CORTEX

The study of the cerebral cortex is one of quite peculiar significance to the physiologist and physician, for to its functions are attributed most of the valued qualities in which the human species excels in the animal kingdom. The neural processes in the cortex determine what distinguishes the character of one man from that of another—his personality. They also enable him to adapt himself to a novel environment by memory, learning, foresight, and other adjuncts to intelligent behaviour. If such terms as the " mind " have any meaning apart from the behaviour of the whole organism, they are clearly more closely connected with the cerebral cortex than with any other part of the body. So it comes about that psychologists and even philosophers have to take the properties of the brain into account when formulating their theories, and since these theories may be of the utmost importance, as in the practice of education and psychotherapy, it behoves us to examine these properties with more than usually critical attention. The temptation to erect elaborate superstructures of psychological theory upon a speculative neurological hypothesis, put forward innocently as a provisional summary of the recorded experiments, is apt to increase the confusion in a field of inquiry already sufficiently obscure. At the frontier between two sciences, the specialist in one often borrows, none too critically, suggestions from the other which happen to enrich his argument. In this, even more than in most branches of physiology, therefore, vigilance is needed in distinguishing between the theories (and facts) which may be believed with some confidence, those which are only suspected as likely, and those which are not known, though various guesses may be under consideration. Individual temperament will play a part in assessing the degree of credibility to be attached to any particular hypothesis. Few things in scientific or medical practice are more valuable than a robust sense of what is likely, and this is probably best developed by a continuous attempt to segregate beliefs and hypotheses, according as they are more or less reliable. In the last resort, one's judgment of a theory depends on the nature of the evidence for and against it, its scientific convenience, and the trust one may place in the discrimination of its sponsors.

The study of cerebral function may be approached in various ways : (1) The anatomical structure of the nervous system must be the basis for all physiological methods, and must be examined by dissection and reading. (2) The significance of the anatomical method is immensely enhanced by comparing the structure of the nervous system in different organisms, and especially by relating the degree of development of the cerebral hemispheres, with differences of behaviour of animals at different stages in the evolutionary scale. (3) The embryological methods include the correlation of defects in the brain due to arrest of development with dislocation of normal function. Another line of investigation depends on the fact that the fibres of different tracts in the central nervous system acquire their myelin sheaths at different ages in the development of the individual, and the belief that these fibres do not convey impulses until the time when they have become myelinated. The function of a particular tract should thus appear at the stage of development when its myelination is complete. (4) Exact histological examination of the cortex has revealed regions with distinct and characteristic arrangements of cells and fibres, corresponding presumably with distinct functions. (5) The physiological methods proper include studies on the behaviour of the whole animal, the effects of stimulating or destroying parts of the cortex on the behaviour of the animal, the investigation of the electrical activity of the cortex and its modification. (6) Clinical observations on men afflicted with circumscribed lesions in nervous disease, or with localised injury, due, for example, to gunshot wounds, have to be relied on to a great extent when information is required concerning cerebral functions peculiar to human beings.

Before considering the results of some of these methods, it may be as

well to point out that the phrase " localisation of function " is used in
connection with the cerebral cortex in two senses. First it is used in
connection with the association of the function of a particular area of the
cortex with a particular part of the body. Although there is a certain
amount of overlapping, there is well-established spatial representation
of the body in the cortex. Secondly, there is the idea that different
kinds of cerebral activity occur during the excitation of different parts
of the cortex. For example, there is said to be a " sensory mechanism "

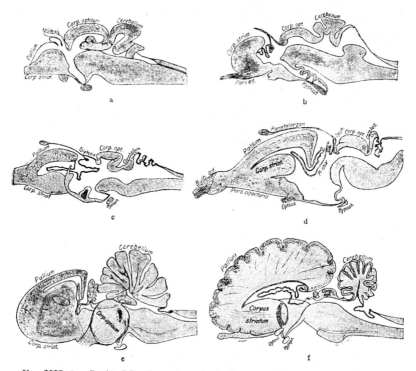

Fig. XII. 9.   Sagittal Sections through the Brains of Vertebrates, showing the
Progressive Development of the Cerebral Hemispheres.

(*a*) Teleosts ;   (*b*) Elasmobranchs ;   (*c*) Amphibia ;   (*d*) Reptiles ;
(*e*) Birds ; (*f*) Mammals. (After Edinger.)

for the foot in the upper part of the post-central gyrus, and a corresponding " motor mechanism " for the foot in the pre-central gyrus. This idea
comes from the observation of the effect of removal of these two areas on
sensation and the power of voluntary movement. There is, however,
no reason to believe that all the neural processes necessary for the
appreciation of touch occur only in these parts of the cortex, and that no
other parts of the cortex are involved. The localisation of a lesion
which destroys an essential link in a neural process is a very different
matter from the localisation of the whole process. There is, in fact, no
opposition between the views that some essential steps in particular

processes are localised in particular cortical areas, and the view that the cerebral cortex works as a whole.

This is not the place in which to deal with the comparative anatomy of the cerebral hemispheres, and we will only recall the dramatic development of these organs, in the mammalia as contrasted with that in the lower vertebrates (see Fig. XII. 9), as an introduction to the consequences of their extirpation. These, as might be expected, involve a more extensive disturbance of the behaviour of an animal, the larger, relatively, is its fore-brain.

It is difficult to detect any dislocation of the normal behaviour of fish (teleosts) after removal of the fore-brain. They swim about, moving spontaneously, seeking food and discriminating between, say, a worm and a less delectable object, such as a thread of cotton. They mingle naturally with their normal fellows, and cannot be distinguished from them by their behaviour. There is little reason to suppose that the fore-brain is any more prominent in the neural mechanism of elasmobranchs, although, since they recognise prey by smell rather than by sight, and the operation incidentally involves removal of the olfactory lobes, extirpation of the fore-brain interferes with the natural feeding habits of these animals.

Loss of the fore-brain seems to inconvenience a frog almost as little as a fish, so long as care is taken to avoid injury to the mid-brain. It moves spontaneously and naturally, and divides its time normally between land and water, in which it swims like any other frog. It leaps and escapes from enemies effectively. There is indeed a suggestion that it is not quite as good at catching flies as its intact fellows, and that some of its reflexes are unusually excitable, so that, for example, it croaks regularly when its back is stroked, but except in inconsiderable details, its behaviour is unaffected.

Removal of the fore-brain in birds has much more obvious consequences. In these, as in mammals, there is much more widespread disturbance of function, and the disturbance is more extensive during the first few days, while they are still under the influence of the shock and irritation due to the local mutilation of the nervous system, than later, when the effects may be ascribed mainly to absence of the excised organ. At first, then, birds treated in this way become quite immobile unless stimulated. They just stand still, with eyes closed, as if asleep, and remain so indefinitely. When disturbed, they show that they can walk and fly normally, and that the balancing mechanism is unimpaired. But they never make a spontaneous movement nor take food naturally, even if they are standing on a heap of grain.

When the stage of relative recovery sets in, as it does if the thalamus has not been damaged, quite a different kind of behaviour becomes apparent. The animal is excessively restless, and constantly on the move. Obstacles are succesfully avoided. The bird responds to sound and light, and can fly and balance normally and sleeps at night. The characteristic disturbance of function is now, however, shown in connection with more complex acts. A male bird avoids a female as it does any other obstacle. A female ignores its young. Food remains unrecognised. All effects of previous training disappear—the carrier pigeon forgets its " home," and the parrot ceases to talk. It is evident that the animal has lost part of a mechanism involved in complex chain reflexes, and in acquiring new reactions to significant stimuli in the environment. Nevertheless, a certain amount of training of such animals may still be possible, and a sound or metronome beat may still become a conditioned stimulus signalling food. (Conditioned reflexes will be considered below.)

The effects of extirpation of the cerebral hemispheres in mammals have been studied most completely on the dog. In Goltz's classical experiment a dog was observed for one and a half years after the operation, and more recent experiments have lasted up to three years. After recovery from the shock such animals can run and jump nimbly, as is described in connection with the " thalamus animal." Sleeping and waking periods alternate regularly, and the animal growls or barks if disturbed, and moves about spontaneously. The decorticated dog is, however, blind, and runs up against obstacles, though the reflex contraction of the pupils to light remains. Smell is abolished owing to interference with the olfactory nerves ; sleep, however, is interrupted by loud sounds. The sense of pain seems unimpaired, for if pinched the animal will growl, and may snap clumsily at the offending hand. Food and drink is taken when brought into contact with the snout.

The most prominent change in the animal is the loss of everything that distinguishes the behaviour of one dog from that of another, and its complete lack of interest in its surroundings. Thus it no longer answers to its name, or recognises the man who feeds it. It is unmoved by the barking of other dogs, or by animals of the opposite sex. It cannot be trained to acquire simple habits. It has, in fact, lost all the characteristics which justify the description of a dog as a relatively intelligent animal.

The decortication of rats results in the loss of previously-acquired habits, and in an almost complete disability to develop new ones by careful training. Similar experiments on monkeys have not been very illuminating, as the animals only survive for a few weeks, nor have the fragmentary observations on anencephalic monsters (human infants born without a cerebrum and who usually survive only a few days).

This brief outline of the comparative physiology of the cerebrum has called attention to the connection between the relative size of the organ and a certain kind of complexity of behaviour of the animal, and this connection has been confirmed by the observation showing that it is just this sort of complexity that disappears when the organ is surgically removed. The relation of the area of the cortex to behaviour is further illustrated within the group of the mammalia, by comparing the number of convolutions on the surface of the brains of the rabbit, dog, monkey and man. The number and depth of these convolutions increases in that order, and in man it is so great that the area of the cortex reaches about 2,000 sq. cm., of which about one-third is actually exposed to the surface.

It is clear that the cortex has increased in size as the special senses have increased in usefulness. The usefulness of a sense is not a question of mere acuity. The eye of a hawk is proverbially sharper than ours, and the range and fineness of grading of a dog's hearing is much greater than ours. Our advantage lies in part in our power of co-ordinating simultaneous impressions from all senses, and associating them with similar sensations in the past. The other difference lies in our power of actively investigating the environment. The cortex is not a mere receptacle and sorting system for sense data. When a dog receives a new stimulus, he cocks his ears and sniffs the air, Pavlov's " What is it ?" reflex. When in man the same situation is followed by reflection and the choice of the best possible method of investigation, the connection between stimulus and response is too complex to be called reflex.

The cortical activity of an animal, aware of his environment by his five senses, and reacting to new stimuli by active investigation, is too complex to observe profitably. The problem can be broken up by first examining the activity of different parts of the cortex, and then applying the information so obtained to the study of the behaviour of the whole animal ; we must then use special methods to control the flood of afferent sense impressions, so as to vary one factor at a time.

The first hint that the functions of different areas of the cortex might differ, came from Gall, a Viennese physician in the early 19th century. He had a school friend with an unusually good memory and very prominent eyes. On this basis he suggested that memory was located in the frontal lobes, and that the development of the mental faculties was accompanied by growth of a corresponding cortical area. This theory was elaborated into " phrenology " by Spurzheim who located a number of spurious psychological faculties, but by the end of the 19th century it had fallen into well earned disrepute. Scientific interest in the subject was revived in 1860, when Broca, a Paris neurologist, described two patients who had become speechless. At postmortem examination, he found in both cases rather extensive lesions which involved the posterior part of the lower frontal gyrus on the left side. About this time, Hughlings Jackson predicted the existence of an excitable motor area from consideration of the type of epilepsy which now bears his name. Usually caused by injury, these convulsions begin with a movement or sensation which, in any one individual, is regularly located in the same place—for example, in a thumb ; and this localising sign is always found to be associated with a circumscribed injury to a corresponding part of the cortex. In consequence, a relation between particular regions of the cortex and particular parts of the body was suspected, and this was confirmed by the discovery that electrical stimulation of a certain portion of the cortex produced movements, and that in a general way the site of stimulation determined the part of the body which moved. This region of the cortex is known as the *motor cortex,* and is situated in front of the Rolandic fissure as shown in Fig. XII. 10.

Histologically, the motor cortex is distinguished by the presence of cells, some of which exceed 15 μ in diameter, and are called giant cells. The axons of the giant and the smaller pyramidal cells give rise to the myelinated fibres of the pyramidal tract, which degenerate after ablation of the motor cortex.

Electrical stimulation of the motor cortex produces discrete movements of the opposite side of the body. It is possible to map out leg, arm and face areas in which movements rather than muscles seem to be the units represented. The relation between the point stimulated and the resulting movement is not a very stable one ; different movements

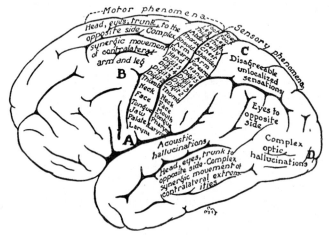

Fig. XII. 10. Diagram of the **Chief Cortical Areas in Man,** showing the principal excitable areas as determined by direct stimulation of the brain under local anæsthesia. (From Fulton " Physiology of the Nervous System.")

may be elicited by exciting the same points under varying conditions of narcosis, blood supply, and temperature, but previous stimulation of the cortex is most effective in modifying the result. The characteristic features of cortical stimulation were described by Sherrington as facilitation, reversal and deviation of response. Continued stimulation of a point may lead to an increase in amplitude of the movement (facilitation), or to its reversal, *e.g.,* of flexion to extension, or to its replacement by another movement entirely (deviation of response). While these terms are useful in describing the results of experiment, they do not tell us much about the normal activity of the cortex. Walshe remarks that " Electrical stimulation appears to sample the motor cortex, revealing fragmentary reactions but not clearly revealing the general design of the cortical representation of movements."

The most detailed knowledge of the results of stimulation of the human cortex is derived from operations under local anæsthesia.

Penfield and Boldrey have summarised the results of some thousands of stimulations in their diagram (Fig. XII. 10). The larger the variety of movement that can be obtained from a part of the body, the larger is its cortical area. There is considerable overlap between the areas responsible for movements of different parts of the body, and some overlapping

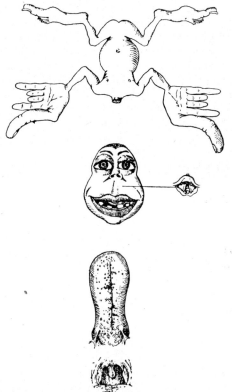

Fig. XII. 11. Sensory and Motor Homunculus, indicating the order and comparative size of the parts of the body as they appear from above down on the Rolandic cortex (compare Fig. XII. 10). The larynx, lying between the nose and the lips, represents vocalisation, and the pharynx, at the bottom, represents swallowing. Note the comparatively large size of the thumb, lips and tongue (between lips and pharynx) indicating that they occupy comparatively long vertical segments of the Rolandic cortex. Sensation in the genitalia and rectum lie above and posterior to the lower extremity, and are not shown. (Penfield and Boldrey, "Brain".)

of motor and sensory areas in front of and behind the central sulcus. A " desire to move " followed stimulation of a number of points in the motor area.

The nature of the outflow from the motor cortex has been made clear by recording simultaneously the electrical activity of the cortex and the impulses in a single unit in the pyramidal tract. Usually, oscillations of electrical potential in the cortex at 7–10 per second were accompanied by single impulses in the pyramidal fibre at the same rate. Occasionally, instead of a single impulse, there were two or three impulses very close together. After sensory stimulation, the rate of discharge rose to 50–150 per second, and during cortical convulsions, each volley of impulses consisted of 30–40 impulses at rates of 500–1000 per second. With an increase in the rate of discharge, there was usually movement of the muscles, in spite of the presence of an anæsthetic. Presumably, therefore, the slow stream of impulses when the cortex is at rest, keeps up a state of subliminal excitation of the neurones of the spinal cord.

The effect of removal of the motor cortex varies considerably with the species of animal studied. The leg area of the monkey, for example, can be mapped out by stimulation, and cleanly removed. When the animal recovers from the anæsthetic, there is a complete loss of " voluntary movement " and of tone in the leg of the opposite side, an immediate flaccid paralysis, which may be followed in some days by an increasing

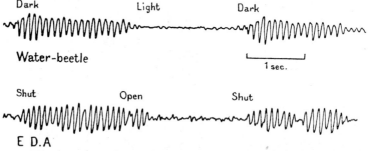

Fig. XII. 12. Comparison of **Action Potential Waves** from the eye of the water beetle in darkness and light, and from the brain of a human subject (E.D.A.) with eyes open and closed. (E. D. Adrian and B. H. C. Matthews, " Brain.")

stiffness. Recovery of gross movements begins in about a week, and after a month, there is no detectable difference between the two sides. In the lower primates, represented by the lemur and the baboon, recovery is slower, and in the chimpanzee, it is slower still, and is never complete. There is a permanent loss of position sense and clumsiness of fine movements which limits the usefulness of the limb. In man, destruction of the motor area for a limb is followed by a flaccid paralysis, and if the lesion could be strictly limited to the motor area, the paralysis would be permanently flaccid. Any recovery in motor power which may occur, is attributed to the activity of cells which had been damaged but not destroyed by the initial lesion. The limb may take part in lower reflex acts and movements expressive of emotion. Smiling for example, can still occur, when there is no voluntary power of moving the lips.

After about a week, there is usually an increase in tone and reflex excitability and the paralysis is said to be spastic. Its mechanism is obscure, but it is believed to be due to the involvement of part of the " extra-pyramidal " system by the rather extensive lesions which are met with clinically. This is a system capable of suppressing the activity of the motor cortex. It consists of the region immediately in front of the motor area, often called the *strip*, the basal ganglia, and their connections with the substantia nigra and the tectospinal tracts. Lesions confined to basal ganglia and mid-brain in man are followed by considerable increases in tone of the muscles, a cog-wheel jerkiness of voluntary movement, and gross tremor which can be diminished by voluntary effort. It is, therefore, possible that disorders in which there is an increase in tone in the limbs may be due to release from the extra-pyramidal system, which normally exerts an inhibitory effect on the pyramidal system.

The Sensory Areas of the Cortex

The same methods of stimulation, excision and the recording of electrical activity have been used to study the sensory cortex. Penfield and Boldrey have mapped out the sensory areas in man, and have found that about two-thirds of their responses were obtained from behind the central sulcus, and the remainder in front of it. Pain was very seldom reported by their patients, and when it was, may have arisen from the stimulation of pain endings on blood vessels. Touch, tickling, warmth, cold, and a sensation of movement were most frequently felt. Another method of stimulation which has been widely used in animals, consists of the application of strychnine to small areas of the cortex. After strychnine, an impulse which would normally have excited a few cells only will now excite a large number, and perhaps all the neurones from that area. This produces a " strychnine spike," a large electrical wave by which the functional connections of the area treated with strychnine can be traced. If small paper squares soaked in strychnine are placed on the post-central gyrus and later removed, the animal will have a corresponding area of hyperæsthesia on the opposite side of the body. Mere touching of hairs will give rise to signs of pain and irritation. In the monkey this method maps out a sensory area which extends over the middle third of the cortex, from the posterior part of the frontal convolutions as far back as the parieto-occipital sulcus. Some functional boundaries are observed, since treatment with strychnine of the arm area does not affect the leg area. The localised injection of minute quantities of strychnine has been used as a method of mapping out the connections between the sensory cortex and the nuclei of the thalamus.

The effects of the excision of the sensory cortex in animals can only be studied if we have an adequate method of testing sensation. Nearly all such work is combined with the establishment of conditioned reflexes or maze running habits, and will be described later. This work has also emphasised the importance of cortical dominance as one ascends the evolutionary scale. If the whole of the occipital cortex of both sides is removed in a rat, all previous visual habits are lost, but those which depend on the distance and direction of objects can be re-established. In a monkey, the only visual conditioned reflexes which can be established after the same operation, depend on simple appreciation of the difference between light and darkness. The animal cannot appreciate the form or position of objects. A man who has both his occipital lobes injured is permanently and completely blind.

The study of the electrical activity of the cortex has confirmed the results of stimulation. It is possible to record the potential changes in the cortex due to the arrival of impulses which were set up by touching the skin. These changes always appear first in the post-central gyrus which is, in fact, the primary projection area for cutaneous sensation. From the study of a number of animals, Adrian has concluded that those parts which are of greatest importance in the investigation of the outside world, have the largest cortical sensory areas. In the pig, the snout is most important, in the cat the claws and the fore-limbs, in the dog the muzzle and in the monkey the hands and face.

In man, the destruction of the sensory area does not abolish sensations of pin prick, touch, heat or cold. It does diminish the power of localising a stimulus sharply and appreciating accurately fine differences. Stereognosis, the power of recognising the shape of an object when it is held in the hand, is always severely impaired in these lesions. The recognition of an object by touch, which seems childishly simple to a normal subject, requires sensations of touch, pressure, joint and muscle sense, the fusion of the separate sensory data, and the recollection of previous similar experiences. This process can only occur in relation to cortical activity. Although the existence of bilateral representation of cutaneous sensations makes the situation a little doubtful, the elementary sensations can probably enter consciousness in the presence of thalamic activity, and in the absence of the sensory cortex.

The occipital cortex is especially concerned with vision, and its functions are considered in the chapter devoted to that subject. The temporal lobe is concerned with hearing. The primary projection area of the auditory pathway is the middle third of the superior temporal convolution and the adjacent cortex in the Sylvian fissure. Bilateral destruction of these areas produces " cortical " deafness in which no significance is attached to any sounds. The hippocampal gyrus receives fibres from the olfactory tracts.

Adrian has pointed out that it is the receptive surfaces of the body which are represented in the sensory cortex. Thus the retina has point to point relationships with the calcarine cortex, the whole sentient surface of the body is represented on the post-central gyrus, and the basilar membrane of the cochlea is represented on the superior temporal gyrus.

Speech

All the areas so far enumerated, somatic, motor and sensory, visual, auditory and olfactory, are closely related to the great tracts which run to and from the cortex. It is their connection with these tracts which makes their behaviour comparatively easy to investigate experimentally. There are as well a few areas whose connections are chiefly intracerebral, and which have been recognised as the result of clinical and anatomical studies. Lesions of these areas are followed by disturbances of the most highly developed forms of behaviour. The first to be recognised, as mentioned above, was the association between Broca's area and disturbances of speech, or aphasia. Later, lesions of the supra-marginal, angular, and superior temporal gyri, were often found to be accompanied by aphasia. It was believed that, surrounding the primary visual and auditory area, there were visual and auditory " association areas " concerned with the interpretation of the sense data. Fitting in with this hypothesis, cases were described of " pure word deafness " associated with lesions of the superior temporal gyrus. Lesions of Broca's area, which adjoins the motor area for the lips and tongue, were said to cause anarthria, or " pure " motor aphasia. It soon became apparent that when they were carefully studied, no clinical cases fitted into these categories. In the war of 1914–1918, Head developed special methods for the study of these cases and soon made it clear that, though there is no general defect of intelligence, far more than speech in these patients' behaviour was affected. A patient who was, for example, unable to name objects, was also incapable of carrying out complex commands, was unable to do more than the simplest arithmetic, and could not match an object unless he could see the two objects side by side. Head believed that the real defect in these cases was an inability to use symbols, and as a great deal of thinking is carried on by symbolic formulations, many mental processes in aphasics were limited and slow. The " higher " intellectual processes which require abstract ideas suffered more than the lower.

He divided his cases into four groups :—

(1) Verbal aphasia, essentially a disorder of word formation. In its exteme form the patient may be almost entirely deprived of the use of spoken words, though he can sometimes convey his meaning in writing. He may be unable to say more than " Da Da," or an occasional exple-ive. In right-handed patients, the lesion in all forms of aphasia is constantly found in the left hemisphere, and in this form it is usually in front of the central sulcus.

(2) Syntactical aphasia. Words are correctly used but there is difficulty in the construction of sentences, and speech degenerates into jargon.

(3) Nominal aphasia. This is one of the commoner forms of aphasia. There is an inability to name familiar objects though they are recog-nised and used correctly. The lesion is usually behind the central sulcus.

(4) Semantic aphasia. The patient is unable to grasp the meaning of complete sentences, though words are correctly used. He can name correctly items in a picture without understanding the content of the picture as a whole.

The investigation of these defects of speech is particularly difficult, since, when the normal chain of events in speech is interrupted, the process does not fall apart into the simpler elements of which it is normally composed. So far, in our analysis of function in the central nervous system, we have found that when the higher processes are interrupted, the lower processes make their appearance modified by depression or release as the case may be. There is no reason to believe that this is true of cortical processes. Faced with the inability to recall a particular word, the patient tries circumlocutions to get round the difficulty. For example, when an officer patient was unable to name colours, which requires the use of an abstract term, he gave concrete instances instead. Presented with red objects, he said, " What the Staff wear," and for black, said, " What you do for the dead." The actual content of an aphasic's speech will depend on his previous mental habits and his attempts to find alternative ways of expressing himself. It will not necessarily demonstrate the elements of which his speech is normally composed. These adaptive efforts represent, of course, the activity of healthy surviving cortex, and in the continental literature, much emphasis is laid on this plasticity and adaptability, which is said to be a characteristic feature of cortical behaviour. Occasionally the lesion seems to interrupt a particular pathway, and there is no " way round." One of Head's patients was presented with a written command which he was quite unable to understand as long as he read it silently. As soon as he was allowed to read the command aloud, he understood it and carried it out.

Perhaps a more reliable method of studying the relation between " words, thoughts and things," is revealed in the development of primitive speech in different human races, the acquisition of words by children, and in other human activities (*cf.* Ogden and Richards : " The Meaning of Meaning.")

In addition to symptoms which formed part of the aphasia complex, such as the inability to read (alexia), and inability to write (agraphia), a number of other symptoms have been described after lesions near the angular gyrus on the left side. These include inability to use objects correctly (apraxia), acalculia, disorientation in space, and disorientation for the right and left sides of the body. Their systematic investigation has barely started.

The Frontal Lobes

Stimulation of the frontal lobes anterior to the pre-motor cortex results in movement of the eyes to the opposite side. There is a cortico nuclear tract, which runs from this, the frontal adversive eye field, to the nuclei of the eye muscles in the mid-brain. More anteriorly is the pre-frontal area, which gives no detectable response to stimulation, and its removal produces no conspicuous clinical symptoms. It is, therefore a " silent area." Its bilateral removal in monkeys and apes leads to loss of immediate memory, and to some restlessness and emotional over activity. Recently, total amputation of one or both frontal lobes has been practised in man. After unilateral amputations, there is perhaps little loss of initiative, with an inability to plan ahead. After removal of both frontal lobes, attention, memory, and the ability to grasp simple situations were unaffected, but the higher intellectual activities, thinking in symbols, and judgment, had deteriorated. No more conspicuous changes occurred in a patient who survived total amputation of the right hemisphere.

The Electrical Activity of the Cortex

While we can follow the arrival of impulses in the sensory areas and their departure from the motor areas, we know little as yet about the intermediate steps. Adrian has shown that excitation of a point on the cortex sets up a wave of activity which spreads a few millimetres out into the surrounding tissue. This wave travels at the very slow rate of about 30 cm. per sec., as it depends on the successive excitation of cortical neurones, each of which is only excited after the usual synaptic delay. Excitation can only spread any distance in the cortex by deep paths involving cortical association fibres. Dusser de Barenne has mapped out eleven bands in the sensori-motor cortex of the chimpanzee. Some of the bands excite all the others, while others inhibit them all. The remainder of the bands have a selective action, inhibiting some and exciting others. One of these areas, *the strip*, lies just in front of the motor cortex, which it inhibits through a path which has cell stations in the basal ganglia and thalamus.

The nature of the individual units in the electrical activity of the cortex is uncertain, but it is probable that, as in the superior cervical ganglion, the important unit is the action potential of the cell body of the neurone. One characteristic feature of the cortical neurones is their tendency to discharge in unison when they are under uniform conditions. This property is shared by the ganglion cells of the water-beetle *Dytiscus*, and the cells of the occipital cortex of man (Fig. XII. 12). In all parts of the cortex, potential waves at a frequency of 10 per sec. can be picked up on occasion, but they occur especially readily in the occipital cortex. When the eyes are shut, the neurones are at rest, and seem to discharge at a steady low frequency, which varies with their metabolic rate. The discharge of the individual cells tends to become related to that of their neighbours, so producing a smooth oscillation in the record of the potential which can be detected by leads on the surface of the brain. If the activity of the cells were random, there would be no external potential change.

Similar 10 per sec. potential waves can be picked up from the scalp in man. First described by Berger in 1924, this potential oscillation is now called the alpha rhythm. It is most conspicuous in a subject at rest with the eyes shut. It is abolished by looking at a pattern but not by looking at a diffusively illuminated screen. If the light is made to flicker, the frequency of the alpha rhythm follows the frequency of the flicker over a narrow range of 8–18 cycles per second. Difficult mental arithmetic or an unexpected touch can abolish the rhythm. It has been described by Adrian as " disappointingly constant," and its usefulness in investigating cortical activity in man has so far been limited.

When we turn to the study of the activity of the cortex in the intact

animal, the outstanding fact is the animal's ability to learn from experience, an ability which is almost entirely absent in a thalamus animal. In
order to study this process of learning, it is necessary to keep the
environment so constant that no random changes occur to distract the
animal's attention, and one must also have some indication that the
animal has been stimulated. The first difficulty is formidable, as it is
quite possible for the animal to be aware of more elements in the
situation than is the experimenter. Both difficulties were brilliantly
solved by Pavlov, who chose to study the process by which the animal
associated new events with stimuli which already give rise to basic
inborn reflexes. This process he called the setting up of conditioned
reflexes, new patterns of behaviour which have been determined by
previous experience.

Conditioned Reflexes

The recognition of conditioned reflexes came about in the following
way. Some forty years ago, Pavlov was studying the conditions which
determine the secretion of saliva in dogs. Introduction of food into the
mouth invariably evoked such a response, even after ablation of the
cerebral cortex. The mechanical and chemical action of a suitable
substance on the buccal mucous membrane is therefore the appropriate
stimulus of the " feeding reflex," which is permanent and adequate under
all ordinary conditions, and is termed the " unconditioned " stimulus.
But the familiar fact that the sight, smell or even the thought of food
may make a man's mouth water did not escape Pavlov's attention, and
he measured the increased salivary secretion in dogs exposed to such
stimuli. This he called " psychic secretion." For such more complex
nervous activity to occur, however, the cortex must be intact.

Any event in the outer world, which usually happens just before or
at the beginning of feeding-time, is a signal for food, and evokes the
salivary response even in the absence of food itself. Any other event
can be made into such a signal if it be combined with feeding often
enough.

The fundamental relation which Pavlov formulated is that a previously inactive stimulus may in itself acquire the capacity of eliciting
any given reflex response if repeatedly applied simultaneously with the
" unconditioned " stimulus. The somewhat stable association so formed
between a new stimulus substituted for the original one, and the reflex
response appropriate to the latter, is known as a " conditioned reflex,"
and its exciting agent as a " conditioned stimulus."

Most of the work on conditioned reflexes has been done in connection with the feeding reflex in dogs, using the amount of secretion
of saliva as a convenient quantitative indication of the intensity of the
response. But conditioned reflexes may also be developed as modifications of other innate reflexes, such as motor reflexes, involving either
skeletal or visceral muscles. Consider, for example, the reflex extension
of a man's finger due to a slight electric shock, and comparable with
the " flexion reflex " of the hind limb discussed in the previous chapter

In an experiment recorded by Watson, the palm of the hand lay prone upon a pad-electrode, while the tip of the middle finger was stimulated by a point electrode applied to it; the upward twitch of the finger was recorded by a lever on a smoked drum. An electric bell served as the conditioned stimulus; its inactivity was first tested, the sound being in no case followed by a twitch of the finger. The bell was then rung and the electric shock applied simultaneously for five times, after which the effect of the bell alone was tested. Five more combined stimulations followed, succeeded by another test of the effect of the bell alone, and this sequence was continued until the conditioned reflex appeared. It first appears haltingly, maybe once occasionally, then twice or more in succession, finally a twitch is regularly evoked by the sound of the bell alone. Some fourteen to thirty combined stimulations are usually sufficient to produce this result. Similarly the sound of a bell can be made to evoke the flexion reflex of the hind limb after some twenty to seventy combined stimulations, or combined action of bell and light on an eye will develop the former into a stimulus for contraction of the pupil.

Any kind of event in the outer world can become a conditioned stimulus, provided (1) that the external event can affect some sense organ in the animal; (2) that its occurrence coincides with application of the unconditioned stimulus (or of a well-established conditioned stimulus); (3) that it is repeated a sufficient number of times. In illustration of the first condition, we may quote the determination of the limits of sensitivity of animals to variation in pitch. Sounds may be made into conditioned stimuli for the feeding reflex, but only if they fall within the range of from 70 to 90,000 vibrations per second for dogs, or from 20 to 20,000 vibrations per second for man. It may be remarked that even nocuous stimuli, such as intense electrical stimulation, pinching, cutting, or burning of the skin, if systematically accompanied by feeding, lose their normal consequences and acquire the conditioned effect, and can thus be made to evoke only the signs of the keenest appetite.

In a conditioned reflex, impulses which were formerly transmitted to one part of the nervous system are now diverted to another, and the question arises, what conditions determine the direction of nervous impulses along special channels in this way? One factor appears to be the functional power or degree of irritability of the alternative reflex arcs, and this is illustrated by the following experiment. Nocuous skin stimulation may be formed into a conditioned stimulus for the feeding-reflex, but not for the reflex salivary secretion elicited by forcible introduction of dilute acid into the mouth. Nocuous stimulation of skin over bones cannot, however, be developed into a conditioned stimulus even for the feeding-reflex. Pavlov attributes the relations between these three reflexes to the greater physiological potency of the mechanism concerned in the consequences of bone stimulation than that concerned in the feeding-reflex, the results of nocuous skin stimulation coming between the latter two.

Great difficulty is experienced during the deliberate formation of conditioned reflexes in achieving the rigid isolation of the indifferent stimulus, which is essential if uncomplicated results are to be obtained. For example, an unnoticed accompanying stimulus, such as an extraneous noise, smell, draught, change in illumination, movement, or change in respiration of the experimenter, may become a conditioned stimulus in the absence of which the desired response will not appear. Elaborate methods have therefore to be adopted to prevent the dog being disturbed either by fortuitous noises or by movements of the observer (Fig. XII. 13).

It is usually impossible to develop a conditioned reflex in an animal by the method of combined stimulation, unless the indifferent stimulus

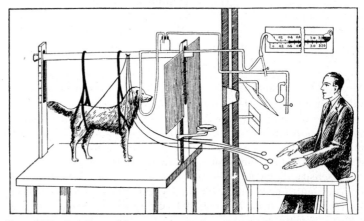

Fig. XII. 13.   General Arrangements adopted in Pavlov's Laboratory for Experiments on Conditioned Reflexes.

The dog is insulated from the experimenter by an opaque and sound-proof partition, through which pass the controls for applying the stimuli to the skin, and for measuring the salivary response.   (Pavlov.)

accompanies the unconditioned stimulus or precedes it ; if the indifferent stimulus follows the unconditioned stimulus by only a few seconds, no relation is established.

Simultaneous combination of conditioned stimulus and food results in a *simultaneous conditioned reflex*. If the offer of food is delayed till the conditioned stimulus has acted for some time, the salivary response in the resulting conditioned reflex is delayed for the same time, and this is termed a *delayed conditioned reflex*. If the conditioned stimulus has ceased before the food is offered, the consequent conditioned salivary response is evoked by the after-effect or " trace " of the conditioned stimulus which remains in the nervous system. The delay in the response of such a *trace-reflex* is the same as the delay in offering food during its formation.

Not all the events within the orbit of an animal's organs of sense at a moment when a fundamental reflex reaction is in progress become stimuli, and it is evident that some mechanism must exist tending to inhibit the influence of most of these, and to enhance the influence of a certain group. If this were not so, the formation of relations such as we have described could eventuate only in chaotic and inappropriate responses. In the formation of a conditioned reflex under experimental conditions, for instance, it is clear that the usual surroundings in the laboratory exert little or no influence, and all visual, auditory, tactile and other stimuli must be inhibited, save only such a group of stimuli as we have isolated for the purpose. We will turn our attention, therefore, to the three main varieties of inhibition, namely, internal, external and generalised inhibition.

Internal inhibition is due to some inherent property of the nervous system, and may further be divided into four sub-groups : (1) If a particular stimulus has become a conditioned stimulus for salivary secretion, and may therefore be regarded as a signal of food, and then acts on several consecutive occasions without confirmation by the unconditioned stimulus, it gradually loses its potency. This is termed *inhibition by extinction*. This effect is not due to abolition of the conditioned reflex, for the same stimulus recovers its effect after a period of rest, and without further intervention of the unconditioned stimulus.

(2) If a conditioned stimulus in a well-established conditioned reflex be accompanied on several occasions by an indifferent stimulus (in the absence of the unconditioned stimulus), the combination fails to produce the effect which follows application of the conditioned stimulus alone. Abolition of the response takes place more rapidly in this way than by simple extinction, and has given rise to *conditioned inhibition*. This interpretation is confirmed by the significant observation that the same conditioned inhibiting agent will now inhibit any other conditioned reflex which may have been derived from the same unconditioned reflex. The process is supposed to be due to excitation of the mechanism of internal inhibition, brought about by repeated action of the indifferent stimulus at a time when inhibition by extinction is taking place.

(3) If in working out a new reflex the conditioned stimulus precedes the unconditioned stimulus by anything from one-half to thirty minutes, as in the trace-reflex, the response in the established conditioned reflex will be delayed just such a period after application of the stimulus ; the inhibition which prevents reaction during the intervening interval is termed *inhibition by retardation*.

(4) Lastly, stimuli which closely approach a conditioned stimulus qualitatively and quantitatively regularly elicit the response at first, but gradually, as the reflex becomes more fully developed, lose their efficacy by a process referred to as *differential inhibition*.

The relations between the processes of conditioned reflexes and internal inhibition are further complicated by the phenomenon of *inhibition of inhibition*. Any of the manifold events which are suitable to form conditioned stimuli may also serve not only as agents of inhibition, but in certain circumstances to become agents effective in releasing the conditioned reflex from internal inhibition.

Take, for example, a sound with a frequency of 1,000 vibrations per second, and by repeated synchronous action of the sound and food, convert it into a conditioned stimulus for the feeding reflex of a dog until the sound of the pipe suffices by itself to elicit salivary secretion. Several repetitions of the conditioned stimulus without offering any food now result in gradual elimination of the response, by the variety of internal inhibition known as " extinction," but the activity of the conditioned reflex will recover of itself if allowed to rest for a time. If instead of waiting for this stage we immediately superimpose any new indifferent stimulus (*e.g.*, a light) upon the still ineffective sound, the " extinguished " stimulus (the sound) at once regains its potency in inducing secretion. Neither sound nor lamp alone is efficacious, but their combination elicits the response. This result can only be explained by supposing that lighting of the lamp inhibited or overcame the internal inhibition, and so released the original conditioned reflex.

The second main class of inhibition, **external inhibition,** is concerned more directly with the effects of external changes. (1) *Simple inhibition* is a variety of external inhibition which occurs during the action of nocuous stimuli. Reflexes initiated by these are, in general, prepotent, and inhibit both unconditioned and conditioned reflexes. Repetition may, however, modify the effect even of nocuous stimuli, which are to some extent subject to the influence of inhibition by extinction, and may even be transformed into conditioned stimuli.

(2) A second variety of external inhibition not infrequently disturbs the formation of conditioned reflexes ; it is a reaction to slight changes in the experimental environment. Contact with a fly, or the dropping of a small piece of plaster from the ceiling for instance, is invariably followed by some action of the skeletal musculature ; eyes, nose, ears, etc., take up particular positions such that the receptive fields of the animal are presented at the most advantageous angle to the direction of stimulation, and this response, known as the *orientation reflex* (distraction of attention) suffices, as a rule, to inhibit all conditioned reflex activity.

Sleep. Animals often become drowsy or go to sleep during experiments on conditioned reflexes, and then all activity ceases and a condition of *generalised or spontaneous inhibition* supervenes. Thermal stimuli are particularly apt to have this effect, and if either warmth (45° C.) or cold (0° C.) be applied to the same spot of skin, repeatedly or continuously, the liveliest animals sooner or later become somnolent and may fall asleep. A stimulus can, therefore, evoke not only active reflexes, but also a passive reflex, namely, inhibition of the " highest centres " of the nervous system. If a conditioned stimulus, for instance, precedes the unconditioned one for something like one-half to three minutes, a retardation of effect follows, as we have seen above. The response approaches more and more closely in time to that of the application of the unconditioned stimulus as the reflex becomes more fully established, and finally these two coincide. During the interval between the two stimuli, the animals remain indifferent owing to the action of internal inhibition. In some cases, the response disappears altogether, the animal becomes cataleptic and inert to stimulation ; it assumes a particular pose, and rigidly maintains it, and finally falls into a profound slumber from which it can be roused only with difficulty. Sleep may thus be as imperatively determined as action ; it involves inhibition of a complete section of nervous function, and probably the phenomena of hypnotism are determined by conditioned inhibition of certain portions of this function only.

Summation and Irradiation. Suppose two different stimuli have been associated with food, so that the salivary response can be evoked by either, *e.g.*, a sound and a light. The combined application of the two conditioned stimuli will evoke a greater reflex response than the application of either one alone, and this phenomenon is called *summation*. A related property of conditioned reflexes is known as *reinforcement*. Consider, for example, a watch-dog whose tendency to attack strange persons is readily aroused, *i.e.*, with an unusually excitable aggression reflex. Alone in the room with his master, the dog keeps quiet, and various conditioned reflexes can be worked out perfectly normally. If a stranger enters and applies the stimuli, however, violent barking ensues, and food will be snatched from the hand with hasty movements ; established conditioned reflexes give abnormally great responses, and saliva flows abundantly. If the stranger keeps as still as possible, barking ceases, though the dog keeps his eye on him. But now the conditioned stimulus is ineffective, and even food is taken only five to ten seconds after it is offered, and then without relish. If, however, the stranger gets up and moves about, there is a renewal of the hostile demonstration, together with heightened conditioned reflex responses. Pavlov concludes that the conditioned aggression reflex, when powerfully excited by movements of the stranger, irradiates to the feeding-reflex apparatus, reinforcing its activity. Diminution in intensity of the former reflex is associated with focussing of excitation which is limited to its own apparatus only, and with relative depression of other parts of the nervous system, so that excitability of the feeding-reflex arc is diminished. This conclusion, that an impulse may spread widely in the higher centres, is confirmed by analogous experiments on the mutual effects of different conditioned feeding-reflexes, and on heat and cold reflexes ; it is also consistent with the well-known observation that stimulation of a point on the motor cortex may give rise to generalised convulsions. The spreading of a wave of inhibition over the cortex seems to be a feature peculiar to the dog, as a pupil of Pavlov's has failed to find any such process in the monkey.

Sensation. Throughout our consideration of conditioned reflexes we have implied capacity on the part of animals to discriminate between different impressions received from the outer world, responding to some and not to others. The analysis of sense data becomes therefore an important preliminary to appropriate behaviour, and merits close scrutiny. In the higher forms special sense organs are differentiated, and their functions have been intimately studied from two points of view, namely, as examples of physical (*e.g.*, optical) apparatus, and as factors influencing subjective judgments when man himself is the subject of inquiry. Objective study of their actual physiological functions may, however, be achieved by the methods now under consideration.

So little was known at the time about what portion of the analysis should be attributed to peripheral sense organs, and what to their central connections, that Pavlov considered the apparatus of analysis as a whole, and includes in the " **analysor** " both sense organ and its neurone derivatives in the brain.

Two classes of problem may be distinguished ; those concerning the range within which a stimulus may vary and yet elicit response from animals, and those concerning the degree of difference between two stimuli which suffices to evoke different responses. The first includes the definition of the limits of audible pitch to which we have incidentally alluded, and the threshold of audible intensity. Analogous experiments have delimited the upper and lower wave-lengths of the spectrum visible to dogs.

The problems of sensory discrimination in animals can also be studied by means of Pavlov's objective technique. In the determination of the minimum differences of pitch appreciated by a dog, for example, a tuning fork of say 256 vibrations per second (middle C) is repeatedly accompanied by electrical stimulation of a paw, until it is established as a conditioned stimulus for the reflex contraction. Another fork (264) half a semi-tone higher will at this stage also produce the movement of the limb, but if it be sounded several times consecutively without accompaniment by the unconditioned stimulus, it loses its effect. The first fork is now tried again, and if not immediately effective, it is again combined with the electric shock. This alternate process is continued until the response invariably follows the sound of one fork and never the sound of the other. A series of such experiments is now undertaken with pairs of forks at diminishing intervals, until an interval is reached when such " differential inhibition " can no longer be established. A trained dog can actually distinguish different sounds at intervals of only fractions of a tone, and can retain such distinction permanently—a capacity known in man as the sense of absolute pitch. Fine shades of tone colour and differences of intensity so small that if compared at intervals of a few minutes an untrained man can scarcely appreciate them, may elicit different reactions in trained dogs after many hours. No less precise is a dog's distinction between intervals of time or the number of sounds repeated in a given time. A metronome beating at 100 per minute can be differentiated from one at 104 per minute, and a trained dog will recognise the difference twenty-four hours or more afterwards. That all such discrimination depends upon equilibrium between excitatory and inhibitory mechanisms is illustrated by its great impairment or even temporary destruction after a dose of a stimulant, such as caffeine.

From what has been said earlier in this chapter on the increase in the development of the cerebral hemispheres in the primates, it is probably wise not to generalise too hastily from Pavlov's results on dogs. Conditioned reflexes can be established in children with some difficulty, but in adults they are difficult to establish and remarkably evanescent. In young babies the increase in the number of behaviour patterns seems to correspond to a process of " conditioning," but as the store of accessible experience increases, the appearance of new forms of behaviour seems to depend on too many factors to be usefully called " reflex." Moreover, Pavlov's experiments are simplified in that the dog is prevented from actively investigating its environment. This was not so in a large series of experiments carried out by Lashley on training rats to run through mazes, and to open the doors of latched food boxes. The animal had not only to associate particular stimuli with the presence of food, but also it had actively to investigate the situation. Lashley concluded that simple association was a very primitive phenomenon, but that the variety of exploratory acts, the capacity to develop specialised movements, and to examine the separate items in a situation, were the important factors in the successful solution of the problem. These abilities were found to suffer in proportion to the amount of cortex previously removed. Attention, insight and initiative are, in fact, functions peculiar to the cortex.

CHAPTER XIII

THE AUTONOMIC NERVOUS SYSTEM AND CHEMICAL TRANSMISSION AT NERVE ENDINGS

THE autonomic (involuntary or vegetative) nervous system is often defined as that part of the peripheral nervous system which is independent of the control of the will. The designation of the system as " autonomic " or " involuntary,". stresses this essential feature. The definition, however, like nearly all attempts at definition, is not strictly correct. Reflexes like the knee jerk are involuntary, but do not involve autonomic pathways. On another hand, by recalling emotions or sensations, the will may exercise more or less control over smooth muscle and glands and in doing so stimulate autonomic fibres. There are, in addition, persons who can control one or another of the autonomic functions. They are able, by effort of will, to slow or to quicken the heart beat, to contract the smooth muscle of the skin or to constrict the pupil.

For our purpose, the autonomic nervous system is best defined as the efferent pathway to the viscera, including all nerve fibres and nerve cells by means of which impulses are sent from the central nervous system to glands, smooth muscles and heart, that is, all efferent nerve fibres with the exception of those to the striped (voluntary) muscle. The definition stresses the efferent character of the system. It excludes the afferent sensory fibres by means of which impulses pass from the viscera to the central nervous system. These fibres do not differ from other sensory fibres either anatomically or in their physiological properties. It must be emphasised, however, that most of our so called autonomic nerves, such as the splanchnic, the vagus or the chorda tympani are mixed nerves containing autonomic (efferent) as well as afferent (sensory) fibres.

The autonomic fibres emerge from the central nervous system either in the motor roots of the spinal nerve or in cranial nerves. But not all spinal or cranial nerves carry autonomic fibres. The outflow is confined to three regions of the nervous system (see Fig. XIII. 1). Autonomic fibres leave with the 3rd, 7th, 9th and 10th cranial nerves ; this is the cranial division of the autonomic nervous system. There is a thoraco-lumbar outflow in all thoracic and in the upper lumbar anterior roots and a sacral outflow in some of the anterior sacral roots (see Fig. XIII. 1). The thoraco-lumbar division is termed the *sympathetic system ;* the cranial together with the sacral division the *parasympathetic system* These two groups form the autonomic nervous system and the sub-division is based on anatomical differences in the origin of their separate peripheral pathways.

Most viscera are supplied by fibres from both systems which often act antagonistically. The double antagonistic innervation, however does not apply to all viscera. For example, most of the systemic blood

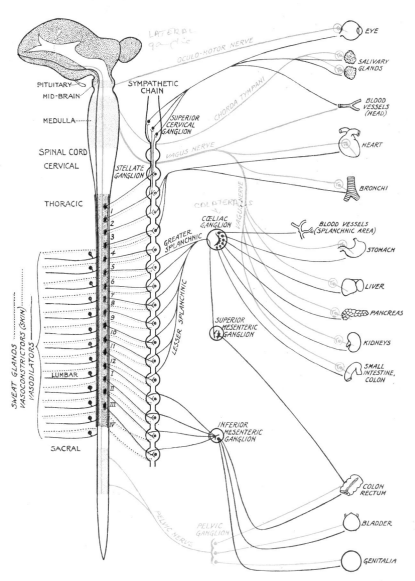

FIG. XIII. 1. Diagram of the connections of the autonomic nervous system. The sympathetic system is shown in red, the parasympathetic system in blue. (After Meyer and Gottlieb.)

[To face p. 448.

vessels are supplied by sympathetic vasoconstrictor fibres only, and centrally induced vasodilatation is brought about by inhibition of vaso-constrictor tone. Some vessels, in skeletal muscle, receive sympathetic vasoconstrictor and sympathetic vasodilator fibres. There is no para-sympathetic innervation of the smooth muscles of the upper eyelid, of the hair muscles in the skin, of the uterus, of the sweat glands or of the suprarenal medulla. Even when a tissue is provided with a dual antagonistic innervation, a too simplified conception of this anta-gonism is misleading. When light falls into the eye the pupil constricts as a result of parasympathetic impulses. When the eye is then shaded, the pupil dilates, not as a result of stimulation of the sympathetic fibres to the dilator muscle of the pupil, but because of diminished discharge in the parasympathetic system. On the other hand, the dilated pupil of a frightened person is mainly a sympathetically stimulated pupil and dilatation can occur despite the fact that bright light may shine into the eye. To understand the difference in the working of the different parts of the autonomic nervous system the anatomical arrangements have to be considered.

Impulses emerging from the central nervous system into autonomic fibres have to cross a *ganglionic synapse* on their way to the periphery. A synapse is a junctional region where one neurone ends and another starts. The peripheral pathway of an autonomic nerve consists of two neurones. The first neurone originates in a cell in the central nervous system and the axon (the *preganglionic fibre*) terminates at a synapse near a cell in a ganglion. The ganglion cell with its axon (the *post-ganglionic fibre*), constitutes the second neurone which terminates at the peripheral effector structure. A preganglionic fibre may traverse one or several ganglia without entering into synaptic junction with a ganglion cell, and each fibre may form a great number of synapses in a given ganglion or give off collateral branches terminating around the cells of different ganglia. With the use of *nicotine*, Langley was able to discover the endings of preganglionic fibres and the origin of the postganglionic ones. Nicotine has no action on nerve fibres, but stimulates, and later paralyses the ganglion cells. If it is painted on an autonomic ganglion, therefore, the nerve cells in the ganglion will be excited and give rise to impulses passing along the postganglionic fibres, thus indicating the origin of a postganglionic fibre to a given peripheral structure. Later on, these cells become paralysed and can no longer be excited when their preganglionic fibres are stimulated. This block will not occur when fibres merely traverse a nicotinised ganglion without entering into syn-aptic junctions. It is, therefore, possible by stimulating fibres proximal to a ganglion, painted with nicotine, to find out if they only traverse the ganglion or form synapses with its nerve cells.

The position of the cell stations or synaptic junctions in the auto-nomic path varies. Preganglionic fibres may be relatively short, relaying in ganglia near the vertebral column (vertebral or lateral ganglia), to long postganglionic fibres. Or the postganglionic fibres may be short and the long preganglionic fibres may terminate around ganglion cells situated within the tissue of the innervated organ (terminal or peripheral ganglia). Or the cell stations may have intermediate positions (collateral or prevertebral ganglia). There is this general difference. Parasympathetic preganglionic fibres relay in peripheral ganglia or in collateral ganglia (ciliary, sphenopalatine, submaxillary or otic ganglia) situated near the innervated tissue. Terminal ganglia, however, are the exception in the sympathetic path. Its main cell stations are the vertebral ganglia forming the paired sympathetic chains with their adjoining cervical ganglia in the neck. In addition there are many cell stations in collateral ganglia, like the cœliac and the mesenteric ganglia.

Since the preganglionic sympathetic fibres are medullated when they emerge from the lateral horn cells of the cord into the anterior roots and pass as fine filaments to the sympathetic chain, these filaments have a whitish appearance (white rami communicantes). The fibres usually lose their myelin sheath near or at the ganglia ; thus the connecting filaments containing the non-myelinated postganglionic fibres which are sent back to the spinal nerves of the trunk and limbs have a more greyish appearance (grey rami communicantes).

The ganglia are distributing centres, in which impulses from a single preganglionic fibre may be relayed to many (twenty or more) postganglionic fibres. In the parasympathetic division the relays are situated in or in close proximity to the innervated tissue limiting the spread of the impulse to a restricted area. The position is different in the sympathetic system. Here the anatomical arrangement clearly favours diffuse distribution of the nerve impulse over wide areas. In addition, on stimulation of the sympathetic, a hormone, adrenaline, is secreted from the suprarenal medulla into the blood stream, mimicking many of the sympathetic nerve effects, thus emphasising the fact that the organism is not concerned with a limitation of sympathetic effects to restricted areas. The anatomical arrangements of the two divisions characterise the fundamental difference in the function of the two systems.

It is possible that some of the parasympathetic ganglia are weak automatic centres independent of the central nervous system from which impulses originate continuously. Such function is attributed to the cells of the nerve plexus in the wall of the digestive tract. To a lesser degree it may be a more general property of parasympathetic ganglia.

Fig. XIII. 5 is a simple representation of the general pathway of all efferent nerve fibres. The uninterrupted course of the motor fibres to skeletal muscle (1) is contrasted with the autonomic pathway consisting of two neurones and showing the characteristic difference in the position of the cell stations (2, 4). There is one exception. The autonomic fibres to the suprarenal medulla do not pass a cell station on their way to the periphery (3). The medullary cells and the sympathetic ganglion cells have a common origin. Both are probably derived from the same primitive masses of neuroblasts, but have followed different paths in their differentiation. The innervation to the suprarenal medulla consists of preganglionic fibres of the sympathetic system, the postganglioni fibres, so to speak, having been converted into a gland of internal secretion. It is interesting to note that the product of its secretion, adrenaline, probably is identical with the substance released from the endings of most postganglionic sympathetic fibres (see p. 457).

The Function of the Sympathetic System

The Emergency Function of the Sympathico-adrenal System. Removal of the paired sympathetic chains with their outlying ganglia, as far as it is technically possible, is compatible with life. Sympathectomised animals show, in fact, no signs of deficiency if kept in sheltered conditions; but when exposed to extreme cold, oxygen lack, carbon dioxide increase, hæmorrhage or anæsthesia they may succumb earlier than control animals. The sympathetic innervation fulfils an important function in making the animal fit for states of emergency. There is a widespread discharge of impulses in the sympathetic system in states of physiological stress : during severe muscular work, in situations of danger, in extreme temperatures, asphyxia, hæmorrhage, under strong emotions such as fear or rage, or when in pain. The discharge affects also the fibres to the suprarenal medulla leading to an output of adrenaline. This widespread discharge has been likened to a reflex action of the organism with the purpose of strengthening its powers of defence and producing those changes necessary for preparing the organism for " fight and flight." It is in this connection, that Cannon referred to the emergency function of the sympathico-adrenal system. Sympathectomised animals show signs of deficiency in many of these adverse circumstances, but the degree of deficiency varies in different species. The capacity for strenuous muscular exercise is definitely decreased in cats but not in dogs which remain excellent fighters. When seen in the light of a protective mechanism for emergencies, the effects of sympathetic stimulation are easily understood and remembered.

The dilatation of the pupil (contraction of the radial muscle of the iris) protrusion of the eye or exophthalmos (contraction of the smooth muscle at the back of the eye) and opening of the palpebral fissure (contraction of the smooth muscle fibres of the levator palpebræ) increase the perception of light. In animals an alarming appearance is produced by bristling of the hairs of the back and tail. Of this effect " goose flesh " alone has survived in man. Broncho-dilatation decreases the resistance to the passage of air into the alveoli of the lung. The movements of the digestive tract are inhibited and the sphincters become contracted. Glucose is mobilised from the liver. There is some evidence that fatigue in skeletal muscle may be counteracted. The heart beats more strongly and more frequently ; the coronary arteries are dilated. The spleen contracts and ejects its store of red blood corpuscles. Vasoconstriction occurs in the systemic vessels, mainly in the splanchnic area and in the skin which becomes pale. Passive or active vasodilatation occurs, however, in skeletal muscles, thus shifting the blood from regions where it is not urgently needed to the active tissues. Active vasodilatation (sympathetic vasodilators) occur in the limb muscles of those animals which like man, dog and hare are capable of sustained muscular effort. The redistribution of blood may occur with little or no rise in arterial blood pressure. No useful purpose would be served if the circulatory effects of sympathetic stimulation, as well as of adrenaline, consisted in an increased activity of the heart in order solely to eject the blood against a greater peripheral resistance. The main effect is redistribution of the blood volume with increased circulation rate. On the other hand, the vasoconstriction following severe hæmorrhage tends to keep up or restore an effective arterial blood pressure by adapting the vascular bed to the reduced blood volume.

Cannon points out that a general sympathico-adrenal discharge may be harmful unless transformed into action. Heart and circulation may be worked just as hard from an armchair as from a rower's seat. " If no action succeeds the excitement and the emotional stress—even worry and anxiety—persists, then the bodily changes due to the stress are not a preparatory safeguard but may be in themselves profoundly upsetting to the organism as a whole."

The Efferent Pathway of Reflexes to Organs Widely Distributed in the Body. The sympathetic system may act as a unit in conditions of physiological stress, but this is one aspect only of its function. It is important to realise that this system is the efferent pathway for those reflexes where the effector organ is widely distributed in the body, *i.e.,* the blood vessels, the sweat glands and the hair muscles. Sympathetic fibres are the sole connection between the vasomotor centre and the blood vessels or between the temperature regulating centre and the sweat glands. Any regulation of vasomotor tone through the vasomotor centre is brought about by increased or decreased sympathetic discharge without participation of the parasympathetic. It is true that the latter system contains vasodilator fibres to some tissues such as the salivary glands ; these fibres, however, are not activated for the purpose of circulatory readjustments but for a specific organ function, salivation. Without a sufficient supply of fluid to the glands, salivation would not continue ; accordingly the pattern of the salivary reflex incorporates a localised vasodilatation mediated by parasympathetic nerves.

It must further be realised that the sympathetic discharge to the vessels and sweat glands may vary in different areas of the body and that different parts of the sympathetic system may act separately from each other and even antagonistically. The following instances will illustrate these points. (1) Emotional blushing is the result of inhibition of sympathetic constrictor tone of the skin vessels. This inhibition is limited and usually does not spread over the vessels of the whole body. In women who blush frequently and vividly, the " blush area " is confined to the face and to the V-shaped area in the neck, areas of skin exposed to sunlight by the cut of modern dress. (2) Sweating, limited to the skin around the lips and nose, may be evoked by gustatory stimuli such as chewing spicy foods. (3) When the environmental temperature rises sufficiently the skin becomes flushed and sweat beads appear. Again the flushing is due to reflex inhibition of sympathetic vasoconstrictor tone in the skin but the secretion of sweat is the result of an apparently antagonistic stimulation of the sympathetic secretory fibres to the sweat glands. When these and the vasoconstrictors are stimulated simultaneously, as in extreme fright, " cold sweat " appears, the sensation of cold being brought about by the restriction of the blood flowing through the skin.

One of the main functions of the sympathetic system is its *rôle* in preserving constant internal conditions, the preservation of what Claude Bernard called the " milieu intérieur." The sympathetic system is in part responsible for man's great adaptability to life in different surroundings and for the conservation of his " inner climate " which he carries about with him. The constant changes in the distribution of the circulating blood volume to adapt the organism to changed environmental conditions and to the changing demands created by muscular activity are brought about, as far as nervous mechanisms are involved, through the sympathetic system. The sympathetic vasoconstrictor tone is influenced continuously by many reflexes. The regulation of heat loss is almost entirely dependent on the sympathetic system, whether we consider the increased heat loss by radiation through vasodilatation or by evaporation of sweat, or whether we consider the regulation in animals by erection of the feathers or hair.

Tonic Activity. There is a continuous sympathetic discharge from the central nervous system to certain innervated tissues whereas to others it occurs only under special conditions. The smooth muscles of the hairs, the sweat glands, the digestive tract and the medulla of the suprarenal belong to the latter groups of tissue. The intrinsic muscles of the eye, the heart, the arteries, arterioles and capillaries are kept in a state of continuous although varying tonic contraction by their sympathetic innervation. When this is interrupted, the pupil contracts, the eye sinks into its socket (enophthalmos) and the upper lid droops (ptosis), giving the eye a sleepy appearance. That the vessels dilate was first shown by Claude Bernard when he cut the cervical sympathetic nerves on one side in the rabbit ; the vessels of the external ear on the denervated side dilated and the skin temperature rose.

Central Control. There are centres in the spinal cord and in the medulla oblongata for tonic and reflex discharges by way of the sympathetic system for different autonomic functions. The cardio-accelerator and vasomotor centres are discussed in the chapter on circulation. Sweat secretion is closely linked with the centre for temperature regulation in the hypothalamus. Stimulation of this region will cause widespread sympathetic discharge and it appears that the sympathetic pattern of emotional reaction is represented here. A cortical representation of sympathetic activity appears to exist in the motor and premotor areas.

We have mentioned the fact that the sympathetic discharge varies in different parts of the sympathetic system and is even absent in some and that reflexes do not affect all sympathetic fibres simultaneously or to the same extent ; there may even be stimulation in one and inhibition in another region.   Little is known about this finer central integration, which is necessary for keeping the internal environment constant. Sympathetic centres in the spinal cord, moreover, may be acted upon reflexly, without bringing the higher centres into action. The functions of the spinal centres become manifest in patients with complete transverse section of the spinal cord. After recovery from spinal shock, reflex sweating has been observed below the level of the lesion, in catheterisation of the bladder or after a warm bath.

The Function of the Parasympathetic Nervous System

Unlike the sympathetic system with its widespread discharge the parasympathetic system is the main efferent pathway for those reflexes which are more localised in character. These reflexes are discussed in detail in the appropriate chapters. Parasympathetic activity usually influences single organs without affecting others. The importance of the parasympathetic system becomes clear, once we realise that the reflexes are abolished when the parasympathetic pathway is interrupted. When this happens in the eye the pupillary reflexes to light and near vision are no longer obtained. When the parasympathetic pathway to the salivary glands is interrupted neither the presence of food in the mouth nor its sight or smell will induce salivary secretion. The reflex secretion of gastric and pancreatic juice and of succus entericus are dependent on the integrity of the parasympathetic fibres in the vagus nerve, stimulation of which, in addition, causes increased bile flow and increased activity of the walls of the digestive tract and inhibition of its sphincters. Cutting the parasympathetic fibres to the lachrimal glands abolishes reflex lachrimation. Through the parasympathetic fibres in the vagus, a continuous discharge is exerted upon the heart's action, as shown by the fact that the heart-rate in man may double when the vagal inhibition is suddenly removed, as after atropine. At birth, this tone is weak. In a new born baby, atropine will only increase the pulse rate from about 140 to 160 per minute. The vagal tone to the heart in man is influenced continuously by many reflexes. The significance of this tone is best realised, when we remember the effect of heart-rate on mechanical efficiency. A given amount of work is performed by the heart with less oxygen when it beats slowly than when it beats quickly.

The parasympathetic fibres from the sacral division are the efferent pathway for the reflex contraction of the urinary bladder and inhibition of its internal sphincter in the micturition reflex. There is no sympathetic control of bladder activity, although sympathetic nerves regulate the blood flow in the bladder muscle. The contraction, produced by stimulating the sympathetic nerve of the muscle of the ureteral orifices and of the trigonum, is linked not with the micturition reflex but with the sex function. Section of the hypogastric nerves which contain the sympathetic fibres does not interfere with micturition whereas the bladder becomes paralysed after section of the pelvic nerves.

The cranial division of the parasympathetic contains vasodilator fibres to the salivary glands and tongue and the sacral division contains similar fibres to the erectile tissue of the external genitalia. The main *rôle* of these vasodilators is, as mentioned before, linked with the specific functions of these organs, salivary secretion and erection of the generative organs respectively and not with general circulatory readjustments. Ejaculation is dependent on the integrity of the sympathetic system ; its removal causes impotence in the male. Thus both divisions of the autonomic nervous system are involved in the mechanism of coitus.

The distribution of the parasympathetic fibres to the different viscera is shown in Fig. XIII. 1. In many instances the parasympathetic system functions against a background of sympathetic tone which diminishes when the parasympathetic is activated.

Summary of the Effects of Stimulation on the Sympathetic and Parasympathetic Nerves

In the following table, a more detailed account is given of the effects obtained on stimulating sympathetic and parasympathetic fibres to different tissues.

TABLE XIII. 1.

Sympathetic and parasympathetic effects.
(Modified from Best and Taylor, 1945.)

Organ	Sympathetic	Parasympathetic
Heart	Acceleration	Inhibition
Impulse formation .	Increased	Reduced
Conduction . .	Quickened	Slowed
Auricular muscle .	Increased contraction	Weakened contraction
Ventricular muscle .	Increased contraction	No innervaton of mammalian ventricle
Blood vessels		
Cutaneous . .	Constriction	No innervation
Muscular . .	Constriction. Dilatation in animals capable of sustained muscular effort ; cholinergic and adrenergic fibres	No innervation
Tongue . . .	Constriction	Dilatation
Buccal mucosa. .	Dilatation (cholinergic fibres)	No innervation
Salivary and lacrimal glands.	Constriction	Dilatation
Coronaries . .	Dilatation (adrenergic fibres)	Constriction
Cerebral . . .	Slight constriction	Dilatation
Pulmonary . .	Slight constriction	Slight dilatation and constriction
Abdominal and pelvic viscera.	Constriction	No innervation
External genitalia .	Constriction	Dilatation (Erection)

TABLE XIII. 1—*continued*

Organ	Sympathetic	Parasympathetic
Glands		
Sweat . . .	Secretion (fibres cholinergic in man and cat, adrenergic in horse and sheep)	No innervation
Nasal mucosa . .		Secretion
Salivary . . .	Scanty mucous secretion	Secretion
Gastric . . .		Secretion
Intestinal . .		Secretion
Pancreas, Acini and islets.		Secretion
Lachrimal . .		Secretion
Liver . . .	Glycogenolysis	Increased bile flow
Adrenal medulla .	Adrenaline secretion	No innervation
Adrenal cortex . .	No innervation but stimulated by adrenaline	No innervation
Smooth muscles of		
Bronchi . . .	Relaxation	Contraction
Eye		
Iris . . .	Midriasis ; contraction of dilator pupillæ	Miosis ; contraction of contractor pupillæ
Ciliary muscle .	Relaxation	Contraction
Smooth muscles of orbit and upper lid.	Contraction	No innervation
Nictitating membrane (third lid) in cat and dog.	Retraction	No innervation
Arrector pili (hair muscles).	Contraction	No innervation
Pharynx . . .		Contraction
Oesophagus . .	Relaxation, usually contraction of cardiac sphincter	Contraction ; relaxation of cardiac sphincter
Stomach wall . .	Usually relaxation	Contraction
Intestine . .	Relaxation	Increased tone and motility
Internal anal sphincter.	Contraction	Relaxation
Detrusor of urinary bladder.	Relaxation	Contraction
Trigone and sphincter of urinary bladder.	Contraction	Relaxation
Vasa deferentia, seminal vesicles and prostate.	Contraction (ejaculation)	
Uterus . . .	Relaxation ; contraction when pregnant	No innervation

CHEMICAL TRANSMISSION AT NERVE ENDINGS [1]

The nerve impulse is associated with an electrical variation, the action potential. The *physical* theory of transmission postulates that this propagated disturbance, when it reaches the nerve endings, is itself able to stimulate the reactive structure ; whereas the *chemical* theory

[1] The concept of chemical transmission is not limited to the autonomic nervous system ; its other application will also be dealt with here.

assumes that there is a functional gap between nerve ending and reactive structure which the nerve impulse is unable to jump. This inability is overcome by the release from the nerve endings of an active substance, the chemical transmitter or mediator, which then in its turn, acts upon the reactive organ. This theory was suggested at the beginning of this century to explain the striking similarity between the actions of adrenaline and sympathetic nerve stimulation and between the actions of drugs like pilocarpine and muscarine and parasympathetic nerve stimulation. In 1921, Otto Loewi, with experiments on the frog heart, brought forward experimental evidence in favour of this theory. Fig. XIII. 2 shows a modification of his original method. Two frogs' hearts are supplied with Ringer solution from the same reservoir, the liquid being mixed by the pumping action of the hearts. On stimu-

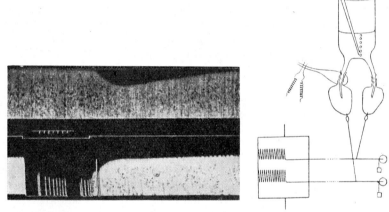

Fig. XIII. 2. Demonstration of **Chemical transmission of vagus effect** on frog's heart. Modification of Lœwi's original experiment. (After Kahn.)

lating the vagi to the first heart, it is inhibited and may stop beating. When stimulation ceases, and the heart starts beating again, a slight but definite inhibition occurs in the second heart which is connected with the first heart only by the Ringer solution. A substance must have been released into the liquid during stimulation of the vagus which on reaching the other heart caused the vagus-like effect. On stimulation of the sympathetic accelerans fibres to the heart an " accelerans substance " was demonstrated similarly. We know now that the substance released from the parasympathetic vagus endings is **acetyl-choline.** The substance released from the sympathetic fibres which Cannon has called **sympathin** is certainly closely related chemically to **adrenaline** and may be identical with it.

Repetition of the experiments with stimulation of the vagus to the mammalian heart perfused with blood, was for a long time unsuccessful, for the following reason. Acetyl-choline once released is quickly destroyed by an enzyme, *cholinesterase*, which hydrolyses acetyl-choline into choline and acetic acid, both pharmacologically inert substances in comparsion with acetyl-choline. Choline has, in fact, actions like acetyl-choline, but only if given in concentrations several thousand times as great. The amounts of choline set free, therefore, are too small to produce reactions and the hydrolysis may be regarded as an effective mechanism of inactivation. In warm blooded animals the enzyme will have acted usually before the acetyl-choline has had time to enter the capillaries. By the use of a tissue from a cold blooded animal, and Ringer solution instead of blood, Lœwi had avoided this danger.

Recent work has distinguished two cholinesterases. A pseudo-cholinesterase present in many tissues and in plasma and the true cholinesterase present in cholinergic nerves and in blood corpuscles and probably solely responsible for the destruction of acetyl-choline released in nervous activity.

Such a rapid mechanism of inactivation has not been provided for the transmitter sympathin. Sympathin is not destroyed by blood, and if it were identical with adrenaline this would not be surprising, because the adrenaline secreted from the suprarenals has to be transported by the blood stream. Sympathin is probably partly destroyed before diffusing into the capillaries by tissue enzymes which either oxidise the side chain (amine oxidase) or the OH groups of the benzene ring (a phenol oxidase). But some of the transmitter certainly reaches the blood stream in an active form and can and has been demonstrated there by its reactions on distant denervated tissues (denervation sensitises the tissues to sympathin or adrenaline). For instance, when in cats the heart, pupil and nictitating membrane (a third eye-lid present in some species), are denervated and the suprarenals removed, to exclude output of adrenaline from this source, stimulation of sympathetic fibres to other tissues will cause quickening of the heart, dilatation of the pupil and withdrawal of the nictitating membrane, all of which are typical effects of adrenaline. It would be useless to employ similar methods for the detection of the released acetyl-choline. Its enzymatic destruction provides an extremely efficient safeguard against any spread of the effects of the nerve impulse and thus makes the acetyl-choline particularly suitable as a transmitter for the peripheral effects of the parasympathetic division with its restricted localised function. In addition, the quick destruction will also ensure a short duration of the effect not out-lasting the nerve impulse for any length of time. But how can the acetyl-choline be detected if it is so quickly destroyed ? This has become possible by the use of eserine (physostigmine).

In the presence of eserine or related substances (such as prostigmine), acetyl-choline is no longer hydrolysed by the esterase in the blood or tissue. Before the acetyl-choline can be acted upon by the cholinesterase it has to be " fixed " to a " receptor " of the enzyme. Acetyl-choline and eserine compete for the same receptor. Acetyl-choline when fixed is at once hydrolysed and the receptor becomes free again. Eserine remains fixed since it can only be acted upon very slowly, if at all by the cholinesterase. If, therefore, sufficient eserine molecules are available all the receptors will, after a time, become blocked for the acetyl-choline. An action such as that of eserine is called competitive inhibition.

In the presence of eserine the released acetyl-choline may escape into the blood stream without being hydrolysed and exert effects on distant organs in the same way as sympathin in the normal course of events. This is illustrated by the experiment shown in Fig. XIII. 3.

At 1 the peripheral end of the cut chorda-lingual nerve is stimulated. It contains secretory and vasodilator fibres to the salivary gland and tongue. The local vasodilatation in these tissues, is too restricted to cause a general effect on the arterial blood pressure. Between 1 and 2, eserine has been injected intravenously and ten minutes later, the nerve has been restimulated. This time the released acetyl-choline escapes destruction and diffuses into the blood capillaries. When it reaches the systemic circulation it causes general vasodilatation. The result is a fall of arterial blood pressure after a latency of some ten seconds, due

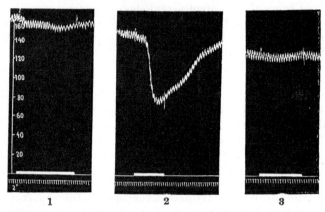

FIG. XIII. 3. Arterial blood pressure of anæsthetised cat. Effect of three stimulations of chorda-lingual nerve on blood pressure. Intravenous injection of eserine between 1 and 2, and of atropine between 2 and 3.

mainly to the time taken to travel round the circulation. Atropine abolishes the vasodilator action of acetyl-choline ; therefore, at 3, after atropine, the depressor effect is no longer obtained on restimulation of the chorda-lingual nerve.

In other experiments, with a similar purpose, the eserinised venous blood from a given organ was collected and tested for acetyl-choline, whilst the nerves to the organ were stimulated ; or the organ was perfused with eserinised Ringer solution, the nerve stimulated and the venous effluent collected and assayed.

The amounts of acetyl-choline released on nerve stimulation and available for analysis are far too small to be detected or identified by our present chemical methods. But acetyl-choline has been identified chemically in extracts of the horse spleen, the human placenta and the ox brain and can be regarded as a substance occurring naturally and being formed in the body. Its identification when released on nerve stimulation is based on pharmacological methods using tissues which respond to minute doses of acetyl-choline with characteristic reactions. Some tests in use for this purpose are shown in Fig. XIII. 4.

(*a*) Contraction of the muscle of the body wall of the leech, the effect being greatly increased in the presence of eserine. The reaction is very sensitive ; it is induced by a concentration of acetyl-choline of only one part in a thousand million. The action is highly specific.

(*b*) Contraction of the rectus abdominis muscle of the frog and the sensitising effect of eserine on the action. Sensitive to about one in fifty million acetyl-choline.

(*c*) Inhibition of the beat of the frog's heart. This was the first test used. The action is abolished by atropine.

(*d*) Depression of cat's blood pressure. The action is sensitised by eserine and abolished by atropine.

In each of these tests, the response to the unknown solution is matched with that of an appropriate dose of a standard dilution of acetyl-choline, and hence the apparent acetyl-choline content of the unknown solution is determined. If the apparent acetyl-choline content is found to be the same in all four tests, and, in addition, the unknown substance is unstable in alkaline solution and destroyed by blood in the absence of eserine, but not in its presence, the identity with acetyl-choline is regarded as proved.

In order to prove that a nerve impulse acts by the release of acetyl-choline the following three facts have to be established.

(1) Release of acetyl-choline on stimulation of the nerve.

(2) The action of injected acetyl-choline must be identical with or approximate closely to, that of nerve stimulation, although we have to take into account the fact that the method of injection does not always imitate closely the release of acetyl-choline by nerve impulses.

(3) Eserine, by delaying the destruction of the released acetyl-choline must potentiate and prolong the effects of nervous stimulation. In some instances, prolonged action of acetyl-choline may paralyse a reactive structure, in that case the response to nerve stimulation should be affected similarly after eserine.

Additional evidence may be obtained by showing that the innervated tissue contains acetyl-choline which disappears on nervous degeneration, indicating that it is contained not in the tissue cells but in the nerve fibres and endings. Similar results may be obtained in many tissues with regard to the content of true cholinesterase. Recently, synthesis of acetyl-choline has been shown to be a property of those nerve fibres which act by the release of acetyl-choline. It is synthesised from choline and the enzyme has been termed *choline acetylase*. The acetylation, however, is not a simple reaction but a complex process in which adenosinetriphosphate is involved. The synthesis has been studied particularly in brain tissue and is greatly accelerated by potassium ions.

A systematic analysis of different nerves soon made it clear that there is no strict relation between the two anatomical divisions of the autonomic nervous system and the two chemical transmitters ; and that the chemical transmission theory is not confined to the autonomic nervous

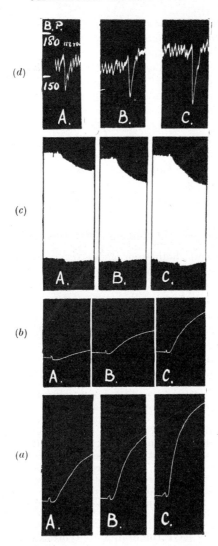

FIG. XIII. 4. Tests of Substance in Perfusion Fluid emerging from Veins of Stomach during Stimulation of Vagus.

(*a*) Eserinised Leech Muscle : (*b*) Frog's Rectus abdominis ; (*c*) Frog's Heart ; * (*d*) Cat's blood pressure. In each case, A shows the effect of a suitable dose of acetyl-choline, B shows the effect of a dose of the perfusion fluid, adjusted to be proportional to the dose A of acetyl-choline. C is the effect of acetyl-choline given in double of the concentration of A. In each of the four reactions, the effects in B are intermediate between those in A and those in C.

Concentrations of acetyl-choline (A): (*a*) $1 : 280 \times 10^6$; (*b*) $1 : 56 \times 10^6$; (*c*) $1 : 56 \times 10^6$; (*d*) 1 c.c. of $1 : 40 \times 10^6$. (After Dale and Feldberg.)

* Owing to the slowness of the drum, the individual vertical lines representing heart beats have overlapped. The vertical distances between the upper and lower borders of the white patch nevertheless indicate the relative amplitudes of the heart beat.

system. Moreover, with one exception—the innervation of the suprarenal medulla—the peripheral pathway of the autonomic nervous system consists of two neurones, so that transmission had to be considered not only at the endings of postganglionic fibres, but also from the preganglionic endings to the ganglion cells of the postganglionic fibres, *i.e.*, the transmission across the ganglionic synapse.

In 1934, Dale introduced special terms to describe nerve fibres or neurones which acted by the release of acetyl-choline or adrenaline; the former he called **cholinergic**, the latter **adrenergic**, nerves. An understanding of the distribution of these fibres is best obtained when considering the pharmacology of acetyl-choline. That of adrenaline is described elsewhere (Chap. XV). Some of the properties of the transmission process may be discussed first.

Some Properties of Cholinergic and Adrenergic Nerves

The adrenergic and cholinergic nature of a nerve is not confined to the endings but is an inherent property of the whole neurone. An adrenergic or cholinergic nerve contains adrenaline or acetyl-choline respectively throughout the whole course of the nerve fibre and when the nerve impulse passes along it, minute amounts of the chemical mediators are released. The difference between the fibre and the ending is only quantitative. At the endings, the process shows a local intensification to ensure transmission to a contiguous cell. No function can yet be postulated for the release along the course of the fibre.

The theory, however, has been put forward that the chemical transmitters are responsible for the electrical variation associated with the nerve impulse. This theory is based on evidence which at present is insufficient. There is no necessity to postulate such a theory in order to explain the presence and release of the transmitter substances throughout the whole course of the nerve fibre, so long as we assume that the property of a naked nerve ending is a property also of the whole fibre. There is no justification for assuming that the ending constitutes a tissue different from the nerve fibre and endowed with an entirely new function. According to our present knowledge, therefore, the release of the chemical transmitter is not necessary for the passage of the impulse but caused by it.

Cholinergic nerves have the ability to synthesise acetyl-choline not only at their endings but along the whole course of the fibre. For synthesis to take place, however, some of the acetyl-choline has to be released first and the store thereby diminished. It is released from a pharmacologically inactive complex, a loose combination with some cell constituent, probably protein. The complex is resistant to the action of the cholinesterase, hence all tissue acetyl-choline exists in the form of such a complex. When acetyl-choline is synthesised in nervous tissues, it is not synthesised as free acetyl-choline but as the complex. About 48 hours after a cholinergic nerve is cut, the peripheral end loses its ability to synthesise acetyl-choline and the acetyl-choline store disappears. At this time, the fibre is still able to conduct nerve impulses.

The nerve impulse releases the acetyl-choline from the bound complex, so that it becomes diffusible and pharmacologically active and can exert its effects on the effector structure ; then it is at once destroyed by the cholinesterase.

The nerve impulse may be pictured as an ionic change passing along the fibre. The ions responsible for this change are thought to be potassium and the passage of the impulse has been likened to a wave of mobilisation of these ions. In this connection, it is interesting that potassium ions were found to release acetyl-choline from the inactive compound. The injection of potassium chloride into an artery of an organ supplied by cholinergic fibres imitates the release of acetyl-choline at the nerve endings caused by the arrival of the nerve impulse. It must be stressed that the actions of potassium which resemble those of acetyl-choline in many respects are not explained wholly by this action. Potassium ions have, in addition, strong direct effects on many cells.

Another observation suggesting that the whole of a neurone is either cholinergic or adrenergic is based on regeneration experiments. When the known facts of regeneration experiments with cross-sutured nerves were reconsidered, in the light of the chemical transmission theory, it became evident that cholinergic fibres could replace other cholinergic fibres and enter into functional connections with them and that adrenergic nerves could replace adrenergic ones, but a cholinergic fibre could not replace an adrenergic one and *vice versâ*.

Pharmacology of Acetyl-choline

The pharmacological actions of acetyl-choline can be divided into two classes.

(a) *The Muscarine-like Action.* Muscarine is a substance of known composition closely related to choline ; it is found in extracts of a common toadstool (*Amanita muscaria*). Its effects are the same as those observed on stimulating the postganglionic parasympathetic fibres (inhibition of the heart, constriction of the pupil, contraction of the urinary bladder, secretion of the glands of the digestive tract, stimulation of its wall, etc.). In addition, it induces general vaso-dilatation, secretion of sweat, contraction of the spleen and of the uterus. These actions, whether induced by muscarine or acetyl-choline, are abolished by atropine.

(b) *The Nicotine-like Action.* Nicotine has two characteristic actions. At first, it excites and subsequently it paralyses the following structures : (1) the autonomic ganglia ; (2) the cells of the suprarenal medulla and (3) the motor endplates of skeletal muscle. Similar actions can be obtained when acetyl-choline is injected. The nicotine-like effects, mostly are not abolished by atropine. In the diagram of Fig. XIII. 5 the structures which are affected by the nicotine-like action of acetyl-choline are marked by the letter N. Acetyl-choline has, in addition, stimulating and paralysing effects on cells of the central nervous system (see p. 469). They are included in the term nicotine-like actions although they are abolished by atropine.

The Distribution of Adrenergic and Cholinergic Neurones

Most of the postganglionic sympathetic fibres are adrenergic, which explains the striking similarity between the effects of adrenaline and sympathetic stimulation. It has long been known, however, that adrenaline will not cause sweating in human beings although the sweat glands are innervated by fibres which anatomically belong to the sympathetic division. Sweating is produced by muscarine, pilocarpine or acetyl-choline, the so-called parasympathomimetic drugs. We can explain this discrepancy thus. The postganglionic sympathetic fibres to the sweat glands are cholinergic and act by the release of acetyl-choline.[1] Similar postganglionic sympathetic but cholinergic fibres are found in the innervation of the uterus and in some animals, in the

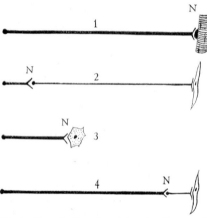

Fig. XIII. 5. Illustration of **efferent peripheral pathway.** Motor nerve fibre to striped muscle (1). Typical sympathetic (2) and parasympathetic (4) pathway to smooth muscle, heart and gland cells. Sympathetic innervation of the suprarenal medulla (3). N = Structures affected by nicotine-like action of acetyl-choline and places where transmission by nicotine-like action takes place.

vasodilator innervation to skeletal muscle. The splanchnic nerve seems to contain a few such fibres to the pancreas.

Cholinergic fibres to the skin (probably the sympathetic innervation of the sweat glands) are responsible for the following phenomenon. In certain people, more commonly females, an itching urticarial rash of the skin is induced regularly by emotions, exercise and warmth. The urticaria, a typical " triple response," must be due to the release of H-substance or histamine from the skin cells (see p. 76). It is known that people may be allergic to a great number of allergens (fish, eggs, pollen, strawberries and certain drugs), which act as injurious agents to the skin cells causing the release of histamine. In this special instance, the people are allergic to acetyl-choline, which when released from cholinergic nerve endings acts as the injurious stimulus and causes the release of histamine.

The postganglionic neurones of the parasympathetic division are

---

[1] In horses adrenaline causes sweating and their sweat glands are innervated by sympathetic adrenergic fibres.

cholinergic, a fact which explains the striking similarity between the effects of parasympathetic stimulation and drugs like acetyl-choline, pilocarpine or muscarine. It is the muscarine-like action of acetyl-choline which is effective in the transmission to the peripheral structures from the postganglionic cholinergic parasympathetic as well as from the postganglionic cholinergic sympathetic fibres and it is therefore not surprising that these nerve effects are abolished by atropine. After atropine, stimulation of the vagus no longer inhibits the heart, and stimulation of the sympathetic no longer causes sweating in human beings. Nevertheless, the nerve impulses still release their acetyl-choline. Atropine, although abolishing the effects of nerves has no action on the nerves or nerve endings themselves, but renders the effector structure insensitive to the action of acetyl-choline, whether released or artificially applied. Many other drugs can still act after atropine. We do not know why drugs like atropine render the cells insensitive to one kind of drug and not to another.

Transmission by the Nicotine-like Action of Acetyl-choline. In Fig. XIII. 5, the letter N indicates the nicotine-like transmissions by acetyl-choline to the cells of the suprarenal medulla, the cells of autonomic ganglia and to the motor endplates of skeletal muscles.

We should distinguish between " release from nerve endings " and " secretion from gland cells." Transmitter substances are released and then act upon cells modifying their activity or initiating new events. In the adrenal medullary cells the activity stimulated by the released acetyl-choline is the secretion of a hormone adrenaline.

New aspects were opened up but also new difficulties arose, when the experimental evidence led to the conclusion that the transmission across the ganglionic synapse and from the motor endings to the endplates of skeletal muscle is effected by acetyl-choline. Two new features are involved in these transmissions ; the rapidity of the transmission and the absence of fusion of the responses on repeated nerve stimulation. The transmission is so quick as to give the appearance of an almost unbroken propagation and each single impulse gives rise to a single impulse in the postganglionic fibre or to a single wave of excitation along the voluntary muscle and with repeated stimulation each impulse gives rise to a new secondary impulse or to a new wave of excitation. The acetyl-choline released by the first impulse must, therefore, have disappeared before the second impulse arrives, and this may be after a very short time interval. As Dale puts it : if acetyl-choline intervenes at all in the transmission of these rapid and individual excitatory events, it can only do so by appearing with an explosive suddenness, as the nerve impulse reaches the preganglionic or motor ending, and having initiated the single excitation wave, it will have to vanish almost as quickly as it appeared.

Transmission Across the Ganglionic Synapse. Although transmission is very quick, there is not an unbroken physical propagation. Records of action potentials in the ganglia have shown that there is electrical discontinuity between the pre- and postganglionic nerve impulse, as postulated by the acetyl-choline theory. There is a short time lag of a few milli-seconds for the transmission of preganglionic impulses across the ganglion. This short *synaptic delay* implies that the acetyl-choline is released and has acted within this short period. When an impulse has crossed the synapse, the ganglion cell is unable to send off a new impulse along the postganglionic fibre during the next few milli-seconds, *i.e.*, during *the absolute refractory period.* Within this period the acetyl-choline must fall below the threshold level, otherwise it would restimulate the ganglion cell to fire off a new impulse. These time factors are not incompatible with the acetyl-choline theory, but emphasise the rapidity of the release and disappearance of acetyl-choline and exclude the possibility of a process of diffusion of the released acetyl-choline to

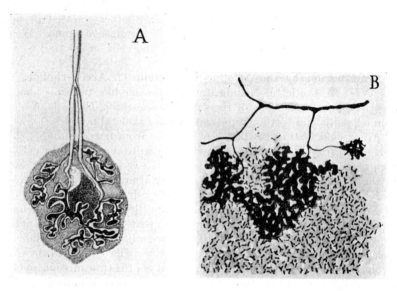

Fig. XIII. 6. Broadening of the nerve ending at (A) the motor endplate of skeletal muscle (after Kuhne), and (B) the plate of an electric organ of *Torpedo.* (After Ewart.)

the site of action. Transmission across the ganglion occurs in one direction only ; postganglionic stimuli when backfired into the ganglion are not transmitted to the preganglionic fibres and they do not release acetyl-choline.

We have seen that nicotine first stimulates and then paralyses the ganglion so that stimulation of the preganglionic fibre becomes ineffective. The ganglionic block is explained as follows. The nerve impulse releases acetyl-choline from the endings of the preganglionic fibre as usual, but the paralysed ganglion cell is no longer excited by it. We have described such an effect for atropine and parasympathetic nerve stimulation. Nicotine produces an exactly comparable effect on the ganglion cells.

Neuro-muscular Transmission. The motor nerve to skeletal muscle does not end directly on the muscle fibre, for a special structure, the motor endplate, has developed and is interposed between the ending and the contractile element of the fibre. In Fig. XIII. 6, the ending of a nerve fibre is shown in relation to the endplate. The nerve fibre loses its myelin sheath near the plate, the naked fibre broadens and forms a large surface of contact with the plate. The chemical transmission theory postulates the release of acetyl-choline from these endings in intimate contact with the upper surface of the plate. The time factors to be reckoned with in this transmission are as small as, or even smaller than, those discussed for the ganglion.

An analysis of the contraction caused by injected acetyl-choline will illustrate some of the features stressed in the foregoing paragraphs.

A single motor nerve impulse causes a short *single* contraction, a

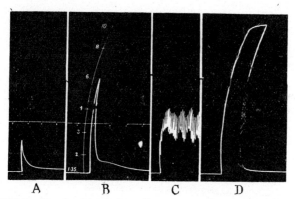

Fig. XIII. 7.   Tension record of a cat's gastrocnemius muscle.   (A) Maximal twitch.   (B) Contraction in response to arterial injection of 20 μg. of acetyl-choline.   (C) Incomplete and (D) complete tetanus in response to nerve stimulation.   Horizontal line at the left: time in seconds. Vertical scale : tension in kg.   (After Brown, Dale and Feldberg.)

twitch.   When a single stimulus is applied to all the fibres in a nerve to a muscle so that all fibres of the muscle contract once, a maximal twitch is obtained.   The rapid injection of acetyl-choline into a muscle artery also causes a short contraction, but the tension developed may be several times that of a maximal twitch (Fig. XIII. 7).   The response to the injected acetyl-choline, therefore, cannot be a twitch.   According to the acetyl-choline theory we should expect the acetyl-choline to act not directly on the contractile elements of the muscle but on the endplates. In that case, the greater tension developed could be explained on the assumption that the acetyl-choline persists in effective concentration at the plates for so long that it restimulates the muscle fibres several times after they have recovered from their refractory periods.   This problem can be decided by recording the electrical changes accompanying the contraction, but some special precautions have to be taken.   The injected acetyl-choline will reach the various endplates at different moments and the contractions of the individual fibres will be so out of phase that

when led off from the whole muscle, the electrical variations will compensate and extinguish each other.   In such instances, the electrodes
must be placed so close together that the changes from a few muscle
fibres only are recorded.   Under this condition, the quick twitch-like
contraction, following the arterial injection of acetyl-choline, was found
to be associated with an irregular outburst of electrical activity (see
Fig. XIII. 8), indicating that it is a *brief asynchronous tetanus*.   Similarly
eserine, which allows the acetyl-choline released by a motor impulse to
persist at the endplate in a concentration sufficient to re-excite the
muscle through several successive refractory periods of the fibre, changes
the reponse to a single motor nerve volley from a single twitch to a
brief waning tetanus.

Curare is a poison which acts on the motor endplate much as atropine acts on heart, smooth muscles or gland cells, or as nicotine acts

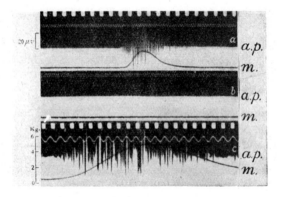

Fig. XIII. 8.   Isometric myograms (m) and action potentials (a.p.), taken
with electrodes very close together, from a cat's gastrocnemius muscle.
Close arterial injection of (*a*) 5 μg. of acetyl-choline, (*b*) saline solution
and (*c*) 25 μg. of acetyl-choline ; higher speed recording surface.   The
time record shows intervals of 70 msecs.   (After G. L. Brown.)

on ganglion cells.   Curare prevents the muscle from responding to stimulation of the motor nerve although the muscle will still respond to direct
stimulation.   During nerve stimulation, acetyl-choline is released at the
motor endings as in the uncurarised preparation but the motor endplates do not respond to it.   Thus, curare acts on the motor endplates,
much as atropine acts in connection with the parasympathetic nervous
system.

What is the normal action of acetyl-choline on the endplates ?
It does not excite the muscle fibres ; they are excited by the change
occurring at the plates when in contact with the acetyl-choline.   Some
idea about this change may be obtained from experiments on the *electric
organs* of certain fish, *e.g.*, *Torpedo*.

This electric organ is an accumulation of hypertrophied motor end
plates derived from skeletal muscle but lacking the contractile element
The motor endplates develop, not in the middle of the muscle fibres a

usual, but at one end which grows until a fully developed plate is obtained. The muscle fibre may remain unchanged, may diminish or may even disappear. The electric organ of *Torpedo* is formed by a great number of columns containing such plates arranged side by side, each column being built up of several hundred superimposed plates. Large efferent nerve fibres enter the plates from the ventral sides covering them with a terminal nerve net (Fig. XIII. 6). Impulses are sent down from the central nervous system along these nerves causing a brief discharge of the organ (40 to 80 volts). The impulses may follow each other at a frequency of several hundred per second. At the moment of the discharge, the ventral sides of all plates become negative to the dorsal nerve-free sides, probably by depolarisation.

This sudden depolarisation which constitutes the discharge is thought to be the effect of minute amounts of acetyl-choline, released simultaneously from all nerve endings at the ventral surfaces of all plates and then destroyed within the brief refractory period. It has been shown that the organ is extremely rich in true cholinesterase and acetyl-choline, that acetyl-choline is released on stimulation of the nerves and that when injected arterially into the perfused organ acetyl-choline causes an electrical discharge. At the electric organ, the depolarising action of acetyl-choline is the final event, devoid of any further stimulating action, whereas in skeletal muscle the depolarisation stimulates the contractile element and at the ganglion cell, it initiates the impulse along the post-ganglionic fibre According to this view, acetyl-choline is a depolarising agent. Evidence has been obtained in support of this view from quite a different source. A model of a polarised surface with a lipoid layer in contact with saline solution can be connected to an amplifier by leads applied to the two surfaces of the interface. A positive electromotive force may thus be obtained, which quickly declines when minute amounts of acetyl-choline are added to the saline solution.

Central Synapses. The analogy between the transmission across a ganglionic synapse and across a central synapse is obvious. In addition, the view is widely held that the motor nerve ending with its endplate has many properties in common with the central synapse, furnishing a kind of pattern for the reactions taking place at this structure. Can we extend the concept of transmission by liberation of acetyl-choline to central synapses ? The question cannot be decided on the basis of suggestive analogies. Perhaps an entirely new experimental approach will have to be found, before a decision can be reached.

By applying to this problem the methods used in the investigation of cholinergic nerves, observations have been made suggesting that acetyl-choline may be the transmitter across a number of synapses in the central pathway of autonomic and motor neurones.

Acetyl-choline stimulates the respiratory, the cardio-inhibitory, the blood pressure centres in the mid-brain and sympathetic centres in the spinal cord. When applied to the motor area of the cortex both acetyl-choline and eserine cause activity of the appropriate muscle on the contralateral side ; when applied to the spinal cord they cause discharge of motor impulses. The central nervous system is rich in true cholinesterase. In the human foetus the cholinesterase appears and increases in different parts of the central nervous system in the order of their morphological differentiation. Brain tissue has a relatively low store of acetyl-choline but a great ability to synthesise it. This may be characteristic for a tissue which like the brain shows continuous spontaneous activity. Acetyl-choline was found to be released continuously from a perfused brain and spinal cord. The release from the cord increased on stimulation of the central end of a cut sensory nerve.

Different parts of the central nervous system contain varying amounts of acetyl-choline and of the enzymes which hydrolyse and synthesise acetyl-choline. A high content is found in the thalamus and in the basal ganglia, a low content in the cerebellum and in the pyramidal tracts. In addition, the content of these enzymes and of acetyl-choline diminish in the more highly developed brains. It is natural to suggest that the transmission by acetyl-choline may be a more primitive type of central transmission, the importance of which receded in higher animals, and which is retained in them at certain synapses only. Our knowledge, however, is too scanty at present to justify a definite statement of this kind.

CHAPTER XIV

THE PHYSIOLOGY OF THE SENSE ORGANS

Our knowledge of the outside world is based on information supplied by our sense organs ; they serve as a fairly well-equipped laboratory for the analysis of the physical world around us. We can judge weight and temperature ; the concentration of hydrogen ions can be judged by the sourness of solutions ; we are aware of the rhythmic variations in air pressure which we call sound and of a certain band in the electro-magnetic spectrum which we call light. Of many physical phenomena, however, such as X-rays, wireless waves, or ultra-violet rays, we remain unaware until their energy is converted into a form capable of stimulating one of our sense organs.

Very small quantities of energy in the form of light are capable of stimulating the eye, and a small quantity of mechanical energy applied to a hair of the skin is felt as a touch. The eye or optic nerve can also be stimulated mechanically, but the quantity of energy required is enormous compared with the amount of light energy necessary to produce the same sensation, and it is important to remember that the resulting sensation is always one of light. Appearances of light due to this cause are seen on pressing the eyeball at one side. In general it can be stated that each type of sense organ is capable of being stimulated by only one type of energy (Müller's Law). Very powerful stimuli of another kind applied to a nerve fibre, its end-organ or its central connections in the brain, give rise to only one type of sensation, namely, that for which the end-organ is specialised. There is no difficulty in determining which organs are stimulated by light, sound, dissolved substances (taste) and gases (smell), and, consequently, one would expect to find separate receptors in the skin for the appreciation of touch, heat and cold. Although we are accustomed to think of the skin as uniformly sensitive, it can be shown that one minute part of its surface may be more sensitive than another to a given type of stimulation. Corresponding to each of these specialised areas we should expect to find a specialised end-organ.

The Sense of Touch. A method much used clinically to determine the presence or absence of the sense of touch is to draw a wisp of cotton wool lightly over the skin. Although rather crude from the physiological point of view, the method gives one interesting result, because if the test is made on a part of the skin which has been shaved, the cotton wool is hardly felt, whereas on the unshaved skin there is no doubt of the sensation. The hairs of the skin, therefore, are an important factor in the appreciation of light touch. A more refined method of investigating the sense of touch is by v. Frey's æsthesiometers, a series of hairs of different thickness, graduated by determining the force necessary to bend them. The skin is shaved and an area of about 1 cm. square marked out on it. This area is then explored by pressing the æsthesiometer-hairs on different parts of its surface. It will be found that there is only a limited number of spots where the touch can be felt and that they are grouped around the hair bulbs. They are called *touch spots*. It will also be found that some of these touch spots require a stronger hair to stimulate them than others and that sensitivity to touch varies in different parts of the body.

Evidence from this type of experiment would lead one to expect microscopical structures beneath the skin specially adapted for the reception of mechanical stimuli. In the case of hairy parts, the touch end-organs are localised in the arborisations of the nerve fibrils around the hair bulbs, stimulation occurring by bending the hairs or by firmer

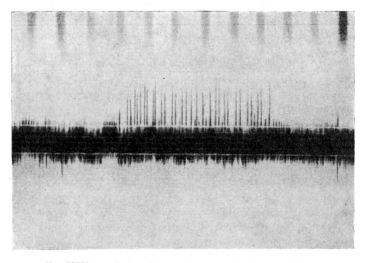

Fig. XIV. 1.   Action Potentials from an End-organ of Touch.

The hairs on the side of a cat's foot were lightly deflected, and the action potentials led off from the cutaneous nerve. Impulses only occurred during actual movement of the hairs. Time marker at the top of the figure records $\frac{1}{20}$th sec. (Matthews.)

pressure at their bases. There are, however, some hairless parts of the body, such as the lips and finger-tips, which are very sensitive to touch. It is believed that Meissner's corpuscles are the end-organs for touch in these areas. These corpuscles are found in the pulp of the finger tips.

The action potentials set up by the sense organs of touch have been investigated by Adrian by recording the electric variations in the cutaneous nerve supplying the toe pad of the hind limb of the cat. A glass disc was lowered on to the pad with a force which was kept less than 10 g. weight. At the moment of contact of the disc there was an outburst of impulses, which declined so rapidly that the response was all over in about one-fifth of a second. Similar rapid adaptation is found in the response to the deflection of the hairs (Fig. XIV. 1).

The Temperature Sense. If an area of skin is mapped out in the same way as for touch spots, but using heated or cooled metal rods, it is found that there are certain areas specially sensitive to warmth and cold. These areas are not so circumscribed as the touch spots, but are areas where a sensation is easily obtained in the centre but less easily in the immediate surroundings. Provided the testing rod is left long enough in contact with the skin, temperature differences can be felt on most parts of the skin owing to the conduction of heat to or from the sensitive spots. The areas sensitive to warmth do not coincide with those sensitive to cold ; neither are they equal in number, there being few or no cold spots in exposed parts of the skin such as the face. Certain " mucous membranes " are relatively insensitive to heat stimulation, so that it is possible, for instance, to drink liquids which are hotter than the skin can bear, and the same also applies to medicinal douches.

Although the warm and cold end-organs thus appear to be different, there seems to be some relation between the sensations, heat or cold spots being stimulated according as the temperature of the surface is greater or less than that of the deeper layers of the skin. If, for example, one hand is put for some minutes into hot water, and the other into cold, the sensations of warmth and cold gradually fade. This adaptation is probably to be explained partly by the properties of the sense organs themselves, and partly by the fact that the whole depth of the skin has taken up a uniform temperature (equal to that of the water). If, now, both hands are plunged into tepid water (about $37°$ C.), the hand which has been in hot water feels cold, while the other feels hot. This may be explained by the fact that in the hand which was in hot water, the temperature now falls from the deeper layers towards the surface, while in the hand which was in cold water the temperature gradients are in the opposite direction.

Extremes of temperature are thought by some observers to be appreciated by separate mechanisms, but since over-stimulation of any end-organ can give rise to pain, and since there is an element of pain in the sensation of heat, it is best to think of the sensation of heat as compounded of warmth and pain. Cool and cold are probably received by the same end-organs. There is evidence that the end-organs sensitive to cold are the end-bulbs of Krause, while those sensitive to warmth are the end-organs of Ruffini.

Pain. Painful sensations are experienced not only by the over-stimulation of any end-organ, but also by stimulation of what are known as pain spots. These, on exploring an area with a needle-point, are found not to coincide with the other spots. One part of the body, the cornea, is sensitive to pain only, and it is here that the microscope should reveal these pain receptors. There are, however, no organised structures but only naked nerve endings and presumably these are responsible for pain reception. It is interesting to note that naked nerve endings are also found in large quantities around the small veins, an arrangement that may be responsible for the severe pain of phlebitis (inflammation of the veins).

Although naked nerve endings appear to be the pain end-organs in many parts of the body, it has been shown that in the skin pain is not appreciated until the sub-epidermal layers are reached. It seems probable, therefore, that the skin end-organ for pain is the network of nerve endings which lie in the sub-epidermal layer.

The action potentials associated with the sense of pain have been investigated by pressing a sharp needle on to a decapitated cat's toe pad and leading off to the oscillograph from the cutaneous nerve. The needle was attached to a lever which was arranged so that a force varying from $\frac{1}{2}$ g. to 100 g. could be applied to the skin at the point of the needle. On human skin, a force in excess of 20 g. is felt as a prick. Two outstanding conclusions emerge from this experiment. First, that the frequency of the impulse is increased by increased intensity of the stimulus, whether this be due to a large constant force applied to the needle or to progressive penetration of the point into the deeper layers of the skin. The frequencies observed vary between 5 and 100 per second in each nerve fibre, being the same as those due to other kinds of cutaneous sensation. This does not favour the hypothesis that pain is due merely to excessive stimulation of any cutaneous end-organ, a view which was at one time held owing to the fact that extreme heat or pressure is painful. The occurrence of distinct pain, heat and touch " spots " on the skin also leads to the rejection of this hypothesis.

Secondly, the duration of the outburst of impulses is greater when the painful stimulus is greater. So long-continued is the sensory discharge due to pain that it has been suggested that the peculiar properties of pain may depend in part on the number of the impulses reaching the nervous system. This would be especially true if a large number of fibres were conducting the sensory disturbances, when the characteristic massive quality of the sensation would be produced.

Other Sensory Skin Functions. It is customary to assume that certain other sensory functions of the skin are served by separate mechanisms. These are : (1) the appreciation of deep pressure which, if excessive, leads to pain ; (2) the ability to localise the position of a stimulus of the skin ; and (3) the ability to discriminate between stimulation by one or two points of a compass. The latter (tactile discrimination) varies very considerably over different parts of the body, a separation of the compass points by 0·22 cm. being appreciable on the tip of the middle finger, whilst a separation of 6·8 cm. is necessary on the back. The muscle and joint senses enable us to judge the position and state of flexion of our limbs. Although not strictly skin functions, they are used in conjunction with touch, localisation, and discrimination to enable us to appreciate the shape of objects held in the fingers (Stereognosis).

The action potentials set up by pressure have been investigated by the same methods as those used for touch. The pressure on the glass disc was increased to between 200 and 500 g. weight, and it was found that the frequency of the impulses varied both with the absolute amount of pressure and with the rate of increase of pressure. If the pressure was maintained at a constant value, the frequency of the impulses declined slowly from its initial value, showing that the pressure end-organs become only slowly adapted to the stimulus.

Visceral Sensations. Sensations from the internal organs differ in many respects from skin sensations. The internal organs are insensitive to certain types of stimulation, *e.g.*, heat, and even when stimulated they may give the patient no information concerning the nature of the stimulus. They are not usually localised, but if they are, it is as likely as not for the sensation to be felt in a region far removed from its origin. This is known as the phenomenon of *referred pain*. Visceral sensations are referred to that portion of the skin whose nerve supply is derived from

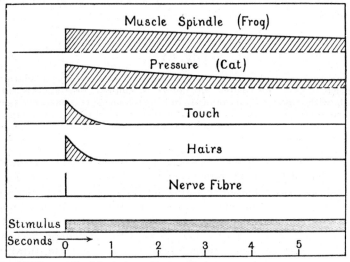

FIG. XIV. 2.   The **Adaptation of Various End-organs** to a Constant Stimulus.

Muscle spindles and pressure receptors give an almost constant response for several seconds, but it subsequently gradually dies away. (Cf. Fig. X. 14, p. 378.)

Touch receptors and hairs give a response which dies away entirely in less than one second (Fig. XIV. 1).

The response of a nerve fibre is included for comparison ; this, as we have seen, is all over in a very small fraction of a second. (From Adrian's " Basis of Sensation.")

the same segment of the spinal cord as that of the internal organ. Gall-bladder pains, for example, are often localised in the right shoulder ; kidney pains in the groin. One finds, however, that the sensory nerves to joints, to the muscles working those joints, and the covering skin are all supplied from the same spinal cord segment. In joint injuries it is usual to find impaired movement due to the fixation by the muscles, and also pain in the overlying skin. Visceral sensations are usually painful and are of the same type whatever their origin. Two very common causes of visceral pain are (1) prolonged contraction of plain muscle such as occurs in a ureter which is trying to pass a stone, and (2) the stretching of organs such as the mesentery, where the end-organs involved are the Pacinian corpuscles.

Sensations during Regeneration of Nerves. After section of a sensory nerve to the skin there is a complete loss of all types of sensation in the area exclusively supplied by that nerve. During recovery from the injury the sensations are different from those arising in normal skin. All types of stimulation tend to be painful, and they do not arouse the appropriate sensation. The pain is diffuse, radiating, wrongly localised, and peculiarly unpleasant, and produces in the subject an almost irresistible tendency to make some motor response. This type of sensation was at one time called " protopathic " as opposed to the finer grades of sensation, which are obtainable from the normal skin and which were known as " epicritic." The finer grades of sensation and accurate localisation recover very slowly and never completely.

THE EYE

In the sections dealing with the eye and the ear a systematic anatomical description of these structures will not be attempted, because this subject is dealt with fully in anatomical and histological text-books. Certain structural details are, however, of such importance to a proper understanding of the physiology of vision and hearing that any account would be unintelligible without some mention of them.

The question that must be answered in considering the problem of vision is that of how light, falling on the eye, can effect the changes in the visual cortex which are responsible for the sensation of vision. It is convenient to divide this main question into three parts ; first, how is light transmitted from the external world to the sensitive end-organs of the eye ; second, what is the mechanism whereby light energy is changed into a form in which it can stimulate the optic nerve ; and, third, how is this stimulus transmitted to the brain ? These three questions will be answered, as far as is possible in the present state of our knowledge, in the following discussion.

The consideration of our first question—that of the transmission of light through the eye—requires, first of all, some knowledge of the structure and properties of the various parts of the eye.

The diameter of the eyeball is approximately 23 mm. Its outer coat is called the *sclera* (the white of the eye), and this becomes continuous in front with the more highly curved *cornea* which is transparent to allow the entry of light into the eye. The shape of the combined cornea and sclera resembles that of a cricket ball with a watch-glass placed on it (Fig. **XIV. 3**).

Acuteness of vision depends very largely on the optical perfection of the anterior surface of the cornea. This structure must be well protected, and this is effected by the lids and secretion of tear fluids. The lids themselves are composed of plates of compressed fibrous tissue, and they are involuntarily closed when a foreign body is seen to be approaching the eye or when the cornea is touched. Birds, fishes and reptiles have a third, semi-transparent, eyelid (the nictitating membrane) moving horizontally beneath the other two.

Tear fluid is secreted by the lachrymal gland ; it irrigates the conjunctival surfaces of the lids and cornea.   In addition to its mechanical action of washing dust and other foreign bodies out of the eye, it has a bactericidal action.   Normally the secretion of tears just about keeps pace with their evaporation.   When, however, tear fluid is being secreted in large quantities, it is siphoned off into the nose through the lachrymal ducts and may also pass between the lids, a course which it is normally prevented from taking by the greasy secretion from the edges of these structures.   The two puncta by which the tear fluids are drained into

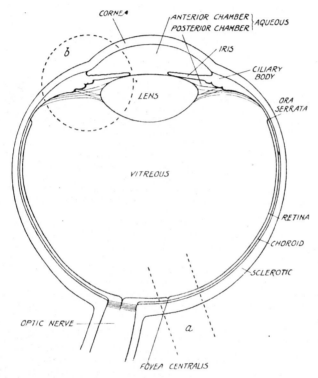

FIG. XIV. 3.   Diagrammatic Horizontal Section of the **Human Eye**.   (Parsons.)

the lachrymal sac and duct can be seen on the edges of the lids on their medial aspect.

The *sclera,* as its name implies, is a tough structure serving as a protective coat to the eye.   The contents of the eyeball are at about 25 mm. Hg above atmospheric pressure, so that if a cut is made in the sclera, they tend to escape.   Normally the sclera resists this intra-ocular pressure, but occasionally it weakens locally and becomes bulged under the strain.   Certain blood vessels and nerves pierce the sclera, and in the case of the optic nerve, the fibres pass through a lattice-work of sclera known as the *lamina cribrosa.*

The sclera is lined on the inside by the *choroid,* a highly vascular coat ; lining the choroid is the retina, the light-sensitive structure of the eye. The choroid not only contains the principal blood supply to the eye, but, since it is very heavily pigmented, it prevents light both from reaching the retina through the sclera and from scattering within the eye ; the pigmentation corresponds to the blacking of the bellows and the backing of the plate in a camera. The structure of the sensitive portion of the retina merits more detailed examination and will be considered later. In the region immediately posterior to the corneo-scleral junction, the retina and choroid become modified and enlarged to form the *ciliary body* (Fig. XIV. 4), which consists of a stroma, a very rich blood supply, some glandular substance and a group of muscles (the ciliary muscle). From the ciliary body there arises the *iris*, a structure composed morphologically of two layers, one continuous with the choroid, the other with the retina. The choroid layer, facing outwards and visible through the cornea, usually develops a heavy pigmentation

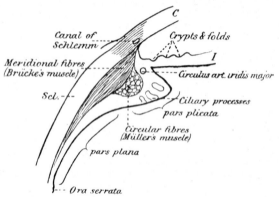

Fig. XIV. 4. The **Ciliary Body**—an enlarged section of the region " b " in Fig. XIV. 3. (Parsons.)

during the period of growth. In those cases where this pigment fails to develop, the retinal coat can be seen and the iris appears blue. The presence of brown pigment on the anterior surface of the iris behaves as a Mendelian dominant character to the absence of such pigment, which is a recessive character. Parents without the pigment have exclusively children who are similarly without it.

By far the greater bulk of the interior of the eyeball is occupied by the *intra-ocular fluid* (also known as the *aqueous humour*) and the *vitreous body* (or *vitreous humour*) separated by the *crystalline lens*. These three are transparent and, with the cornea, make up the optical system of the eye. Together they are capable of forming an inverted image of external objects on the retina in much the same way as the lens of a camera forms an inverted image on the photographic plate.

The anterior chamber of the eye and that part of the posterior chamber which lies in front of the lens contain intra-ocular fluid only. The rest of the posterior chamber, comprising about two-thirds of the bulk of the eyeball, is occupied by the vitreous body. At one time it was thought that the intra-ocular fluid was a simple dialysate from blood in the vessels of the ciliary body, but more accurate methods have shown that this cannot be so since its osmotic pressure is, in fact, slightly higher than that of plasma. There are also discrepancies between the chemical composition of intra-ocular fluid and of plasma which do not fit in with this explanation of its origin. A discussion of the question of the formation of intra-ocular fluid will be found in Chapter III.

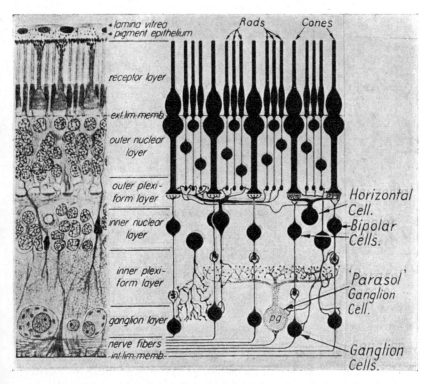

Fig. XIV. 5. The **Human Retina.**

At the left, a vertical section through the retina in the nasal fundus, as it appears in ordinary histological preparations ($\times$ 500). Note cross-section of capillary in inner nuclear layer.

At the right, a " wiring diagram " of the retina showing examples of its principal elements. (After Walls.)

Many people think that there is a fairly rapid production of intra-ocular fluid by the ciliary body. This is supposed to pass through the pupil into the anterior chamber to escape through the spaces of Fontana —minute openings in the sclera immediately posterior to the cornea— to enter the canal of Schlemm and then the venous blood. Other people think that the flow is normally sluggish but is accelerated by inflammations of the interior of the eye. There is no obvious reason for a rapid flow since the metabolism of the lens is small and the iris probably derives oxygen from its own blood vessels.

The vitreous body is a thin transparent jelly of about the consistency of the white of a raw egg ; it has no obvious microscopic structure. Chemically it may be regarded as a gel formed by the combination of the intra-ocular fluid with two specific proteins—the mucoprotein and the residual protein. The mucoprotein appears to be associated with the maintenance of the transparency of the vitreous (a similar protein is characteristic of the cornea), while the residual protein is responsible for the gel formation. The quantity of water associated with the colloid molecules of the vitreous varies with the pH ; when alkaline the vitreous swells and the rise in intra-ocular pressure produces an expulsion of fluid. The vitreous is a much more stable constituent of the eye than the aqueous and losses may have to be compensated for by a serous exudate behind the retina often leading to retinal detachments.

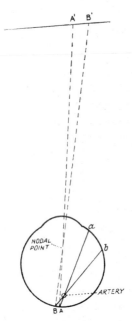

Fig. XIV. 6. **Shadows of Arteries** on the Retina.

A brightly illuminated point on the sclera " a " casts a shadow of the artery on to the retina at " A," and this shadow appears to occupy a position " A¹ " in the outside world. When the illumination moves to " b," the shadow appears to move to " B¹."

Microscopically the *retina* (Fig. **XIV.** 5) is composed of several layers, the outermost of which contains rods and cones, the light sensitive end-organs. The nuclei of these form the outer nuclear layer. There are two other cell layers, the inner nuclear and ganglion cell layers, the latter giving rise to the axons of the optic nerve. The arborisations of the nerve fibres connecting the cell layers form two intermediate ones called the outer and inner fibre layers. It is a remarkable thing that the rays of light, before they can reach the actual sensitive layer of end-organs, have to pass, not only through the inner layers of the retina, but also between the branches of the retinal vein and artery as they ramify on its surface. Simple eyes, such as those of cephalopods, have the sensitive elements of the optic nerve endings pointing towards the light and away from the other coverings of the eyeball. Although the retina is fairly transparent, its presence in the path of the beam must cause some interference with the perfection of the image in man and animals having this type of retina. It has the advantage, however, of bringing the rods into close relation with the vascular choroid.

The presence of the retinal blood vessels can be appreciated in one's own eye under certain conditions. One of the best ways of doing this is to illuminate a small area of the sclera very brightly from outside the eye (Fig. **XIV.** 6). This illuminated area casts a shadow of the vessels on to the sensitive layer, and one sees a large branching tree pattern in one's field of vision. On moving the light the vessels appear to move. By measuring the actual movement of the light, and the apparent movement of the vessels, it is possible to calculate the distance between the vessels and the sensitive layer. Since this calculated distance is found to be the same as that between the vessels and the rod and cone layer, it follows that the latter must constitute the ultimate end-organs of vision.

At the posterior pole of the eye there is a small depression on the retinal surface called the *fovea centralis* (central pit) (Fig. XIV. 7) which plays an important part in vision. It will be considered in detail later, but it must be pointed out at this stage that when we look at a small object, the eye is moved so that the image of that object falls on the fovea. The fovea is the region of most distinct vision.

The Formation of the Retinal Image

The optical system of the eye is such that an inverted image of external objects is formed on the retina. By applying the laws of optics to the refracting surfaces and the refractive indices of the eye media, it is obvious that the retinal image must be inverted just as it is on the focusing screen of a camera. Such an inverted image can be seen in the excised eye of an albino rabbit by looking at it from behind through the non-pigmented sclera. In infancy, during the period when the sense of vision is being developed, we learn to associate the inverted image with the uninverted external object. If from any cause in later life an uninverted image is formed on the retina, the object itself appears inverted. This can be demonstrated by casting the shadow of an object, held very close to the eye, on to the retina by means of a point source of light. If

FIG. XIV. 7. A cross-section of the Retina showing the Fovea Centralis. An enlarged section of the region "a" in Fig. 178. (After Sobotta.) There are no rods in the retina at this point.

NERVE FIBRE LAYER — GANGLION CELL LAYER — INNER MOLECULAR LAYER — INNER NUCLEAR LAYER — OUTER MOLECULAR LAYER — OUTER NUCLEAR LAYER — ROD AND CONE LAYER the object is a pin head upwards, it is seen head downwards. For a similar reason, when an effusion of blood has made its way into the vitreous and the clot sinks from the top to the bottom of the eye, the shadow of the clot appears to pass from below upwards. Additional evidence of an inverted retinal image is derived from the relative positions of the *fovea centralis* and the place of entry of the optic nerve (blind spot). Also, in diseases leading to blindness of one half of the retina, objects in the outer world lying on the side opposite to the lesion are not seen. This point will be referred to later.

Before reaching the retina the rays of light have to pass through the cornea, the anterior and posterior chambers of the aqueous humour, the lens and the vitreous. The absorption of visible rays by these eye media is very small except in old age, when there is an appreciable absorption of the shorter spectral waves by the lens. Infra-red and ultra-violet radiations, both of which are capable of damaging the retina, are absorbed by the eye media before reaching it. Both these types of radiation are harmful to other structures in the eye. The infra-red rays, for instance, can cause cataract of the crystalline lens (*e.g.*,

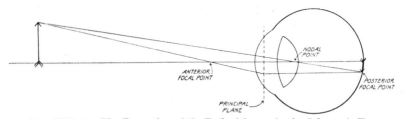

Fig. XIV. 8.—The **Formation of the Retinal Image** in the Schematic Eye.

amongst glass-blowers), whilst the ultra-violet rays cause intense inflammation of the conjunctiva (film-star's eye, snow-blindness). The retina is protected against intense visible radiation by changes in the pupil diameter, the iris contracting reflexly under these conditions and dilating again more slowly in the dark. Even when the pupil is fully contracted, the absorption of visible light by the retina at the site of a very bright image may lead to a rise of temperature sufficient to cause a burn resulting in local blindness. This condition is common after an eclipse of the sun.

The eye is often said to resemble a camera, the lens in each case focusing an image on to a light-sensitive structure which is either the retina or a photographic plate. It is important to remember, however that the strongly curved outer surface of the cornea is the chief refracting surface of the eye. The lens is very powerful if examined in air, but since it is suspended in fluids whose refractive indices are only a little less than its own, it loses most of its power when in the eye. The lens is responsible for the fine focusing of the image on the retina.

Both in the case of the eye and the camera it is possible to predict the size and position of the image from a knowledge of the cardinal points of their optical systems. The most useful of these is the *nodal point*, a imaginary point at the optical centre. In the case of a thin lens it is at its centre, whilst in the case of the eye it is in the crystalline lens near the posterior surface, 15 mm. in front of the retina (Fig. XIV. 8). A pencil of light directed towards the nodal point behaves as though it had passed through undeflected, although this does not mean that the pencil actually follows this path. Its use is in the calculation of the size of the retinal image, when the size and distance of the external object are known. The calculation is made by the use of the principle of similar triangles. It can be applied, for instance, to the calculation of the distance between the blind-spot (optic disc) and the region of most distinct vision (fovea centralis). A circle and, 60 mm. to its left, a cross are made on a piece of paper, and, looking at the cross with the right eye only, the paper is moved away from the eye. At about 220 mm. distance the circle will be invisible because its image will fall on the blind-spot, at which point the retina is absent (Fig. XIV. 9). By " similar triangles " we have :—retinal distance required : 15 mm. :: 60 mm. : 220 mm. The

FIG. XIV. 9. Figure for illustrating the Presence of the **Blind-spot**. Look at the cross with the right eye only and hold the book at about 22 cm. from the eye.

distance between the fovea and the centre of the optic disc works out to be 4 mm., a result which agrees with histological observations.

The *anterior focal point* is 13 mm. in front of the cornea, and a pencil of rays which has passed through it is refracted parallel to the optic axis when it meets the *principal plane*, which lies 2 mm. behind the anterior surface of the cornea (Fig. XIV. 8). Using these quantities in conjunction with the nodal point, the position of the image within the eye can be determined.

The eye also behaves like other optical instruments in that it is subject to some of their defects. Amongst these can be mentioned *spherical aberration*. The power of a spherical lens is greater at the periphery than at the centre, that is to say, the image formed by its periphery is nearer to the lens than the image formed by its centre. In the eye the outline of the refracting surfaces is slightly hyperbolic and in this way spherical aberration is diminished. *Chromatic aberration* of a lens system is due to the fact that the short (blue) waves of the spectrum are more refrangible than the long (red) waves, and so come to an earlier focus. Actually the eye, on looking at a point source of light, focuses the middle wave-lengths, giving the light a halo of red and blue. These halos can be seen by looking at a small light through a piece of cobalt glass which transmits only blue and red rays.

Accommodation. A normal eye at rest brings distant objects to a focus on the retina, and its *far point* of distinct vision is said to be at infinity. If an object is brought close to the resting eye, the image becomes blurred just as the image of a near object on a photographic plate is blurred unless some readjustment of the lens system is made. In the case of the eye this readjustment is known as accommodation ; in the case of the camera it is known as focusing. There is a limit beyond which the eye cannot further accommodate, and the nearest point at which objects can be seen after maximum accommodation is known as the *near point.* The mechanism of accommodation by which the divergent rays from near objects are converged to a focus on the retina is not the same in all animals. In the mollusc, *Pecten,* the eye is elongated as in focusing with a camera ; birds increase the radius of curvature of

Fig. XIV. 10.—The Changes in **Sanson's Images** during Accommodation.

A 3-point source of light forms mirror images at the anterior surface of the cornea and at the anterior and posterior lens surfaces. During accommodation (right) only the anterior lens image changes. Notice the contraction of the pupil. (Fincham.)

the cornea and lens and may, in addition, change the position of the fovea ; mammals, including man, increase the power of the lens by increasing its curvature.

Certain changes can be seen to occur in the human eye when it accommodates for near objects. If a candle is held slightly to one side of a subject's eye in a darkened room, an observer sees images of the flame formed by the principal refracting surfaces (Sanson's images) The anterior surface of the cornea acts like a convex mirror and forms a bright uninverted image. The anterior surface of the lens functions similarly, but the image is faint and often very difficult to see, and normally is larger than that formed by the cornea. The image from the posterior surface of the lens is inverted and much smaller than the others. When the eye accommodates alternately for far and near objects a marked change occurs in the image from the anterior lens surface there is a very slight change in the image from the posterior lens surface and no change at all in the image from the cornea, showing that this structure is unchanged during accommodation (**Fig. XIV. 10**). In order to focus near objects the curvature of the anterior lens surface is increased and consequently the mirror image formed at its surface becomes smaller. It can be shown by direct microscopical measurement that the anterior lens surface moves forward during accommodation. This is not due to a forward displacement of the lens, since the posterior surface moves backwards very slightly. The inner margin of the iris rests against the anterior surface, and the forward movement during accommodation can be seen when the eye is viewed at an angle of 90 degrees with the line of vision ; the observation is complicated, however, by the accompanying contraction of the iris.

If a lens is excised it is found to be more spherical than it is within an eye accommodated for distant vision. The reason for this is that the lens is an elastic body which assumes a more spherical shape when it is free from restraint. In the unaccommodated eye there are forces at work which keep the lens under tension, whilst for the clear vision of near objects these forces are relaxed, and since the lens is elastic it becomes more spherical and therefore more powerful. The radius of

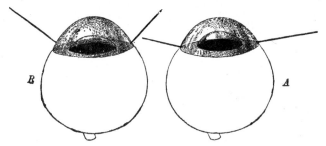

Fig. XIV. 11. **Accommodation** in the Cat's Eye. R for distant vision
A for near vision.

Two needles have been passed through the edge of the cornea into the ciliary bodies ; these are seen to move forward during accommodation for near vision. (Beer.)

curvature of the anterior lens surface at rest is 10 mm. and about 6 mm. during maximum accommodation ; the radius of the posterior surface changes from about 6 to 5·5 mm.

The tension,is supplied to the lens through its *suspensory ligament,* which is composed of some delicate strands of fibrous tissue attached to the periphery of the lens capsule and radiating outwards to become attached to the ciliary body. There are two muscles in the ciliary body, both of which contract on accommodation, and this contraction leads to a slackening of the suspensory ligament. The first of these, the *radial muscle,* arises from the corneo-sclerotic junction and its contraction pulls the ciliary body forwards towards the cornea. The second— the *circular muscle*—encircles the lens within the substance of the ciliary body which is drawn inwards towards the lens during contraction. Both these movements release the tension on the suspensory ligament. If a needle is pushed through the sclera into the ciliary body, its movements during accommodation are communicated to the needle and move it (Fig. XIV. 11). These movements of the ciliary body have also been seen directly through a window cut in the sclera.

The changes during accommodation can be summarised into (1) contraction of the ciliary muscles, (2) the approximation of the ciliary body to the lens, (3) relaxation of the tension of the suspensory ligament, (4) increased curvature of the anterior surface of the lens due to its elasticity (Fig. XIV. 12). In addition, during accommodation, the pupil contracts and the optic axes converge. These three reflexes are very closely associated with one another and they are often grouped together as the *near reflex* or *accommodation reflex*. All three are mediated by the IIIrd (oculo-motor) nerve and are designed to facilitate the production of a sharp image on corresponding points of the two retinæ. The relationship between accommodation and convergence will be considered later.

Until recently the view was held that the lens could not become

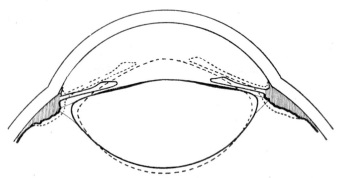

Fig. XIV. 12.   Diagrammatic Cross-section showing the **Changes during Accommodation** (dotted lines).   (After Helmholtz and Fincham.)
Note the regional variation in the thickness of the lens capsule.

accommodated by virtue of its own elasticity, since it is only the central portion of its anterior surface which becomes more spherical, the whole outline becoming hyperbolic.   It is now known that the capsule of the lens plays an important part in the determination of the final outline. The lens substance proper is held under pressure, and so, flows out when a small cut is made in the lens capsule.   The thickness of the capsule is not uniform, and in those regions, such as the anterior pole, where it is thinnest, the increase in curvature during accommodation is greatest (Fig. XIV. 12).   During accommodation the pupil contracts, so cutting off the peripheral parts of the lens and allowing only the most curved portions to take part in the formation of the retinal image.

The ability to accommodate is gradually lost with age owing to progressive hardening of the lens.   The condition is known as *presbyopia* (old sight).   At the age of twenty the near point of the normal eye is a 9 cm. ; at fifty it has receded to 53 cm., and objects nearer than this are seen indistinctly ; at the age of eighty all power of accommodation is lost.   Presbyopia is treated by giving the patient convex spectacles for near work.   They give the incidental rays an initial convergence, the necessary final convergence being supplied by the crystalline lens.

TABLE XIV. 1.

Amplitude of Accommodation in Dioptres and Near Point in Metres for a Normal Eye (after Duane)

Age.	Accommodation in Dioptres.	Near Point in Metres.
10	13·4	0·075
15	12·3	0·08
20	11·1	0·09
25	9·9	0·10
30	8·7	0·11
35	7·3	0·14
40	5·8	0·17
45	3·6	0·28
50	1·9	0·53
55	1·3	0·77
60	1·2	0·83
65	1·1	0·91

Errors of Refraction. It is unusual amongst either man or other animals to find an eye which is " normal " in respect to its optical system. Two of these optical defects (*errors of refraction*) are very common ; *hypermetropia* (long sight), in which the focus of the unaccommodated eye is behind the retina, and *myopia* (short sight), in which the focus of the unaccommodated eye lies in the vitreous (Fig. XIV. 13). The eye is always hypermetropic at birth, since the lens is then almost full sized and grows very little in after life ; the growth of the rest of the eyeball follows more closely that of the body generally. At birth, therefore, the eyeball is too short relative to the power of the lens and the rays fall on the retina before coming to a focus. With the subsequent growth in after years this defect is normally remedied, but in some people the growth of the eyeball is arrested and the eye remains hypermetropic. Myopia is almost always due to a lengthening of the eyeball, a fact which can be readily verified by asking a myope to look as far as possible towards his nose, so exposing an unusually large area of sclera.

People suffering from hypermetropia can usually remedy the defect by accommodating ; indeed they must continually use accommodation to see anything, including distant objects, clearly. " Eye-strain " is common in this condition, and is possibly due to constant use of the ciliary muscle. Myopes can never see distant objects clearly unless the incident rays are slightly diverged by concave spectacles (Fig. XIV. 13). Their far points, at which objects are focussed accurately without accommodation, are not at infinity, but are relatively close to them. Hypermetropes have to use an amount of accommodation in excess of the normal and so cannot see objects so close to the eye as the normal ;

their near point is farther off. Myopes, on the other hand, although they have faulty distant vision, have a near point which is closer to the eye than normal. Hypermetropes begin by having a too-distant near point and, since this recedes progressively with age, they have to take to reading glasses earlier. A myope may never need reading glasses since his near point only recedes as far as his far point which may be within reading distance.

In myopia and hypermetropia we have just seen that the distances over which clear vision can be maintained are very different. The lens

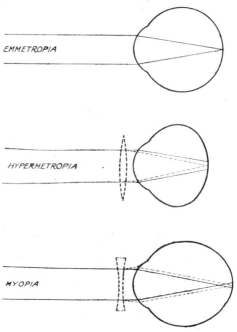

Fig. XIV. 13.   **Errors of Refraction.** Diagram of the Paths of Parallel Rays on entering the Emmetropic (normal), Hypermetropic and Myopic Eyes. The dotted lines show the paths taken when a correcting lens is introduced.

and its changes during accommodation are, nevertheless, normal. Let us suppose that three people of the same age, a myope, a hypermetrope and a normal, are given a printed page and told to hold it at the near point, that is, with maximum accommodation. They are then told to relax the accommodation and convex glasses are placed in front of the eyes until the print, held in the same position, is again clearly seen. The power of this lens is a measure of the amount by which the lens in the eye had to increase its power in order to see the print clearly in the first place. All three people, although the positions of their near points would be very different, would require the same strength of lens if they were the same age, showing that the increase in the power of the crystalline lens during accommodation is the same in all cases. If the same experiment were done with people of advancing ages it would decrease progressively.

In ophthalmology the power of a lens is expressed, not by its focal length, but in *dioptres* (D), that is, the reciprocal of the focal length in metres with the sign changed.[1] A convex lens with a focal length of —2 m. is a +0·5D lens. The advantage of this system is that the powers of lenses are additive. Two lenses of +4 and —5D (focal lengths —0·25 m. and +0·2 m.) when placed together are equivalent to one —1D lens (focal length +1·0 m.).

Degrees of myopia and hypermetropia are usually expressed in terms of the number of dioptres necessary to give normal vision ; thus, a myopic eye which needs a concave lens of —3D would be said to have three dioptres of myopia. Accommodation is best expressed in the same manner. For instance, a normal eye focuses distant objects when it is at rest and, in order to see an object clearly at 0·2 m., it will have

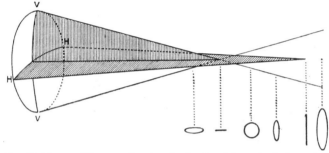

FIG. XIV. 14.   Diagram showing the Paths of Rays in **Astigmatism**.
The vertical meridian (V, V) of the refracting surface is curved more than the horizontal meridian (H, H).   Cross-sections of the conoid of light are shown below.

to increase the power of its lens system until its focal length is —0·2 m., or +5D. This is called exercising five dioptres of accommodation. A hypermetrope of the same age who ordinarily has to accommodate by, say, +1·5D in order to see clearly in the distance, must increase his accommodation by the same amount (+5D) as the normal, *i.e.*, must exercise +6·5 D, in order to focus an object at the same distance (0·2 m.).

One other common optical defect of the eye must be mentioned, namely *astigmatism*. This is a condition where the foci for vertical and horizontal rays entering the eye are different (Fig. XIV. 14). Astigmatism is usually due to differences in the curvature of the cornea in two directions, although astigmatic lenses occur, too. If, for instance, the horizontal curvature of the cornea were normal but vertically it were too great, then with a horizontal slit in front of the eye the rays would all come to a focus on the retina, but with a vertical slit they would be focused in front of the retina.

The Pupil.   The iris can be looked upon as a diaphragm capable

[1] With the new convention of describing lenses the sign, of course, is unchanged.

of varying the size of its aperture in response to different stimuli. The aperture is called the *pupil* and through it light enters the eye. The contraction of the pupil not only prevents the eye from receiving too much light but also improves the definition of objects.

The iris has two muscles, the circular muscle (*sphincter pupillæ*) contraction of which constricts the pupil, and the radial muscle (*dilator pupillæ*) stimulation of which causes dilatation of the pupil. The circular muscle is supplied by the IIIrd nerve and the radial by the sympathetic. Both sets of muscle fibres are also in a state of tone which is independent of their nervous connections, but the circular are stronger than the radial fibres, and normally are able to overcome them. Under ordinary circumstances, the iris is in a constant state of activity governed by the antagonism between these two muscles. Cutting the IIIrd nerve fibres to the eye causes a moderate dilatation of the pupil while stimulation of the cut ends makes it contract. Stimulation of the sympathetic produces dilatation.

The size of the pupil is constantly changing in response to various external stimuli, the most important of which is light. An increase in the amount of light entering the eye causes contraction of the pupil while a decrease causes dilatation. Most of this reaction is due to a reflex following stimulation of the retina, but it is probable that light also has a direct effect on the iris muscle even in man. In all animals in which there is partial decussation of the optic nerve, illumination of one retina produces contraction of the pupil in the unstimulated as well as the stimulated eye. This is known as the *consensual reflex*.

The effectiveness of light in eliciting pupillary constriction depends upon *changes* of illumination rather than upon the absolute quantity of light entering the eye. Thus, a rapid increase in illumination will produce a much greater initial constriction than a slower increase over the same range. Also, if two people are brought under the same moderate illumination, one after having been in the dark and the other after subjection to a high illumination, the pupils of the first will contract and those of the second will dilate. Later, as the eyes of both become adapted to the new illumination, the pupils of the first subject will dilate and those of the second contract until, for both, they have reached the physiological size for those particular conditions of illumination. This property of responding by pupillary constriction to a higher and dilatation to a lower illumination than that to which the eye happens to be attuned at the time is bound up with the general phenomenon of adaptation to different conditions of illumination. This whole subject of adaptation will be dealt with in detail later.

The Action of Drugs on the Eye. The ciliary muscle is supplied by the IIIrd nerve. If this is stimulated electrically the muscle contracts and the eye becomes accommodated for near objects ; similarly if the nerve is cut accommodation is paralysed. Atropine, homatropine and allied drugs, by inhibiting the action of acetylcholine on the muscle, have the same effect and are used clinically to abolish the power of accommodation. Since they keep the intra-ocular muscles at rest they are used in the treatment of intra-ocular inflammations. The effect of one drop of 1 per cent. homatropine on the eye is maximal in about an hour and takes about twenty-four hours to wear off completely. The effect of atropine lasts nearly a week. Eserine (physostigmine) and pilocarpine have the opposite effect ; they cause a spasm of the ciliary muscles and the eye is focused for near objects. The action of atropine is partially overcome by these drugs and they are often used to make reading possible after an examination of the eye. Eserine is interesting because it renders the suspensory ligament of the lens completely slack and the lens itself can often be seen to lie loose in the eye.

These drugs have the same effect on the circular muscle of the iris as they have on the ciliary body. Atropine and homatropine, therefore, cause dilatation of the pupil by knocking out the circular muscle and leaving the normal tone of the radial muscle to assert itself. The pupil can no longer contract when a strong light is shone into the eye, so that everything appears dazzlingly bright. Cocaine also dilates the pupil and, if a drop of 2 per cent. cocaine is given after homatropine, a further slight dilatation of the pupil results. Cocaine acts as a sympathetic stimulant by potentiating the action of adrenaline and, therefore, causes contraction of the radial muscle fibres. Homatropine and cocaine make a useful combination since not only do they together ensure a maximum dilatation of the pupil, but also cocaine anæsthetises the conjunctiva and homatropine is apt to make it smart. Novocaine cannot be used for the eye since it does not penetrate either the cornea or the conjunctiva. Eserine, on the other hand, contracts the pupil by preventing the destruction of acetylcholine so that impulses from the IIIrd nerve have a more lasting effect, while pilocarpine, by acting directly on the circular muscle, produces the same end result. These drugs are used in the treatment of *glaucoma*, a disease in which the intra-ocular pressure is raised owing to blockage of the spaces of Fontana by the margin of the iris. Morphia contracts the pupil to the size of a pin's head. The action is on the nucleus of the IIIrd nerve, and cutting the IIIrd nerve abolishes the effect.

The Duplicity Theory

Two kinds of end-organ can be found in the retinæ of most animals ; they are called rods and cones on account of their shape (Fig. **XIV. 14**). The human retina contains both rods and cones. There are very important differences between human vision in feeble illumination (night-vision) and in a bright light (day-vision), and it is generally thought that the rods are connected with night-vision and the cones with day-vision. This idea is embodied in the Duplicity Theory.

The duplicity theory has to explain why there are such remarkable differences between our vision at illuminations over 0·01 foot-candles (day-vision) and our vision at illuminations below this level (night-vision), and why we associate these differences with the reactions of the rods and cones of the retina. At high illuminations we can appreciate colour (differences in wave-length), and the most sensitive part of the retina is the fovea which we use for all activities requiring distinct vision. At low illuminations we are colour-blind, and find that, while the fovea is comparatively insensitive, the sensitivity of the peripheral retina is enormously increased. In day-vision, the brightest part of the spectrum appears to be the " yellow " but at night, while the spectrum

is appreciated in shades of grey only, the brightest wave-length has shifted to the " green." The long-wave end of the spectrum tends to disappear altogether and the short-wave end becomes relatively much brighter. These changes (which occur only in the periphery) in the relative brightness of colours with illumination are known collectively as the *Purkinje phenomenon*. At low illuminations the fovea is unable to see the spectrum at all until it is made bright enough for the colours to appear, while even in day-vision, the extreme periphery of the retina is practically colour-blind. We can, then, connect the fovea with the acute coloured vision characteristic of high illuminations and the peripheral retina with the colourless vision of low ones. The fovea is most sensitive to a wave-length of about 555 mμ (yellow) but can be stimulated by all parts of the visible spectrum, while the periphery (in the dark-adapted eye) is most sensitive to wave-lengths between 500 mμ. and 505 mμ. (green) and hardly at all to those over 650 mμ. (Fig. XIV. 16).

Microscopic study of the retina shows that the fovea is composed entirely of cones while around it they become mixed with rods and, in general, as one goes farther out towards the periphery the relative number of rods to cones becomes progressively higher. In man the number

FIG. XIV. 15. A **Rod** (1) and a **Cone** (2) of the Human Retina. (After Walls.)

of retinal elements per unit area decreases towards the periphery so that, although the ratio of rods to cones increases, the actual rod count is highest in a ring at about 20° from the fovea. Therefore, we can definitely connect the cones with day-vision and the rods with night-vision, and this idea is borne out by the fact that, in general, animals that live mostly by night or in dark places have a great predominance of rods in their retinæ, while animals which spend much time in the sun have mostly cones. This relationship between the rod and cone content of the retina and the habit of a species is particularly well developed in certain day- and night-living species of the lizard family as well as in the primates.

Visual Purple. Having, as it were, accompanied the light rays through the eye, and seen how they reach the sensitive end-organs of the retina, we have now to consider the second of the three questions formulated at the beginning of this section, namely :—What is the mechanism whereby light energy is changed into a form in which it can stimulate the optic nerve ? We are now in a position to put this question in a rather more concrete form. We can ask :—What is it that happens in the rods and cones, when light falls on them, so that the result is a

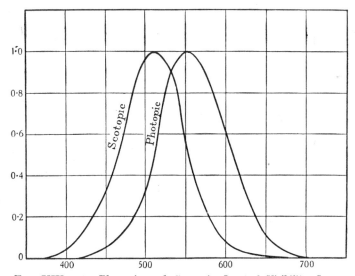

FIG. XIV. 16. Photopic and Scotopic **Spectral Visibility Curves.**
Abscissæ—wave-length in mμ.
Ordinates—relative sensitivity of the eye, the sensitivity at the most effective wave-length (505 mμ for scotopic conditions, and 550 mμ for photopic conditions) being made, arbitrarily, equal to unity. (From Rawdon-Smith, after Hecht and Williams.)

series of impulses in the nerve fibres of the retina and finally of the optic nerve ? We have to confess here that we do not know what happens in the cones, but we have got a great deal of information about the changes which light produces in the rods.

It is known that light, as such, is incapable of stimulating a nerve. It can only do so through some end-organ which, according to our present ideas, must contain a *photochemical substance*—that is, a substance which is decomposed by light. Such a photochemical substance— *visual purple*—is found in the rods of all vertebrate eyes, and if we examine its properties we find that they will explain most of the phenomena of scotopic or night-vision.

If the retina of a dark-adapted animal is removed it is found to be deep pink in colour, and this colour changes rapidly on exposure to light, so that, after a few minutes, an isolated retina becomes yellow or white. The original pink colour is due to visual purple and the change to the bleaching of this substance by light.

The fact that visual purple is coloured means that it does not absorb all the spectral wave-lengths to an equal extent, and, since it is pink in colour, it must transmit relatively more of the red and blue and absorb more of the yellow and green. Also, since light cannot affect a photochemical substance unless it is absorbed, it follows that the green and yellow wave-lengths must be more potent in bleaching visual purple than those at the ends of the spectrum. Both the absorption and bleach-

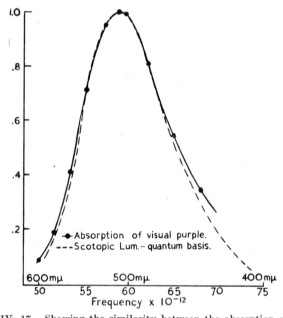

Fig. XIV. 17. Showing the similarity between the absorption of **Visual Purple** and the relative brightness of different wave-lengths as seen by **Night Vision** (scotopic luminosity curve).

ing curves of visual purple have been worked out experimentally. It has been found that, not only do both curves practically coincide with one another, but also that they agree very closely with the curve of the sensitivity of the dark-adapted (scotopic) eye to the different parts of the spectrum (Fig. XIV. 17). Thus, corresponding to the maximum sensitivity of the rods to the green and their lack of sensitivity to the red wave-lengths, visual purple is most readily bleached by green and is unaffected by red light.

Visual purple can be extracted from the rods by digitonin, bile salts and certain other hæmolytic agents. A deep pink solution is obtained which is bleached by light in the same way as the retina itself. Such solutions, as well as isolated retinæ, have been used to study the chemistry of visual purple and, although we still know very little about this complicated and difficult subject certain helpful facts have emerged as a result of recent work.

It appears that light, acting on visual purple, produces a distinct chemical compound called *transient orange*, which is very unstable and decomposes spontaneously to form *indicator yellow*. Indicator yellow, as its name implies, changes colour with *p*H, being yellow under alkaline and almost colourless under acid conditions : it seems probable that the " visual yellow " and " visual white " described by earlier workers were both really indicator yellow although " visual white " may have been either indicator yellow or its decomposition product(s).

Visual purple is made up of a reacting, or *chromophore*, group attached to a protein ; this chromophore and its bond with the protein being responsible for the characteristic absorption curve of visual purple. (The chromophores are responsible for the existence of the absorption while the shape of the absorption curve may be modified by the bond between them and the protein). Like so many other biologically important proteins, visual purple is a phospho-protein, and contains phospholipin. Light apparently causes a loosening of the bond between the protein and its chromophore, so rendering the latter more readily soluble in organic solvents. The substance extracted by such solvents is called *retinene*, and has recently been shown to be vitamin A aldehyde. We shall return to this point later. It seems, therefore, that light somehow weakens the chemical link which joins the protein to its chromophore group in the visual purple molecule and thereby destroys the absorption curve (colour) of visual purple producing indicator yellow via transient orange. Indicator yellow itself appears to be the chromophore still in some sort of association with the protein, although it is not known whether the link is a chemical one as in the original visual purple molecule or whether it is only physical, possibly an adsorption. *In vitro* the alteration of the protein-chromophore bond by light (bleaching) is accompanied by an increased positive charge on the visual purple protein molecule. Since the iso-electric point of visual purple is 4·5, this means that at the *p*H of the body, bleaching probably entails a decrease in the negative charge of the molecule It is not known, but is, at least, a possibility, that it is this electrical change (probably involving the release of ions from the visual purple molecule) which is responsible for the actual initiation of the nerve impulses which result from the impact of light on the retina.

In the living eye, visual purple is bleached by light but reappears slowly in the dark ; at the same time the eye becomes slowly more sensitive to light during a stay in the dark and, therefore, since the photo-chemical effect of a given amount of light is proportional to the concentration of the light-sensitive substance concerned, it appears that the regeneration of visual purple is responsible for this increase in sensitivity which is called *dark adaptation*. Any failure in the capacity of the eye to increase its sensitivity at low illuminations will produce the condition of *night blindness*.

There are several causes of night blindness all due to some disturbance of the scotopic mechanism which may involve either the rods or visual purple. For instance, the congenital form of night blindness (which may be inherited) appears to be caused by the absence of rods from the retina, just as complete colour blindness is due to a congenital absence of cones. The same effect is produced by the destruction of the rods by disease as in retinitis pigmentosa. Night blindness can also be caused by vitamin A deficiency, and here the failure appears to be in the production of visual purple since it has been shown that animals deprived of vitamin A either regenerate no visual purple or only do so slowly and in insufficient quantity. This form of night blindness is well

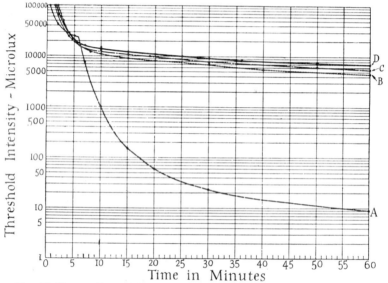

FIG. XIV. 18. **Dark Adaptation Curves** of one normal (A) and three congenitally night-blind (B, C and D) subjects.

1 lux = 1 metre-candle = 0·1 foot candle (very nearly). (After Dieter.)

known among people living under conditions of privation and can easily be cured by adding vitamin A to the diet.

Dark Adaptation. The adaptation of the eye to low illuminations is a slow process, taking at least an hour, but the change in sensitivity is very great. The actual increase in sensitivity depends on the illumination to which the eye has been previously subjected but it is usually in the region of a thousandfold and the fully dark-adapted eye can appreciate a light of only one ten-thousandth the intensity necessary to stimulate it when it is light-adapted. The smallest brightness necessary to stimulate the eye in any given state of dark-adaptation is known as the *visual threshold* ; the *absolute threshold* is that brightness which can just be appreciated by the fully dark-adapted eye, it is usually about 0·000001 equivalent foot candle.

During dark-adaptation there is, of course, a considerable increase in pupil size which would cause some increase in sensitivity, but the pupil changes alone can only account for an increase of about twelve times so that the greater part must be due to the increasing concentration of visual purple in the retina.

The measurement of dark-adaptation has been the subject of a vast amount of work and many instruments have been designed for the purpose but the basic principle of all methods is the same. After a preliminary subjection to light of high intensity designed to bleach all the visual purple out of the retina, the subject is put into the dark and the lowest intensity of light which he can recognise is measured at various intervals up to about an hour after the beginning of the test. The results are usually presented in the form of a dark adaptation curve (Fig. XIV. 18). Of the four curves shown in Fig. XIV. 18, one (curve A) illustrates the normal course of dark adaptation while the others (curves B, C, D) represent that of persons suffering from congenital night blindness. It will be seen that the normal dark adaptation curve is not continuous but is divided into two quite distinct parts. It is really made up of two separate curves superimposed, the upper one being due to the adaptation of the cones and the lower to that of the rods.

The dark adaptation curve of the cones can be obtained by using a red light of wave-length too long to stimulate the rods ; such a curve corresponds to that of the night-blind subjects shown in the figure so that it is clear that the small amount of dark adaptation of which the night-blind eye is capable is due to cones alone. We see, therefore, that although the cones are also able to increase their sensitivity at low illuminations, the extent of this increase is very small compared to that of the rods and that the enormous changes in sensitivity experienced by the normal eye are due to the rod-visual purple mechanism of the retina. This is the explanation of the phenomenon known as the physiological night blindness of the fovea because, since the rods become so much more sensitive than the cones, a dim light, such as that given by a feeble star or faint patch of light, will be invisible on direct fixation but can be seen by slightly averted vision when the image falls on the rods.

We have seen that the duplicity theory in its simple form states that day vision is a function of the cones and that night vision is a function of the rods and due to their content of visual purple. The implication is that the cones are too insensitive to be stimulated by a brightness of less than 0·01 equivalent foot-candles, and that the rods do not function above this illumination because, under these conditions, the regeneration of visual purple is unable to keep pace with its destruction ; the rods are, in effect, deprived of their photo-chemical substance. Actually, this cannot be the whole truth for two reasons at least. First, if the dark adaptation of the cones alone is tested, it is found that they are, in fact, able to respond to intensities considerably below 0·01 e.f.c., and, secondly, illuminations very much higher than this are not sufficient to bleach all the visual purple in the living eye. Visual purple can still be extracted from the retinæ of rats and frogs even after quite long exposures to direct sunlight. However, the fact remains that under ordinary conditions, there *is* a rather sharp switch-over from day t night vision as the brightness falls below 0·01 e.f.c. It seems as thoug at high illuminations the response from the cones can swamp tha from the rods, while at low illuminations the rod response is able t monopolise the situation.

Most of what has been said so far about the adaptation of the eye ha been concerned with adaptation to low illuminations after exposure t high ones. It is now being realised, however, that dark adaptation is onl a special case of a fundamental change which is always occurring whe the eyes are being used. The eye works well under a wide range c illuminations but to expect it to work at one brightness when it : adapted to another much higher or lower brightness is like using a ammeter with the wrong shunt in the circuit. The term " adaptation is now used to describe the adjustment of the retinal mechanism to tł general prevailing brightness of the objects in the field of view. It ma mean either the process of adjustment or the final " stationary state after adjustment is complete.

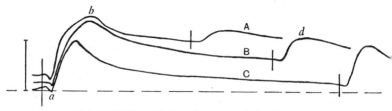

FIG. XIV. 19.   **Electroretinogram** of the Frog.
The short vertical lines show the beginning and end of the stimulus :
1 sec. in A ;   1·5 sec. in B ;   2 sec. in C.   (From Granit and Riddell.)

The Nerve Impulse and the Sensation

Having dealt, as far as our knowledge will allow, with the first tw of our three questions, we now come to a consideration of the thirc We must enquire into the changes produced in the nervous pathway– the optic tract—which connects the end-organs of the retina with tł visual cortex of the brain. It is also necessary to associate these change so far as we are able, with the conscious visual sensations produced.

Action currents are produced in the optic nerve when light falls o: the eye in exactly the same way as they are produced in other sensor nerves when their end-organs are stimulated by appropriate mean It must be remembered, also, that in the case of the optic tract, the firs two synapses are located in the retina itself (at the bipolar cells of th inner nuclear layer and the ganglion cells) and one would, therefor expect to find action currents occurring in the inner layers of the retin as well as in the optic nerve. Experiment has shown that this is indee the case. If one electrode is placed on the retina and one on the sclera o some other neutral point, the complicated pattern of potential change illustrated in Fig. **XIV. 19** is obtained when a light is shone on to th retina. Such a diagram of the electrical changes in the retina followin stimulation is called an electro-retinogram. One very interesting point about these records is the " off " effect—there is a fresh burst of activity both in the retina and in the optic nerve when the light is removed, and this means that cessation of illumination can act as a positive stimulus to the eye. It has been found possible to record the action currents in single optic nerve fibres, and these experiments have shown that in the frog, there are three distinct types of response and that any one fibre only exhibits one of these three. One set of optic nerve fibres discharges all the time the eye is illuminated ; when the light is switched on the second set produces a burst of impulses which quickly disappears, and another burst when it is switched off again ; while the third set responds only to turning off the light (Fig. **XIV. 20**). The

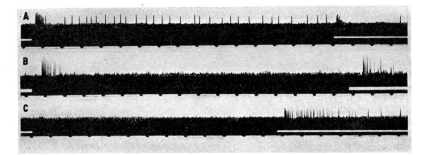

Fig. **XIV. 20**. Oscillograph Records of the **Action Potentials** in three single intraocular optic nerve fibres of the frog's eye, showing three characteristic response types.

A. Response to illumination of the retina consisting of an initial burst of impulses, followed by a maintained discharge lasting throughout the illumination. There is no response to cessation of illumination in this fibre (the off response in this record is partly due to retinal potential, partly to another fibre which discharged several small impulses).

B. Response only to onset and cessation of light.

C. Response only to cessation of light.

At the bottom of each record is a time marker in 1/5 sec. ; the signal marking the period of illumination fills the white line immediately above. (From Hartline. *Amer. J. Physiol.*)

second set of fibres—those which respond both to " on " and to " off "—will also respond to a *change* in the illumination, whether this is an increase or a decrease, and also to movements of light or shadow across the retina. The magnitude of the " off " response of the third type of fibre is dependent on the previous illumination ; the higher the foregoing illumination the greater the " off " response. This response can also be suppressed immediately by turning the light on again.

The great majority of nerve fibres leaving the mammalian retina have proved to belong to the first two groups ; they are either " on " or " on-off " fibres. The retinæ of the usual laboratory mammals contain a much greater preponderance of rods and far fewer cones than does that of the frog and it has been suggested that pure " off " responses are associated with the cones. This suggestion is borne out by the fact that during dark adaptation, the "off" response recorded on the electro-retinogram of the frog gradually disappears while the *b*-wave becomes bigger. In general the electro-retinogram of the dark adapted frog resembles that of the mammalian retinæ tested, as one might expect if dark adaptation causes the rods to dominate the total retinal response.

A single fibre of the optic nerve represents a single ganglion cell of the retina, but probably it is only at the fovea that it also represents a single end-organ. Experiments with frogs have shown that a given nerve fibre can be excited by stimulating an area of the retina containing many rods and cones. Such an area is called the "receptive field" of the ganglion cell or nerve fibre involved. It is also true that one very

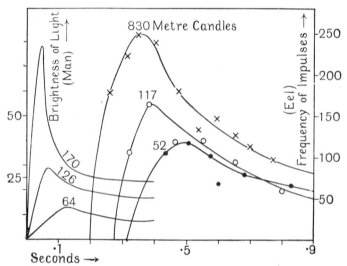

FIG. XIV. 21. A Comparison between the **Brightness** of the Sensation produced by Short Flashes of Variable Intensity in Man and the **Frequency** of Impulses in an Eel's Optic Nerve under similar conditions. (From Adrian : " Basis of Sensation.")

small spot of light, stimulating only a very few end-organs, will produce impulses in several different fibres and this means that the receptive fields of different nerve fibres must overlap considerably. These results are borne out by recent work on the histology of the nervous connections of the primate retina which has shown that, except in the fovea, a number of end-organs, which may include both rods and cones, is usually in nervous connection with one ganglion cell. In the fovea, on the other hand, there is always a one-to-one relationship between the end-organs—in this case cones only—and their ganglion cells. We shal return to this point later when we consider visual acuity.

As one would expect, the relationship of the intensity of the stimulus (in this case light) to the number of impulses passing up the optic nerve in a given time is the same as that for other sensory systems, so that the higher the illumination used, the greater the frequency of nerve

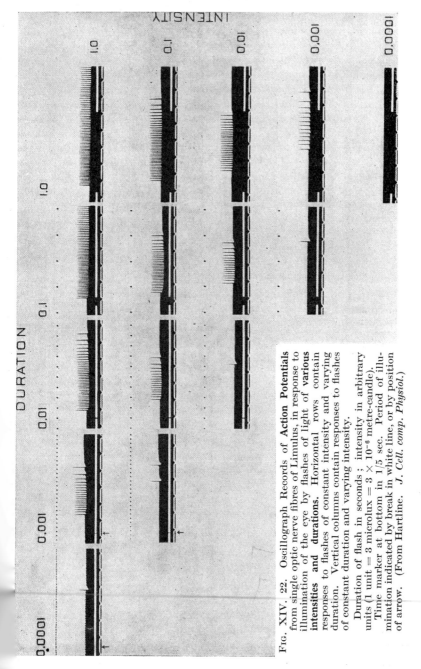

Fɪɢ. XIV. 22. Oscillograph Records of **Action Potentials** from single optic nerve fibres of Limulus, in response to illumination of the eye by flashes of light of **various intensities** and **durations**. Horizontal rows contain responses to flashes of constant intensity and varying duration. Vertical columns contain responses to flashes of constant duration and varying intensity.

Duration of flash in seconds ; intensity in arbitrary units (1 unit = 3 microlux = 3 × 10⁻⁶ metre-candle).

Time marker at bottom in 1/5 sec. Period of illumination indicated by break in white line, or by position of arrow. (From Hartline. *J. Cell. comp. Physiol.*)

pulses. The changes in frequency of the optic nerve impulses with tensity of light vary in much the same way as the subjective sensation brightness (Fig. **XIV. 21**). Both sets of curves in the figure rise to a higher peak and die away more quickly when the intensity of the stimulating light is increased. Within limits, the frequency of the optic nerve impulses appears to depend on the *amount* of light used for stimulating the eye. In other words, in order to obtain a given response the product of intensity and duration of the light must be kept constant (Fig. XIV. 22). There is also another factor—the *area* of the retina stimulated. Thus it has been found that increasing the illuminated area on the retina has the same effect on the frequency of the impulses as raising the intensity of the light. Both effects also occur subjectively— a light which is not of sufficient intensity to produce a sensation may do so if it is increased in size, or (if the original stimulus was a short flash) if the length of exposure is increased.

Fig. XIV. 21 shows that raising the brightness of a retinal image has other effects besides increasing the frequency of the optic nerve impulses. The latent period is shortened and the maximum frequency is attained more quickly. With short flashes of light the frequency also dies away more quickly if the light is made brighter. It has been shown by experiments on man that the sensation produced by a short flash of light outlasts the stimulus, so that if a series of flashes separated by a short interval of darkness is presented to the eye the resultant sensation may be one of continuous illumination. This phenomenon is known as the " persistence of vision." In this case, too, the brighter the flash the shorter the latent period of the sensation and the more quickly does the sensation die away. Therefore it appears that the intensity of the *sensation* is very closely associated with, and is probably dependent on the frequency of the impulses passing up the optic nerve.

If we look at a white surface which is illuminated by bright flashes separated by dark intervals of equal duration, the appearance of the surface will vary with the rate of alternation of black and white. If this rate of alternation is increased progressively a time will come when the sensation produced by a flash will still be in existence when the sensation from the next flash arrives ; the surface viewed will then appear to be continuously illuminated and not flickering. The frequency of alternation where flicker disappears is known as the " critical frequency of flicker." An increase in the illumination of a flash leads to a decrease in the duration of the sensation. If, therefore, the critical frequency has been reached for one illumination, an increase of illumination will cause the flicker to reappear.

In cinematograph projection there is a dark interval on the screen whilst one " frame " is being changed to the next, but owing to the persistence of vision these dark intervals are not appreciated. Under most conditions the peripheral parts of the retina are more sensitive to flicker than the central parts. This can be demonstrated by looking away from the screen, when the flicker will be observed.

Since the critical frequency of flicker depends on the brightness of the flashing light this method can be used to measure the subjective brightness of lights of different intensities. The method is useful for measuring the relative subjective brightness of different parts of the spectrum where the judgments are complicated by the presence of colour.

The Functions of the Cones

The fovea centralis, the small depression in the centre of the retina, is a late development in mammals, and its evolution can be followed in the primates, the lower members of the series having none, whilst it becomes gradually more marked, reaching its highest development in man. The structure of the fovea is such that it allows more distinct vision than any other part of the retina. It is encircled by blood vessels but itself has none, so that the path of the light rays is uninterrupted. For the same reason the nuclear and fibre layers of the retina are swept to one side from the fovea. The fovea lies in the centre of the macular plexus, a region of the retina where the ganglion cell layer and the outer fibre layer are much proliferated. Although not so sensitive as the fovea, the macular plexus is more so than the rest of the retina. This region appears to be specially represented in the cerebral cortex.

Corresponding with the macular plexus is a thin layer of pigment on the surface of the retina known as the macula lutea (yellow spot). Its function is unknown ; its presence is troublesome in colour vision experiments, since it interferes with colour matching, and its amount varies in different people. Its presence can be appreciated subjectively by opening and closing one eye in front of which is a bottle containing a green solution of chrome alum ; on looking at the sky the macula lutea can be seen as a pink spot, subtending about 5 degrees, lying on the green ground formed by the rest of the sky.[1] The fovea and its immediate surroundings (4 degrees) contain cones only, the end-organs of day-vision capable of " appreciating " colour and having a high acuity for the form of objects. At the fovea it is possible to study the reactions of the cones uncomplicated by the rods. Beyond this rod-free area the cones become progressively fewer in number towards the periphery of the retina.

The perception of fine detail is a characteristic of day-vision and of the cones and is most highly developed at the fovea which contains rather specialised cones, each of which seems to be connected to one nerve fibre only. This difference between the anatomical structure of the fovea and the periphery of the retina (where many end-organs may be linked to the same optic nerve fibre) explains the difference in the resolving power of these areas. The ultimate mosaic of sensitive elements of the fovea as represented in the optic nerves and probably in the visual cortex, is much finer than that of the peripheral parts of the retina.

The Form Sense. Two points of light subtending an angle of not less than 1 minute at the eye, can be resolved, that is, we are aware that

[1] With a clenched fist, the distance between the second and fifth knuckles subtends an angle of 8° at the eye when the hand is held at arm's length. The distance between the second and third knuckles subtends 3°.

there are two points and not one. Now the nodal point of the eye is 15 mm. in front of the retina and, therefore, the distance between the images of the two points on the retina will be 4·4 μ.[1] The diameter of a foveal cone is about 3·5 μ, so that the images can be made to stimu-

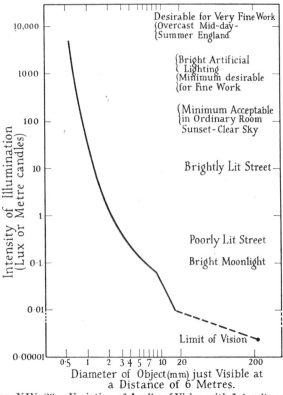

FIG. XIV. 23. Variation of **Acuity of Vision** with **Intensity of Illumination**.

The diameter of a white object which is just visible at a distance of 6 metres is plotted against the intensity of the illumination (both on logarithmic scales). 1 lux = 1 metre-candle = 0·1 foot-candles. The visibility of an irregular object is the same as that of a symmetrical object of the same area.

The acuity of vision is about doubled by increasing the illumination from that of an ordinary artificially lit room, to that of bright daylight (100,000 lux or more), and is increased some 400 fold from the minimum at which vision is possible, to bright daylight. The break in the curve indicates, approximately, the intensity at which cone vision becomes dominant. (From data by K. J. W. Craik.)

late two cones with an unstimulated cone between them. If the images were to fall on two neighbouring cones, the points would appear as one. It is possible to test the perfection of an eye's optical system by this method, but the use of two points of light is inconvenient and the letters of the alphabet (*test types*) are commonly employed for the

[1] One μ = 1/1000 of a millimetre.

routine testing of visual acuity. It is usually stated that a person with standard vision can recognise a letter when its details (breadth of the stroke and spaces) subtend an angle of 1 minute at the eye. This value applies only to black letters on a white ground and when the illumination is approximately that of a well-lighted room. The letters composing a sheet of test types are arranged in different sizes and, opposite each size of letter, there is a figure indicating the distance at which a person with standard vision can read that size. If a person cannot read the 18 m. line further off than 6m., his visual acuity is expressed as a fraction of the standard, namely 6/18. It should be noticed that at 6 m., the details of the 18 m. line subtend an angle of 3 minutes and the fraction 6/18 is the reciprocal of the smallest visual angle recognisable by the patient.

Visual acuity is, to some extent, dependent on the illumination (Fig. XIV. 23). The higher the illumination the greater the visual acuity, in other words, a line of print which is too small to be read at a given distance may become easily recognisable if it is more brightly lit. The reason for this improvement is not fully understood.

The Perception of Light and Shade. We obtain a very great deal of information about the outer world by judging the relative illumination of objects. It is often of importance to measure the smallest increase of brightness which can be appreciated visually, and for this purpose it is usual to project a small additional illumination (ΔI) on to an evenly illuminated surface (I). The added illumination is increased until it is just visible, its value then being known as the difference threshold. If this quantity is divided by the illumination of the larger surface, the fraction is found to be fairly constant over a very wide range of values (ΔI/I = constant).

This is a particular case of Weber's Law which states that a just appreciable increase in any kind of sensory stimulation bears a constant ratio to the intensity of the original stimulation. The law applies to the estimation of temperature, loudness, weight, etc.

Colour Vision. It must be confessed at the outset that, in spite of important recent discoveries, the whole subject of colour vision is still in an unsatisfactory state. We have not, as yet, got any theory which goes more than part of the way towards explaining all the phenomena associated with our ability to differentiate between different wavelengths.

It is possible to recognise 120 different hues in the visible spectrum (400–800 mμ) and about 1,000 different shades altogether if one includes the purples, magentas and other colours which do not occur in the spectrum. Since 120 different hues can be distinguished in a range of 400 mμ, it follows that the eye can differentiate between wave-lengths that are less than 4 mμ different. The problem of colour vision is : how is this accomplished ? We do not yet know the answer to this question and probably the best way of approaching the subject is to describe some of the phenomena which must be explained by any theory designed to provide the answer. Let us, therefore, begin with certain facts, leaving possible explanations of them till later.

The colour of an opaque object depends on the wave-lengths *reflected* from it into the eye, while that of a transparent object depends on the wave-lengths *transmitted through* it. Therefore, the effect of mixing colours by means of an opaque medium such as paint will be quite different from that obtained by mixing coloured lights. For instance, a mixture of yellow and blue *paints* produces green and a mixture of red and green produces a dirty brown colour, but a mixture of suitable blue and yellow or red and green *lights* produces white. When we speak of colour mixing in physiology we always mean mixing lights of different wave-lengths.

It is found that by mixing different quantities of a spectral red and green all the intermediate spectral hues of orange and yellow can be matched exactly, and similarly that mixtures of blue and green can reproduce the spectral blue-greens. Further, it is found that by mixing red, green and blue in appropriate proportions, most known colours (including white) can be matched. These three colours are, therefore, called the *primary colours*. Two colours, such as green and red, which can be mixed to give white are known as *complementary colours*.

The astonishing fact that two different stimuli such as red and green light can, when added to one another, produce a sensation which is qualitatively distinct from that produced by either stimulus alone is one of the fundamental problems which has to be explained by any theory of colour vision. The theory which we owe to Young and Helmholtz, and which is generally known as the **Young-Helmholtz Theory** of colour vision still provides a fairly satisfactory explanation.

We have already seen that a pure spectral yellow of, say, 590 mμ is subjectively indistinguishable from a mixture of the right proportions of a red of 670 mμ and a green of 550 mμ, and it seems probable that the actual optic nerve impulses are the same whether they are initiated by the yellow wave-length or by the red-green mixture. If this is true, the implication is that the analysis of colour takes place in the retina. The Young-Helmholtz theory suggests that there are three colour sensitive mechanisms in the retina corresponding to the three primary colours. These might be three photo-sensitive substances, perhaps contained in three different types of cone. One of these mechanisms is assumed to respond maximally to blue, less to green and not at all to red ; another would respond maximally to green, less to blue and yellow and not at all to red ; the third would respond maximally to red, less to green and not at all to blue (Fig. XIV. 24). Thus, it will be seen that a mixture of red and green light would stimulate the red and green end-organs to an extent depending on the proportions of the mixture and that this stimulus could be exactly imitated by a mono-chromatic yellow of intermediate wave-length. The two stimuli would, therefore, produce the same effect on the optic nerve and the resulting sensations would be identical. By extending this idea we can state that any colour will stimulate the three retinal mechanisms in varying proportions and that this stimulus can be reproduced exactly by a suitable mixture of the three primary colours, red, green and blue.

Unfortunately, the Young-Helmholtz theory does not cover many of the facts of colour vision nor does it even provide a really satisfactory explanation of all the results obtained by mixing spectral wave-lengths. A study of the hypothetical sensation curves for the three suggested colour mechanisms illustrated in **Fig. XIV. 24**, might lead one to suppose that three quite specific wave-lengths and no others represent the primary colours and that by making suitable mixtures of these three, *all* the colours recognisable by the eye can be reproduced. This is not, in fact, the case. Any colour can be produced by mixing three wave-lengths chosen from the red, green and blue regions of the spectrum, but the actual wave-lengths which must be chosen to imitate one colour may not be the same as those needed to reproduce another.

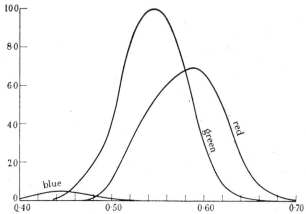

Fig. XIV. 24. König and Dieterici's suggested **Sensation Curves** for three retinal mechanisms of colour vision (corrected by Judd).

Abscissæ—wave-length in mμ.
Ordinates—relative sensitivities of the three mechanisms at different wave-lengths, the maximum sensitivity of the green mechanism being made equal to 100. (From Walters : *Proc. Roy. Soc.*)

One cannot consider the curves in **Fig. XIV. 24** as representing the fixed properties of three retinal mechanisms whose physical nature now only remains to be discovered. Nor can these curves be regarded as providing a recipe for the preparation of any colour by the mixture of three primaries. One should rather join Young in looking on the figure as a diagram illustrating the sort of retinal properties which may be postulated to account for the phenomena of colour vision.

The Young-Helmholtz theory has, so far, no anatomical basis in the retina ; no one has been able to find three structurally different sorts of cone or three suitable photo-chemical substances.[1] In the last few years, however, a considerable amount of very suggestive electro-physiological information has been collected. A study of the responses

---

[1] Some people believe that the rods with their visual purple may be one of the colour end-organs, although opinions seem to differ as to whether they are responsible for the perception of the blue or the green wave-lengths.

of single optic nerve fibres when the retina is stimulated by mono-
chromatic light has shown that some fibres give a maximal response
when wave-lengths from the blue region of the spectrum are used, others
when the stimulating wave-length was in the green region and yet
others when it was in the red. The last type of nerve fibre was only
found in eyes containing a certain proportion (33 per cent. or more) of
cones. No fibres were found which gave responses exactly corresponding
to the three " sensation curves " of Fig. XIV. 24, instead it appears that
as many as seven different types of end-organ may be concerned, two
responding maximally to wave-lengths in the blue, three in the green
and two in the red region of the spectrum.

It must be emphasised that the results described above do not tell
us anything about the *colour vision* of the animals concerned—this
would involve difficult and laborious conditioned reflex experiments—
but it does suggest the presence of retinal mechanisms of some sort
which are especially sensitive to specific wave-lengths. Further, it
suggests that the sensation curves of the Young-Helmholtz theory are a
brilliant approximation to the true state of affairs and also provide an
explanation of the difficulties encountered by the generations of workers
who have tried to fix the shapes of its three fundamental curves.

Earlier in this chapter (p. 491), it was implied that all cone vision
is colour vision and that rod vision is colourless. Further, the Young-
Helmholtz theory assumes that for the appreciation of white and grey
(and therefore of brightness) in daylight vision all three of the colour
sensitive mechanisms must play their part. The electro-physiological
investigations just described indicate that these assumptions are not
valid for cone vision.

If the reactions of the nerve fibres of a pure rod retina to single
wave-lengths are explored, the great majority of sensitivity curves are all
the same, and always correspond to the scotopic luminosity curve and
the visual purple absorption curve shown in Fig. XIV. 17. This is true
whether the eye is tested in the light or the dark adapted state. Further,
when similar experiments are done on an eye with a mixed rod and cone
retina, the sensitivity curves are always of the scotopic type so long
as the eye remains dark adapted. In all these cases, we are obviously
dealing with the results of rod reactions. If, however, light-adapted
mixed retinæ are used, the majority of the sensitivity curves correspond
to the photopic luminosity curve given in Fig. XIV. 16, although there
are nearly always fibres giving curves of what one might perhaps almost
call " the Young-Helmholtz type." Curves suggestive of colour vision
are also found in pure cone eyes and in these, as might be expected,
the majority of the fibres give curves of the photopic type even when
the eye is dark adapted. These findings strongly suggest, that, in day
vision, one type of cone end-organ mediates our sensations of brightness
and so our photopic luminosity curve while other types are responsible
for our sensitivity to colour. Futher evidence on this point will be
considered in the section on defective colour vision.

It has been found that the optic nerves of certain animals possess three separate sets of nerve fibres which end in three distinct layers of the lateral geniculate body. It has been suggested that these are the conducting paths from the three fundamental retinal mechanisms postulated by the Young-Helmholtz theory. There is, however, no direct evidence connecting these three nervous pathways with colour vision.

In man, colour sensitivity is at its best in the central area where the cones are tightly packed, and decreases as coloured objects are viewed with increasing obliquity. It is often necessary to determine the greatest angle at which white objects can be seen or coloured ones recognised. This process is known as mapping the field of vision. It is

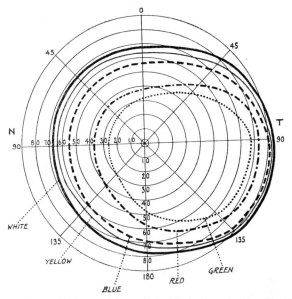

Fig. XIV. 25.   Perimeter Chart of the Right Eye showing the **Fields of Vision** for Different Colours.

done on a perimeter, an apparatus for presenting the object at different angles with the line of vision whilst keeping it at a constant distance from the eye. When mapping a visual field, it is necessary to specify the size and brightness of the object because the greater these quantities the farther out can it be seen and its colour recognised. When a coloured object is viewed with increasing obliquity, the colour appears to change in hue, the long wave-lengths tending to look yellow and the short wave-lengths blue. There are, however, four colours which do not suffer any apparent change. These are a yellow and its complementary blue, and a green and its complementary purplish-red. The colour fields for the yellow and the blue coincide, provided their brightnesses are the same ; the red and green fields also coincide, but they are not so extensive. The type of perimetric chart obtained with unselected coloured papers is shown in Fig. XIV. 25.

Defective Colour Vision. From reasons which have been given earlier it will be clear that the cones are predominantly the end-organs of colour vision, whilst the rods give rise to a colourless sensation. There is a rare condition of colour-blindness in which the whole world is seen in shades of grey. In this condition the patient behaves at all intensities of illumination as normal people do at night—the brightest part of the spectrum being in the green, in other words, he has a scotopic luminosity curve. In addition, the fovea, which contains only the cones, is blind. These patients, on attempting to fixate an object, move the eyes so that the image passes over the retina towards the fovea, but since this region of the retina is blind, the eye overshoots the mark, moves in the opposite direction, overshoots the mark again and so on. Rapid involuntary oscillations of the eye of this kind are called *nystagmus*, and total colour-blindness is one of many causes.

Slightly defective colour vision is common, 8 per cent. of males being affected. Although commonly called colour-blindness, the abnormality is often not detected until the colour vision is tested, and the sufferers may go through life without being aware of the defect. These colour-defectives tend to confuse certain colours, especially reds and greens, a fact which has led to some disastrous railway accidents. The condition is explained by the Young-Helmholtz theory by assuming that one set of colour-sensitive cones, one of the colour receptors, is absent or ill-developed. Usually it is either the red or the green receptor. The characteristic feature of the condition is that all colours can be matched by mixtures of two spectral primaries, and vision is said to be dichromatic, as opposed to the normal, which is trichromatic. Just as a normal person can match white by mixing three primaries, so a dichromat can match white by mixing two primaries. In passing along the spectrum, therefore, they will come to a wave-length, which will stimulate the two receptors in the same proportion as that necessary to produce white. This wave-length is, to the dichromat, indistinguishable from white.

If the Young-Helmholtz theory were entirely correct, one would expect the photopic luminosity curve of the dichromatic colour defective to differ markedly from the normal, since it would be the result of only two instead of three colour sensitive mechanisms. In point of fact, the luminosity curves of many of these people do not fall outside the normal individual variations. This lends added weight to the suggestion that cone vision is mediated by several types of end-organ, one responsible for sensations of brightness and others for the differentiation of colour. In dichromatic colour deficiency one or more of the second group may be supposed to be missing, while the first functions in the normal manner.

The detection of deficiencies in colour vision is not a task which can be undertaken light-heartedly, since there are all grades of severity, and when a defect is present in a mild form, it may only be possible to detect it when the conditions are made difficult. A subject may, for instance, show no signs until the area which he is required to recognise is very small, feebly illuminated, or the colour mixed with a lot of white light, as happens in a fog. In the Board of Trade test the candidate is required to name the colour of a small illuminated area of variable size. This is the basis of the Edridge-Green colour perception lantern. Another method is to present the suspect with a skein of wool, and ask him to pick out the one which matches it from a pile of variously coloured skeins. In the third method, which is the most convenient for rapid use, a series of cards are printed with figures in coloured spots on a background of similarly shaped spots, but in a colour which is liable to look the same as that of the figure to a colour defective.

In addition to the Young-Helmholtz theory another theory of colour vision should be mentioned, the **Hering theory**. In it the whole series of our visual sensations are regarded as made up of three pairs of six primary sensations—red and green, yellow and blue, black and white. Adherents of the theory think that yellow should be classed as a primary colour and not as a mixture of red and green sensations. Each of these pairs of sensations depends on the action of a special substance, in which the " anabolism " is produced by one colour of the pair and " katabolism " by the other—the two colours of each pair are complementary, that is, mixed together, they give a white. In the discussion of the fields of vision for colours it was stated that both complementary red and green cease to be appreciated at the same angle in the peripheral retina. Hering explained this as a loss of the red-green substance, the yellow-blue substance being lost more peripherally, and beyond this all colours are seen by the black-white substance, that is, in shades of grey. Further evidence for this theory is given by the phenomena of contrast colours.

If a small piece of grey paper is placed on a large square of red paper, the grey appears tinged with complementary green. Each colour can evoke the complementary colour sensation. This is known as the phenomenon of *simultaneous contrast*. *Successive contrast* is experienced when a coloured square is fixated for a few seconds, and the eyes are then turned towards a large piece of grey paper. The space previously occupied by the coloured square is now seen in the complementary colour. This is the commonest type of after-image. Hering's theory states that when anabolism is induced in one area katabolism is induced in neighbouring areas and subsequently in the same area.

There is not so much difference between the two theories of colour vision as appears at first sight. They both agree that there is a mechanism for colour analysis in the retina and that most colours result from stimulation of primary sensations in different proportions. The Young-Helmholtz theory has the great advantage of simplicity, whilst the Hering theory gives a more plausible explanation of colour fields and simultaneous contrast, both of which phenomena require an extension of the other theory. It must be admitted, however, that Hering's theory does not accord with modern views of photochemistry.

Vision with Two Eyes

The eyeball, its muscles, nerves and blood vessels are lodged in the orbit, the rest of the orbital cavity being filled by a mass of soft fat. Surrounding the eyeball is Tenon's capsule, a tough loose-fitting envelope, which is attached to the sclera just behind the corneo-scleral junction, and which sends prolongations to blend with the sheaths of the muscles and nerves. In addition, the eyeball is underslung by a thickening of Tenon's capsule, called the suspensory ligament. This method of supporting the eye allows very free movements in all directions.

The *extrinsic muscles* responsible for the movements of the eye are arranged in pairs, namely, the superior and inferior recti, the internal and external recti, and the superior and inferior oblique muscles. They are supplied by the IIIrd (oculo-motor) nerve, with the exception

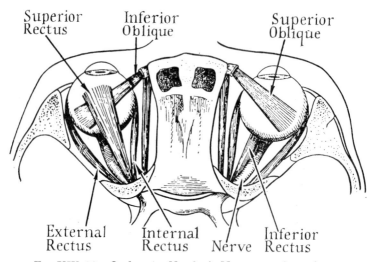

FIG. XIV. 26.   **Oculomotor Muscles** in Man as seen from above.
On the left, a portion of the superior oblique muscle has been cut away to reveal the inferior oblique ; on the right, the superior rectus muscle has been removed, so as to show the inferior rectus. (Modified from Adler.)

of the superior oblique (IVth, trochlear), and the external rectus (VIth, abducent). Their actions are easy to understand from a knowledge of their origins and insertions and of the centre of rotation of the eyeball, which is approximately in its centre. The internal and external recti run horizontally forwards from their origin at the optic foramen, to be inserted into the sclera ; on contraction, they rotate the eye inwards towards the nose and outwards respectively (Figs. XIV. 26 and 27). The optic foramen is on the medial side of the orbit, and the superior rectus runs forwards and outwards to be inserted in front of the equator of the eye. On contraction it turns the eye upwards, and, since it lies medially to the centre of the rotation, it also turns the eye inwards and at the same time rotates the right eye in a clockwise direction and the left eye anti-clockwise when looked at from the front. The inferior rectus turns the eye downwards and inwards, and rotates the right eye anti-clockwise.

Although the superior oblique arises from the optic foramen, it passes through the trochlea, situated to the upper, medial side of the front of the orbit, and it exerts its pull from this point on the upper, posterior lateral quadrant of the eye, where it is inserted. Its action is, therefore, to turn the eye down and out and to rotate the right eye clockwise. The inferior oblique arises from the medial floor of the orbit and is inserted into the lower, posterior and lateral quadrant of the eye. It turns the eye upwards and outwards and rotates it anti-clockwise. When the superior rectus and inferior oblique contract simultaneously, the eye is moved vertically upwards, the other muscular actions cancelling one another out.

The field of vision for one eye is more than 180 degrees. With two eyes arranged on the sides of the head, an animal can therefore see all round itself. In man, the eyes look directly forwards, so that the total field of vision is little more than 180 degrees ; the advantage of seeing parts of the outside world simultaneously with the two eyes has entailed

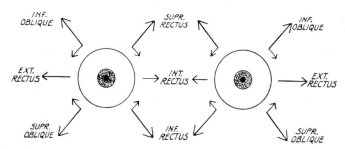

Fig. XIV. 27. **Eye-movements.** Diagram showing the direction in which the Extrinsic Eye Muscles operate. Rotational movements about the Optic Axis are shown by short arrows.

a loss in the total size of the field of vision. Certain portions of the outside world form almost identical images on the two retinæ, and both these images must be transmitted along the optic nerves. There is no doubt that we are conscious of both images simultaneously, because two sets of objects can be arranged each hidden to one eye but visible to the other, and in these circumstances all the objects can be seen and not only those visible to one eye only. This faculty of blending the two visual images into one conscious picture is known as *binocular vision.* By suitable devices, entirely different pictures can be presented to each eye and normally we are conscious of both, but when the need arises it is possible to suppress one image, as for instance on looking down a microscope with both eyes open. There are people, however, who have not got this faculty of fusing the images from the two eyes, and habitually suppress one image.

When we look straight at an object, the eyes are moved so that its image falls on the fovea of each eye, and other objects in the field of vision fall on geometrically corresponding points on the two retinæ. If we prevent the images from falling on corresponding points as by pressing on the eyeball, then we see double (Diplopia). This is a very distressing condition, usually arising from paralysis of one of the eye muscles, often the external rectus, owing to the long exposed intracranial course of the nerve. The maintenance of single vision demands a very fine mechanism for co-ordinated eye movements, the most important of which is *convergence* or the adjustment of the optic axes for near objects.

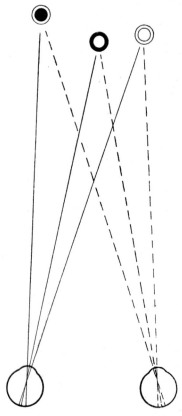

Fɪɢ. XIV. 28a.   This shows the Angles subtended to each Eye when Three Circles are viewed naturally.

In Fig. XIV. 28b, a diagram has been placed in front of each eye reproducing these angles. This is the principle of the **Stereoscope,** with which instrument the circles would be seen in relief.

In order to look at a near object, not only do we converge, but also accommodate ; there is a connection between the two processes, the act of accommodation producing a tendency to converge, and *vice versa.* If a weak prism is placed in front of one eye, so as to cause an apparent displacement of external objects horizontally, momentary diplopia may result, but the eyes are capable of changing the convergence independently of the accommodation so as to regain single clear vision. If the prism is inserted so as to cause a vertical displacement, the diplopia which results cannot be overcome unless the displacement is very small ; the eyes have never been trained to make vertical readjustments relative to one another.

The similarity of the two retinal images acts as a stimulus to convergence. If the retinal images are dissimilar, this stimulus no longer exists, and any defect in the association between convergence and accommodation can be investigated. These are known as defects in *muscle balance.* A subject looking through a Maddox rod (made up of a series of cylinders of red glass) at a point source of light, will see the light as a streak with one eye, whilst with the other eye he will see it naturally. The white point and red streak are so dissimilar that there is no stimulus to visual fusion, and the amount of convergence of the

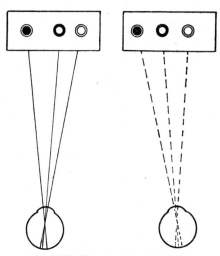

Fig. XIV. 28b.   See Fig. XIV. 28a.

subject's eyes is that which is inherent in the accommodation necessary to focus the light. If a concave lens is placed in front of the naked eye, a certain amount of accommodation will result, and with this will be associated additional convergence. Under these conditions the distance between the white spot and the red streak will change. Normal eyes should converge to exactly the right amount to correspond with accommodation for any distance, but it is usual to find some abnormality. Provided the eyes do not deviate vertically in their position of rest, the defect does not usually require correction.

Strabismus (squint) is a condition where it is obvious that the visual axes of the two eyes do not meet at the point of fixation. The condition may be due to paralysis of an eye muscle, but it is often found in hypermetropia. The chain of events leading to squint in hypermetropia is interesting. In order to focus objects, hypermetropes must accommodate more than normal people, and with this is associated a stimulus to converge more than is necessary. Usually it is possible for the patient to counteract this urge to converge, but in cases where this is impossible the patient suppresses the image from one eye in order to avoid diplopia. This suppression of one retinal image becomes habitual, and being virtually blind it does not matter what position the eye takes up—it may become a squinting eye. Unless the hypermetropia is treated by glasses in early years so as to encourage binocular vision, the squinting eye becomes almost blind owing to disuse.

Stereoscopic Vision. The images falling on the two retinæ are not quite similar, and advantage is taken of these differences in order to judge the relative distances of outside objects. By closing the eyes alternately it will be seen that where the differences between the two retinal images are great, one or more of the objects regarded will be seen double, but where the differences are only small the objects are seen single, but acquire an additional appearance of solidity, by which their relative distances can be judged. Fig. XIV. 28a shows the angles subtended at the two eyes by three circles. If these objects are photographed, first from the position of the left eye, and then from that of the right eye, the two pictures which result can be arranged so that each is visible to the appropriate eye and not to the other (Fig. XIV. 28b). The conditions of vision of the original objects have now been reproduced, and under these conditions the combined photographs have the same quality of depth as had the original objects. Owing to the urge to converge when accommodating for the photographs, most people require prisms to displace the images into a convenient position for fusion, but it is possible to " let the eyes go," so that the two parts of the figure coincide, in which case the circles will appear to be at different distances from the eyes.

Very small differences in angle are sufficient to make a judgment of relative distances ; stereoscopic vision is, in fact, one of the most exact visual judgments. It is surprising to find, therefore, that people can get on quite well without it. It is possible, for instance, to drive an automobile with one eye only. In this case distances are judged in other ways, as, for instance, by the relative sizes of objects, the overlapping of contours and shadows, the place where the base cuts the road and by their colours, distant objects having a tendency to look blue.

The Anatomical Basis of Binocular Vision. In man, with his overlapping fields of vision, there is a considerable field where objects are seen binocularly. Lower mammals, such as the rabbit, can have no binocular vision since their visual fields do not overlap. These differences are associated with changes in the relative distribution of fibres in the optic nerve and tract. In the rabbit practically all the optic nerve fibres cross in the chiasma, the whole of one retina being represented in the cerebral cortex of the opposite side. In man and monkeys, the left field of vision is represented both on the nasal half of the left retina and on the temporal half of the right retina (Fig. XIV. 29). In the chiasma, these right temporal fibres do not cross but become closely intermingled with those fibres which convey similar impressions from the left nasal retina and which do cross in the chiasma. Fibres from the extreme nasal

retina convey impressions which are not represented in the other retina
and cross in the usual way. As a result of the anatomical distribution of

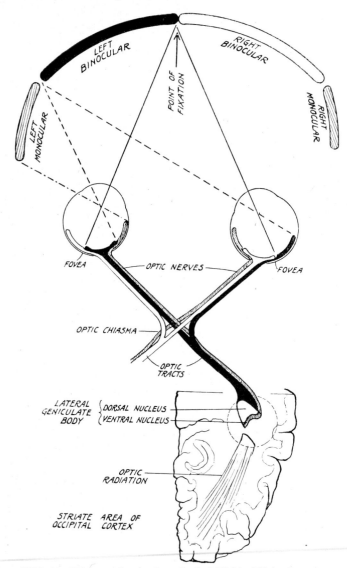

Fig. XIV. 29. Diagram showing how the Left Field of Vision is represented
on both Retinæ and how the Fibres from these Regions are gathered
together to form the Right Optic Tract, to reach the External Geniculate Body, whence they are relayed to the Occipital Cortex.   The
macular fibres are not shown.

fibres, the left field of vision is represented in the right cerebral cortex,
whether the eyes are placed laterally as in rabbits or frontally as in man
and monkeys.

Many people think that the partial decussation of the optic nerve in the chiasma which is characteristic of those mammals with frontally placed eyes, and therefore overlapping visual fields, is necessary if there is to be binocular fusion. It seems hardly likely that this is really the case, however, because many non-mammalian vertebrates (owls, some fish, etc.) have frontally placed eyes with overlapping of the visual fields but total decussation of the optic nerves. Such animals always use both eyes for choice when observing an object and it seems that they must be capable of fusing their two visual fields ; in other words, that their binocular vision must be *single* vision. The mammals do, however, differ from all other vertebrates, not only in having developed a partial decussation of the optic nerve where necessary, but also in having *conjugate eye movements*. No mammal is able to move one eye independently of the other ; under normal circumstances the eyes always move as one, not necessarily of course always in the same direction, but always, as it were, with the same end in view. Where the mammalian eyes are placed laterally, as in the rabbit, there are usually no spontaneous eye movements at all, but if a mammal has overlapping visual fields it is also found to have conjugated eye movements and a corresponding degree of partial decussation in the optic chiasma. It seems probable, therefore, that the partial decussation of the optic nerves is not fundamentally associated with binocular fusion so much as with the continuous conjugation of the two eyes.

The paths taken by optic nerve fibres on their way from the eye to the brain have been studied by destroying portions of the retina and following the resultant degeneration in serial sections stained by appropriate methods. In the optic nerve the arrangement of the fibres corresponds to their origin in the retina, and it is possible to recognise their division into superior, inferior, nasal and temporal fibres, together with a large bunch of fibres from the region of the macular plexus when this is present. Those of the inferior fibres which cross in the chiasma remain on the inferior aspect (ventral), and the superior fibres cross in the upper part. Since the inferior nasal fibres lie below and medially in the optic nerve as far as the chiasma, it is these fibres which first get compressed by pituitary tumours, with a consequent loss in the superior temporal field of vision.

In the optic tracts there is a fairly obvious division into superior, inferior and macular fibres, but the nasal and temporal fibres are intermingled. The fibres in the optic tract pass on and 95 per cent. end in the lateral geniculate body. A few fibres end in the medial geniculate body, and the superior colliculus, but none in the pulvinar of the thalamus. From the lateral geniculate body fibres arise which form the optic radiations passing to the occipital cortex (Fig. XIV. 29). The external geniculate body has a dorsal nucleus which becomes progressively more developed from the lower animals to man, and appears to vary with the degree of binocular vision. The ventral nucleus is supplied by fibres from the extreme nasal retina, where images are not represented in the other eye, and its functions are probably connected with monocular vision and possibly also with night-vision, since it is well developed in *Nycticebus*, a night-hunting lemuroid. The dorsal nucleus is subdivided into regions for the reception of macular, upper and lower retinal fibres, and there is some clinical evidence that this distribution is maintained in the optic radiations. From clinical evidence, obtained from cases of gunshot wounds, vascular lesions, cerebral tumours, etc., it appears that there is some segregation of fibres in the occipital cortex ; the macular region is represented very extensively about the posterior end of the posterior calcarine fissure ; the lower retinal fibres are situated below, and the upper fibres above the fissure, but more anteriorly ; the extreme peripheral fibres are situated still more anteriorly.

It will be obvious from a study of Fig. XIV. 29 that destruction of the right occipital cortex will lead to loss of the left field of vision. This condition is caused not infrequently by obstruction of the posterior cerebral artery. In these cases, however, macular vision is usually spared, probably owing to the fact that the extreme tip of the occipital cortex also derives a blood supply from a branch of the middle cerebral artery.

THE EAR

The ear (Fig. XIV. 30) is divided anatomically into three parts—the *outer ear*, the *middle ear*, and the *inner ear* or *labyrinth*. Each plays its part in the events leading up to the sensation of sound. The pinna and external auditory meatus which comprise the outer ear are responsible for the collection of sound waves. The bony ossicles of the middle ear conduct the sound to the cochlea, a specialised part of the inner ear where the sound wave is analysed and the auditory nerve impulses are originated. There are two other parts of the inner ear, the vestibule and the semi-circular canals. They are concerned with the sensations due to movement and orientation.

The *pinna* of most animals can be moved to the best position for the collection of the sound waves, but in man this organ is of little use and sounds can be heard almost as well without it. The *external auditory meatus* is protected against foreign bodies by hairs projecting outwards and from insects by a secretion of bitter wax. The meatus is 25 mm. long, and its end is blocked by the *tympanum* (ear drum), which is a diaphragm of connective tissue covered externally by modified skin continuous with that of the meatus, and internally by a mucous membrane continous with that of the middle ear. The tympanum is conical in shape, with its concave surface facing outwards and downwards. It is supposed to be aperiodic, that is, it does not resonate in response to any particular frequency as do the diaphragms of some loud speakers. Attached to the apex of the cone on its inner side is the handle of the *malleus*, the first of the three bony ossicles of the middle ear. Movements of the tympanum with the variations in air pressure due to the incoming sound waves are translated into movements of the malleus. Large variations of external air pressure are liable to rupture the tympanum, but this danger is minimised by the *Eustachian tube* (auditory tube) leading from the cavity of the middle ear to the naso-pharynx. It allows equalisation of air pressure on the two sides of the tympanum. There is a valve at the lower end of the auditory tube which is opened by the tensor palati muscle during the act of swallowing, in order to allow free communication between the ear and the pharynx. This valve is normally closed, so preventing one from hearing one's own speech unduly loudly—a painful phenomenon experienced by some patients in whom the muscle is inactive. Airmen and divers equalise the pressure on the two sides of the tympanum by swallowing occasionally.

Movements of the malleus are communicated to the second of the

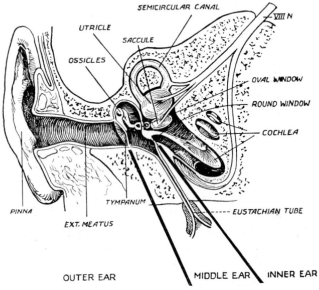

Fig. XIV. 30. Diagram of the **Ear.**

middle ear ossicles, the *incus*, and from this to the *stapes*. There is a saddle-shaped articulation between the malleus and incus, and movements are communicated both by this and a spur of bone on the malleus. There is a ball-and-socket joint on the lower process of the incus with which the stapes articulates (*the incudo-stapedial junction*). The oval footplate of the stapes fits into the oval window of the inner ear, and is held in position by an annular ligament, which also prevents the escape of fluid.

Attached to the ossicles are two small muscles, the *tensor tympani* which is attached to the malleus, and the *stapedius* which, as its name implies, is connected to the stapes. The stapedius is extremely minute, and is said to be the smallest muscle in the body. The function of these two muscles appears to be twofold ; first, the tensor tympani, owing to its tonus in the resting state, keeps the tympanic membrane taut, a necessary condition if its sensitivity to air-borne vibration is to be maintained. Thus, if the tendon of this muscle is cut, the Wever and Bray response of the ear falls by about one-fifth (see p. 532). The stapedius probably performs a similar office for the membrane of the oval window. Secondly, reflex contractions of both these muscles have been observed in dogs and rabbits, in response to loud

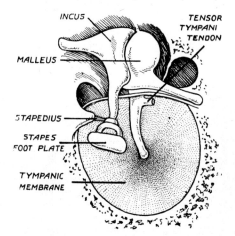

FIG. XIV. 31.   Semi-diagrammatic representation of the **Middle Ear.** (Modified from Beatty.)

sounds ; reflex contraction of the stapedius to such stimuli has been reported in man. Such contractions would be expected to have the effect of so damping the movements of the ossicles as to reduce the amplitude of vibration of the stapes footplate, and so of the oval window ; they would thus have a protective action against injury of the cochlea by very loud sounds.

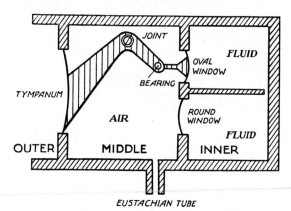

FIG. XIV. 32.—Model illustrating the method of transmission of vibrations from the outer to the inner ear. (Modified from Beatty.)

The function of the middle ear is to reduce the amplitude and increase the force of the vibrations imparted by the tympanum. When a lightly damped diaphragm, such as the tympanic membrane, which is easily set into vibration by air-borne sound waves, is to be used to transmit these movements to a device such as the oval window, which is heavily damped by the cochlear fluids, it may be shown that greater efficiency of transmission will be obtained if a reduction of the amplitude of vibration of the second moving part is provided for. Such a mechanism is well seen in any gramophone sound box, where the short needle is attached to a lever, the other end of which is connected to the centre of the diaphragm. The pivot about which this lever moves is much nearer the needle end than the diaphragm end, thus a small movement of the needle produces a relatively large movement of the diaphragm.

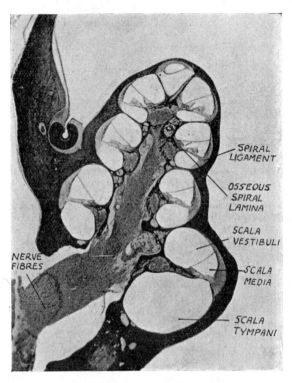

Fig. XIV. 33.   Section of the **Cochlea** of a guinea-pig, magnification × 7.
(From a photograph kindly supplied by Dr. C. S. Hallpike.)

In the middle-ear conditions are reversed, and a large movement of the tympanum must provide a small movement of the oval window. In fact, the travel of the stapes footplate is only about one-third of that of the centre of the tympanic membrane ; the ossicles, therefore, appear to provide just such a reduction ratio as is necessary to ensure efficient transmission of air-borne vibrations to the inner ear.

The functions of the inner ear are threefold. The semi-circular canals are sensitive to movements of the head, especially rotational movements ; of the two parts of the vestibule, the utricle is believed to give information about the position of the head, and the saccule has recently been shown in the frog to be sensitive to low-frequency vibrations. The cochlea is sensitive to sound, that is, to displacements of fluid which follow the variations in air pressure.

In spite of the elaborate anatomical detail of the cochlea, its bare architectural outline is not difficult to understand (Fig. XIV. 33). It is a cavity in the temporal bone shaped like a snail's shell; from this it derives its name. Thus it resembles a tube coiled into the form of a conical helix, round a central core of bone—the *modiolus*. The top of the tube is closed, but the bottom end contains in its bony wall two windows, each sealed by a membrane. The lower of these two is known as the *round window*, whilst the upper is called the *oval window*. With the margins of the latter the stapes foot-plate engages. A section made through the apex of the cochlea reveals the cross-sections of the tube in outline, and the blood vessels and auditory nerve embedded in the modiolus. The lumen of the tube of the cochlea is divided into three compartments by two membranes and their attachments. The basilar membrane is stretched between two linear projections on the inside walls of the tube. The first of these projections is composed of bone, the *osseous spiral lamina*, and may be regarded as a projection of the wall of the modiolus into the lumen of the tube. It therefore forms a ridge running from the apex to the base of the cochlea and resembles the marking of a screw. On the opposite side of the tube, also forming a projecting ridge along its whole length, is the *spiral ligament* composed of fibrous tissue. Reissner's membrane arises from the inner side of the *Organ of Corti*, and runs upwards and outwards at an angle to become attached to the wall of the tube above the spiral ligament. The space enclosed between these two membranes is known as the scala media, and it contains a fluid, *endolymph*. The space above Reissner's membrane contains *perilymph*, and is known as the scala vestibuli ; the space below the basilar membrane also contains perilymph, and is known as the scala tympani. These two spaces are continuous at the apex of the cochlea, through an opening known as the *helicotrema*. The oval window is between the scala vestibuli and the middle ear cavity, the round window between the scala tympani and the middle ear. The escape of fluid from the inner ear is prevented at both windows by a membranous covering.

It will now be necessary to consider how the movements of the middle ear ossicles are transmitted to the basilar membrane, movements of which stimulate the auditory nerve. When the foot of the stapes is displaced inwards into the oval window, pressure is applied to the peri-lymph, tending to compress it. Since this fluid in its bony casing is incompressible, movements in it must find some outlet. This is provided by the round window membrane, which bulges into the air cavity of the middle ear, the movements being, therefore, a counterpart of those at the oval window. Slow displacements of perilymph in the scala vestibuli could be transferred to the perilymph in the scala tympani by the helicotrema ; the movements are so rapid, however, that this cannot take place. The most important channel for accommodating the displacements of fluid is, therefore, by means of the scala media and its two limiting membranes. A displacement of the stapes inwards causes a downward movement of the basilar membrane, and a displacement outwards causes an upward movement. These movements of the basilar membrane are intimately connected with the perception of sound.

The basilar membrane and its associated structures, in particular the organ of Corti, are shown in Fig. XIV. 34. The *basilar membrane* itself is composed of fibrous tissue lined on its under side with connective tissue ; its length from base to apex of the cochlea is about 32 mm. ; its breadth at the base is about 0·17 mm., and at the apex about 0·47 mm. The organ of Corti is situated on the inner and upper aspect of the basilar membrane and forms a continuous chain from apex to base.

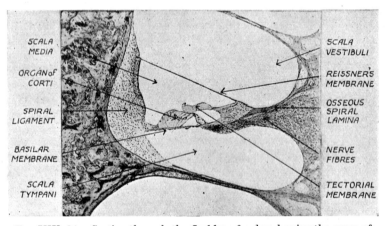

Fig. XIV. 34. Section through the **Cochlea** of a dog showing the organ of Corti ; magnification × 75. (From a photograph kindly supplied by Dr. C. S. Hallpike.)

Each segment of the organ of Corti consists of two pillars forming an arch of Corti which supports the inner and outer hair cells. From the upper extremity of each cell hairs protrude, movements of which are an effective stimulus to the sensory endings of the auditory nerve. The hairs themselves are embedded in the tectorial membrane, a flap of connective tissue with its internal edge attached forming a roof to the organ of Corti. Impulses on the cochlea nerve are initiated by deformation of the hair cells of the organ of Corti, owing to movements of the basilar membrane.

The Physical Properties of Sound

If a tuning fork is struck the " prongs " of the fork are set into vibration, that is, they move backwards and forwards with great rapidity, at one moment coming nearer to one another, at the next farther away. If, now, a small mirror is attached to one such prong, so that a beam of light reflected from it moves in sympathy with the movements of the prong, it will be possible, by arranging that this beam falls on to a moving strip of photographic film, to obtain a record of the movements of the prong over a given time. In other words, the record will constitute a graph showing the position of the prong (ordinates) against time (abscissæ). Such a graph is shown in Fig. XIV. 35. The completed record is said to show the *wave-form* of the tuning fork vibrations, and the distance between the resting position of the fork and its position of maximum deflection gives a measure of the *amplitude* of swing of the fork ; where this distance is large, the vibrations are said to be of large amplitude, and where it is small, of small amplitude. It is easily demonstrable that a fork vibrating at greater amplitude will produce a louder

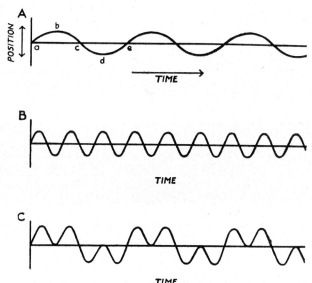

FIG. XIV. 35.   Wave-form of Vibrations of Tuning Forks.
A. a b c d e constitutes one complete cycle.
B. Frequency of fork three times that of A.
C. Composite wave-form produced by sounding forks A and B simultaneously.

sound ; the record from such a fork will show a similar number of waves in a given time, but the amplitude of each wave will be greater.

When the wave-form of a good tuning fork is examined in this way, it may be shown that the curve thus reproduced is almost exactly the same as that obtained by plotting the sine of an angle against the angle itself. Such a wave is thus known as a *sine-wave*, and the vibrations of the fork which give rise to it as *sinusoidal*.

A similar record may be obtained without a mirror on the fork. When the prongs of the fork vibrate, air pressure changes are set up in their vicinity, and these in turn set up pressure changes near-by ; thus the sound travels through the air in the form of waves, the direction of wave motion being the same as that in which the sound is travelling, unlike waves on the surface of water, whose motion is clearly at right angles to their direction of travel ; these propagated pressure variations are perceived by man as sound. If a light diaphragm is arranged near a source of sound such as a fork, it will vibrate in sympathy with the changes in air pressure initiated by the source. By placing the mirror on this diaphragm, it will be possible to obtain a graphical record of its movements, and thus of the air pressure changes. Such a record will be found to be exactly as Fig. XIV. 35), except that in this case the ordinates represent *air pressure changes*. The number of complete cycles, a b c d e, in one second of time is known as the *frequency* of the fork or note, and is usually measured in *cycles per second*. The wire set into vibration by striking the note " Middle C " on a piano has a frequency of 256 cycles per second, that is, it performs 256 complete double vibrations in one second.[1]

The *pitch* of a note depends on its frequency ; the higher the pitch the higher is the frequency. The octave above a given note has double the frequency ; thus, the octave above " Middle C " has a frequency of 512, and the octave below it has a frequency of 128.

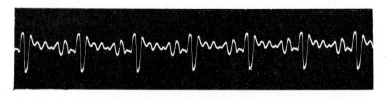

FIG. XIV. 36. **Wave-form** of an **English Vowel** of the type " **ah.**"
(D. B. Fry, from " Science and Speech.")

If, now, a fork of three times the frequency of the first fork be set into vibration, the result in diaphragm movements will be as shown in Fig. XIV. 35). Should forks of both of these frequencies be set going at the same time, the resultant wave will be that shown at (C). Thus, it is evident that the wave-form of the air vibrations set up by two forks sounding simultaneously is quite different from that obtained from either fork alone. Most of the sounds commonly met with in daily life have an infinitely more complicated wave-form than this, the *quality* of a sound depending on its wave-form. The wave-form of the vowel " ah " is shown in Fig. XIV. 36. According to Fourier's theorem, however, just as the relatively complicated wave-form of (C) is the result of adding together (A) and (B), so the wave-form of any periodic vibration, however complicated, may be resolved into a series of simple waves, consisting of a *fundamental* with the lowest frequency found, and a number of *overtones* or *harmonics*, whose frequencies are multiples of that of the fundamental. Each of these single component frequencies will be of the same wave-form as Fig. XIV. 35, *i.e.*, sinusoidal, and in the

---

[1] A frequency of 256 cycles for the note " Middle C " is accepted by physicists. A frequency of 261·6 cycles per second is employed on pianos tuned to the international standard pitch (A = 440), and equal temperament.

case of highly complicated sounds, the number of these components may be very great.

The analysis of a complex wave-form into its sinusoidal constituents in the ordinary way requires much tedious mathematical manipulation ; but mechanical frequency analysers have been developed which have made possible the estimation of the frequency and power of the fundamental and harmonics of most sounds commonly met with in daily life. The frequency of these harmonics will bear a simple numerical relationship to that of the fundamental. They are called second, third, etc., harmonics, according as their frequencies are respectively twice, three times, etc., that of the fundamental or first harmonic. A sound whose wave-form is not strictly periodic will be found upon analysis to contain components whose frequencies are not simple multiples of that of the fundamental. These components are called *anharmonics.* " Noises," whose wave-form is highly irregular, contain many such constituents.

Besides frequency and wave-form, sounds have one other important attribute, that of *intensity* or loudness. Intensity and loudness are not quite the same. When a sound is emitted from a source, power is radiated in the form of pressure variation in the surrounding air, and the term intensity is used to denote the amount of energy per unit time passing through a given area at right angles to the direction of propagation of the sound. Intensity, then, is a physical term. Loudness, on the other hand, is of psychological significance, and describes a characteristic of the sensation evoked by the sound. That these two are not synonymous is due to a peculiar property of the ear, in that it is not uniformly sensitive throughout the range of frequencies. It requires a smaller *power* of sound at 1,000 to 2,000 cycles per second to produce a just perceptible sensation than it does for frequencies higher or lower than these. This point will be referred to in greater detail later. The unit by which intensity is measured is defined simply as the power passing through an area of one square centimetre ; for sound, power is usually measured in *microwatts*, that is, millionths of one watt, and thus it is customary to speak of a given sound as having an intensity of so many microwatts per square centimetre at the particular point at which it was measured.

It is clear that the intensity of a sound must bear some relation to the amplitude of vibration of the diaphragm previously referred to, for the diaphragm is directly measuring the variation in air pressure set up by the source of sound. The intensity is directly proportional to the square of the difference between the maximum and minimum values of the pressure.

At 2,000 cycles per second, a just perceptible sensation is produced by a sound of intensity less than 10^{-9} microwatt per square centimetre ; the power of this sound is of the same order as that received as light from a candle eight miles distant, if the intervening air is perfectly transparent. In the corresponding case for the eye, the minimum intensity for visibility in the green region of the spectrum, at which point the eye is most sensitive, is about 10^{-8} microwatt per square centimetre ; thus the ear is some ten times more sensitive than the eye.

Consideration of the enormous range of intensities called for in dealing with audible sounds has led to the adoption of a somewhat different type of scale. What is required is a unit which expresses, not the absolute intensity of a sound, but changes in the intensity of sound ; such a unit is the *bel*, which is defined thus : if the intensity of a sound increases ten times, its intensity level is said to have risen by one bel ; if one hundred times, by two bels. Consequently the rise in bels is simply the common logarithm of the ratio of the two intensities. For practical purposes, however, such a unit is inconveniently large, and for this reason the *decibel* is more often used. This is simply one-tenth of a bel, and represents an increase in intensity of roughly 25 per cent. This is, as it happens, about the least change in intensity that can ordinarily be detected (see p. 535). The effectiveness of the decibel scale of intensity is illustrated by the following table of the intensities of certain noises in relation to the faintest perceptible sound (after Beatty). The *loudness* of any of these noises would be measured in phons, as defined below, and the figures would be somewhat different.

Decibels

130	Sounds felt as well as heard.
120	Pneumatic drill at operator's position.
110	Steel plate hammered by four men—2 feet.
100	Loud motor horn—23 feet.
90	Lion roaring—17 feet.
80	Very heavy street traffic. New York.
70	Loud peal of thunder.
60	Busy traffic. London.
50	{ Quiet motor car—30 feet. { Conversational voice—12 feet.
40	Centre of New York quietest time of night.
30	Quiet surburban street. London.
20	Whisper—4 feet.
10	Rustle of leaves in gentle breeze.
0	Faintest audible sound.

A sound is audible if the intensity of a noise going on at the same time is not more than 12 decibels greater, even though the frequency of the sound is within the region of frequencies covered by the noise.

From the graph shown in **Fig. XIV. 37** it may be seen that, provided the intensity is neither too small nor too large, a pure tone may be heard if its frequency lies between some 20 and 20,000 cycles per second. Beyond these limits of frequency a " sound " is no longer heard, but, if sufficiently intense, is felt by parts of the body other than the ear. If, within these limits of frequency a sound is too quiet, it is not perceived, whilst a sound too loud is not only heard but also felt by the ear, often a somewhat painful sensation.

It is evident that, since the ear is not uniformly sensitive over the whole of the audible frequency range, tones which are equal in intensity but widely differing in frequency will not give rise to the same loudness sensation in a listener. Hence, it is desirable to have some unit for measuring loudness differences, as distinct from intensity differences. The *phon* is the unit commonly used for this purpose. A pure tone of

1,000 cycles per second is adopted as a reference sound. To measure the loudness of a complex sound in phons, it is necessary to compare it with a pure tone of 1,000 cycles per second, the intensity of which is adjusted until both reference sound and complex sound are judged to be equal in loudness—a subjective judgment which may not always be very easy.

In practice, such measurements are often made, not by subjective judgment, but by using a sound intensity meter (*i.e.*, an instrument

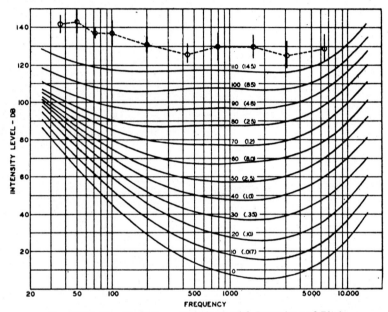

Fig. XIV. 37. Variation of **Loudness** with **Intensity** and **Pitch**.
Each curve shows the variation of the intensity level of a sound with its frequency, for a constant loudness in phons, as given by the figure against the curve; the values are for the average normal subject. Thus, for example, the threshold of hearing (0 phons) lies at an intensity level of 5 dB at 2,000 cyc./sec. and at 25 dB at 250 and 10,000 cyc./sec. The values of the intensity level are given in decibels above a sound pressure at the ear drum of 0·0002 dynes/sq. cm.
The dotted curve at the top gives the threshold of feeling. (From Stevens and Davis " Hearing.")

measuring sound power directly) whose frequency characteristic can be varied to match that of the ear.

The Physiology of Hearing

A physiological theory of hearing should account for the two most fundamental characteristics of the ear. These are, first, its power to discriminate frequency (a difference in frequency of only less than 5 parts in 1,000 is perceptible over most of the musical scale—that is, one can tell the difference between a note of 1,000 cycles per second and one of 1,005 cycles per second), and secondly, its power to discriminate intensity (under the best conditions, an increase of intensity of about 10 per cent. (0·4 decibels) can just be detected). Let us consider first the discrimination of frequency, and the analysis of frequency such as a musician performs when he resolves a chord into its component notes. If a note is played on a violin or other instrument near a piano with the dampers lifted, the piano will emit an " echo " of that note ; another note played in the same way will also produce a response from the piano, the frequency of the echo being the same as that of the note played. This occurs because the strings of the piano vibrate sympathetically with the incoming sound, each string responding only to one frequency. The string is said to be *resonant* or tuned to that particular frequency. The bass strings of the piano are long, heavy and slack, and thus resonate to low frequencies, while the treble strings are short, light and tightly stretched, and resonate to high frequencies. The basilar membrane of the cochlea at the basal end is short, small in cross-section, and its supporting spiral ligament gives the appearance of being able to withstand considerable strain ; at the apical end, however, it is relatively long, heavy and apparently more loosely supported. Consideration of the varying width of the basilar membrane led Helmholtz to enunciate his famous *Resonance Theory of Hearing*, which states essentially that the " fibres ". of the basilar membrane are tuned to various frequencies somewhat like the strings of a piano. These fibres are very short compared with the corresponding strings of the piano (the longest fibre is only about one-half a millimetre in length) ; but the loading effect of the fluids of the inner ear are probably sufficient to lower the resonant frequencies to appropriate values. The

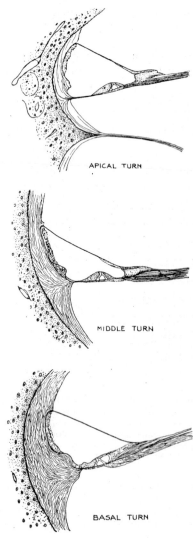

APICAL TURN

MIDDLE TURN

BASAL TURN

FIG. XIV. 38. Showing the relative sizes of the Spiral Ligament and the breadth of the Basilar Membrane at different levels of the Cochlea. (From photographs by Wilkinson and Gray.)

discrimination of frequency thus becomes a function of the cochlea, the auditory cerebral cortex serving to discriminate from what particular region of the basilar membrane the received nervous impulses arise.

But unlike the strings of a piano, the basilar membrane is continuous ; consequently, the greater the intensity of the received sound (and therefore the greater the amplitude of vibration of the resonant fibre), the greater will be the spread of the movement to adjacent parts of the membrane. Hence, the louder the sound, the greater will be the number of receptors stimulated, and so the greater the number of nerve fibres conveying impulses from the cochlea to the brain.

It has now been agreed that the basilar membrane, within the cochlea, does respond differentially to tones of different frequency, but there has recently been some dispute as to the precise mechanism whereby this is brought about. Several workers in this field now adopt the view that the phenomenon of resonance is not involved, though no precise specification of the mechanism whereby the differential response of the basilar membrane is brought about has so far been suggested. For this reason, however, in the ensuing discussion we shall use the term " *Place Theory*," and this should be understood to include both the resonance theory and all theories presupposing discrimination by the basilar membrane by some other mechanism. The Place Theory has not always found acceptance in the past, its best known rival being the *Frequency Theory*, according to which the function of the cochlea is to translate vibrations into nervous impulses, the frequency of which is exactly the same as that of the sound. But the highest frequency at which any single fibre of the auditory nerve can transmit impulses is approximately 1,000 per second, whereas sound can be heard up to a frequency of 20,000 per second ; it is clear, therefore, that the Frequency Theory would be untenable if the auditory nerve trunk contained only a single nerve fibre. To overcome this difficulty, the *Volley Theory* has been proposed ; it supposes that several fibres may operate for a single note, and that one fibre will conduct an impulse whilst others are non-conducting ; thus with only 20 fibres a 20,000 cycle note could be heard, each fibre conveying 1,000 impulses in one second out of step with those travelling in the other fibres. In all probability, many more fibres than this would be operative.

Recent research on the ear has progressed along two distinct lines. First, experimental investigation has shown that the mammalian cochlea does, in fact, contain some mechanism, different parts of which respond to stimuli of different frequencies ; and that, as suspected, the basal end is most sensitive to high frequencies whilst the apical is most sensitive to low. Secondly, it has become possible to demonstrate the presence of action potentials in the auditory tracts of the mid-brain, and to show that the frequency of these potentials corresponds within limits to that of the sound giving rise to them. Both these advances have been made largely as a result of progress in the evolution of apparatus with which small electrical potentials, such as those produced by the passage of nervous impulses, may be detected. Such an instrument usually takes the form of an amplifier similar to that used in an ordinary wireless set, together with an oscillograph and camera. Its uses in detecting action potentials in peripheral nerves were considered in Chapter X.

Experimental demonstration that the cochlea contains a mechanism for frequency discrimination has resulted from enquiries of two kinds. First, when the ear is subjected to intense continuous stimulation for a long time, the organ of Corti, which is a highly delicate structure, suffers some disorganisation. If the stimulating sound is a pure tone, the Place Theory would lead one to expect that only that part of the organ would be injured which responds to the particular frequency used in the experiment.

In guinea-pigs and other small mammals subjected to such stimulation, injury to the apical turn of the cochlea in response to low tone stimuli, and basal disorganisation for high tones has been demonstrated histologically. More recently despite the very considerable histological difficulties which arise when dealing with human material, lesions in the basal turn have been demonstrated in boiler-makers and others, whose working conditions are such that they are subjected to loud noises of high frequency for some years. Such men become deaf to high tones; by correlating the range of frequencies over which the patient was deaf with the position of the cochlear injury, examined histologically after death, those regions of the human basilar membrane which are resonant to frequencies from 2,000 cycles per second upwards have been roughly located.

[1] The second type of evidence supporting the theory of frequency discrimination by the basilar membrane depends on a study of the amplitudes of the electrical potentials in the cochlea which accompany stimulation of the ear by notes of different frequency. When the ear is stimulated by a sound, small oscillating electrical potentials of frequency exactly, and wave-form roughly, corresponding to that of the sound, are produced within the cochlea. This is known as the *Wever and Bray effect* or simply the *cochlear effect*. The following observations (Hallpike and Rawdon-Smith) show that these potentials are greater at the basal end for high notes, and at the apical end for low notes :—

Frequency of Sound. (Cycles per second.)	Response at apical electrode. (Micro-volts.)	Response at basal electrode. (Micro-volts.)
250	150	45
2,050	30	110

Other evidence indicates that these potential changes are due to mechanical vibration of the organ of Corti and that the potentials are roughly proportional to the magnitude of these vibrations. Hence the above

---

[1] In the remainder of this section the data given are those for the cat. In essence, however, they apply to man.

observations demonstrate that the amplitude of the mechanical vibration is greater at the apex for low notes, and greater at the base for high notes. This is exactly the condition implied by the theory that the cochlea contains a frequency discriminating structure.

The ratio between the electrical response to high and low tones is about 4 : 1 at either point ; that this is not greater is due to electrical spread from one point to the other by conduction through the inner ear fluids themselves.

The frequency of the action potentials in the auditory nerves corresponds fairly accurately with that of the incoming sound, up to 2,400 cycles per second. The *Volley Theory*, already described, accounts for the passage of impulses at this high frequency along a group of nerve fibres, no one of which can conduct more than 1,000 impulses per second. Above 2,400 cycles per second, the volley mechanism breaks down, and stimulation at a higher frequency produces irregular and asynchronous action potentials. This is due to the facts that different fibres conduct impulses at different velocities, and that the higher the frequency the greater the number of fibres necessary for its transmission.

Recent investigations have shown that the reproduction of the stimulus frequency by the impulses in the auditory nerve does not occur at all accurately in the mid-brain and other parts of the central nervous system. This effect is due partly to the delays which are occasioned in the passage of nervous impulses through the synaptic junctions of the C.N.S., and partly to the different conduction rates in different nerve fibres which result from variations in diameter and other factors. For these reasons, the frequency theory has now been abandoned as a mechanism for explaining the discrimination of pitch. The most widely accepted theory of pitch discrimination at the present moment remains, therefore, the " Place Theory," according to which the pitch of a note is recognised by the identity of the nerve fibres conducting the impulses to which it gives rise, and consequently by the spatial position of the responding part of the basilar membrane.

A note appears louder if the total number of nerve fibres active is greater ; this will occur if the amplitude of vibration is so great as to impose a considerable movement on those parts of the basilar membrane adjacent to that exactly tuned to the note—the greater the amplitude, the further will be the spread of the disturbance up and down the membrane, and so the greater the number of nerve fibres excited.

Auditory Acuity

When the intensity of a sound is continuously decreased, it reaches a value where no sensation of sound is produced. The smallest intensity of sound required to produce a sensation is said to be on the *threshold of audibility*. When the intensity of sound is increased until it is felt as well as heard, such a sound is said to be on the *threshold of feeling*. Within these limits of intensity, the auditory spectrum has a limited range of frequency.

The human ear is capable of appreciating a range of frequencies between about 20 and 20,000 cycles per second. Many animals, such as dogs, can hear notes too high for men to hear ; the upper limit is very variable. If a sound of frequency above 20,000 cycles or below 20 cycles is sufficiently intense, it is felt but not heard in the true sense of the word. Notes of frequency higher than 20,000 cycles cannot be heard, probably because there are no basilar membrane fibres designed for their reception, and also because the inertia of the ossicles in the middle ear limits their vibration at high much more than at low fre-

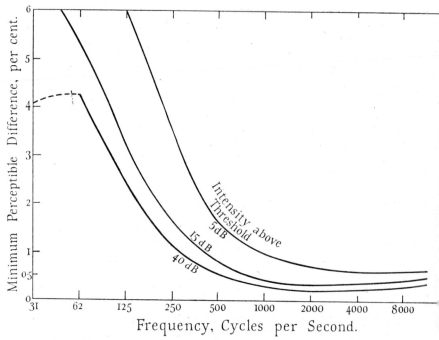

Fig. XIV. 39. The **Minimum Differences in Frequency** which can be detected at various frequencies and at various intensities above the threshold (expressed as a percentage of the frequency of the stimulus). At intensities greater than 40 dB, the changes in sensitivity are small. The values given are for listening with one ear ; if both ears are used, the minimum perceptible differences are smaller. (From data by Shower and Biddulph.)

quencies. The complete auditory spectrum may, therefore, be represented by the curves shown in Fig. **XIV. 37**. The frequencies of most speech sounds lie between 80 and 6,000 cycles per second.

The human subject is capable of discriminating small differences of frequency ; the minimum perceptible difference of frequency is smallest between 500 and 4,000 cycles per second; expressed as a percentage of the frequency, this is about 0·3 per cent. (Fig. **XIV. 39**). A note having a frequency of 1,000 cycles has a pitch which is noticeably different from one having a frequency of 1,003 cycles, which is 1/22 of a semitone higher. Over the whole range there are approximately 1,600 perceptible changes in pitch, and since the basilar membrane is 32 mm. long, each change is equivalent to an average shift of 0·02 mm.

A rise in intensity of an auditory stimulus must lead to an increase in the length of the portion of basilar membrane vibrating. Further, a rise in intensity of an auditory stimulus is correlated with a rise in amplitude of the electrical response in the auditory nervous tracts. Consequently, the loudness of a sound is judged by the number of fibres operative. The acuity of the ear for differences in sound intensity is not so good as the acuity of the eye for differences in light intensity. Under the best conditions the fractional increase in sound intensity which can just be detected by the ear is between 5 and 10 per cent., whilst an increase in light intensity of 0·5 per cent. can be detected by the eye. Intensity discrimination is not so good for low notes or low intensities ; at a frequency of 60 cycles and at a moderate intensity, a change of 20 per cent. is just perceptible, whilst at low intensities an increase of as much as 200 per cent. is necessary.

Owing to imperfections in the structures that translate the variations in air pressure in the external air into movements of the oval window, the wave-form of these movements is not identical with that of the incoming sound. In other words, *wave-form distortion* takes place ; if a pure tone (sinusoidal) were impressed upon the ear drum, then this tone, together with various powers of all its harmonics, would be impressed on the fluids of the inner ear. If a pure tone of frequency n cycles/second causes the ear-drum to vibrate, then the vibrations of the cochlear fluids will contain notes of frequency n (the *fundamental*), $2n$, $3n$, etc., cycles/second (second, third, etc., *harmonics*). These harmonics are known as the *subjective* harmonics, as they are introduced by the ear itself.

From further calculations on the behaviour of the components of the middle ear, one would expect that the distortion of notes of low frequency, and therefore large amplitude, would be relatively greater than that for notes of high frequency, which, for the same power, are smaller in amplitude. That this is so has recently been shown by the fact that the wave-form of the cochlear response produced by pure tone stimulation of the ear becomes more distorted as the frequency of the stimulus is reduced.[1]

Masking. It is a common experience that the presence of one sound reduces our ability to hear other weaker sounds. This is known as *masking*. The masking effect differs, according to whether the second tone is above or below it in pitch. This result is shown in Fig. XIV. 40 for a continuously sounding masking tone of 1,200 cycles. While this masking sound is being impressed on the ear at a constant intensity, another sound is gradually increased until it is just heard and its intensity is then measured. The difference between the thresholds of the second sound in the presence and absence of the masking sound is shown on the ordinates of the graph. The graph also shows the effect of increasing

---

[1] Some of this distortion is due to admixture of potentials due to the passage of nerve impulses in the auditory nerve with the cochlear effect itself; these have been eliminated in some experimental work by previous section of the auditory nerve. This results in degeneration of the latter and consequent absence of action potentials. Normally, however, these potentials limit the lowest frequency of stimulus which can be used in this experiment.

the intensity (20, 40, 60, etc.) of the masking sound. At low intensities of the masking tone, only notes immediately above and below it in frequency are affected. If its intensity is raised, however, the effect spreads to all frequencies above, whilst notes of much lower frequency remain quite unaffected. If, for instance, one produces a complex sound consisting of a fundamental frequency A and progressively higher notes of a, b, c, etc., all the constituents may be heard. On doubling the intensity of all the constituents, A may mask a. On redoubling the intensity A may mask both a and b, and so on, until finally nothing will

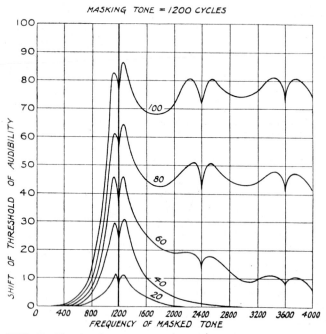

FIG. XIV. 40. Showing the **Masking Effect** of a continuously sounding note of 1,200 cycles per second on the threshold of audibility (in decibels), tested at various frequencies. The intensity of the masking sound is represented by the numbers on the curves in decibels above the normal threshold. (Fletcher.)

be heard but the single frequency A, which therefore gains in prominence as the sound is amplified. This state of affairs is reminiscent of the booming of speech in loud speakers having a large output.

The Localisation of Sound. The ability to recognise the direction from which a sound proceeds is poorly developed in man. Under the best conditions it is rarely possible to localise the direction of a sound more accurately than within 10 degrees in the horizontal plane and considerably more in vertical planes. Man's ability to localise sound is due to two factors ; first, that there will be a time difference between the arrival of a given vibration at one ear and at the other, unless the source of sound is equidistant from the two ears ; and secondly, for high frequency tones, that there will be a difference of intensity at the two ears due to the " shadow " effect of the head.

The velocity of sound is 1,100 feet per second. A sound from a source at an angle of 45 degrees from the sagittal plane will, therefore, reach one ear approximately 0·0004 seconds before it reaches the other. It is supposed that a sound is localised on the basis of such a time difference. This can be shown by conducting a sound through two tubes, one leading to the right ear and the other to the left. When both tubes are of equal length the sound appears to be in the mid-line, but if the right tube is made longer, the sound is located to the left of the mid-line. The other mechanism mentioned above comes into play in the localisation of high notes. At high frequencies the intensity of the sound reaching the distant ear is very small and the sound is localised to the side where it is loudest.

Many animals have another way of localising sounds ; they rotate their pinnæ until the apparent intensity is greatest, when the pinnæ will be facing the source of sound.

Auditory Fatigue. If the ear be subjected to prolonged loud sound it suffers a transient loss of sensitivity, *i.e.*, it becomes fatigued. This means that the intensity of a note, if it is to be just perceived, must be made greater after such stimulation than before. A sufficiently intense stimulus applied to one ear only causes a loss of sensitivity in both ears ; that is to say, the fatigue is binaural. The loss in the nominally unstimulated ear is not produced by the residue of sound reaching it (due to bone conduction, slight leaks, etc.), as is shown by the following experiment. Suppose a sound of intensity only 70 decibels above the threshold be applied to the right ear, then no loss of acuity will be found in either right or left ears. If, however, the intensity of the fatiguing sound is raised, although still applied only to the right ear, the left ear, as well as the right, will suffer a loss of sensitivity. Yet the residue of sound reaching the left ear is at least 60 decibels below that in the right ear, and thus can exert no fatiguing effect on it. It follows, therefore, that stimulation of one ear, if sufficiently intense, lowers the sensitivity of both ears ; this effect is probably central. The loss in the stimulated ear, however, is somewhat greater than that in the unstimulated one. The greater fatigue of the stimulated ear is presumably due to a loss of sensitivity in the peripheral mechanism.

In general, tones of frequency above 1,000 cycles produce much more fatigue than do tones of frequency below this.

Deafness. The common types of deafness are due to :—

(*a*) *External Ear Obstruction*, that is, obstruction of the external auditory meatus by a wax plug, by dirt, or by inflammation and swelling of the meatal wall (otitis externa).

(*b*) *Middle Ear Disease*, in which the ossicles are prevented from functioning properly. This condition frequently follows a nasal catarrh, and starts as an inflammation of the middle ear (otitis media), the infection entering *viâ* the Eustachian tube. Later, a pathological condition of the bone round the inner ear may develop (*otosclerosis*). This mainly results in the formation of new bone in the neighbourhood of the oval window which causes fixation of the stapes footplate to the bony capsule, with consequent loss of hearing. In the later stages, the organ of Corti often shows degeneration.

(c) *Inner Ear Disease* usually involves loss of function of the organ of Corti or of the cochlear nerve, and is thus sometimes referred to as " nerve deafness." It may be due to :—

(1) *Injuries to the Inner Ear*, such as boilermakers' deafness (Chronic Labyrinthine Concussion) which has already been described (p. 532).

(2) *Diseases of the Inner Ear and Auditory Nerve*, due to local hæmorrhages or inflammation or to general disease (*e.g.*, syphilis, malaria, rheumatism). The commonest cause of internal ear disease, however, is middle ear disease.

The tests for deafness normally employed are the spoken voice, whisper, the tick of a watch, and tuning forks of various frequencies. Such tests are inaccurate, but in experienced hands can give a fair indication of the degree of loss of hearing. A more accurate instrument, with which the sensitivity over almost the whole auditory spectrum may ·be tested, frequency by frequency, is the *audiometer*. In this, pure tones produced electrically are led to the ear by a special telephone ; the intensity of the tone may be altered at will, and that point at which the patient no longer hears the sound is readily estimated.

External and middle ear deafness may often be distinguished from inner ear (nerve) deafness by making use of the phenomenon of " bone-conduction." If the auditory meatus be carefully plugged, a tuning fork will be heard without difficulty if its stem is placed on the bones of the head (*e.g.*, the *mastoid* bone). The vibrations from the fork set up similar vibrations in the cochlea, transmission taking place through the bones of the skull, and not along the chain of ossicles in the middle ear. It is clear, therefore, that if air-conducted sound is not heard, whilst bone conducted vibrations are readily audible, loss of middle ear function must be suspected. This diagnosis may often be strengthened by inspection of the tympanic membrane, which, in the case of most middle ear disease, presents an abnormal appearance.

Deaf Aids take many forms, but all depend for their action upon raising the intensity of the received sound above normal. In the better types of apparatus this is done electrically by means of a microphone, amplifier, and headphone. With such an instrument the relative intensity of high and low tones may be altered at will, thus compensating for losses over a specific range of frequency. It is difficult, however, to avoid some unwanted distortion, and for this, and other reasons, they are not always entirely satisfactory.

TASTE AND SMELL

Both these sensations are superficially related, in that the sense organs are stimulated by specific chemical substances. When examined in more detail, however, it is seen that there are very considerable physiological differences between them.

Taste

The mucous membrane of the epiglottis and soft palate, and of the tip, sides and root of the tongue, contain special sense organs known as taste-buds. These are the receptors for the sense of taste. All tastes can be divided into four (or perhaps six) groups : the sour, the salt, the bitter and the sweet, to which are sometimes added the metallic and the alkaline. It is significant that although many substances give rise to mixed sensations of taste, it is nearly always possible to distinguish the components, and it is impossible to create an entirely new taste by combining any or all of the " pure " tastes. The sense of smell, as we shall see, differs very markedly in this respect. It must be remembered that in most cases, the actual flavour of any substance present in the mouth depends upon its smell almost as much as on its taste *sensu strictu.*

Sourness is a property of all solutions containing hydrogen ions in sufficient concentration. For the mineral acids, such as HCl, the threshold concentration is about 0·001 M. The organic acids, such as acetic, and also carbonic acid, appear more sour than would be expected from their hydrogen ion concentration, probably owing to their greater ease of penetration through cell membranes.

Saltness is a property of the salts of the strong acids, and appears to be due solely to the anions, *e.g.*, Cl^-, Br^-, I^-, NO_3^- and $SO_4^=$. The least concentration of Cl^- which can be tasted is about 0·02 M.

Bitterness is a property of the alkaloids, such as strychnine and quinine, and of many innocuous substances such as quassia. Mg^+, Ca^+ and NH_4^+, and perhaps nearly all cations, have a bitter taste, and so have ether, most glucosides, and some other substances. The threshold concentration for strychnine is about $1·5 \times 10^{-6}$ M or 0·0006 g. per litre.

Sweetness is a property primarily of the sugars, but a number of other completely unrelated compounds also taste sweet, *e.g.*, beryllium salts, lead acetate, chloroform and saccharin. The least concentration of cane sugar which can be tasted is about 0·5 per cent. Saccharin is about 500 times as sweet.

There appear to be four different kinds of taste-bud, one for each kind of taste. The four kinds are not uniformly distributed over all the sensitive areas, and certain substances, such as magnesium sulphate and dulcamarin (the glucoside from bitter-sweet) which stimulate more than one kind of taste-bud, have different tastes according to the part of the mouth with which they happen to be in contact. Again, there are several drugs which abolish the sense of taste if applied to the mucous membrane of the tongue and mouth, and the different sensations of taste are lost separately one after the other. Thus cocaine extinguishes them in the order : bitter, sweet, salt, sour. The sweet taste appears to be specially prone to alterations in sensitivity by drugs and other agents, and the phenomenon of " after-taste " is due largely to this property. As an instance, we may quote the statement that a cigar tastes sweet, if smoked after the mouth has been rinsed out with very dilute copper sulphate.

The taste-buds may be stimulated electrically, and the effect is not due merely to the taste of the products of electrolysis at the electrodes. The different taste-buds, indeed, have different thresholds for electrical stimulation.

Smell

The sense organs for smell are situated in the upper parts of the nasal cavities in a position which is not ordinarily swept by the incoming air. Odorous substances in the inspired air can thus only reach them as a result of eddies and by diffusion. These substances dissolve in the mucus covering the sensitive cells, diffuse into the hairs which protrude from the cells into the mucus layer, and so set up the sensation of smell.

In contrast with the sense of taste, it is quite impossible to classify the various types of smell into definite components ; each substance has its own distinctive smell. There are certain general resemblances, however, and it has been suggested that odorous substances can be grouped into the spicy, the flowery, the fruity, the resinous or balsamic, the burnt and the foul. Unlike taste, again, the combination of two or more smells may produce a completely new smell, which cannot be analysed into its components. One smell, again, can mask, or neutralise, another (the action of perfumes in this connection is well known), and this can take place even if the two odorous substances are applied to different nostrils.

One of the peculiarities of the sense of smell is its rapid fatigue ; air which initially has a powerful smell may seem quite odourless within a few minutes. Recovery is equally rapid. This fatigue only applies to the particular substance exciting it, and another substance, even though it has a very similar smell, may be perceived normally. Different substances fatigue the sensory apparatus at different rates, but for any given substance, the rate of fatigue increases with the intensity of the smell. Some people are completely deficient in the sense of smell and many are incapable of smelling certain substances which have a strong odour to others (hydrocyanic acid is a typical instance). This deficiency may be congenital or acquired.

The actual quantity of an odorous substance which can just be detected is extremely small. The most powerful odour known (from this point of view) is that of ionone, the synthetic substitute for the perfume of violets ; 1 milligram of this substance can be detected by most people in 10,000 cubic metres of air, *i.e.*, in a room 100 feet square by 30 feet high. Now the nasal cavity is estimated to contain rather less than 50 c.c. of air, so that the least quantity of ionone in this cavity that can be detected is about 5 millionths of a microgram (5×10^{-12} grams) ; even in this quantity there are, however, about 100 million molecules present.

The sensitivities of different people to certain odours may be compared by means of the Zwaardemaker *olfactometer*. This consists of a glass tube, one end of which can be inserted into one of the nostrils ; over the outside of this is another tube of glass or metal, arranged to slide to and fro. The inner surface of the outer tube is coated with the substance under investigation. Thus the amount of surface coated with the odorous material which is exposed to the incoming air can be adjusted by sliding the outer tube relatively to the inner. The length of the outer tube so exposed when the subject can just detect the odour is a measure of his sensitivity to the odour of the substance under investigation.

CHAPTER XV

THE DUCTLESS GLANDS

In our review of the functions of the various systems in the human body, we have had occasion to refer to a number of instances of chemical co-ordination concerned with the maintenance of constant conditions in the " internal environment." The intricate buffering arrangements in the blood, and the respiratory and renal adjustments which contribute to the maintenance of the neutrality of the body fluids may be quoted as an example of co-ordination, the range of which extends to every portion of the organism. In contrast with such diffuse mechanisms, we may set those which are more circumscribed, and among them we may distinguish two classes : first, those in which the co-ordinating substance is derived from an anatomically distinct structure, but which exerts its influence over a wide field ; and secondly, those in which the substance has a specific action which is revealed predominantly by a particular tissue. Insulin, considered in Chapter VI., may be named as a member of the first class, and secretin, considered in Chapter V., as one of the second class.

The identification of ductless glands as the unique seat of manufacture of certain substances with specific actions and of extreme potency has attracted considerable attention to the important part played by such actions in the animal economy. Substances of this kind are commonly termed **hormones,** but since this implies a stimulant action which not all of them possess, the name " chalone " is occasionally employed to denote substances with an inhibitory action, and " autacoid " is applied non-committally to the whole group of substances with a normal regulatory function, whether their actions are regarded as excitatory or inhibitory.

Hormones are unsuited to effect changes with the speed of nervous reflexes, but some of them are concerned in regulatory processes involving fairly rapid adaptations, for example, the influence of adrenaline and acetylcholine on the arterioles. Other substances are concerned with the slower processes of growth and metabolic equilibrium, for example, thyroxine.

The study of the actions of extracts of the ductless glands is properly a branch of pharmacology, for it must not be supposed that such an action, however specific or potent, necessarily represents the normal function of the gland. One might as well imagine that the effect of digitalis on the vertebrate heart was a normal function of the glucoside in the foxglove from which it had been extracted. The assertion that a particular action is a normal function of a ductless gland depends on the correspondence between the consequences of excision of the organ, and of replacement by injections of extracts, or of implantation of gland tissue.

To avoid confusion, it is essential to distinguish between the specific

and the non-specific actions of tissue extracts. All crude tissue extracts
contain histamine, and produce capillary dilatation and a fall of blood
pressure when injected intravenously (Fig. XV. 1) ; in exceptional circumstances, this depressor effect may be masked by the action of a
sufficiently potent pressor substance. A specific depressor effect can,
therefore, only be distinguished from the non-specific action of histamine, if the effective substance in a tissue extract can be isolated and
purified. The actions of acetylcholine and of the minutest doses of

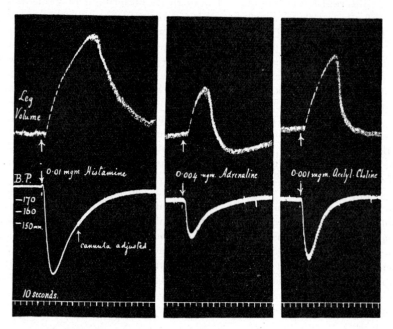

Fig. XV. 1.   The Action of **Histamine, Adrenaline** (in minute concentration)
    and **Acetylcholine** on the Arterial Pressure and the Volume of the
    Denervated Limb of a Cat.
    Histamine and acetylcholine are produced during activity of the vaso-
dilator nerves in the skin and muscles respectively (Chapter II.). A
larger dose of adrenaline (say, 0·05 mg.) would have given the more characteristic vaso-constrictor effect, *i.e.*, rise in arterial pressure and diminution
in limb volume (*cf.* Fig. XV. 4). (Dale and Richards.)

adrenaline, shown in Fig. XV. I, are instances of evidence of this kind. A
pressor action, on the contrary, is readily recognised as a specific effect
of the extract which induces it, as exemplified by extracts of the posterior lobe of the pituitary gland, and of the suprarenal glands in all but
minute doses.

Many of the regulatory mechanisms in which hormones play a
part have been considered in previous chapters under their appropriate
systems. The secretions of the gonads, and anterior lobe of the pituitary
gland (Chapter VIII.), of the pancreas and the thyroid (Chapter VI.), of
the intestinal mucosa (Chapter V.), and of the suprarenals (Chapter

II.), have been discussed, and it remains only to give a more detailed account of certain features of some of them. Various other organs have been numbered among the ductless glands in the hope that a suitable function would be found for them ; some, like the carotid body, are now known to have quite a different kind of function (Chapter II.), while others, like the pineal body, can as yet have no function confidently assigned to them.

THE SUPRARENAL GLANDS

The two suprarenal bodies are situated immediately above the upper poles of the kidneys, as shown in Fig. XV. 2. Each consists of two

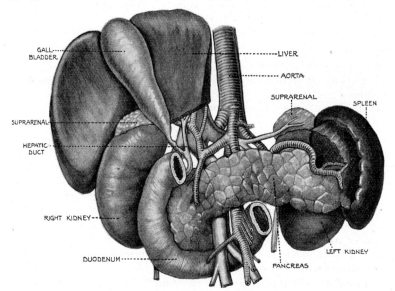

Fig. XV. 2. Supra-renal gland, gall-bladder, liver, pancreas and spleen shown in their relative positions. (After Sobotta.)

histologically distinguishable portions : (1) the cortex, which is the paler, and stains darkly with silver nitrate ; it completely envelops (2) the medulla, which is smaller and darker ; it stains brown with chromates, and is consequently referred to as " chromaffine tissue." The cortex arises from the cœlomic epithelium, while the medulla arises from the ectoderm, in close association with the sympathetic system. The two portions of the gland are thus distinct in origin and appearance, and, as their functions are also entirely different, it will be convenient to consider them separately.

The Function of the Suprarenal Medulla

Complete extirpation of the medulla without destruction of all the cortical tissue is an operation of some difficulty, but when it has succeeded, it has not proved fatal ; the victims suffered from no untoward symptoms and exhibited no lowering of the arterial pressure.

Extracts of the organ, however, are of great physiological potency, and their actions have been traced to a substance chemically related to tyrosine, and named **adrenaline.** It has the following formula :—

$$HO \underset{HO}{\underbrace{\langle\quad\rangle}}\!\!- CH(OH) - CH_2 . NH . CH_3$$

The naturally occurring form is lævo-rotatory, and this has been found to be about twelve times as active physiologically as the dextro-rotatory isomer. Adrenaline in solution is rapidly destroyed on exposure to air. At body temperature most of the adrenaline injected intra-venously is decomposed in a few minutes. Owing to its instability, administration by mouth has little effect.

Adrenaline acts on all the organs in the body innervated by the sympathetic system, and has the same action on them as has stimulation of the sympathetic nerves. The sweat glands in man are, however, unaffected by adrenaline, and so form the only outstanding exception to the rule.

Instances of the sympathomimetic action of adrenaline on the cardio-vascular system have already been considered in Chapter II. : the rise of arterial pressure, which is greater after section of the vagi ; the augmentor and accelerator action on the heart ; the intense con-strictor action on all the arterioles except those in the brain, lungs and coronary system of the heart, and the vaso-dilator action produced after the vaso-constrictor nerves have been paralysed by ergotoxin, have all been mentioned. The vaso-dilator effect, moreover, is often more easily evoked than the vaso-constrictor effect by a very minute concen-tration of adrenaline, so that in suitable animals vaso-dilatation may be produced particularly in voluntary muscle by injection of minimal doses of adrenaline with a consequent fall in blood pressure (see Fig. **XV.** 1). The musculature of the alimentary canal and of its outgrowths, such as the bronchi, is relaxed though the sphincters may contract. The pupil is dilated, and glycogen is discharged from the liver with consequent hyperglycæmia, and possibly glycosuria (Chapter **VI.**).

The manner in which adrenaline acts on tissues is a matter of some interest, more particularly because it is suspected that this substance, or one resembling it, is formed in the tissues themselves when the sympathetic nerves are stimu-lated. It was mentioned in Chapter XIII., in connection with the " humoral theory " of nervous action, that stimulation of the sympathetic supply of a frog's heart resulted in liberation of a substance with physiological actions resembling those of adrenaline.

Adrenaline undoubtedly acts directly on the tissues rather than on the nerves, because its action persists after section of the nerves, even if time has been allowed for complete degeneration of their peripheral ramifications; the heart and the pupil are, in fact, more sensitive to adrenaline when this has been done. On the other hand, the action of adrenaline may be prevented by drugs, such as ergotoxin and apocodeine, which also interrupt the influence of the sympathetic system, but which do not abolish the contractile response of the muscle to direct electrical stimulation, or to the application of certain other drugs, such as barium chloride. These facts are usually summarised by the statement that adrenaline acts on an **excitatory** mechanism in the tissue, whereas certain abnormal stimuli (*e.g.*, an electrical shock and barium chloride) can act more directly on the contractile mechanism.

Small quantities of adrenaline can be estimated by matching their effects with those of a known concentration of the pure substance on isolated muscles suspended in Ringer's solution. The contraction of the rabbit's uterus, or relaxation of its intestine, are convenient indicators for this purpose, and are sensitive to concentrations varying from 1 in 10^{10} to 1 in 10^{6}, the latter producing a nearly maximal effect (Fig. XV. 3). A quantity of adrenaline as small as 0·002 mg. per kilogram suffices to raise the blood pressure of a pithed cat by a perceptible amount. These

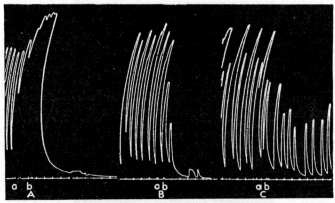

FIG. XV. 3. **Estimation of the Adrenaline Content of Blood :** Adrenaline inhibits the Rhythmic Contractions of the Intestinal Muscles of a Cat.

The muscle was initially beating in Ringer's Solution (upstroke of the lever indicates contraction). At *a*, in each case, this solution was removed and at *b* was replaced by cat's blood containing : A, 1 : 1,000,000 adrenaline, B, 1 : 2,000,000 adrenaline, and C, 1 : 3,000,000 adrenaline. After a preliminary contraction, due to the action of the blood, inhibition of the spontaneous activity was produced, which was complete in the first two cases, and very marked in the last. (Cannon.)

figures serve to emphasise the extreme physiological potency of the substance.

The suprarenal medulla is under the control of the splanchnic nerve, the stimulation of which is followed by changes in the organism which are in part due to direct stimulation of the sympathetic system, and in part due to the discharge of adrenaline, which reinforces and prolongs the immediate effects of the nervous stimulation (this is shown in Fig. II. 21, p. 56). The way in which stimulation of the suprarenal gland depends on the liberation of acetylcholine at the nerve endings within it has been described in Chapter XIII. It has been estimated that the normal concentration of adrenaline in the blood leaving the suprarenals is equivalent to 0·002 mg. per minute per kilogram body weight under ordinary experimental conditions. This is reduced to a negligible quantity after section of the splanchnic nerves, and increased ten to twelve fold by electrical stimulation of these nerves.

Reflex stimulation of the sympathetic system is produced under a variety of conditions, such as (1) physical exercise, (2) emotional states of fear and rage, (3) pain produced by stimulation of a sensory nerve, (4) asphyxia, (5) exposure to cold, and (6) general anæsthesia. The effects on the organs of the body are identical with those described above as resulting from injection of adrenaline, and they may be summarised as a mobilisation of those resources of the body primarily concerned in the executive actions which are natural in the presence of an emergency, and an inhibition of those functions which are not of immediate importance under such conditions. This is the foundation of the

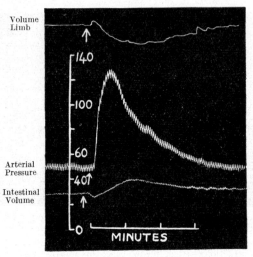

Fig. XV. 4. The Effect of Intravenous **Injection of Adrenaline** on the Volume of the Denervated Limb, the Arterial Pressure, and the Volume of a Loop of Intestine of a Decerebrate Cat.
   0·01 mg. of adrenaline was injected at the moment indicated by the arrow. The vagi and splanchnics had been cut previously. A fall in the plethysmograph record indicates vaso-constriction. Note the constriction of the skin vessels (limb volume) and passive dilatation of the intestinal vessels. (G. A. Clark.)

emergency theory of the function of the suprarenal medulla. It asserts that many of the physical changes which accompany intense emotion are due to the activity of the sympathetic and suprarenal systems. Such activity results in a rapid pulse, and rise in blood pressure, hair " standing on end," dilatation of the pupil and inhibition of the digestive processes, which are among the well-known signs of emotional excitement. Closer analysis of the action of adrenaline reveals a redistribution of the blood supply, that to the skin being less, and that to the muscles greater. It is usually supposed that a vaso-constriction in the abdominal organs—the " splanchnic area "—and in the skin is one of the more important contributors to the increased peripheral resistance, which, together with the augmented output of the heart, produces the characteristic rise in arterial pressure. Certain experiments have shown, however, that in many circumstances this is not the case (Fig. **XV. 4**). The crucial test of the emergency theory depends upon direct observation of the rate of discharge of adrenaline in the suprarenal veins of an animal suitably stimulated. Exposing a cat to a barking dog, for example, increases the secretion of adrenaline, as shown in Fig. **XV. 5**. The emergency theory seems the more likely because it fits in happily with the conception of an organism well adapted to changes in its environment.

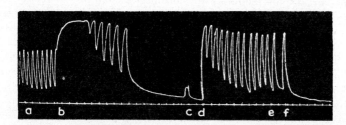

Fig. XV. 5. **The Secretion of Adrenaline during Excitement :** Record of a Rhythmically Beating Intestinal Muscle.

The muscle was initially beating in Ringer's solution. At *a*, this solution was removed, and at *b*, was replaced by blood taken from the inferior vena cava of a cat which had been excited by being " barked at by a dog for 15 minutes." After a preliminary contraction complete inhibition was produced. At *c*, this blood was removed, and at *d*, was replaced by blood obtained in a similar manner from a quiet cat ; the muscle immediately began to contract rhythmically. This blood was removed at *e*, and " excited " blood again added at *f* : the contractions ceased. Compare this with Fig. XV. 3, which shows the effect of blood containing known amounts of adrenaline on an intestinal muscle under similar conditions. (Cannon.)

The Functions of the Suprarenal Cortex

About thirty crystalline steroids have been isolated from the suprarenal gland, of which seven are active in maintaining the life of an animal lacking all suprarenal cortical tissue. The formulæ of three of these are given below. It is difficult to assign to any one of these

Corticosterone Deoxycorticosterone Dehydrocorticosterone

substances the chief place in cortical function, particularly as the latter is not easy to define. The suprarenal cortex probably plays several

18—2

parts in the body, and a mixed deficiency syndrome follows removal of the glands.   At the present time, two fields of activity are fairly well established and are associated with certain of the compounds which have been isolated ; but we must first describe as a whole the effects of deprivation.

Removal of the Suprarenal Glands and Substitution Therapy.   In the following sections, the effects of removal of the whole suprarenal glands (cortex plus medulla) are considered.   Unless otherwise stated, the effects of such removal may be taken as being the result of a deficiency of the cortical portion only of the glands.   Animals submitted to adrenalectomy recover from the surgical interference, but after about a week begin to show muscular weakness, loss of appetite, reduced temperature and blood pressure, and finally more severe symptoms such as diarrhœa, vomiting and anuria.   Death occurs two or three days after the first signs of illness.   **Addison's disease** in man is characterised by muscular weakness, loss of weight, low blood pressure, low temperature and vomiting.   The similarity to the effects of suprarenal deficiency is obvious, and the condition is, indeed, due to disease of the suprarenal ; frequently to infection with the *B. tuberculosis*.   An additional feature, which has not been reproduced in animals, is bronzing of the skin and of the mucous membrane of the mouth in areas of pressure or friction.   It must be borne in mind that successful treatment of deficiency in man may not influence the underlying disease.

Cortical extracts restore adrenalectomised animals to health and maintain them, so far as is known, indefinitely.   For example, the urea, chlorides, phosphates and creatinine retained because of renal failure are secreted, and no kidney damage remains.   Similar extracts are administered in human cases of cortical deficiency, and are frequently referred to as if they contained an active principle " cortin."   This term, though convenient, refers to no particular chemical substance. In estimating the effects of treatment, the *survival time* of animals after adrenalectomy is an important criterion, but it cannot be used in man since it depends for its significance on total deprivation of cortical tissue at a definite moment.

Closer investigation of adrenalectomised animals shows that they secrete in the urine excessive amounts of sodium and chloride, and retain potassium.   In conformity with this, it is found that the administration of large quantities of sodium chloride causes a dramatic improvement in the condition of deficient men and animals, and greatly prolongs the life of the latter after complete adrenalectomy.   Animals so treated are, however, not normal, because they cannot withstand stress.   The ability to withstand stress is usually tested by exposure to low temperature, starvation, or severe muscular exercise.   Starvation also induces symptoms of hypoglycæmia, a phenomenon believed to be independent of failure to endure stress.   The optimal conditions for treatment of the deficiency by administration of suprarenal extract are secured by the adoption of a diet rich in sodium chloride and in carbohydrate.   A very much smaller dose of " cortin " then becomes sufficient to maintain deficient men in good condition, and adrenalectomised animals alive indefinitely.

De-oxycorticosterone (desoxycortone) is the most potent of the isolated cortical products in raising the concentration of sodium and decreasing the concentration of potassium in the serum of both adrenalectomised and normal rats. It has little or no effect on carbohydrate metabolism.

Corticosterone, and other derivatives with an oxygen atom (hydroxyl or ketone) at C_{11} of the steroid nucleus have the greatest influence in protecting adrenalectomised animals against the hypoglycæmia induced by procedures such as starvation or the administration of phlorrhizin. This group of compounds has another characteristic effect. Its members restore to voluntary muscle the power, lost after adrenalectomy, of responding to prolonged direct electrical stimulation.

After removal of the crystalline compounds, the remainder of a suprarenal extract is known as the " *amorphous fraction.*" It has little influence in combating hypoglycæmia, or in restoring the efficiency of muscle for prolonged work, but in *adrenalectomised animals*, it is the most potent cortical product in maintaining life.

Resistance to stress seems to be restored in some degree by all cortical products, whatever their other main action.

Since the tendency to hypoglycæmia and the low efficiency of muscle are compatible with life, it follows that treatment with products which have little or no effect on carbohydrate metabolism is quite successful symptomatically, so long as the animal or individual is not starved or exposed to low oxygen pressure.

Overactivity of the Suprarenal Cortex. When this occurs, very pronounced effects are seen, particularly in children of both sexes and in women.

In *females* of any age, from intra-uterine life onwards, overgrowth of cortical tissue may give rise to a form of hermaphrodism. Hair appears on the face, the pubic hair assumes a male distribution, the voice becomes deeper, the clitoris enlarges and amenorrhœa supervenes. Young girls in whom these changes occur precociously may never menstruate. If the condition is established before birth, it may be difficult or impossible to distinguish the sex of the child, who might equally well be a boy with undescended testicles. This is because external genitalia may be influenced before their development is complete.

In *boys* precocious sexual maturity may take place, and is associated with muscular hypertrophy. In both sexes, mental changes appropriate to these conditions may accompany them, *i.e.*, a masculine outlook in women and girls, and a mature attraction for the opposite sex in boys. Girls with only moderate signs of masculinisation may excel others of their sex in athletic prowess.

The relation between these predominantly sexual manifestations of supra-renal activity, and the metabolic ones which we discussed previously is not known, but it seems probable that androgens are produced from the cortical steroids by some abnormality in metabolism. Removal of the abnormal or excessive suprarenal cortical tissue gives good results, if the growth is not malignant.

THE THYROID GLAND

In various parts of the world, enlargement of the thyroid gland is common, and if it gives rise to embarrassment in no other way, it may be

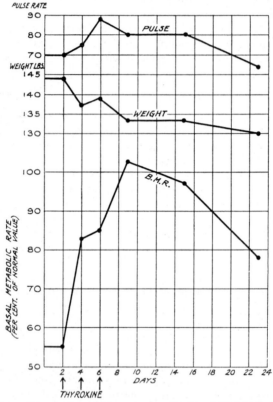

FIG. XV. 6. The Action of **Thyroxine** on the Basal Metabolic Rate, the Weight and the Pulse Frequency of a Patient with Myxœdema.

Five mg. of synthetic thyroxine were injected intravenously on the second day, 4 mg. on the fourth day, and 5 mg. on the sixth day ; in addition to the increase in basal metabolic rate, fall in weight, and rise in pulse frequency shown on the chart, the injections produced a rise in temperature, diuresis and diarrhœa. (After Lyon.)

disfiguring and the enlarged gland may press on neighbouring organs. During the last century two lines of treatment were adopted ; the administration of iodine in various forms, which softened the gland and reduced the swelling, and surgical removal. Sometimes the whole gland was excised, and a temporary relief from symptoms lasting for about six months was succeeded by the signs typical of thyroid deficiency. This " *cachexia strumipriva* " was similar to a condition, *myxœdema*, occurring spontaneously in middle-aged or elderly adults.

With the demonstration that administration of animal thyroids by the mouth, or the injection of extracts of them, relieved both ailments, an unusually complete chain of evidence on the origin of a human endocrine deficiency was forged. Animal experiments, carried out at the time and subsequently, amply substantiated these findings, and showed, in addition, that thyroid tissue transplanted to other parts of the body of a thyroidectomised animal was a satisfactory substitute for the animal's own gland.

Certain similarities of myxœdema to *cretinism* had early been noticed, and successful treatment of the latter with thyroid established the fact that it was due to thyroid deficiency, this time congenital. By indicating briefly the outstanding features of cretinism and myxoedema, we may gain some insight into the functions of the thyroid gland.

Myxœdema is superficially characterised by a thickening of the subcutaneous tissue, coarsening of the features, dryness and pallor of the skin, and falling out of the hair. The patient is mentally dull, sluggish in action, with a slow pulse and perhaps a subnormal temperature. A history of constipation and, in women, amenorrhœa, may be obtained. These features of the disease are variable and may not all occur simultaneously. A definite diagnosis depends on the demonstration of *a reduced basal metabolic rate*, which may be 30 or 40 per cent. below the normal (Fig. XV. 6). Since no independent way of reducing basal metabolic rate for a long enough period has been found, it is impossible to state categorically that all the other signs and symptoms are secondary to the reduction, but many of them certainly are, and thyroid deficiency is believed to reduce the activity of all tissues.

Cretinism may occasionally occur in an infant for no apparent reason, when it is said to be " sporadic." Nearly always, however, it occurs in those regions of the globe where goitre is prevalent, and is there " endemic." In its most severe form, it begins to be apparent at the age of 3 months, but in addition to the features it has in common with myxœdema, others occur due to *arrested development*. The child, even should he grow up, never achieves a mental capacity greater than that of a normal child of about 3 years, and may actually lack initiative to feed himself at the age of 12. The long bones fail to grow at the epiphyses, leading to much loss of stature, but the skull does enlarge, giving a characteristic deformity. The fontanelles are late in closing. The visceral organs also grow, so the individual becomes pot-bellied. The muscles become disproportionately large (without achieving any great strength) with the consequence that the tongue is too big for the mouth, from which it protrudes, causing a dribble of saliva. To these grotesque abnormalities may be added pads of fat, deposited on the shoulders and buttocks.

Whether the two fundamental phenomena of arrested development and diminished metabolism of the tissues are inter-related, it is impossible to say. If they are, the relationship is not the simple one that cells fail to grow because their vital activity is sluggish. Growth and development are not the same. Tadpoles treated with thyroid undergo premature metamorphosis, becoming frogs at a much smaller size than normally. But in the course of other experiments, tadpoles have been known to grow abnormally large without undergoing metamorphosis.

Perhaps the most striking feature of cretinism is its complete response to thyroid therapy if this is begun early enough. In cases of several years' standing, irreversible changes have occurred, and improvement is all that can be hoped for. It must be emphasised that cessation of treatment in either myxœdema or cretinism leads to a prompt relapse into thyroid deficiency (Fig. XV. 6). We shall see, however, that there is hope that all but the sporadic cases of cretinism may be prevented in another way, and in order to understand this we return once more to the treatment of thyroid enlargement.

Endemic Goitre. Any generalised enlargement of the thyroid gland is called a " goitre." Goitres have been described from ancient times in all races and even in a great many animals. It is now generally accepted that the geographical distribution coincides with deficiency of iodine in the drinking water, or in the soil (and therefore presumably in the vegetable food of the region). Other causes of endemic goitre, such as low grade infection, have not been excluded, but there is no doubt that inaccessibility or deficient absorption of iodine is the chief. Goitre has been connected not only with a deficient intake of iodine, but also with an abnormally low iodine content of the gland itself. The structure of the latter is more difficult to explain, but it is believed that hyperplasia is the primary result of iodine deficiency, and is followed by partial atrophy. This leads to a hard gland, with an overgrowth of secretory and supporting elements, some fibrosis, and irregularly-shaped almost obliterated colloid vesicles. Improvement in the supply of iodine, not necessarily due to deliberate treatment, gives rise to distension of the vesicles with secreted colloid, and to remission of hyperplasia. This leads to a softer gland, and a different histological picture, typical of " colloid goitre." When iodine again becomes deficient, it reverts to its " hyperplastic " state.

Treatment with iodine leads ultimately to a reduction in the actual size of the gland, but although it has been known from ancient times (in the shape of ingesting burnt sponge, with or without incantations), it fell somewhat into disrepute during the latter part of the last century on account of the toxic symptoms of overdosage. The most important consequence of the reinstatement of iodine as a therapeutic agent has been the discovery that by giving iodides in small quantities to the population of a goitre region (for instance, by adding 1 part in 5,000 to the salt which they buy), the disease is prevented. This has been carried out with success in the United States and Switzerland, and in other places on a smaller scale. The minute additional intake of iodine is thought to be harmless to normal persons, and iodisation of all the salt consumed in England has been advocated. Goitre is common in a belt running roughly from Somerset through Derbyshire to Durham, but is not restricted to it.

Supplementary iodine is also an important means of eliminating endemic cretinism, for although several generations must pass before the result is certain, there is little doubt that congenital thyroid deficiency is usually associated with a familial history of iodine deficiency, usually in the shape of goitre, and that it takes intermediate forms between frank cretinism and simple goitre, being responsible for many idiots and deaf-mutes. The provision of adequate iodine for the populations of areas where goitre and cretinism are prevalent is likely to make the incidence of these diseases negligible.

It must be borne in mind that simple goitre is not, as a rule, accompanied by overt symptoms of hypothyroidism. This suggests that the hyperplasia of the gland does, in some ill-understood way, compensate for the deficiency of iodine, although this element is an essential constituent of the active principle of the gland.

Fig. XV. 7.   **Exophthalmic goitre.**
Note the swelling in the neck (due to enlargement of the thyroid gland) and the protruding eye-balls (exophthalmos).   (Parsons.)

Exophthalmic goitre (Fig. XV. 7) is an enlargement of the thyroid, often slight, in which hyperplasia is accompanied by *hyperthyroidism*. Administration of iodine again seems to check the hyperplasia, and lead to a distension of the vesicles with colloid, while the symptoms are much relieved. After a few weeks, however, they tend to return in a more intense form. The most reasonable though admittedly incomplete, theory at present is that the secretory activity of the thyroid is " set " at a higher rate. The gland may, therefore, find itself short of iodine and undergo the histological changes already described (sometimes, myxœdema ultimately ensues, presumably owing to " exhaustion " of the gland). The histological results of iodine treatment are similar to those in simple goitre, but the simultaneous reduction in the output of secretion is not explained. The eventual relapse into over-secretion, however, falls into line with expectation, and with the results of iodine overdosage in simple goitre, which in the past frequently led to hyperthyroidism.

The signs and symptoms of hyperthyroidism (which may also result from localised tumours of the thyroid) contrast, as might be expected, with those we have so far considered. *The basal metabolic rate is greatly increased*, and the skin is flushed and moist. There is loss of weight and tachycardia, the apex beat being diffuse, and its position suggesting an enlargement of the heart which is not, however, apparent *post mortem*. Mental activity is accelerated, with exaggerated responses to sensory and emotional stimuli. Just as the increased frequency of the heart beat may cause cardiac failure, so the heightened susceptibility of the nervous system may lead to insanity. Protrusion of the eyeballs, for which there is no complete explanation (though it can be produced in animals by anterior pituitary) is typical but not invariable. It is doubtful whether the overactivity of the secretory cells is a primary defect, or is secondary to some other change, such as excess of the thyrotrophic hormone.

Thyroxine. A substance with the following structure :—

$$\text{HO} \underset{\underset{\text{I}}{|}}{\overset{\overset{\text{I}}{|}}{\bigcirc}} \text{O} \underset{\underset{\text{I}}{|}}{\overset{\overset{\text{I}}{|}}{\bigcirc}} \text{CH}_2 \cdot \overset{\overset{\text{NH}_2}{|}}{\text{CH}} \cdot \text{COOH}$$

has been isolated from the thyroid gland, and for all practical purposes its activity is qualitatively the same as that of dried thyroid gland. It takes, however, a longer period to achieve its maximum effect, and it probably must be built up into a more complex molecule before it becomes identical with the actual substance secreted by the thyroid. The fact that 65 per cent. of its molecule by weight is iodine explains the avidity of the gland for this element, although half the iodine content of the thyroid may be due to its content of di-iodotyrosine.

Thiourea $\text{C} \cdot \text{S} \overset{\nearrow \text{NH}_2}{\underset{\searrow \text{NH}_2}{}}$ and its derivatives and 2-thiouracil appear to inhibit the formation of thyroxin, and have been successfully used in the treatment of hyperthyroidism, although the gland itself appears histologically overactive. These compounds may have undesirable secondary effects, for instance, on the granulocytes of the blood, but their anti-thyrotoxic action has become the basis of treatment of suitable cases.

THE PARATHYROID GLANDS

Two pairs of very vascular bodies, about the size of lentils, attracted the attention of surgeons in the early days of therapeutic removal of the thyroid glands (Fig. XV. 8). Unless one or more of them was left undisturbed, tetany supervened, and the consequences were usually fatal.

The parathyroid glands are necessary for life. Sudden extirpation of all parathyroid tissue results, after a delay of three or four days during

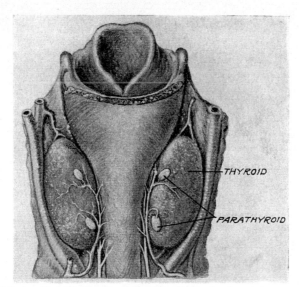

FIG. XV. 8.   Thyroid Gland and Parathyroid Glands, shown from the back.
(After Halstead and Evans.)

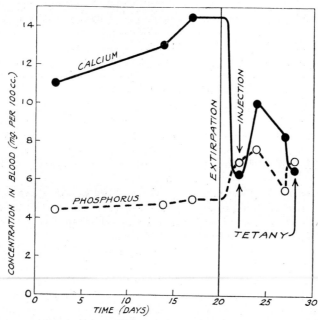

FIG. XV. 9.   The Effect of **Extirpation of the Parathyroid Glands and Subsequent Injections of Parathormone** on the Concentrations of Calcium
and Inorganic Phosphorus in the Blood, showing their action in inducing
and preventing Tetany in a Dog.

Tetany occurred whenever the calcium concentration fell below about
7 mg. per 100 c.c.   (After Weaver and Reed.)

which no untoward effects are apparent, in periodic tonic spasms of the musculature, high fever, increased irritability of the peripheral nerves, and death due to asphyxia during one of the " tetanic " convulsions. This condition of *tetany* is associated with an abnormally low concentration of calcium salts in the blood ; it can be alleviated by administration (oral or intravenous) of calcium salts, and permanently controlled by periodic injections of parathyroid extracts.

Deprivation of parathyroid, by surgical removal of the gland, is always followed by a fall in the concentration of calcium in the blood, which, if sufficiently extensive, is associated with tetany, as just remarked. Injection of parathyroid extract (**parathormone**), on the other hand, results in an increased concentration of calcium in the blood, the extra calcium being derived from the bones. These relations are illustrated in Fig. XV. 9, which also indicates the characteristic variations in concentration of inorganic phosphate produced by the same agents ; the phosphate and the calcium concentrations vary in opposite directions.

The parathyroid glands appear, therefore, to exert a specific control over the utilisation of calcium salts in the body, and the effects produced by excessive and inadequate functioning of these glands are essentially the same as those produced by excess and deficiency of calcium.

The normal level of concentration of calcium salts corresponds with about 10 mg. Ca per 100 c.c. of plasma, about half of which is held by protein and is indiffusible through collodion membranes.

Hypercalcæmia (more than 20 mg. Ca per 100 c.c. plasma) when produced in the dog by repeated large doses of the hormone is associated with a rise in the viscosity and the osmotic pressure of the blood and with an increase in the concentration of phosphates, proteins and urea ; diarrhœa, vomiting, vascular failure, coma and death may ensue. Parathormone injections have been given to man in cases of lead poisoning to remove the lead which has accumulated in the bones. Calcium comes away with the lead and produces a hypercalcæmia, and cases are recorded in which the blood calcium rose to nearly 20 mg. per 100 c.c. without producing severe symptoms.

Hypocalcæmia (less than 7 mg. Ca. per 100 c.c. plasma) results in the muscular twitchings and tetanic convulsions mentioned above ; the effect of immersing isolated muscles in saline solutions deficient in calcium may be recalled in this connection.

Ancillary evidence connecting the parathyroid glands and calcium metabolism is derived from the pathological changes in the glands associated with diseases involving failure in the normal calcification of bone. For example, overgrowth of the glands accompanies malnutrition on calcium-deficient diets, rickets, and osteomalacia ; a similar hypertrophy is usual during pregnancy and lactation (we remarked in Chapter VIII. on the relatively high concentration of calcium in milk, as compared with that in blood). Partial excision of the glands, moreover, results in deposition of defective dentine in the teeth, and in an imperfect development of callus about bone fractures—

abnormalities which can be rectified, at least in rats, by implanting additional parathyroid tissue.

Very large quantities of vitamin D have been found to raise the concentration of calcium in the serum (about 100 times the anti-rachitic dose is needed). This is apparently the result of a direct action in releasing calcium from the bones and of promoting absorption from the gut, as already mentioned in Chapter VI. The parathyroid gland is not involved. It has been found, also, that a substance known as *tachysterol* which is an intermediate product in the formation of calciferol (vitamin D$_2$) by irradiation of ergosterol, is also effective in a similar way, and that di-hydroxy-tachysterol is even more effective. This substance, known as " A.T. 10 " is in use clinically to raise the serum calcium concentration, and to counteract the effects of chronic hypoparathyroidism.

THE PITUITARY GLAND

The pituitary gland weighs about one-half a gram in man, and is attached to the base of the brain, occupying a fossa in the sphenoid bone, known as the *sella turcica*. The gland consists of the *body* (divided into an anterior and a posterior lobe by the " cleft "), the *stalk* (infundibulum) and the *pars tuberalis* in contact with the base of the brain. With the exception of the *pars nervosa*, the gland is developed as an outgrowth (Rathke's pouch) from the roof of the mouth ; later it is separated, and comes into close association with the neural portion. The " cleft " is a survival of the lumen of the pouch, and the pars intermedia, lining the posterior aspect of the cleft, is thus also derived from the pouch. The *anterior lobe* is a very vascular organ, and consists of epithelial cells, the appearance of which has justified the alternative name " pars glandularis " for this portion of the pituitary body. The *pars tuberalis* is a flat, tongue-like projection of the gland moulded over the base of the brain as far as the tuber cinereum, and ensheathing the stalk. The *posterior lobe*, lying behind the cleft, is divided into the *pars intermedia* lining the posterior surface of the cleft, and the main

Scheme of the Development and Anatomy of the Pituitary Gland

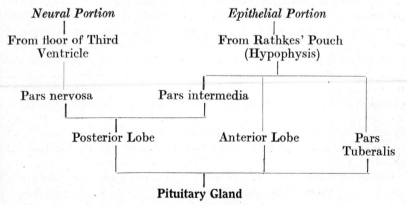

body of the lobe—the *pars nervosa*—which is developed as an outgrowth from the brain, and consists mainly of cells resembling neuroglia in appearance. The blood supply of the posterior lobe is not a rich one, except immediately beneath the pars intermedia, but there is an intimate connection both by vascular and nervous channels with the base of the brain. The term *hypophysis* is often applied to the whole pituitary gland, though its use originated in connection with the epithelial portion of the gland.

Abnormal enlargement of the pituitary gland results in an extension of the bony pituitary fossa, which can be detected in X-ray photographs of the skull.

The pituitary gland is probably not necessary for life, though extirpation is followed by the extensive abnormalities described below. The consequences of the earlier methods of operative removal of the gland were always fatal, but this may be attributed to the associated injury to the base of the brain. Newer methods of hypophysectomy, designed to prevent mutilation of the brain, may be followed by survival for long periods ; owing to the very close association of the pars tuberalis with the brain, however, some of this portion of the gland is always left behind ; the interpretation of these experiments is not quite certain, therefore, especially since the remaining portion of the pars tuberalis subsequently hypertrophies and yields abnormally potent extracts.

The Anterior Lobe

This portion of the gland has two groups of functions : (*a*) those concerned with growth and metabolism, and (*b*) those concerned with control of the sexual cycle. A great many potent extracts have been obtained from the gland with as many different kinds of activity, but they may represent only fractions of larger molecules, and their actions may give a distorted impression of the function of the whole anterior lobe. The following " hormones " have some claim to be regarded as separate entities : the growth, thyrotrophic and adrenotrophic hormones ; and the follicle-stimulating, luteinising (interstitial cell-stimulating) and lactogenic hormones.

The **growth-promoting function** of the gland has been shown in the following way : (1) Extirpation of the gland in young animals (*e.g.*, puppies six to eight weeks old) leads to an almost complete arrest of growth, the hair remains soft and infantile, the milk-teeth persist throughout life, and no junction of the epiphyses occurs though the bone structure is normal. This condition may be referred to as " experimental dwarfism." (2) Repeated injection of saline emulsions of the gland into young animals leads to a corresponding condition known as " experimental gigantism," as illustrated in Fig. XV. 10. (3) Human diseases attributed on histological grounds to over- or under-activity of the gland show signs which are consistent with these experimental results. Thus, overgrowth of the gland in the young is associated with " gigantism," heights of over 8 feet being reached if hyperpituitarism has been in progress for some time before junction of the epiphyses.

If the derangement does not set in until after the junction of the epiphyses, further growth of the long bones is no longer possible, and the disease is manifested by an ingravescent overgrowth of the extremities and the head, known as "acromegaly." In these conditions of over-activity of the anterior lobe there is frequently a diminished sugar tolerance leading to glycosuria. The activity of the gland in carbohydrate metabolism is discussed in Chapter **VI**. It is often called **diabetogenic,** but it is clear that the factors concerned are complex, and intimately associated with the function of the growth hormone whose function may not be the same at all times of life.

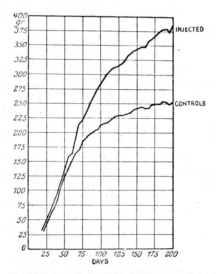

Fig. XV. 10.　The Effect of Injection of Extracts of the **Anterior Lobe of the Pituitary Gland** on the Growth of Rats.

Two groups of thirty-eight rats each were selected ; the rats in one group served as controls, while those in the other were injected daily, and the average weight of the animals in each group was plotted against the time. Note the "gigantism" produced in the injected group. (Trendelenburg, after Evans and Long.)

The Thyrotrophic Hormone. Extirpation of the pars anterior of the pituitary body results in a reduction of the basal metabolic rate by some 30 per cent., the nitrogen excretion being particularly diminished. Conversely, if the thyrotrophic hormone is injected daily into hypophysectomised rats the basal metabolic rate is raised to normal in three or four days. That it acts through the thyroid may be shown by the discharge of colloid and hyperplasia of the epithelial cells. When it is injected into the normal animal, the metabolic rate is raised, but in spite of continued injection this returns to normal in two or three weeks and indeed falls 20 or 30 per cent. below normal if the injection is long continued. This is due to the gradual production of a substance which is not only antagonistic to the hormone, but inhibits its production by the

pituitary. In view of the action of the thyroid extract on growth and
development already described, it is necessary to state here that the
lack of growth following hypophysectomy is not corrected by administration of thyroid gland, *i.e.*, it is not to be attributed wholly to absence
of the thyrotrophic hormone, though this deficiency plays its part.

The Adrenotrophic Hormone.   The suprarenal cortex atrophies after
removal of the anterior pituitary, though the medulla remains normal.
Certain pituitary extracts restore the cortex to normal, and are thought
to contain a specific hormone with this action. The most important
question raised by this and various confirmatory observations is whether
the " diabetogenic " activities of the anterior pituitary are exerted
directly on the liver and peripheral tissues, or whether the suprarenal
cortex is the immediate " diabetogenic " agent, the *rôle* of the pituitary
being limited to providing the initial stimulus in the shape of adrenotrophic hormone. The answer seems to be that part of the effect of the
anterior pituitary may be so explained, but that it has also a direct
action which can be demonstrated in the absence of the suprarenals.
This point is discussed in more detail in Chapter **VI.**

The **gonadotrophic** and **lactogenic** activities of the anterior pituitary
are explained in Chapter **VIII.**   Like the suprarenals, the gonads
atrophy after removal of the pituitary, but the restorative effects of
extracts are more complicated owing to the dual function of gametogenesis and endocrine secretion which the gonads possess. In addition,
the activities of the ovary, and in some species the testis, are cyclic, and
the ratio between the amounts of the two gonadotrophic hormones
produced is subject to constant fluctuation. The *follicle-stimulating
hormone* (FSH) causes spermatogenesis, ripening of Graafian follicles
and secretion of œstrogen by the ovaries. The *luteinising* or *interstitial-
cell-stimulating* hormone (LH or ICSH) maintains the interstitial tissue
of both gonads, and causes secretion of androgen by the testis. It
acts synergically with FSH in producing ovulation, and determining
the formation of the corpus luteum. Artificially administered, it is
capable of luteinising all follicles just as they stand, without ovulation
taking place.   *Prolactin*, the lactogenic hormone, is necessary for the
secretion of milk by the mammary glands, in the actual development
of which it and other less well attested pituitary hormones may play a
part. Removal of the anterior pituitary during lactation promptly
stops the secretion of milk.   It has now been found that while injections
of LH fail to *maintain* the corpus luteum in the hypophysectomised
animal, prolactin will do so. It is, therefore, *luteotrophic* as well as
lactogenic.

Clinical Pituitary Syndromes.   *Gigantism, acromegaly* and *dwarfism*
are readily explicable by supposing an over- or under-secretion of
growth hormone. Gigantism and acromegaly are associated with an
overgrowth of the acidophil cells of the anterior pituitary and may be
accompanied by glycosuria. This is in accordance with the suspected
close relation or identity of the growth and " diabetogenic " factors.
Sexual hypofunction, which also may be present, is presumably due to

pressure of the proliferating acidophil cells on the remaining elements of the gland. Surrounding structures, notably the optic chiasma, may also suffer from pressure. There are various types of dwarfism in which deformity, mental deficiency and sexual hypofunction may be present in different degrees or absent altogether. Perfectly formed midgets are of special interest, because their intelligence is normal, and some of them are capable of reproduction (the children are of normal size and are delivered by Cæsarean section). This implies that deficiency of the growth hormone can occur without an associated deficiency of thyrotrophic or gonadotrophic hormones.

Other pituitary syndromes are not so easy to reconcile with the physiological analysis of the gland, although " there is sufficient variety of findings to give comfort to almost any kind of hypothesis, and a mere physiologist is poorly qualified to winnow the chaff from the grains of wheat " (Carlson). *Cushing's disease* or pituitary *basophilism* is associated with an adenoma of the basophil cells, and a variety of signs and symptoms may be exhibited. Among the more constant are adiposity, confined to the face, neck and trunk, often with tenderness : kyphosis, possibly accompanied by rarefaction of the vertebræ : sexual dystrophy which may start in females with precocious development, but which ends with amenorrhœa in women and impotence in men ; a tendency to a masculine distribution of hair in females ; a high coloured or dusky skin ; purple abdominal striæ, initiated by the stretching of the skin by abdominal fat ; high blood pressure and polycythæmia. The subjects are generally young adults and the suprarenal cortex is hypertrophied.

Two rare diseases are attributed to generalised atrophy of the anterior pituitary : Simmond's disease and progeria. The former, *pituitary cachexia*, is accompanied by atrophic changes in the adrenal cortex, gonads and other viscera. It is characterised by extreme emaciation, with premature signs of age, low metabolic rate, amenorrhœa or impotence, and physical and mental weakness. *Progeria* is a similar condition occuring in childhood. " As though touched with the wand of some malign fairy, the child does not remain infantile, but skips adolescence, maturity and manhood, and passes at once to senility, looking at eleven or twelve years like a miniature Tithonus ' marred and wasted,' wrinkled and stunted, a little old man among his toys." (Osler).

The commonest anterior pituitary lesion is a tumour of the chromophobe cells, but in the typical picture of the ensuing disease, signs and symptoms due to pressure on the more active acidophil and basophil cells are mingled with the results of hypothalamic involvement. In the adult, *dystrophia adiposo-genitalis* leads to regression of the sexual organs, loss of hair and adiposity of feminine distribution. In childhood, when it is known as *Fröhlich's* syndrome, the sexual organs fail to develop at puberty, and secondary sexual characteristics do not appear ; the obesity is again of feminine distribution. Growth may be impaired. Signs of diabetes insipidus and somnolence may be present, but the children are not necessarily stupid. The obesity is at present regarded as being of hypothalamic origin, but it must be remembered that fat is also deposited, though differently, in Cushing's syndrome, where the lesion may be very small and unlikely to yield pronounced pressure effects on the hypothalamus. It may be said in general that clinical lesions, though they may involve primarily only one type of cell, fail to provide an analysis of pituitary function because of the unknown factors introduced by locally disturbed nervous functions and secondarily deranged internal secretions.

The Posterior Lobe

Three important groups of actions can be demonstrated by injection of post-pituitary extracts into mammals, namely, the pressor (cardio-

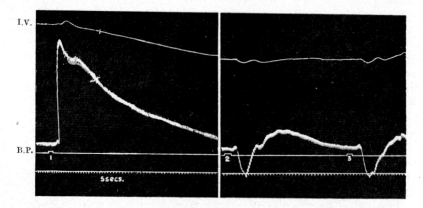

FIG. XV. 11. The Action of Extracts of the **Posterior Lobe of the Pituitary Gland** on the **Blood Pressure** of a Cat.

From above downwards : intestinal volume ; arterial pressure ; injection signal ; time in five second intervals. Note that the second and third injections had practically no vaso-pressor action ; the fall in pressure actually produced was due to the presence of histamine as an impurity in the extract. Note also the prolonged constriction of the intestinal vessels. (Schafer and Swale Vincent.)

vascular) action, the oxytocic (uterine) action, and the anti-diuretic (renal) action.

The chief action on the cardio-vascular system of an intravenous injection of a considerable dose is a marked rise in the blood pressure (as shown in Fig. XV. 11). This characteristic **pressor effect** has certain properties which distinguish it from other pressor responses. For example, in the cat the post-pituitary action is more prolonged than that due to adrenaline, and it has the curious property of rendering the vessels insensitive for some time (*e.g.*, half an hour) to a further dose of the same substance. Similar but rather more transient effects on the arterial pressure are produced by injection in man.

The pressor action is due to **constriction of the arterioles,** including those of the coronary, pulmonary and cerebral circulations. There is, in many circumstances, one exception to this general vaso-constrictor action, the renal arterioles ; the consequent increase of glomerular pressure may be sufficient to overcome the specific anti-diuretic effect on the tubules, and to induce a diuresis. The vaso-constrictor action is not prevented by denervation, or antagonised by ergotoxin, and is therefore attributed to a direct action on the plain muscle in the vessel walls.

The second important action of post-pituitary extracts on the vascular system is a **constriction of the capillaries.** This is shown in man by the immediate blanching of the skin after intravenous injection, and microscopically by intradermal injection of the extract. Less important actions of the post-pituitary substances on the cardio-vascular system include a contraction of the spleen, and a slowing of the heart and reduction in circulation rate which may suffice, in some preparations (dog anæsthetised with chloralose), to cause a fall of arterial pressure in spite of the vaso-constriction.

There is no sufficient reason for associating any of these pharmacological actions with normal functions of the gland in man The capillary-constrictor action, however, like the melanophore-dilator action, is undoubtedly a normal function of the organ in amphibia, and it is not unlikely, therefore, that pituitary secretion normally contributes to the maintenance of capillary tone in mammals.

The **oxytocic action** of post-pituitary extracts deserves more attention as a candidate for physiological significance, for, as shown in Chapter VIII., it may play a *rôle* in producing the contractions of the uterus at parturition. Injections of the substance induce contractions of the gravid uterus, which result in abortion, and are of such violence that they may, in certain circumstances, rupture the organ. The action on the isolated uterus is one of great sensitivity and regularity, and is employed as an indicator for the comparison of the concentration of an unknown with that of a standard solution of the post-pituitary substances. The organ of an immature guinea-pig is chosen for this purpose, since when immersed in Ringer's solution its responses are uninterrupted by spontaneous contractions, and so regular that distinction between 10 per cent. differences of contraction can be detected.

The post-pituitary substances are often described as general plain muscle stimulants, but this is an error, based on reports of experiments with extracts from which the histamine had not been removed. Nevertheless, a few plain muscles in addition to the uterus are affected by considerable concentrations of genuine and purified extracts, and it is believed that the beneficial influence of pituitary injections on the loss of intestinal tone which sometimes interferes with abdominal surgery is due to a stimulant action on the plain muscle of the gut.

The **anti-diuretic action** of post-pituitary extracts is now well established. This has been discussed in Chapter VII., and we will here only summarise the essential points. Presence of the anti-diuretic factor in the blood stream has a specific action in stimulating the renal tubules to re-absorb water, and so to reduce the rate of urine flow. The secretion of this hormone has been shown experimentally to be promoted by an increase in the osmotic pressure of the blood, provided that this increase does not occur very slowly (over a period of days). The secretion is diminished if the solute concentration of the blood is reduced, as occurs when water is absorbed from the alimentary canal. This diminution in the secretion does not occur in the presence of most anæsthetics.

Changes in the osmotic pressure of the blood do not act directly on the posterior pituitary body itself, but are mediated through the supra-optic tracts from the supra-optic and para-ventricular nuclei in the hypothalamus, acetyl-choline acting as a transmitter agent. Interference with the tracts, either surgically or as a result of a lesion, results in the permanent polyuria of *diabetes insipidus*—the pars nervosa degenerates and the secretion of the anti-diuretic hormone can no longer occur. A permanent polyuria however, can only be produced if some part, at least, of the *anterior lobe* is intact and functional. Complete removal of both parts of the hypophysis does not result in permanent polyuria, although a temporary one, lasting for a few days, is usually observed. Moreover, after removal of the posterior lobe, either alone or together with the anterior lobe, the response to the administration of water is nearly, or completely, normal; but the maximum rate of urine flow is generally reduced unless a substantial part of the anterior lobe is intact.

There are many difficulties in the interpretation of the experimental evidence, but the hormonal action of the supra-optic-posterior lobe system in normally maintaining a small rate of urine flow is undoubted. It seems to be necessary, also, to ascribe to the anterior lobe, not so much the elaboration of a definite diuretic hormone, as the release of a factor which permits the onset of a permanent or large polyuria in the absence of the anti-diuretic hormone. The relatively normal response of the kidneys after hypophysectomy to dilution of the blood must be ascribed to the presence of some mechanism alternative to that involving the neuro-hypophyseal system; there is no definite evidence as to what, or where, it is.

The separation of specific substances in post-pituitary extracts has been possible on account of differences in their chemical stabilities and solubilities. None of the substances has, however, yet been isolated. *Vasopressin* is an extract of high potency and purified by removal of both the non-specific substances and specific oxytocic substance; it exerts its action on the vascular system. *Oxytocin* is similarly separated from vasopressin, and exerts its action on the uterus. The anti-diuretic action may be due to a third substance, but is associated with vasopressin. The melanophore expanding action in amphibia is due to a substance present in the pars intermedia. The action on plain muscles other than the uterus is attributed mainly to vasopressin, and this applies also to the so-called *galactogue action*, *i.e.*, the expression of milk by constriction of the ducts of the mammary glands. Evidence has recently been brought forward suggesting that these substances may be breakdown products of a single protein, but it is still uncertain whether this can function as a whole, or whether its activity is dependent on its fragmentation.

INDEX

Figures in **heavy type** refer to pages in which illustrations or tables occur.

Abdominal reflexes, spinal cord
    segments involved in, 412
Acclimatisation to high altitude,
    mechanism of, 154–156
Accommodation, mechanism in eye
    of, **484–487**
    nerve showing, 367–368
    reflex, nature of, 486
Aceto-acetic acid, amino-acid
    metabolism and, 204
    fat metabolism and, 208, **209**
Acetylcholine, anti-diuretic hormone
    stimulation by, 268
    assay of, 460, **461**
    autonomic ganglia affected by, 386
    blood pressure affected by, **542**
    blood vessels affected by, 56–**57**
    central nervous system affected by,
        403, 469–470
    chorda-lingual nerve stimulation
        liberating, **459**
    electric end-organ affected by, 469
    nerve impulse effected by, 375–376
    nerve storage of, 462
    nerve-muscle junction liberation
        of, 383–384
    skeletal muscle stimulation by,
        467–468
    vagus nerve stimulation liberating,
        457
Acetylene, cardiac output measured
    by use of, 39
Acidosis, causes of, 241
Acromegaly, nature of. 559, 560
Action potential, acetylcholine
    affecting skeletal muscle, **468**
    auditory tract showing, 531
    nature of, 312–**313**
    in nerve of, 356
    optic nerve fibres showing, **499**
    pain stimulation and, 474
    properties of, **370–371**
    retina showing, 498–499
    semicircular canals showing, **420**
    touch end-organ stimulation and,
        472
Adam-Stokes attack, nature of, 27

Adaptation, light brightness on eye,
    498
    sense organs showing, **475**
    sensory endings showing, 380
    touch end-organ showing, **472, 475**
Addison's disease, nature of, 548
Adenosinetriphosphate, acetylcholine
    synthesis affected by, 460
    skeletal muscle containing, 320, **321**
    skeletal muscle contraction
        involving, 326
    ultra-violet light absorption by,
        326
Adrenal cortex, ascorbic acid in, 226
    Cushing's disease affecting, 561
    functions of, 547–550
Adrenal cortical hormones, blood
    sugar affected by, 214–215
Adrenal glands, structure and
    function of, 543–550
Adrenal medulla, adrenaline output
    by, 545, **547**
    innervation of, 450–451, **464**
Adrenalectomy, effects of, 548
Adrenaline, actions of, 451,544
    blood sugar affected by, 213
    blood vessels affected by, **56–57**
    chemical structure of, 544
    circulatory effects of, 64
    denervated tissues affected by,
        458
    estimation on intestine of, **545**
    glomerular capillary pressure
        affected by, 255
    glycosuria caused by, 243
    plain muscle viscosity affected by,
        346
    site of action of, 544–545
    skeletal muscle blood vessels
        affected by, 75
    vasodilator action of, **542**, 544
Adrenaline apnœa, cause of, 163
Adrenergic nerves, blood vessels
    affected by, 61–**62**
    nature and properties of, 462
Adrenotrophic hormone, action of, 560
Aerotonometer, use of, 145

Æsthesiometer, use of, 471
After-discharge, crossed extensor
reflex showing, 396
flexor reflex showing, 394–395
shortening reaction relation to, 407
After-potentials, significance in nerve
of, 370
After-taste, cause of, 539
Age, blood pressure variation with, 54
calorie requirement variation with,
220
near point of eye affected by, 487
protein requirement variation
with, 223
Agglutinins, blood groups containing,
91, 92
nature of, 89
Agraphia, nature of, 438
Albuminuria, causes of, 242, 244
Alcaptonuria, nature of, 243
Alcohol, diuretic action of, 268–269
metabolism and actions of, 227–228
nerve conduction affected by, 372
Alexia, nature of, 438
Alimentary glycosuria, nature of, 216
Alkaline rigor, nature of, 325
Alkalosis, causes of, 241
Allergic reactions, nature of, 90, 123
Allergy, acetylcholine and, 464
All-or-none response, cardiac muscle
showing, 336
definition of, 363
nerve showing, 372–373
skeletal muscle showing, 314–317
α nerve fibres, conduction rate in,
371
Alpha rhythm, nature of, 439
Alternating current, plain muscle
viscosity affected by, 347
Alveolar air, composition of, 133–134,
135
Alveolar carbon dioxide partial
pressure, constancy of, 147–148
exercise effect on, 163
high altitude effect on, 154, 157
Alveolar oxygen partial pressure, high
altitude effect on, 154, 157, 158
respiration affected by, 149
Alveolar water vapour pressure, high
altitude effect on, 157–158
Alveoli, conditions affecting
permeability of, 160
Amenorrhœa, nature of, 298
Amino-acids, essential in diet, 202

Amino-acids, heart usage of, 340
intestinal absorption of, 185
metabolism of, 202–203
Ammonia, renal production of, 241
Amyl nitrite, respiration affected by,
143
Anabolism, definition of, 188
Anæmia, circulatory adjustments in,
67
colour index in, 99–100
red blood cell fragility in, 88
Anaerobic metabolism, skeletal
muscle showing, 324–325
skeletal muscle, heat production
in, 327
phosphate concerned in, 333
nerve fibre type of, 377
Anaphylactic shock, nature of, 89
histamine relation to, 123
Androgens, adrenal cortex production
of, 549
assay of, 292
castrates affected by, 292
nature of, 290
Androsterone, structure of, 289
Angina pectoris, nature of, 73
A nerve fibres, properties of, 370
Aneurin. See Thiamin.
Anharmonic, nature of, 527
Ankle jerk, spinal cord segments
involved in, 412
Anoxia. See Oxygen lack.
Anserine, nature of, 320
Anterior horn cell, structure of, 384
Anterior pituitary gland, androgen
and œstrogen control by,
290–291
development of, 557
functions of, 558–562
lactation affected by, 304–305
ovary affected by, 281
ovulation affected by, 284
reproduction affected by, 301
spermatogenesis control by, 279
Anterior pituitary hormones, blood
sugar affected by, 214–215
diabetes produced by, 217
Antibody, nature of, 88
reticulo-endothelial system and, 83
Anti-diuretic hormone, function of,
563–564
nervous control of, 267, 564
Antidromic impulses, c.e.s. affected
by, 400

Antidromic nerves, blood vessels controlled by, 63
histamine liberation by, 63–64
Antigen, nature of, 88
Aorta, pressure changes during cardiac cycle in 29, 30
structure and function of, 44
Aortic valve disease, pulse wave affected by, 44
Aphasia, types of, 437
Apneustic centre, nature of, 138
Appetite, nature of, 232
Apraxia, nature of, 438
Aqueous humour, formation of, 124, 479
Argininephosphoric acid, nature of, 320
plain muscle activity and changes in, 344
Arm muscles, maximum work with speed of movement of, 13
Arm plethysmograph, use of, 46–47
Arterial anoxæmia, causes of, 159–160
Arterial pressure. See Blood pressure.
Arterioles, blood viscosity in, 93
drugs affecting calibre of, 56–57
post-pituitary action on, 562–563
structure and function of, 44
Arteriolo-venous communications, body temperature regulation and, 75
Arteriosclerosis, nature of, 43
Arterio-venous oxygen difference, high altitude effect on, 156
Artificial respiration, methods of, 161–162
Artificial synapse, properties of, 382–383
Ascites, nature of, 42
Ascorbic acid, actions of, 226
daily requirement of, 221
renal excretion of, 262–263
Asphyxia, chain of events in, 161
nerve fibres effected by, 374
Assay, adrenaline on gut, 545
methods of acetylcholine, 460, 461
Astasia, nature of, 425
Asthenia, nature of, 425
Asthma, nature of, 129
Astigmatism, nature of, 489
A.T.10, action of, 557
Atmospheric pressure changes, blood nitrogen affected by, 98
Atonia, nature of, 425

Atropine, acetylcholine liberation affected by, 465
eye affected by, 490–491
Atwater-Benedict respiration calorimeter, use of, 195, 196
Audibility threshold, masking effect on, 536
Audiometer, use of, 538
Auditory acuity, 533–538
Auditory fatigue, mechanism of, 537
Auditory nerve, impulse frequency in, 533
Auditory tract, action potentials in, 531
Auricle, pressure changes during cardiac cycle in, 29, 30
Auricular fibrillation, jugular pulse in, 25
nature of, 28
Auricular flutter, nature of, 28
Auriculo-ventricular node, position of, 21, 22
Autocoid, nature of, 541
Autonomic ganglion. nicotine action on, 449
synaptic transmission in, 385–386
Autonomic nervous system, circulatory control by, 61–64
definition of, 448
digestive glands supplied by, 165–166
nerve fibre size in, 371
Aviator, high altitude effects on, 156–157
Axon, structure of, 354–355
Axon reflex, triple response and, 76

Baby, heart rate in, 454
Bainbridge reflex, nature of, 41
Barbiturates, central nervous system affected by, 385
respiration affected by, 163
Barometric pressure, alveolar carbon dioxide affected by changes in, 148, 154
Basal metabolic rate, factors affecting 196–199
pregnancy effect on, 298
thyrotrophic hormone action on, 559
thyroxine action on, 550
Basilar membrane, action in hearing of, 523–524

Basilar membrane, function in hearing of, **530**–531

Basophil, description of, 82

Bel, definition of, 528

Benedict respiration apparatus, use of, **195,** 196

Berger rhythm, nature of, 439

β-**hydroxybutyric** acid, fat metabolism and, 208

β-**nerve** fibres, conduction rate in, **371**

β-**oxidation,** fat metabolism and, 207–208

Bicarbonate, buffering action of, **108**–110

carbon dioxide dissociation curve of, **113**

Bile, fat absorption affected by, 187

secretion of, 178–180

Bile pigments, formation of, 180

renal excretion of, 243

Bile salts, entero-hepatic circulation of, 180

Bilirubin, nature of, 86

Binocular vision, anatomical basis of, 516–**517**

nature of, 513

Bird, eye accommodation in, 484

fore-brain removal effects on, 429–430

Birth, lung changes at, 131

Bitterness, perception of, 539

Bladder, nerve supply to, 272–273

pressure changes with filling of, **271**

Blind spot, measurement of, **483**

Blink reflex, location of centre for, 417

Blood, adrenaline estimation in, **545**

buffering power of, 110

calcium, parathormone action on, **555,** 556

carbon dioxide, carriage of, 111–118

dissociation curve of, **113**

distribution of, **96**

speed of processes involved in transport of, 116

carbon monoxide determination in, 107

chemical properties of, 95–**96**

" chloride shift " in, 114–116

coagulation, mechanism of, 84–85

methods of prevention of, 85–86

composition, constancy of, 14

pregnancy effect on, 298–299

Blood composition, renal secretion affected by, 265

flow, measurement of, 46–**47**

rate in different vessels of, **45**–46

gases, amounts of, **96,** 97–98

analysis of, 101–102

groups, nature of, 90–92

hæmoglobin concentration in, 99

lactate, exercise effect on, **119**

oxygen debt relation to, **332**

Locke's solution comparison with, **351**

oxygen capacity, determination of, 100

high altitude effect on, 155

oxygen content, continuous measurement of, 192

dissociation curve, factors affecting, 102–**103**

distribution of, **96**

partial, pressure, measurement of, 145

saturation, high altitude effect on, **157, 158**

pH, renal regulation of, 240–241

phosphate, parathyroidectomy effect on, **555,** 556

plasma. *See* Plasma.

platelets, formation and function of, 83–84

pressure. *See* Blood pressure.

red cell, composition of, **96**

description of, 80

life history of, 86

Na/K ratio in, 95

permeability of, 87–88

viscosity affected by concentration of, **94**

red cell count, high altitude effect on, 155

redistribution in exercise of, 451–452

reservoirs, organs acting as, 59

sedimentation, factors affecting, 92

sugar, glucose ingestion effect on, **215,** 216

liver glycogen equilibrium with, 211

regulation of concentration of, 213–216

temperature changes effect on, 235, **236**

transfusion, blood volume measurement by, 58

Blood urea, protein diet effect on, 97

vessels, nervous control of, 61–64

volume, circulation affected by changes in, 59–60

measurement of, 58

viscosity, factors affecting, 93–94

white cells. *See* Leucocyte.

Blood pressure, acetylcholine action on, **459, 461, 542**

adrenaline action on, **542**

cardiac output affected by, 34, **36**

carotid sinus control of, **68–70**

CO_2 excess and deficit effect on, 63

coronary blood flow relation to, **72**

depressor nerve stimulation effect on, **65, 67**

exercise effect on, **6**

factors determining, **55–56**

function of, 451–452

glomerular capillary pressure relation to, 252–**254,** 255

hæmorrhage effect on, 59–60

histamine action on, **542**

methods of measurement of, **48**–51

post-pituitary extract effect on, **562**

renal blood flow affected by changes in, 263

respiration affected by, 143, **144**

respiration effect on, 73–74

urine composition affected by changes in, 252, **253**

Blue, colour mixing with, 506

field of vision of, **509**

Blush area, nature of, 452

B nerve fibres, properties of, **370**

Body fluids, division of, **229**

Body surface, basal metabolic rate relation to, 197–**198**

nomogram for calculation of, **198**

Body temperature, exercise effect on, **7**

regulation, 14, 232–237

hypothalamus and, 423

skin circulation relation to, 48

sympathetic system involved in, 453

Body weight, body surface relation to, **198**

thyroxine action on, **550**

Boiler-maker, tone deafness in, 532

Bomb calorimeter, use of, 193

Bone marrow, blood cell formation in, 82

Boutons terminaux, nature of, **384**–385

Bragg and Paul pulsator method of artificial respiration, 162

Brain, acetylcholine present in, 459

acetylcholine synthesis by, 460

blood vessels, adrenaline action on, **62, 70**

circulation maintenance in, 71–72

development in vertebrates of, **428**

foodstuffs used by, 213

Broca's area, effects of damage to, 437

Bronchi, structure of, 127–128

Bronchial breathing, nature of, 131

Bronchial muscles, innervation of, 129

Bronchiole, structure of, 129

Brunner's glands, secretion of, 180

Buffer action, nature of, **108**–111

Buffy coat, nature of, 92

Burns, circulatory changes following, 60

Cachexia strumipriva, nature of, 550

Caffeine, diuretic action of, 269

glomerular capillary pressure affected by, 255

respiration affected by, 163

Caisson disease, nature of, 98

Calciferol, actions of, 226

Calcium, blood clotting affected by, 84

dietary requirements under different conditions for, **220**

functions in body of, 224

heart beat affected by, **350,** 351

nerve accommodation affected by, 368

nerve excitability affected by, 382

sensory endings adaptation affected by, 380

tetany affected by, 556

Calorie, definition of, 3

requirements under different conditions for, 218–**219**

Calorimetry, direct and indirect, **195**–196

Cane sugar, taste threshold of, 539

Capillary dilatation, permeability affected by, 123

Capillary pressure, factors affecting, 54–55

measurement of, 51–52

Capillary pressure, normal value of, 53
tissue fluid relation to, 120–121
Capillaries, drugs affecting calibre of, 56–57
permeability of, 120–121
post-pituitary action on, 563
pressure resistance in, 75–76
structure and functoin of, 44
Carbamino-hæmoglobin, nature of, 117
Carbohydrate, energy value of, 193
fat production from, 206–207
metabolism, 210–217
water balance of, 230
respiratory quotient of, 190
Carbon dioxide, blood carriage of, 111–118
dissociation curve, arterial and reduced blood, 113
oxygen dissociation curve affected by, 103
respiration control by, 147–148
scheme of liberation from blood to air of, 117
transport, speed of processes involved in, 116
vaso-motor centre affected by, 63
Carbon monoxide, blood oxygen partial pressure measurement by use of, 145
blood volume measurement by, 58
poisoning, mechanism of, 106–107
Carbonic acid, titration curve of, 108
Carbonic anhydrase, action of, 116
gastric cells containing, 169
pancreas containing, 177
Carboxyhæmoglobin, formation of, 106
Cardiac asthma, nature of, 42
Cardiac cycle, nature of, 23
pressure changes during, 29, 30
Cardiac muscle, all-or-none response of, 316
electrolytes action on, 350, 351
ketone body utilisation by, 209
metabolism of, 339–341
properties of, 308, 334–339
structure of, 22
Cardiac output, factors affecting, 34, 39–40
hæmorrhage effect on, 59
heart failure effect on, 42
high altitude effect on, 155

Cardiac output, measurement of, 37
pregnancy effect on, 299
renal blood flow relation to, 264
venous pressure relation to, 33, 35
Cardiometer, use of, 34
Carnosine, skeletal muscle containing, 320, 321
Carotene, vitamin A relation to, 225
Carotid body, respiration affected by blood gas composition on, 151–152
Carotid sinus, anatomy of, 66
reflex, nature of, 68–70
normal function of, 69, 70
Caseinogen, milk containing, 307
Castration, effects of, 291–292
Catabolism, definition of, 188
Cell membrane, electrical behaviour of, 359–360
permeability, factors affecting, 353
Central excitatory state, nature of, 398–402
Central inhibitory state, duration of, 400
mechanism of, 402–403
Central nervous system, alcohol action on, 228
blood supply to, 125
high altitude effect on, 156
integrative activity of, 15, 398
localisation of function in, 413
micturition control by, 273
parturition control by, 304
synapse, conduction at, 469–470
synaptic delay in, 386–387
Cerebellum, functions of, 423–426
Cerebral cortex, acetylcholine action on, 469
area of, 431
cerebellar connections with, 424–425
electrical activity of, 439–440
localisation of function in, 428, 432
mind relation to, 426–427
sensory-motor connections in, 439
sympathetic activity representation in, 453
Cerebral function, history of knowledge of, 431
methods of study of, 427
Cerebral hæmorrhage, blood pressure affected by, 63
Cerebral hemispheres, comparative anatomy of, 428
effect of removal of, 429–430

Cerebrosides, nature of, 206
Cerebro-spinal fluid, formation of, 125–126
Chain-reflex, nature of, 410
Chalone, nature of, 541
Chemoreceptors, afferent nerves from, 142
Cheyne-Stokes respiration, nature of, 149–150
Chloride, renal excretion of, 240, 251
  renal tubule reabsorption of, 256
" Chloride shift," mechanism of, 114–116
Chlorocruorin, nature of, 99
Cholecystography, nature of, 179–180
Cholecystokinin, action of, 179
Cholesterol, structure of, 289
Choline acetylase, action of, 460
Choline, acetylcholine-like action of, 458
Cholinergic nerves, atropine action on, 465
  blood vessels affected by 61–62
  nature and properties of, 462
Cholinesterase, action of, 457–458
  central nervous system containing, 469–470
  electric end-organ containing, 469
  motor end plate activity and, 384
Chorionic gonadotrophin, nature of, 282
Choroid, nature of, 477–478
Choroid plexus, function of, 125
Chromaffine tissue, nature of, 543
Chromatic aberration, nature of, 483–484
Chronaxie, nature of, 363, 364
Chylomicrons, fat absorption affecting, 186–187
Cilia, properties of, 308–309
Ciliary body, accommodation of eye and changes in, 485
  structure of, 478
Ciliary muscles, action of, 485
  drugs action on, 490–491
Circulation, asphyxia effect on, 161
  chemical regulation of, 64–66
  exercise effect on, 78–79
  rate, measurement of, 37
  scheme of, 20
Circus movement, nature of, 28
Clasp knife reaction, nature of, 405
Climate, temperature regulation and, 234, 237–239

Clonus, mechanism of, 393, 394
C nerve fibres, properties of, 370
Cocaine, nerve fibres affected by, 374
  pupil affected by, 491
  taste-buds affected by, 539
Cochlea, resonance theory and anatomy of, 530
  structure and function of, 522–524
Cochlear effect, nature of, 532
Coitus, autonomic system control of, 455
  mechanism of, 276
Cold spots, location of, 473
Cold sweat, nature of, 453
Colic, cause of, 343
Colloid osmotic pressure, lymph formation relation to, 122
Colon, movements of, 183–184
Colonic secretion, nature of, 184
Colostrum, nature of, 305
Colour blindness, cause of, 496
  types of, 510
Colour brightness, light intensity effect on, 492–493
Colour index, definition of, 99
Colour vision, defects in, 510–511
  Hering theory of, 511
  mechanism of, 505–509
  Young-Helmholtz theory of, 506, 507
Compensatory pause, nature of, 338
Complement fixation, nature of, 89
Complemental air, nature of, 132
Complementary colours, nature of, 506
Condenser discharges, properties of, 364
Condenser, stimulation by use of, 361
Conditioned inhibition, nature of, 443
Conditioned reflexes, properties of, 440–447
Conduction, heat loss by, 234
Cone, dark adaptation of, 496, 497
  diameter of, 504
  function of, 503–511
  " off " response associated with, 499–500
  red appreciation by, 508
  structure and distribution of, 492
Consensual reflex, nature of, 490
Convection, heat loss by, 233–234
Convergence, accommodation relation to, 514–515
  spinal reflexes and, 395

Convulsions, pyramidal tract impulses during, 434
Copper, daily requirement of, 221
Cornea, pain receptors in, 473
Coronary circulation, regulation of, 72
Coronary occlusion, results of, 73
Corpus albicans, nature of, 284
Corpus luteum, formation of, 282, 283
    function of, 296
    nature of, 282
    pregnancy dependence on, 301–302
Corti, organ of, 524
Corticosterone, actions of, 549
    chemical structure of, 547
Cortin, nature of, 548
Coughing, mechanism of, 143
Coughing reflex, location of centre for, 417
Creatine, renal excretion of, 241
Creatinephosphoric acid, anaerobic metabolism affecting, 324–325
    cardiac muscle containing, 339
    energy changes in breakdown and resynthesis of, 327
    lactacid mechanism relation to, 326, 329
    oxygen debt relation to, 331–332
    skeletal muscle containing, 320, 321
Creatinine clearance, inulin clearance relation to, 260–262
Creatinine, production of, 204
Cretinism, iodine treatment of, 553
    nature of, 551–552
Cross agglutination test, nature of, 91
Cross-circulation experiment, arrangement of, 67, 69
Crossed extensor reflex, c.e.s.
    duration in, 400
    nature of, 390
Crossed-flexor reflex, stepping and, 409
Crystalloids, intestinal absorption of, 185
Curare, body temperature affected by, 233
    skeletal muscle affected by, 468
Cushing's disease, nature of, 561
Cutaneous sensation, cortical representation of, 436
Cyanide, kidney affected by, 251
Cyanosis, definition of, 6
Cystoscope, use of, 270
Cytozyme, nature of, 84

Dark adaptation, mechanism of, 496–498
Day-vision, cone distribution in eye relation to, 492–493
Dead space, measurement of, 136
Deaf aids, types of, 538
Deafness, causes of, 537–538
    cochlear damage relation to, 532
Decerebrate preparation, postural reactions in, 405–407
    properties of, 416–419
Decerebrate rigidity, cerebellum stimulation effect on, 426
Decibel, definition of, 528
Decidua, nature of, 296–297
Deciduoma, nature of, 296
Decortication, effects of, 430
Defæcation, mechanism of, 184
    nerve centre for, 413
Delayed conditioned reflex, nature of, 442.
Dendrites, nature of, 354–355
Dentate nucleus, function of, 425
Dentine, parathyroid effect on, 556
Deoxycorticosterone, actions of, 549
    chemical structure of, 547
Depolarisation, acetylcholine effecting, 469
Depressor reflex, nature of, 65, 67
    normal function of, 70
Detonator action, spinal reflexes and, 401
    autonomic ganglion cells showing, 386
Diabetes insipidus, cause of, 564
Diabetes mellitus, blood sugar after glucose ingestion in, 215, 216
    description of, 216–217
    ketosis in, 208
" Diabetic puncture," nature of, 213
Diabetogenic hormone, nature of, 559
Diaphragm, respiratory movements of, 131
Diaphragm slip, respiration effect on movements of, 140
Diastole, definition of, 23
Diastolic murmur, significance of, 31
Diastolic pressure, measurement of, 49–51
    normal value of, 53
Dicrotic wave, nature of, 43
Diet, composition of, 222
    essential constituents of, 218, 220

Diet, heat production relation to type of, 233

Differential inhibition, nature of, 443

Differential white cell count, 82

Diffusion potential, nature of, 358

Digestion, nature of, 164

Digestive glands, innervation of, 165–166

secretory work of, 166–168

Digestive products, absorption of, 184–187

Dilator pupillæ, action of, 490

Diodone clearance, renal blood flow measurement by, 264

Diodone, renal secretion of, 259, 261

Tm, value of, 261, 263

Dioptre, definition of, 489

Diplopia, nature of, 513–514

Direct current, plain muscle viscosity affected by, 347

skeletal muscle affected by, 361

Disease, physiology of, 2

Dissociation constant, buffer action and, 109

Diuretics, action of, 267–270

Donnan membrane equilibrium, " chloride shift " and, 115

Douglas bag, metabolic studies by use of, 195

Drinker and Shaw apparatus for artificial respiration, 162

Dropsy, nature of, 123

Duodenal cap, action of, 174

Duodenum, stomach emptying control from, 175, 176

Duplicity theory of vision, 491–498

Dwarfism, nature of, 558, 561

Dystrophia adiposo-genitalis, nature of, 561

Ear, eye sensitivity comparison with, 527, 535

frequency differences detectable by, 534

structure and function of, 519–521

wave-form distortion by, 535

Edridge-Green colour lantern, use of, 511

Ejaculation, mechanism of, 277–278

Electric currents, plain muscle viscosity affected by, 347

Electric end-organ, acetylcholine action on, 469

Electrical stimulation, types of, 361

Electrocardiogram, nature of, 25, 26

Electrodes, polarisation at, 358

Electrolytes, cell membrane permeability affected by, 353

heart affected by, 350, 351

Electro-retinogram, nature of, 498–499

Electrotonic potentials, nature of, 360

Electrotonus, accommodation in nerve and, 367

Emergency, sympathico-adrenal system in, 451

Emergency theory of adrenal medulla, 546, 547

Emotion, adrenaline secretion caused by, 547

digestive processes affected by, 165, 166

Endemic goitre, nature of, 552–553

Endogenous protein metabolism, nature of, 204–205

Energy balance sheet, nature of, 197

Energy expenditure, measurement of, 3

Enterogastric reflex, nature of, 175, 176

Enterogastrone, action of, 173

Enterokinase, action of, 178

Eosinophil, description of, 82

Epicritic sensation, nature of, 476

Epineurium, permeability of, 359

Equiline, structure of, 289

Ergotoxin, adrenaline action affected by, 544

Erythroblast, nature of, 86

Erythrocytes. See Blood, red cells.

Eserine, cholinesterase affected by, 458, 459

eye affected by, 491

Ether, respiration affected by, 163

spinal cord affected by, 387

Ethereal, sulphate, source of, 240

Eustachian tube, function of, 519–520

Evans blue dye, blood volume measurement by, 58

Excitation threshold, nature of, 363

Excitation time, nature of, 364

Excitatory state, nerve showing local, 365

Exercise, arterial pressure in, 6

body acidity affected by, 118–120

body temperature affected by, 2, 232

Exercise, cardiac output affected by, **40**
circulatory changes during, 78–79
climatic effect limiting, **238**
efficiency with speed of, **10**, 14
energy expenditure in, 3
fatigue, causes of, 16
homeostasis and, 15
intestinal blood flow during, 74
maximum work with speed of, **13**
muscle blood flow affected by, 75
muscle capillary bed in, 104
myoglobin function in, 105
oxygen consumption in, **4, 9**
oxygen requirement variation with speed of, **11**
pulse rate in, 5, **9**
respiration affected by, 162–163
speed with duration of, **8**
sympathetic vasodilatation in, 451–452
Exogenous protein metabolism, nature of, 204–205
Exophthalmic goitre, nature of, **553–554**
Expiration, movements in, 131
Expired air, collection of, 133
composition of, **135**
Extension reflex, conditioning of, 440–441
Extensor muscles, cerebellum action on, 426
Extensor reflex, spinal shock effect on, 415
stepping and, 409
External auditory meatus, function of, 519
External inhibition, conditioned reflex and, 444
External rectus, eye movements caused by, **512, 513**
Extracellular fluid, volume and composition of, **229**
Extra-pyramidal system, function of, 434–435
Extra-systole, cause of, 338
Eye, accommodation in, **484–487**
drugs acting on, 490–491
ear sensitivity comparison with, 527, 535
movements, conjugate nature of, 518
posture affected by, 422
muscle balance, investigation of, 515

Eye, optical defects in, 487–**489**
structure of, 476–481
uterine endometrium graft in, 296
Eyeball, muscles concerned in movement of, **512–513**

Facilitation, autonomic ganglion cells showing, 386
cerebral cortex stimulation and, 432
spinal reflexes and, 400, 402
Factories Act, atmospheric conditions required by, 239
Fainting, circulatory changes in, 60
heart rate affected by, 42
Fallopian tube, ovulation and movement of, **284**
Faradic stimulation, effect of, **361,** 362
Fat, bile secretion affected by, **179**
carbohydrate conversion to, 206–207
composition of, 206
dietary requirements of, 223
energy value of, 193
intestinal absorption of, 185–187
metabolism, water balance of, **230**
milk containing, **307**
oxidation of, 207–208
respiratory quotient of, 190
storage of, 206
Fatigue, auditory, 537
economy of contraction caused by, 329
nature of, 15
sense of smell, 540
Fatty acids, β-oxidation of, 207–208
body fat containing, 206
Female generative organs, **277**
Female pseudohermaphrodism, cause of, 289
Fertilisation, nature of, 285
site of, 280
Fibrin, nature of, 84
Fibrinogen, nature of, 84
Fick principle, use of, 37
Filtration-fraction, nature of, 264
Final common path, nature of, 395
Fish, fore-brain removal effect on, 429
Flavo-proteins, riboflavin relation to, 226
Flexor reflex, c.e.s. duration in, 399
conditioning of, 441

Flexor reflex, internuncial activity in, 402
  mechanism of, 394–396
  nature of, 390
Flicker, critical frequency of, 502
Fœtal blood, oxygen carriage by, 299–300
  oxygen dissociation curve of, 104
Fœtal circulation, arrangement of, 302
Fœtus, lungs in, 131
Follicle-stimulating hormone, actions of, 281, 282, 560
Foodstuffs, energy value of, 193
  water balance in metabolism of, **230**
Form sense, foveal structure relation to, 503–504
Fourier's theorem, sound waves and, 526
Fovea, light wave-length sensitivity of, 492, **493**
  night blindness of, 497
  structure of, **481,** 503
Fractionation, flexor reflex showing, 395
Fragility curve, nature of, 88
Free-martin, nature of, 288
Frequency difference, detection by ear of, **534**
Frequency discrimination, cochlear mechanism of, 532
Frog blood, composition of, **351**
  fore-brain removal effect on, 429
  heart, perfusion of, 334–**335**
  rectus abdominis, acetylcholine action on, 460, **461**
Fröhlich's syndrome, nature of, 561
Frontal lobes, functions of, 438–439
FSH, actions of, 281, 282, 560

Galactogue, post-pituitary action as, 564
Gall-bladder, X-ray view of, 1**79**–180
Galvanic stimulation, effect of, **361**
Ganglionic synapse, transmission across, 465–466
Gas analysis apparatus, principle of, 101
Gas diffusion, factors controlling, 134–135
Gastric fistula, studies on subject with, **165, 170**
Gastric juice, composition of, 169

Gastric motility, duodenal control of, **175, 176**
  emotion effect on, **165,** 166
  histamine effect on, **170**
" **Gastric** pump," action of, 174
Gastric secretion, emotion effect on, **165,** 166
  histamine effect on, **170**
  osmotic work done in, 167–168
  stimulation of, 1**71**–**173**
Gastrin, nature of, 173
Gastrocnemius muscle, time relations of contraction of, 319
Gastro-ileal reflex, nature of, 183–184
Genetic sex differentiation, nature of, **286–287**
Giant nerve fibre, action potential records from, **356, 369**
Gigantism, cause of, 558, 560
Glaucoma, treatment of, 491
Glomerular capillaries, pressure in, 252–**254,** 255
Glomerular filtration, colloid osmotic pressure effect on, 252–254
  rate, measurement of, 259–260
Glomerular fluid, composition of, 248
Glomerular membrane, area of, 258
  permeability of, **250,** 251
Glomeruli, diuretic agents acting on, 269–270
  functions of, 248–256
Gluconeogenesis, insulin action on, 214
  nature of, 212–213
Glucose, amino-acids as source of, 203
  diuretic action of, **268,** 269
  glycogen equilibrium with, 211
  heart usage of, 339
  intestinal absorption of, 185
  metabolism, hormones action on, 215
  renal excretion of, 243
  renal threshold of, 213
  renal tubule reabsorption of, 256, **261**
  Tm, value of, **261,** 262
  tolerance test, nature of, **215,** 216
Glycogen breakdown, iodoacetate action on, 324
Glycogen, glucose equilibrium with, 211
  skeletal muscle containing, 320, **321**
Glycosuria, blood sugar relation to, **215,** 216

Glycosuria, causes of, 243
   growth hormone causing, 559, 560
Glyoxal. See Pyruvic aldehyde.
Goitre, nature of, 552
Gonadotrophic hormones, action of,
   281–282, 560. See also FSH and
   LH.
   androgen and œstrogen control by,
   290
Gonadotrophin, urinary excretion in
   pregnancy of, 300, 301
Graafian follicle, structure of,
   280–281
Gramophone, ear comparison with,
   522
Granulocytes, description of, 82
Gravity, venous pressure affected by,
   55
Green, colour mixing with, 506
   field of vision of, 509
Growth, thyrotrophic hormone action
   on, 560
Growth hormone, actions of
   558–559, 560

Hæm, nature of, 100
Hæmatin, nature of, 100
Hæmatocrit, use of, 81
Hæmochromogen, nature of, 100
Hæmocyanin, nature of, 99
Hæmocytometer, use of, 80
Hæmoglobin, acidity of
   oxyhæmoglobin and of, 113–114
   bile pigment formation from, 180
   buffering action of, 109–110, 112
   carbon dioxide bound by, 117
   high altitude effect on, 155
   molecular weight of, 104
   oxygen combination with, 100–104
   properties of, 98–104
   renal excretion of, 252
   speed of oxygenation of, 105
Hæmoglobinometer, use of, 99
Hæmolysis, causation of, 87
Hæmophilia, nature of, 85
Hæmopoietin, nature of, 87
Hæmorrhage, circulatory
   adjustments following, 59–60
   vasoconstriction following, 452
Hair, touch sense affected by presence
   of, 471, 472
Haldane gas analysis apparatus,
   principle of, 101

Haldane hæmoglobinometer, use of,
   99
Harmonics, nature of, 526
Harvey, circulation demonstrated by,
   19
Haustra, nature of, 183, 184
Hearing, acuity of, 533–538
   cortical representation of, 436
   ear structures concerned in,
   519–524
   loudness measurement in, 528–529
   physiology of, 529–533
Heart, acetylcholine action on, 457,
   461
   anatomy of, 21
   beat, origin and conduction of, 25
   block, jugular pulse in, 25
   nature of, 338
   efficiency of, 37
   electrical changes origin and spread
   in, 27
   electrolytes action on, 350, 351
   failure, mechanism of, 42
   pulmonary circulation affected
   by, 159, 160
   innervation of, 41
   law of, 37
   murmurs, nature of, 31
   output of. See Cardiac output.
   rate, exercise effect on, 40, 41
   nervous control of, 41–42
   sounds, cause of, 31
   " tone " of, 348
   valves, position of, 22
   volume, arterial pressure effect on,
   36
   work done by, 36
   See also Cardiac muscle.
Heart-lung preparation, use of, 32, 33
Heart-lung-kidney preparation, use
   of, 249–251
Heat loss, methods of, 233
Heat paralysis, frog showing, 411
Heat production, factors affecting,
   233
   nerve impulse accompanied by,
   376
   skeletal muscle, 327–331
Heat spots, location of, 473
Helicotrema, nature of, 523
Heparin, nature of, 85
Hering-Breuer reflex, nature of,
   140–142
Hering theory of colour vision, 511

Hermaphrodism, adrenal cortex connection with, 549
types of, 288–289
Hexokinase, anterior pituitary hormones action on, 215
Hibernation, respiratory quotient and, 207
High altitude, acclimatisation to, 154–156
gas pressures at, 135
mechanical effects on body of, 158
oxygen secretion by lungs at, **146**
Hill's thermopile, nature of, **328**
Hind-limb, blood viscosity measurement in, **94**
Hippuric acid, nature of, 207
His, bundle of, **21, 22**
Histamine, anaphylactic shock and, 90
blood vessels affected by, 56–**57**
bronchial muscle affected by, 129
capillaries affected by, 123
gastric secretion resulting from, **170**
reactive hyperæmia relation to, 77
tissue extracts containing, **542**
Histiocyte, nature of, 83
Homeostasis, nature of, 15
taste used in, 232
Hooke's law, bladder filling relation to, 272
Hormone, nature of, 541–**542**
"H substance," triple response and, 76
Humidity, temperature regulation and, 234
tolerance of body to, **238**
Hunger contractions, nature of, 174
Hunger, nature of, 231
Hydrocephalus, nature of, 125
Hydrogen ion concentration, regulation of, 107–111
taste of, 539
tissues affected by, 352
Hydrothorax, nature of, 130
Hydrotropic substances, action of, 228–229
Hypercalcæmia, effects of, 556
Hypermetropia, nature of, 487–**488**
strabismus due to, 515–516
Hyperpnœa, respiration affected by, 149–150
Hypertensin, action of, 65
Hypertension, causes of, 57
Hyperthyroidism, effects of, 553–**554**
Hypnotism, mechanism of, 445

Hypocalcæmia, effects of, 556
results of, 213
Hypophysectomy, renal function affected by, 269
results of, 558, 559, 560, 564
Hypophysis, definition of, 558
Hypothalamus, anti-diuretic hormone control by, 564
digestive processes affected by, 166
fat distribution affected by, 561–562
nerve centres in, 422
sympathetic centres in, 453

ICSH. *See* LH.
Illumination, visual acuity variation with, **504**
Immunity reactions, 88–90
Incus, action of, 520, **521**
Indicator yellow, nature of, 495
Induction coil, skeletal muscle affected by stimulation with, **361,** 362
Inertia flywheel, use of, **12**
Infection, blood sedimentation rate affected by, 92
body temperature affected by, 232
neutrophils action in, 82
shock resulting from, 60–61
Inferior oblique, eye movements caused by, **512, 513**
Inferior rectus, eye movements caused by, **512, 513**
Infra-red rays, lens affected by, 482
Inhibition by extinction, nature of, 443
by retardation, nature of, 443
of inhibition, nature of, 443–444
sleep relation to, 444
spinal reflexes showing, 396–**397**
Inhibitory after-discharge, nature of, 397
Initial length, plain muscle response to changes in, 343, **344**
Injury potential, nature of, 312, 357
Inner ear, structure and function of, **522**–524
Inspiration, movements in, 131
Inspired air, composition of, **135**
Insulin, blood sugar affected by, 214
hexokinase activity affected by, 215
ketosis affected by, 216

Intermittent claudication, nature of, 73

Internal environment, hypothalamus effect on, 423
  nature of, 14
  sympathetic system in regulation of, 453

Internal inhibition, conditioned reflex and, 443–444

Internal rectus, eye movements caused by, 512, 513
  time relations of contraction of, 319

Interneurones, reverberatory chains in, 401

Interstitial fluid, volume and composition of, 229

Intestinal juice, secretion of, 180–181

Intestine, exercise effect on blood flow in, 74
  movements of, 181–184

Intracellular fluid, volume and composition of, 229

Intra-ocular fluids, nature of, 124
  secretion of, 479

Intra-pleural pressure, respiration effect on, 130

Intrarenal pressure, effects of, 266

Intra-thoracic pressure, pulmonary circulation affected by, 73

Inulin clearance, nature of, 259–262

Involuntary muscle. See Plain muscle.

Iodine, daily requirement of, 221
  goitre associated with lack of, 552

Iodoacetate, action of, 324–325
  cardiac muscle response to, 339

Ionone, smell sensitivity to, 540

Iris, muscles in, 490
  structure of, 478

Iron, daily requirement of, 220
  functions in body of, 224
  hæmoglobin and content of, 104
  red blood cell formation and, 87

"Iron lung," nature of, 161

Iron wire model, nerve impulse and, 368

Irradiation, conditioned reflex showing, 445
  spinal reflexes and, 400

Irreciprocal conduction, nature of, 387

Isolated kidney, arterial pressure changes effect on, 252, 253
  temperature effect on, 249, 251

Isometric contraction, nature of, 309, 310

Isometric lever, nature of, 310

Isometric tension, heat production in contraction relation to, 329

Isometric twitch, tension and heat production in, 311

Isotonic contraction, nature of, 300

Isotonic solution, definition of, 87

Isotopes, amino-acid interchange shown by, 205
  fat metabolism demonstrated by use of, 209
  fat metabolism studied by use of, 206
  metabolic studies with use of, 200–201

Jaundice, forms of, 86

Joint, sensory impulses from 474, 475

Jugular pulse, recording of, 24, 25

Kata-thermometer, use of, 238

Keratin, chemical structure of, 322

Keto-acids, amino-acid metabolism and, 203

Ketone bodies, metabolism of, 209–210
  production of, 208–209

Ketosis, causes of, 208, 243
  insulin effect on, 216
  nature of, 204

Kidney, buffering action of, 111
  denervation effect on, 264
  efficiency of, 257
  intrarenal pressure in, 266
  post-pituitary actions on, 562, 563, 564
  structure of, 244–247, 250
  work done by, 247
  See also Renal.

Knee-jerk, mechanism of, 392–394
  nature of, 390
  reflex inhibition of, 397
  spinal cord segments involved in, 412

Krause end-bulbs, function of, 473

Kupffer cells, bile pigment formation by, 180
  nature of, 83

Labyrinth, cerebellum connections with, 426
structure and function of, **420–421**
Labyrinthine reflexes, nature of, 419
Lactacid mechanism, creatine-phosphate breakdown relation to, 326, 329
nature of, 324
oxygen debt relation to, 331–**332**
Lactation, dietary requirements during, **220, 223**
factors affecting, 304–306
parathyroid gland hypertrophy in, 556
Lacteal, fat absorption into, 185–186
Lactic acid, buffering in body of, 119
cardiac muscle production of, 339
heart usage of, 341
liver/muscle exchanges of, 334
liver and muscle glycogen relation to, 212
milk production of, 306
oxygen debt relation to, 331–**332**
plain muscle production of, 344
skeletal muscle containing, **321**
Lactogenic hormone, corpus luteum affected by, 291, 297
Lactose, milk containing, **307**
Lamina cribrosa, nature of, 477
Latent period, central excitatory state and, **399**
skeletal muscle twitch showing, 311–312
Lateral geniculate body, optic tract connection with, **517,** 518–519
Law of conservation of energy, metabolism and, **197**
Law of Forward Direction, 387
Law of the heart, basis of, 339
Law of Mass Action, oxygen combination with hæmoglobin and, 104
Lead poisoning, parathormone effect in, 556
Leech muscle, acetylcholine action on, 460, **461**
Lengthening reaction, nature of, 405–**406**
Lens, accommodation of eye by changes in, **484–486**
infra-red rays action on, 482
properties of, 482, 483
Lens capsule, accommodation and function of, **486**

Leucocyte, description of, 81
Leucocytosis, nature of, 81
Leucopenia, nature of, 81
Leukæmia, white blood cells in, 83
LH, actions of, 281–282, 560
actions on sex hormones of, 290–291
Lieberkuhn's glands, secretion of, 180
Light, appreciation of differences in, 505
intensity-duration, optic nerve impulses variation with, **501**
Lipiodol, Fallopian tube movements shown by, **284**
Lipoid, metabolism of, 205–210
Liver, bile salt production by, 180
blood capacity of, 74
blood reservoir action of, 59
glycogen, adrenaline action on, 213
blood sugar equilibrium with, 211
insulin action on, 214
ketone body production relation to, 210
ketone body production in, 208–209
lactic acid removal by, 334
specific dynamic action of foodstuffs and, 200
urea formation in, 203
Locke's solution, composition of, **351**
Loudness, intensity-pitch relationship in, 528, **529**
measurement of, 527
mechanism of appreciation of, 533
Lovèn reflex, nature of, **70, 71**
Lumbar puncture, nature of, 124–125
Lung, gaseous exchange between blood and, 144
movement, sounds of, 131
oxygen secretion in, 145–147
stretch receptors, activity of, 380
respiration affected by stimulation of, 140
structure of, **127**
surface area of, 128
Luteinising hormone. *See* LH.
Lymph, formation of, 121–123
Lymphagogues, action of, 122
Lymphocyte, description of, 83
Lysins, nature of, 89

Macula lutea, perception by, 503
Macular plexus, nature of, 503

Maddox rod, use of, 515

Magnesium, intestine affected by, 352

Magnus animal, nature of, 422

Male, generative organs of, **276**
  production from female of, 287
  pseudohermaphrodism, cause of, 288–289

Malleus, action of, 519, **521**

Malpighian body, structure of, 244–245

Mammary gland, hormones action on, 304–305

Marching, optimum speed of, 11

Masking, nature of, 535–536

Mass reflex, nature of, 415

Mast cell, description of, 82

Masticating reflex, location of centre for, 416

Maximal stimulus, nature of, 316

Mechanical efficiency, body and engine, 3
  speed of movement relation to, **10,** 14

Medulla, nerve centres in, 416–417
  respiration affected by section of, 139

Medullated nerve, structure of, 354–355

Megakaryocyte, nature of, 83

Meissner's corpuscles, function of, 472

Membrane manometer, use of, **49**

Membrane permeability, factors affecting, 353

Membrane theory, nerve potentials and, 374–376

Meningitis, cerebro-spinal fluid changes in, 125

Menstrual cycle, events in, 292–298

Menstruation, mechanism of, 294–295

Mental processes, cortical site of, 437, 439

Mesenteric vessels, blood flow and pressure changes in, 45–46, **54**

Mesentery, pain end-organs in, 475

Metabolic rate, temperature change effect on, 236–**237**

Metabolic studies, methods of, 189

Metabolism, definition of, 188
  inborn errors of, 243
  isotopes used in studies of, 200–201, 205
  methods of determination in man of, 194–196

Metabolism, water balance of different foodstuffs in, **230**

Methæmoglobin, nature of, 100

Microrespirometer, use of, 190–191

Micturition, mechanism of, 270–274
  nerve centre for, 413
  parasympathetic action in, 454

Mid-brain animal, properties of, 421–422

Middle ear, structure of, **520, 521**

Midget, nature of, 561

Milk, properties of, 306–**307**

Mind, cerebral cortex relation to, 426–427

Mineral salts, dietary requirements of, 223–224

Miner's cramp, nature of, 224

Modiolus, nature of, 523

Monocyte, description of, 83

Morning sickness, cause of, 298

Morphine, pupil affected by, 491
  respiration affected by, 163

Motoneurone, central excitatory state in, **399**
  composition of, **355**
  definition of, 381
  structure of, **384**

Motoneurone pool, excitation of, **395**

Motor cortex, cerebellar stimulation effect on, 425
  electrical activity of, 433–434
  function of, 431–**432**
  removal, effects of, 434

Motor end-plate, nature of, 355
  transmission of impulse at, 383

Motor nerve cell, structure of, **384**

Motor unit, definition of, 381

Movement, efficiency with speed of, **10,** 14

Mucous membrane, heat sensitivity of, 473

Muller's law, nature of, 471

Muscarine, acetylcholine actions resembling those of, 463

Muscle. *See* Cardiac muscle, Plain muscle, Skeletal muscle.

Muscular exercise. *See* Exercise.

Muscular pump, nature of, 45

Muscular "tone," nature of, 348

Muscular weakness, adrenal cortex relation to, 548, 549

Music notes, wave frequency of, 526

Myelin sheath, nature of, 354

Myelin nerve impulse conduction affected by, **370**, 376
Myelinated nerve fibres, properties of, 370–371
Myeloblast, nature of, 82
Myelocyte, nature of, 82
Myenteric reflex, nature of, **182**
Myoglobin, cardiac muscle containing, 341
function in exercise of, 105
high altitude effect on, **155**–156
oxygen dissociation curve of, **103**
Myopia, nature of, 487–**488**
Myosin, chemical structure and function of, 322
skeletal muscle contraction involving, 326
Myxœdema, nature of, 551

Nausea, nature of, 177
Near point, nature of, 484
reflex, nature of, 486
Neck reflexes, nature of, **418–419**
Neocerebellum, connections of, **424**
Nephritis, urine secretion in, 265–266
Nerve, acetylcholine synthesis by, 460
action potential measurement in, **356**, 357
all-or-none response of, **372**–373
artificial synapse made with, **382–383**
excitation of, 361–368
theory of, 364–367
fibres, properties affected by size of, **370–371**, 374
mammalian, properties of, **370**
myelin sheath relation to, 354
metabolism of, 377
regeneration of, 355
adrenergic and cholinergic, 463
sensations during, 476
resting potential of, 357–360
structure of, 354–357
Nerve cell, permeability of, 357
permeability to carbon dioxide and H ions of, 153
structure of, 354–**355**
Nerve centres, nature of, 139
Nerve deafness, nature of, 538
Nerve endings, chemical transmission
Nerve 456–470
at, impulse, acetylcholine liberation relation to, 462

Nerve conduction rate of, 368, **370–371**
electrical changes in nerve during, 369–371
energy requirements of, 376–377, 378
excitability changes in nerve following, 373–**374**
membrane theory of, 374–376
Nerve plexus, plain muscle tonus and, 349
Nerve-muscle junction, properties of, 383–384
Nerve-muscle preparation, use of, 309
Nervous disease, knee-jerk affected by, 392–393
Neurilemma, nature of, 355
Neuritis, thiamin relation to, 225
Neurofibrils, nature of, 354
Neuro-hypophyseal system, function of, 564
Neuro-muscular transmission, mechanism of, 466–469
Neurone, definition of, 356
Neutrophil, description of, 82
Niacin. *See* Nicotinic acid.
Nicotine, acetylcholine actions resembling those of, 463
autonomic ganglia affected by, 385, 449
ganglion cells affected by, 466
Nicotinic acid, actions of, 226
daily requirement of, **221**
Nictitating membrane, nature of, 476
Night blindness, mechanism of, 495–**496**
vitamin A relation to, 225
Night vision, rod distribution in eye relation to, 492–493
visual purple in relation to, **494**
Nitrogen balance, pregnancy effect on, 298
Nitrogen equilibrium, determination of, **201**–202
Nitrogen excretion, hypophysectomy effect on, 559
Nodal point, position in eye of, **482**–483
Node of Ranvier, nature of, **355**
Noise, wave form of, 527
Nominal aphasia, nature of, 437
Non-medullated nerve, fibre size in, 354

Non-polarisable electrodes, use of, 358–359

Normoblast, nature of, 86

Nucleo-protein, metabolism of, 204

Nystagmus, colour blindness causing, 510
nature of, 421

Occipital cortex, effects of removal of, 435–436
electrical activity of, **434**, 439
visual fields represented in, **517**, 518

Occlusion, flexor reflex showing, 395

Occupation, calorie requirement variation with, **219**

Œdema, heart failure causing, 42
nature of, 123

Œsophagus, swallowing and movements of, 168

Œstradiol, structure of, **289**

Œstriol, structure of, **289**

Œstrogens, assay of, **293**, 249
castrates affected by, 292
excretion in pregnancy of, **300**, 301
lactation affected by, 306
mammary gland affected by, 304–**305**
nature of, 290
uterine mucosa affected by, 294–**295**

Œstrone, structure of, **289**

Œstrus cycle, nature of, **293**–294

Olfactometer, use of, 540

Optic disc, position of, 483

Optic nerve, action potentials in, **499, 501**
colour stimulation to retina affecting responses in, 508
decussation, significance of, 518
visual sensation relation to impulse frequency in, **500**

Optic tracts, composition of, **517**, 518

Orientation reflex, conditioned reflex affected by, 444

Ornithine, urea formation from, 203

Osmotic pressure, blood-lymph relation affected by, 122–123

Otitis media, results of, 537–538

Oval window, nature of, **521**, 523

Ovary, œstrogen secretion by, 290 296
structure of, 280, **283**

Ovulation, course of, 282–**284**
time of, 297

Ovum, development of, 280–**281**
ovulation affecting, 282–285

Oxidation, enzymes concerned in, 191

Oxidative enzymes, vitamins relation to, 224–226

Oxygen consumption, energy production measurement from, 193
consumption, exercise effect on, **4, 9**
nerve impulse requirement for, 377
debt, chemical basis of, 331–333
nature of, 9
dissociation curve, factors affecting, 102–**103**
lack, acclimatisation to, 154–156
carotid body affected by, **151**–152
nervous system affected by, 410–411
spinal cord affected by, 387
poisoning, nature of, 159
requirement, exercise speed relation to, **11**
respiratory quotient relation to energy production from, **194**
secretion by lungs, evidence for, 145–147
skeletal muscle contraction in, **323**
heat production in presence of, 327

Oxyhæmoglobin, acidity of hæmoglobin and of, 113–114
hæmoglobin relation to, 100

Oxytocin, action of, 563, 564
uterus in parturition affected by, 303

Pace maker, action of, 27–28

Pacinian corpuscles, function of, 475

Pain, conditioned stimulus use of, 441
cortex stimulation and, 435
end-organs sensitive to, 473–474
thalamus concerned with, 423

Paleocerebellum, connections of, **424**
functions of, 426

Pancreas, blood sugar concentration effect on, 214

Pancreatic cells, secretion effect on structure of, **167**

Pancreatic juice, composition of, 177
    secretion of, 177–178
Pancreozymin, action of, 178
Panting, temperature regulation by, 235
Pantothenic acid, actions of, 226
Papilloedema, nature of, 126
Para-amino hippuric acid, clearance of, 264
Parasympathetic ganglia, site and function of, 450
Parasympathetic nerves, distribution of, **448**
    pathway of, 450, **464**
    stimulation, effects of, **455–456**
Parasympathetic system, central origin of, 448
    functions of, 454–455
    micturition and, 273
Parathormone, action of, **555–556**
Parathyroid gland, function of, 554–557
Parietal cells, secretion by, 169
Paroxysmal tachycardia, nature of, 43
Parturition, mechanism of, 302–**303**
Pavlov pouch, nature of, **172**
Pecten, eye accommodation in, 484
Pellagra, nicotinic acid and, 226
Pendular movement, nature of, **182**
Penis, erection of, 277
Pepsinogen, secretion of, 169
Perfused organs, metabolism measurements on, 192
Pericardium, anatomy of, 21
Perikaryon, nature of, 354
Perimeter, use of, **509**
Periodic breathing, high altitude causing, 154
    nature of, **149–150**
Peristalsis, nature of, **182**
Pernicious anæmia, cause of, 86–87
    red blood cell size in, 81
Pflüger's law, nature of, 367
pH, definition of, 109
Phenaceturic acid, nature of, 207
Phenol red, renal secretion of, 258
Phlebitis, nature of, 473
Phlorhizin, action of, 203
    action on kidney of, 243
Phon, definition of, 528–529
Phosphate, buffering action of, **108**–109
    glycogen breakdown in muscle involving, 333

Phosphate, urine buffering by, 241
Phospholipoids, nature of, 205–206
Phospho-protein, visual purple and, 495
Phosphoric acid, titration curve of, **108**
Phosphoric esters, glycogen breakdown in muscle involving, 333
Photopic luminosity curve, colour blindness effect on, 510
    colour vision relation to, 508
Photopic vision, spectral visibility curve of, **493**
Phrenology, development of, 431
Physician, functions of, 1
Physostigmine. See Eserine.
Piano, cochlea comparison with, 530–531
Pinna, function of, 519
    sound localisation by, 537
Pitch discrimination, mechanism of, 533
Pitch, wave frequency relation to, 526
Pituitary, anterior. See Anterior pituitary.
Pituitary extract, blood vessels affected by, 56
Pituitary gland, functions and structure of, 557–564
Pituitary, posterior. See Post-pituitary.
Pituitary tumour, vision affected by, 518
Place theory of hearing, 531, 533
Placenta, acetylcholine present in, 459
    functions of, **299, 301**
Plain muscle, pain impulses from, 475
    post-pituitary action on, 563
    properties of, 308, 341–**344**
    tone, bladder pressure affected by, 272
    mechanism of, 349–350
    progesterone effect on, 301–302
    viscosity of, 345
Plantar reflex, spinal cord segments involved in, 412
Plasma calcium, concentration of, 556
    carbon dioxide dissociation curve of " true " and " separated," 115
    composition of, **96**
    Na/K ratio in, 95
    phosphate, buffering action of, 112

Plasma, proteins, buffering action of, 112
  glomerular filtration relation to concentration of, 254
  nature of, 97
  osmotic pressure of, 252
  osmotic pressure, capillary pressure relation to, **54**
  tissue fluid formation relation to, 120, 122
Plasma clearances, nature of, 259–263
Plasmaphorӕsis, nature of, 122
Plethysmograph, use of, 46–**47**
Pleural cavity, pressure in, 130
Pleurisy, nature of, 130
PMS, nature of, 282
Pneumo-taxic centre, nature of, 139
Pneumothorax, nature of, 130
Polarisation potential, nature of, 358
Polygraph, use of, **24**
Pons, respiration affected by section of, 139
Pontine nuclei, connections of, 424–425
Pore electrode, all-or-none response of muscle shown by use of, 315–**316**
Portal blood flow, digestion effect on, **166**–167
Portal vein, pressure in, 185
Post-pituitary anti-diuretic hormone, nervous control of, 267
Post-pituitary extract, circulatory effects of, 64–65
Post-pituitary gland, development of, **557**
  functions of, **562**–564
  renal tubules affected by, 265
Posture, cardiac output affected by, 40
  plasma protein concentration affected by, 254
  reflexes involved in, 422
  reflex mechanism involved in, 405
Potassium, acetylcholine release by, 463
  acetylcholine synthesis affected by, 460
  adrenal cortex action on excretion of, 548
  heart beat affected by, **350**, 351
  muscle affected by, 352
  nerve cell permeability to, 357
  skeletal muscle excitability affected by, **353**

Potential changes, nerve excitation causing, **366**
P–P factor. *See* Nicotinic acid.
Precipitin, nature of, 89
Pregnancy blood sedimentation rate affected by, 92
  course of, 298–304
  dietary requirements during, **220, 223**
  parathyroid gland hypertrophy in, 556
Pregnancy urine, gonadotrophic hormones in, 282
Pregnanediol, excretion of, 297
  excretion in pregnancy of, **300**, 301
  structure of, **289**
Presbyopia, nature of, 486
Pressor substances, hypertension relation to, 57
Pressure, adaptation to, **475**
Progeria, nature of, 561
Progesterone, assay of, 297
  factors affecting secretion of, 291
  mammary gland affected by, 304–**305**
  œstrus cycle affected by, 294
  pregnancy dependence on, 301
  structure of, **289**
  uterine mucosa affected by, **295**, 296
Prolactin, actions of, 560
  mammary gland affected by, 304
Prolan, nature of, 282
Proprioceptive mechanism, dual nature of, 407
Proprioceptive sensation, cortical representation of, 436
Prostigmine, action of, 458
Protein, biological value of, 202
  buffering action of, 109–110
  dietary requirement under different conditions for, **220, 223**
  energy value of, 193
  heart usage of, 340
  metabolism of, 201–205
    water balance of, **230**
  renal excretion of, 244, **250**–251
  respiratory quotient of, 190
  specific dynamic action of, 199–200
Prothrombin, nature of, 84
  vitamin K and, 227
Protopathic sensation, nature of, 476
Pseudo-pregnancy, nature of, 297

Ptosis, sympathectomy causing, 453
Ptyalin, action of, 165
Pulmonary circulation, conditions reducing, 159
factors affecting, 73–74
pneumothorax effect on, 130
vital capacity affected by, 133
Pulmonary venous blood, sampling in man of, 38
Pulse pressure, definition of, 49
normal value of, 53
Pulse rate, exercise effect on, 5, 9
respiration effect on, 74
thyroxine action on, 550
Pulse wave, velocity of, 43
PU, nature of, 282
Pupil, accommodation reflex and changes in, 486
dilatation, nervous control of, 449
drugs action on, 491
light effect on, 484, 490
sympathetic tonic action on, 453
Pupillary reflex, conditioning of, 441
parasympathetic action in, 454
Purines, metabolism of, 204
Purkinje phenomenon, vision and, 492
Purkinje tissue, nature of, 22
speed of conduction in, 27
Pyloric sphincter, action of, 174
Pyroxidine, actions of, 226
Pyruvic acid, amino-acid metabolism and, 203
thiamin action in metabolism of, 225
Pyruvic aldehyde, heart usage of, 340

Quinidine, action on heart of, 28–29

Radial pulse, character of, 43
Radiation, heat loss by, 233
Reaction time, nature of, 389
Reactive hyperæmia, nature of, 76–77
Rebound phenomenon, spinal reflex showing, 408, 410
Reciprocal innervation, nature of, 408–409
Red blood cells. See Blood, red cells.
Red cell count, nature of, 81
Red, colour mixing with, 506
field of vision of, 509

Reduced reflex time, analysis of, 401
nature of, 389
spinal reflexes showing, 396
Referred pain, nature of, 475
Reflex action, definition of, 387–388
Reflex, experimental analysis of, 390–391
Reflex inhibition, nature of, 396–397
Reflex mechanism, theory of, 398–403
Reflex tonus, mechanism of, 404–407
Refraction, errors in eye of, 487–489
Refractory period, auricular fibrillation and, 28
autonomic ganglion cells showing, 466
Refractory period, cardiac muscle showing, 336–337, 338
nerve fibre size relation to, 370
nerve showing, 373
skeletal muscle showing, 317
Reinforcement, conditioned reflex showing, 445
knee-jerk affected by, 393
Reissner's membrane, nature of, 523, 524
Relaxin, nature of, 302
Renal activity, factors concerned in, 264–265
Renal blood flow, measurement of, 263–264
Renal blood vessels, arrangement of, 245–246
Renal disease, intrarenal pressure in, 266
Renal function, theories of, 247–248
Renal plasma clearances, nature of, 259–263
Renal secretion, control of, 264–267
nature of, 257
Renal tubules, functions of, 256–259
diuretic agents acting on, 270
length of, 258
Renin, blood vessels affected by, 56
Renin-hypertensin system, function of, 65–66
Reproduction, hormones concerned in, 301
Residual air, nature of, 133
Resonance theory of hearing, 530
Respiration, asphyxia effect on, 161
blood pressure affected by, 73–74
changes effect on, 143, 144
bronchial tree changes in, 128
chemical control of, 147–153

Respiration, drugs affecting, 163
exercise effect on, 162–163
high altitude effect on, 154
nervous control of, 137–143
vagus nerve function in, 140–142
Respiratory centre, buffering action of, 111
carbon dioxide effect on, 147–148
decerebration effect on, 417–418
description of, 138
oxygen and carbon dioxide action on, 152–153
Respiratory movements, nature of, 130
recording of, 137
Respiratory quotient, energy production of oxygen used in relation to, 194
fat production from carbohydrate effect on 207
isolated heart, 340
nature of, 190
Resting potential, nature in nerve of, 357
Reticulocyte, nature of, 86
Reticulo-endothelial system, bile pigment formation by, 180
nature of, 83
Retina, cortical representation of, 436
flicker sensitivity of, 502
nervous connections in, 500
sensitivity to light wave-lengths of, 492, 493
structure of, 479
Retinal image, formation of, 481–484
Retinal vessels, position of, 480–481
Retinene, nature of, 495
Reverberatory chains, c.e.s. affected by, 401
Rheobase, nature of, 363, 364
Riboflavin, actions of, 225
daily requirement of, 221
Rickets, cause of, 226
Right auricle, blood sampling in man from, 38.
Righting reflexes, nature of, 421
Rigor, chemical composition of muscle in, 321
Ringer's solution, composition of, 351
nature of, 335
Rod, structure and distribution of, 492
Rouleaux formation, nature of, 91–92
Round window, nature of, 521, 523
Rowing, mechanical efficiency in, 7

Ruffini end-organs, function of, 473
Running, oxygen requirement variation with speed of, 11

Saccharin, sweetness of, 539
Saccule, function of, 420, 522
Saliva, composition and function of, 165
secretion of, 167
Salivary gland, acetylcholine, liberation on nerve stimulation to, 459
Salivary reflex, location of centre for, 416
nature of, 164
vasodilatation in, 452
Salivary secretion, conditioning of, 440
Salt, adrenal cortex action on excretion of, 548
taste threshold of, 539
Sanson's images, nature of, 484
Scala media, nature of, 523, 524
Scala tympani, nature of, 523, 524
Scala vestibuli, nature of, 523, 524
Schafer method of artificial respiration, 162
Schwann cells, nerve regeneration and, 355
Sclera, nature of, 477
Scotopic luminosity curve, visual purple comparison with, 494
Scotopic vision, nature of, 493
Scratch reflex, mechanism of, 410
nature of, 390
Scrotum, temperature of, 279
Secondary sex characters, development of, 287
Secretion, action of, 177, 178
Sedimentation rate, factors affecting, 92
Segmentation movement, nature of, 182
Semantic aphasia, nature of, 437
Semicircular canals, function of, 420
Seminal vesicles, castration effect on epithelium of, 291
Seminiferous tubules, length of, 278
Sensation, analysis of, 445–446
spinal cord hemi-section effect on, 415
Sensory cortex, localisation of function in, 432, 433, 435–436

Sensory discrimination, limits of, 446
Sensory end-organs, action potentials set up by, **378–379**
adaptation in, 475
Sensory nerve, action potentials in, **378–379**
Sertoli, giant cells of, 279
Serum globulin, properties of, 97
Sex, calorie requirement variation with, 219, **220**
Sex chromosomes, nature of, **286**, 287
Sex determination, nature of, 285, **286**
Sex differentiation, chemical factors affecting, 287–288
Sex hormones, chemical relationship of, **289**
inter-relationship of, **301**
Sex ratio, factors affecting, 285–286
Shallow breathing, results of, 160
" Sham-feeding," nature of, **171**
Sham rage, nature of, 422
Sheath of Schwann, nature of, 355
Shock, circulatory changes in, 60
Shortening reaction, nature of, **406–407**
Simmond's disease, nature of, 561
Simultaneous conditioned reflex, nature of, 442
Simultaneous contrast, colour vision showing, 511
Sine-wave, nature of, **525**
Sino-aortic reflexes, respiration affected by, **151–152**
Sino-auricular node, action of, 27–28
position of, **21, 22**
Sinus venosus, rhythmic contraction of, 335
Skeletal muscle, acetylcholine action on, **467–468**
action potentials in, 312–**313, 314**
adrenal cortex action on, 549
all-or-none response of, 314–317
anaerobic mechanism in, 323
blood flow in, 75
blood vessels, nerve supply to, 449
cardiac muscle comparison with, 336–337
chemical composition of, 320–322
chloride diffusion in and out of, 352–353
contraction, chemical basis of, 322–327
economy affected by speed of, 329

Skeletal contraction, shortening effect on heat production during, 329–**330**
speed affecting heat production in, 329
curare action on, 468
fatigue, chemical changes in, 323
fatigue effect on composition of, **321**
glycogen, adrenaline action on, 213
blood sugar relation to, 211
insulin action on, 214
muscle, heat production in, 327–331
hexokinase, hormones action on, 215
iodoacetate action on, 324–**325**
ketone body utilisation by, 209
lactic acid, glycogen relation to, 212
motor nerve endings in, 383
oxygen debt incurred by, 331–333
phosphate in metabolism of, 333
potassium action on excitability of, 353
properties of, 308
reciprocal innervation of, **408**–409
relaxation heat in, **330**
spindle, action potentials set up by, **378–379**
adaptation in, **475**
stretch receptor action potentials in, **378–379**
sub-microscopic structure of, 321–322
summation and tetanus in, 317–**319**
synchronous and asynchronous volleys effect on, **390**, 391
tension development of, 319
heat production relation to, 325
stretch reflex affected by, **393**–394
theoretical maximum work of, 331
theory of contraction of, 326–327
tone, cerebellar control of, 425
nature of, 348
twitch of, 309–314
viscosity, nature of, 12, 345
Skin, allergic reactions of, 123
blood flow, temperature regulation and, 235
blood reservoir action of, 59
blood vessels, adrenaline action on, **546**
carotid sinus reflex effect on, 71
factors affecting, 75–77

Skin, circulation, sympathectomy effect on, 453
colour, cause of, 47–48
nerve supply distribution to, **414**
sense receptors in, 471–**475**
Sleep, conditioned inhibition and, 444–445
hypothalamus and, 423
urine secretion during, 265
Small intestine, gastric secretion stimulation from, 173
rhythmic contractions of, 342
Smell, nature of, 539–540
Smoking, carbon monoxide in blood from, 107
Sneezing, cause of, 143
Sneezing reflex, location of centre for, 417
Snow-blindness, nature of, 482
Sodium, adrenal cortex action on excretion of, 548
heart beat affected by, **350,** 351, 352
Sound, cochlea response to different wave-lengths of, **530,** 531
conditioned stimulus use of, 441
intensity, discrimination of, 535
localisation of, 536–537
physical properties of, 524–**529**
velocity of, 537
Sounds, loudness in decibels of, **528**
Sourness, perception of, 539
Spastic paralysis, nature of, 434–435
Special senses, cerebral cortex development relation to, 431
Specific dynamic action, nature of, 199
Speech, cortical damage affecting, 437
wave-frequency of, 534
Speed records, duration and speed relation in, **8**
Spermatogenesis, androgens action on, 292
nature of, **278**–279
Spermatozoa, development of, **278**–**279**
pH effect on life of, 280
Spherical aberration, nature of, 483
Sphincter pupillæ, action of, 490
Sphygmograph, use of, 43
Sphygmomanometer, use of, **50**–51
Spinal animal, properties of, 414–416
Spinal cord, acetylcholine action on, 469

Spinal, central excitatory state in, 398–402
oxygen lack effect on, 387
structure and function of, 381
sympathetic centres activity in, 454
Spinal frog, reactions of, 389
Spinal reflex arc, structure of, **388**
Spinal reflexes, acetylcholine action on, 403
characteristics of, 390–398
spinal shock effect on, 415
Spinal shock, nature of, 413
recovery from, 415
Spinal ligament, nature of, 523, **524**
Splanchnic blood vessels, adrenaline action on, **546**
post-pituitary action on, **562**
Splanchnic nerve stimulation, blood pressure and heart volume affected by, **56**
Spleen, acetylcholine present in, 459
blood capacity of, 74
blood reservoir action of, 59
rhythmic contractions of, 342
Stance reflexes, nature of, 422
Standing, fatigue in, 16
reflexes involved in, 422
Stannius ligatures, nature of, 335
position of, 26, **27**
Stapedius, action of, 520–**521**
Stapes, action of, 520, **521**
Starling's law of the heart, 37
Statokinetic reflexes, nature of, 422
Steady states, nature of, 15
Stepping reflex, mechanism of, 409–410
Stercobilin, nature of, 86
Stereognosis, cortical damage effect on, 436
mechanism of, 474
Stereoscope, principle of, **515**
Stereoscopic vision, mechanism of, 516
Sterility, factors in male causing, 279
Sterols, nature of, 205
Stethograph, use of, 137
Stimulation, types of electrical, **361**
Stomach, movements of, 173–176
rate of emptying of, 169
Strabismus, cause of, 515–516
Strength-duration curve, nerve showing, **363, 364**
Stress, adrenal cortex function in relation to, 548, 549

stretch receptor, action potentials set up by, **378–379**
respiration affected by stimulation of, **140**
stretch reflex, internuncial activity in, 402
stretch reflex, mechanism of, 403–**404**
plain muscle exhibiting, 342
shortening reaction involving, 406–407
stepping movement and, 409–410
striated muscle. *See* Skeletal muscle.
strip, function of the, 435, 439
strychnine, nervous system affected by, 411
sensory cortex mapped by use of, 435
taste threshold of, 539
Subjective harmonics, nature of, 535
Subliminal fringe, nature of, **395, 396**
Successive contrast, colour vision showing, 511
Suckling, lactation stimulation by, 306
Sulphate, renal excretion of, 240
Summation, c.e.s. concerned in, 400
conditioned reflex showing, 445
skeletal muscle showing, 317, **318**
plain muscle showing, 347
Summation interval, nerve excitation and, **365**
Summation of stimuli, flexor reflex showing effect of, 396
Superior oblique, eye movements caused by, **512, 513**
Superior rectus, eye movements caused by, **512, 513**
Supplemental air, nature of, 132
Supra-maximal stimulus, nature of, 316
Supra-optic-post-pituitary system, function of, 564
Supra-optic tracts, kidney affected by section of, 269
Suspensory ligament, action of, 512
eserine action on, 491
function in eye of, 485
Swallowing, mechanism of, 168
Sweat glands, cholinergic innervation of, 464
sympathetic control of, 452
Sweating, control of, 235
heat loss by, 234
local occurrence of, 452
spinal cord centres for, 454

Sweetness, appreciation of, 539
Swimming, labyrinthine function in, 421
Sympathetic ganglia, site and function of, 450
Sympathetic nerves, cholinergic nature of, 464
distribution of, **448**
pathway of, 450, **464**
stimulation effects of, **455–456**
blood vessels affected by, **62**
Sympathetic system, central origin of, 448
function of, 451–454
heart affected by, 41
reflex stimulation of, 546
temperature regulation and activity of, 235
Sympathectomy, circulatory effects of, 64
Sympathico-andrenal system, emergency function of, 451
Sympathin, nature of, 457
Synapse, acetylcholine action at, 469–470
nature of, 355
properties of, 381–**382**
Synaptic delay, nature of, 466
Synaptic potential, nature of, 385–**386**
Synaptic transmission, structures used in, **384**–385
Syneræsis, nature of, 84
Syntactical aphasia, nature of, 437
Syphilis, Wassermann reaction and, 89
Systole, definition of, 23
Systolic murmur, significance of, 31
Systolic pressure, measurement of, 49–51
normal value of, 53

Tachysterol, serum calcium affected by, 557
Tadpole, thyroid effect on, 551
Taste, nature of, 538–539
use of, 232
Taste-buds, location of, 539
Tear fluid, action of, 477
Tectorial membrane, function of, **524**
Teeth, pressure receptors activity in, 380
Temperature, body temperature regulation and, 234

Temperature, metabolic rate response to changes in, 236–237
reflex circulatory response to changes in, 71
tolerance of body to, 238
Temperature regulation. See Body temperature.
Temperature sense, cortical representation of, 436
end organs of, 473
Tenon's capsule, nature of, 512
Tension-length curve, plain muscle showing, 343–344
theoretical maximum work and, 331
Tensor, palati, action of, 520
Tensor tympani, action of, 520–521
Testis, androgen secretion by, 290
structure of, 278
Testosterone, structure of, 289
Tetanus, acetylcholine causing, 467–468
heat production and chemical changes during, 328–329
skeletal muscle showing, 317–318, 319
Tetanus toxin, nervous system affected by, 411
Tetany, nerve accommodation in, 368
parathormone effect in, 555, 556
Thalamic animal, brain section causing, 416
properties of, 422–423
Thalamus, consciousness in, 436
digestive processes affected by, 165, 166
functions of, 423
Thermopile, principle of, 327, 328
Thermo-regulatory centre, action of, 235–237
Thermostromuhr, use of, 46
Thiamin, actions of, 225
daily requirement of, 221
Thiourea, thyroid gland affected by, 554
Thirst, mechanism of, 231
Thiry-Vella loop, nature of, 181
Threshold, nerve excitation showing, 363
Threshold of audibility, nature of, 533
Threshold substance, nature of, 257
Thrombin, nature of, 84
Thrombocyte. See Blood platelet.
Thrombokinase, nature of, 84

Thromboplastin, nature of, 84
Thrombosis, nature of, 85
Thyroid gland, basal metabolic rate affected by, 199
functions of, 550–554
pregnancy effect on, 298
Thyroid secretion, heart rate affected by, 42
Thyrotrophic hormone, action of, 559–560
Thyroxine, actions of, 550
chemical structure of, 554
Tidal air, definition of, 132
Tissue extracts, histamine in, 542
Tissue fluid, formation of, 120
Tissue metabolism, measurement of, 190–191
Tissue respiration, enzymes concerned in, 191
Tissues, blood supply regulation to, 78
Tm, meaning of, 262
Tobacco, carbon monoxide from smoking of, 107
Tocopherol, actions of, 227
Tone deafness, cochlear damage in, 532
Tonometer, use of, 101
Tonus, plain muscle exhibiting, 342
Torpedo, electric end-organ in, 466, 469
Touch, adaptation to, 475
cortical representation of, 435, 436
sense of, 471–472
Trace-reflex, nature of, 442
Trachea, structure of, 127–128
Transfusion, blood group testing for, 91
Transient orange, nature of, 495
Trigger-reaction, nature of, 387
Triple response, nature of, 76
Trophoblast, functions of, 300
Trypsin, formation of, 178
Tuberculosis, pulmonary circulation affected by, 160
Tuning forks, wave form of vibrations of, 525
Tympanum, properties of, 519

Ultra-violet light, adenosine derivatives absorption of, 326
conjunctiva affected by, 482
Unmyelinated nerve fibres, properties of, 370–371

Unsaturated fatty acids essential in diet, 206

Unstriated muscle. *See* Plain muscle.

Urea clearance, inulin clearance relation to, 262

Urea, diuretic action of, 269
formation from protein of, 203
renal excretion of, 241

Ureter, contractions of, 270

Uric acid, production of, 204

Urine acidity, causes of variation in, 241
composition, arterial pressure changes effect on, 252, **253**
plasma composition compared with, 242
flow, variations in, 240
*p*H variations in, 241
secretion, nervous control of, 264
theories of, 247–248

Urobilinogen, nature of, 86

Urochrome, nature of, 242

Uro-erythrin, nature of, 242

Urticaria, acetylcholine causing, 464

Uterine mucosa, œstrogen and progesterone effect on, 294–**295** 296

Uterus, cholinergic innervation of, 464
contractions in parturition of, 302–**303**
post-pituitary action on, 563
spermatozoa survival time in, 280

Utilisation time, nature of, 364

Utricle, function of, 420, 522

Vaginal smear, œstrus cycle effect on, **293**

Vagus nerve, action potentials during respiration, 141, **142**
heart affected by, 41
gastric secretion from stimulation of, 169
pancreatic juice secretion control by, 177
respiration affected by afferent fibres of, 140–**142**
tonic action on heart of, 454

Vagus stimulation, acetylcholine liberation by, **457**

Van Slyke blood gas analysis apparatus, principle of, 102

Vasodilatation, local occurrence of, 452

Vaso-dilator substances, normal production of, 78

Vaso-motor centre, function of, 63

Vaso-motor nerves, action of, 61–**62**
mode of action of, 63

Vaso-motor reflexes, 66–71

Vasomotor tone, sympathetic regulation of, 452

Vasopressin, nature of, 564

Vein, pain receptors in, 473
structure and function of, 45

Vein valves, demonstration of, **19**

Venous pressure, capillary pressure affected by, 55
cardiac output affected by, **33, 35, 40**
heart failure effect on, 42
measurement of, 52–**53**
normal value of, 53

Venous return, exercise effect on, 78–79
factors determining, 57–61

Ventilation rate, carbon dioxide effect on, **148**
definition of, 132
high altitude effect on, 154, 157

Ventricle, pressure changes during cardiac cycle in, 29, **30**
volume changes during cardiac cycle in, 29, **30**

Verbal aphasia, nature of, 437

Vesicular breathing, nature of, 131

Villi, function and structure of, 184–**185**

Virilism, adrenal cortex connection with, 549

Visceral sensations, nature of, 475

Viscosimeter, blood viscosity variation with type of, **94**

Viscosity, plain muscle exhibiting, 343
skeletal muscle affected by, 345

Vision, alpha rhythm affected by, 439
duplicity theory of, 491–498
fields of, **509**
light wave-length discrimination in, 505
nerve impulse frequency relation to sensation of, **500**
nervous pathways of, **517**–518
" persistence of," 502

Visual acuity, light intensity effect on, **504**

Visual field, cortical representation of, 517, 518
Visual purple, properties and function of, 493–496
Visual threshold, variation in, 496
Vital capacity, nature of, 132
Vitamin, definition of, 224
 A, actions of, 225
  daily requirement of, 221
  visual purple relation to, 495, 496
 B, daily requirement of, 221
  fat production from carbohydrate affected by, 207
 B₁. See Thiamin.
 B₂. See Riboflavin.
 C. See Ascorbic acid.
 D, actions of, 226
  daily requirement of, 221
  serum calcium affected by, 557
 E, actions of, 227
 K, actions of, 227
  new-born needs for, 221
Vitreous humour, composition of, 124
 nature of, 480
Volley theory of hearing, 531, 533
Voltage-capacity curve, nature of, 364
Voluntary movement, cerebellar lesions effect on, 425, 426
Voluntary muscle. See Skeletal muscle.
Voluntary muscular contraction, nature of, 319–320
Vomiting, mechanism of, 176–177

Vomiting reflex, location of centre for, 417
Vowel, wave form of, 526

Wallerian degeneration, nature of, 355
Warburg's microrespirometer, use of, 190–191
Wassermann reaction, nature of, 89
Water balance, factors concerned in, 229–231
 renal control of, 240
Water, properties of, 228
 renal tubule reabsorption of, 256
Water diuresis, factors affecting, 267
 inulin clearance in, 262
Water-hammer pulse, nature of, 44
Weber's law, light difference appreciation and, 505
Wever and Bray effect, nature of, 532
 tensor tympani action on, 520–521
White cell count, nature of, 81–82
White reaction, nature of, 75–76
Work, calorie requirement variation with, 219
Wound shock, circulatory failure in, 60

Yellow, field of vision, 509
Young-Helmholtz theory of colour vision, 506, 507

PRINTED IN GREAT BRITAIN BY THE WHITEFRIARS PRESS LTD.
LONDON AND TONBRIDGE